Perspectives in Modern Physics

Perspectives in Modern Physics

Essays in Honor of Hans A. Bethe

On the occasion of his 60th Birthday
July 1966

EDITED BY

R. E. MARSHAK
University of Rochester

WITH THE ASSISTANCE OF

J. WARREN BLAKER
Vassar College

Interscience Publishers
a division of John Wiley & Sons
NEW YORK   LONDON   SYDNEY

49613

Preface

In July 1946, Hans Bethe and I were both consultants at the General Electric Research Laboratories in Schenectady, trying to communicate to this active laboratory the new wonders of "atomic energy". My wife learned from Rose Bethe that Hans was attaining the "ripe old age" of forty (how senior Hans seemed to us youngsters at that time!) and we threw a party in his honor. Ever since then, it was easy to remember Hans' age and to know that he would be celebrating his sixtieth birthday this year.

It seemed appropriate to honor this occasion by dedicating a volume to Hans Bethe which would reflect and recapture the broad and versatile contributions which he has made to almost every branch of physics. The title "Perspectives in Modern Physics" was chosen to enunciate the scope and intent of this "Festschrift". The response of former students and associates and friends of Hans Bethe has been overwhelming, as is evident from the size of this book.

The contributions to this volume range from a personal assessment of Bethe's career by two of his oldest friends, through a series of articles on nuclear physics (which has been his "first love" over the years), through particle physics (which was a natural extension of his interests in nuclear physics), through some articles on accelerators (on which mundane subject Bethe was willing to work at a very early date), through quantum electrodynamics (to which he made such a timely contribution), through an up-to-date appraisal of the Bethe-Salpeter equation (which is still a valuable tool for model testing), through cosmic ray physics (in both its old and modern versions), through a series of provocative papers in astrophysics (to which Bethe made one of the major contributions of the past several decades), through papers on phase transitions and solid state physics (to which he made several pioneering contributions) and finally through a series of papers in what might aptly be called "applied physics" (which cover such diverse fields as nuclear power and geophysics—the last area being one in which Bethe performed so well in his recent role as a "scientist-statesman").

The broad spectrum of physics represented by the forty or so articles contained in this volume only partially reflects the variety and richness of Hans Bethe's scientific career—as his list of publications (placed at the end of the volume) makes abundantly clear. But it should convey to the younger generation of physicists and to all readers the useful lesson of an outstanding physicist maintaining wide interests and resisting fragmentation in physics.

It is a pleasure to thank all the contributors to this volume for their gracious and enthusiastic cooperation—a measure surely of the universal regard and affection which everyone holds for the man we are honoring. Thanks are due Ed Salpeter, for helpful advice generously given, Warren Blaker, for general assistance with the manuscripts and proofs, and Eric Proskauer, Vice-President of John Wiley & Sons, for taking a personal interest in this pleasant undertaking.

R. E. Marshak

Contributors

N. AUSTERN
University of Pittsburgh

R. F. BACHER
California Institute of Technology

M. BARANGER
Carnegie Institute of Technology

GREGORY BREIT
Yale University

R. BROUT
Université Libre du Bruxelles

LAURIE M. BROWN
Northwestern University

S. T. BUTLER
University of Sydney

P. CARRUTHERS
Cornell University

E. D. COURANT
Brookhaven National Laboratory

R. E. CUTKOSKY
Carnegie Institute of Technology

FREEMAN J. DYSON
Institute for Advanced Study

WILLIAM A. FOWLER
California Institute of Technology

H. FRÖHLICH
University of Liverpool

G. GAMOW
University of Colorado

KENNETH GREISEN
Cornell University

J. HAMILTON
Nordisk Institut for Teoretisk Atomfysik

FREDERIC DE HOFFMANN
General Dynamics Corporation

H. HURWITZ, Jr.
General Electric Co.

M. KAC
The Rockefeller University

ARTHUR KANTROWITZ
Avco-Everett Research Laboratory

TOICHIRO KINOSHITA
Cornell University

E. J. KONOPINSKI
Indiana University

SERGE A. KORFF
New York University

J. A. KRUMHANSL
Cornell University

K. KUMAR
Michigan State University

WILLIS E. LAMB, Jr.
Yale University

J. S. LEVINGER
Rensselaer Polytechnic Institute

M. STANLEY LIVINGSTON
Harvard University

F. LOW
Massachusetts Institute of Technology

R. E. MARSHAK
University of Rochester

P. MORRISON
Massachusetts Institute of Technology

ROBERT OPPENHEIMER
Institute for Advanced Study

FRANK PRESS
Massachusetts Institute of Technology

K. F. RATCLIFF
University of Rochester

F. ROHRLICH
Syracuse University

M. E. ROSE
University of Virginia

BRUNO ROSSI
Massachusetts Institute of Technology

E. E. SALPETER
Cornell University

T. B. TAYLOR
Defense Atomic Support Agency

EDWARD TELLER
University of California

D. J. THOULESS
University of Birmingham

S. M. ULAM
Los Alamos Scientific Laboratory

V. F. WEISSKOPF
Massachusetts Institute of Technology

ROBERT R. WILSON
Cornell University

Contents

The Career of Hans Bethe

R. F. BACHER

California Institute of Technology

and

V. F. WEISSKOPF

Massachusetts Institute of Technology

We live in an industrial age today wherein craftsmanship is becoming a lost art. Specialization is the order of the day. Where is the man who can work with his own hands on any kind of material and create a finished product which reflects his insight and knowledge and bears his personal mark? The great craftsman of our profession, the master of the trade, is Hans Bethe.

Hans Bethe was born at the right moment. The beginning of his productive years coincided with the renaissance of physics in the late 1920's. This was the time when the foundations of the new quantum mechanics had been laid and an instrument created with which almost all known natural phenomena could be explained and understood. Men were needed who could make use of this magnificent instrument. It was a wonderful time for a theoretical physicist. Whatever group of phenomena was attacked, the new quantum mechanics gave explanations for the observed facts; a rational way of ordering the phenomena was obtained; insight was gained into the essential processes.

Within a few years successful theories were created for the spectra of atoms, for the chemical bond, for the solid state, metals and insulators, and for many other phenomena. Each of these theories opened up a new field of research, experimental and theoretical. The new way of looking at things created new concepts and lines of approach which in turn required new systematic experimental studies of the phenomena.

1

Hans Bethe was one of these explorers and pathfinders. But he differed from others by his universality. He was active on all fronts at the same time and he possessed an encyclopedic knowledge of what was known and what had been accomplished. Three monumental review articles written within a period of only five years give us proof. The first one gives a review of one-and-two electron problems in the Handbuch der Physik; the second deals with electrons in metals, in the same Handbuch, written with A. Sommerfeld; the third one is a group of three articles on nuclear physics written with the collaboration of R. F. Bacher and M. S. Livingston in the *Reviews of Modern Physics*. These articles are not reviews in the ordinary sense of the word. They are systematic recreations of the knowledge of the time, supplemented by original work wherever there were gaps and omissions in the current knowledge, and each bears the strong imprint of Bethe as the principal author. The work of other physicists is redone, reformulated and often corrected so that the review article has its own unity and clarity in the style of Bethe.

The first of these reviews is unusual in several respects. Perhaps most unusual is that its reedition in 1959 (in collaboration with E. Salpeter) is almost identical with the original version. Not much, apart from new experimental results and some refinements in theory, had to be added in order to bring it up to date after twenty-five years. But it is also unusual in its breadth. It contains under its modest title all essential parts of atomic and molecular physics: not only is there an exhaustive study of the one-and-two electron spectra, transition probabilities, etc., but also relativistic effects, fine and hyperfine structure, collision processes, Stark and Zeeman effects, radiation phenomena, electromagnetic field couplings, etc. In short, it is a textbook of nonrelativistic and relativistic quantum mechanics.

The second review of electrons in metals is equally complete. It contains the basis of what today is solid state physics. It is astounding how clear, simple and complete Bethe's presentation was in the year 1933 when this branch of physics was in its infancy. We find an exhaustive discussion of Brillouin-zones, of radiative processes in metals, of dia-, para-, and ferromagnetism, of all kinds of thermoelectric and galvanomagnetic effects, and, of course, a thorough discussion of the theory of conductivity.

The review articles on nuclear physics represent the first comprehensive presentation of this field as a branch of science. It contains the knowledge of that time (1937) presented with the usual clarity and order, characteristic of Bethe's work.* This review has a great influence on the further development of nuclear physics. It was seen on the desk of every nuclear physicist for many years.

The three great reviews are characteristic of Bethe's broad and encyclopedic knowledge but they by no means give a complete picture of it. His interests cover a much broader horizon. Bethe steps in productively whenever a new physical phenomenon is discovered. He is among the first with an exhaustive explanation on the basis of the latest theoretical ideas; or whenever a new theoretical method is conceived, he is among the first with an exhaustive application to some yet unexplained observations. He has his own personal way of simple and direct approach to theory and experiment and his typical trademark of thoroughness. It is all "handmade". He does not take the experimental results for granted. He analyzes them himself, often making corrections for effects that had been overlooked, and taking great pains in numerical work, in fitting curves, and in estimating errors. Here we observe him, the master of his trade, with thoroughness of approach, respect for detail, and clarity of execution.†

* Bethe wrote these articles seated under a very dim light in Rockefeller Hall at Cornell, a large pile of blank paper on his right and a pile of completed manuscripts on his left. Bethe always wrote in ink with some, but not very many, corrections even to complicated calculations. He was and is indefatigable and worked regularly from midmorning till late at night—but would always stop cheerfully to answer questions. His method of work is like his approach to a mountain. He has the steady swinging stride of a Swiss guide. The pace looks slow, but is deceiving and usually puts him ahead of anyone not a quarter of a century his junior.

† The following anecdote may illustrate one aspect of his work. One of the authors (V.F.W.) intended to embark on a calculation of pair creation of Bose particles by light. He went for advice to Bethe who had just published his famous paper with Heitler about electron pair creation. The required advice was freely granted. When Bethe was asked how long such calculations would take, he answered honestly: "It would take three days for me and it will take three weeks for you!" and so it did.

It should be added, however, that the published result of this calculation is wrong by a factor four, which would never have happened if Bethe had calculated it. The author was at that time assistant to W. Pauli, who hired him with the remark, "I intended to hire Bethe, but Bethe is working in solid state; I don't like solid state physics although I started it." After several months, Pauli despairingly remarked: "I should have taken Bethe after all!"

Bethe's scientific work covers all interesting fields of theoretical physics. For the sake of orderliness, one can indicate a number of fields in which his contributions were particularly important:

A. Solid state problems and the interaction of moving particles with matter
B. Electrodynamical problems
C. Nuclear physics
D. Astrophysics
E. Meson theory
F. Material physics
G. Hydrodynamics

His first publications belong in category A. During his early years, he collaborated with Sommerfeld on the problems of electron motion in metals. He wrote several papers about electron wave functions in crystals and about the theory of x-ray and electron diffraction. We find in this work one of the first applications of group theory to quantum mechanics when he used the crystal symmetries to determine electron wave functions. He continued to work on this problem as late as 1947, when he published several papers on the same subject. The problem of the energy loss of fast particles in matter caught his interest from the beginning and he has worked on these questions throughout his life. His contributions set the pace in his field. It is a subject which he unravelled almost single-handedly.

The second group, electrodynamics, was always in the forefront of his interest. His contributions are characteristic of his approach to physics. When it became clear that the Dirac equation describes the electron pair situation, Bethe and Heitler calculated the pair creation cross sections and corresponding phenomenon—the Bremsstrahlung—for all angles and energies. They arrived at the well-known formulas which remained the basic approach to this problem for over thirty years until today. Twenty years later he took up the problem again, in collaboration with F. Rohrlich and L. C. Maximon, in order to refine the results for the more exact requirements of modern experimentation. When Lamb and Retherford were able to measure the electromagnetic shift of atomic levels, Bethe was the first to apply the new ideas of renormalization to the problem and give a quantitative account of the observed effect. When more accurate relativistic calculations of the interaction of two charged fermions became necessary, Bethe and

Salpeter developed a method which allowed calculations to a higher degree of approximation than the Breit treatment of this problem. Some results of this method were impressively confirmed by measurements of the positronium spectrum.

His contributions to nuclear physics make up the largest part of his work. These began in 1934 with his treatment of the proton-neutron system. In collaboration with R. E. Peierls he worked on neutron-proton scattering and on the properties of the deuteron. Fifteen years later he introduced the useful concept of "effective range" into the theory of particle scattering. In 1935 Bethe was impressed by the new experimental results of Fermi and his collaborators in regard to nuclear reactions with slow neutrons. He tried to deal with the problem of neutron reactions with the simple nuclear model available at that time, in which the nucleons move as almost independent particles in a potential well. This model was very close to the current shell model, but it gave wrong results for reactions with very slow neutrons since these reactions are dominated by many particle effects. The coarse structure of the neutron cross section, however, would have been reproduced by a simple potential well model as Bethe has used. Had the Fermi experiments been made over a larger energy range with much poorer energy resolution, the results would have been in agreement with Bethe's paper on neutron reactions in 1935. As it was, however, the paper was considered as an incorrect approach for two decades until very similar calculations were again the fashion of the day.

When the strong interaction picture was introduced in nuclear physics by Bohr and Kalckar, the concept of level density became important. Bethe was the first to come up with an approximate calculation in 1936 and has always been interested in this problem. In his work with Hurwitz (1951), for example, he determined semiempirically the differences in level density for even and odd nuclei. In a paper in 1940 he applied the same simple approach to the strong-interaction picture as he did in 1936 to a weakly interacting model: he introduced the "continuum" theory of compound nucleus formation which later on was widely used and led to the "clouded crystal ball" model. The same direct treatment of a nucleus as a strongly absorbing "black" sphere resulted in his calculations with G. Placzek of nuclear "shadow-scattering".

When the concept of the meson was introduced into nuclear physics, Bethe was one of the first to study the representation of nuclear forces by meson exchange. He worked intensively on the interpretation of experimental results in regard to meson–nucleon scattering in terms of phase shifts. When Bethe works in a new field, he accumulates and digests the knowledge of the day and presents it in his own special form for the daily use of other less able physicists. Today we find on the desk of everyone who works on meson physics, the two volumes "Mesons and Fields" written by him with S. Schweber and F. de Hoffmann.

During the war, Bethe's main work was done at Los Alamos. But before the beginning of that laboratory he made other important contributions. It started when he read in a newspaper that effects of the explosion of artillery shells were not understood sufficiently. He tackled the problem from first principles, writing an article which was a foundation for much of the later work. Bethe contributed to microwave radar development in 1942 as a member of the Radiation Laboratory at M.I.T.

At Los Alamos his thoroughness, encyclopedic knowledge, and quick understanding were invaluable. Here he brought to bear not only his great strength in nuclear physics, but his ability and experience in hydrodynamics and electromagnetic theory. As head of the theoretical physics division, Bethe insisted that every unknown avenue be explored thoroughly. He altered his own efforts to meet the need, and his contributions were of tremendous importance to the project. After the war he continued to act as consultant at Los Alamos where, even though it would be brief, his visit was always marked by some significant result.

Bethe worked on nuclear reactors as a consultant to industry. His work on fast neutron reactors, particularly on neutron characteristics and the use of oscillator experiments to predict reactor behavior at higher power, has his usual insight and thoroughness. He made extensive studies of the safety of such reactors and his work in this field has had many practical applications to reactor design.

In 1958 Bethe served as a member of the United States delegation to the first International Test Ban Conference in Geneva. Solid experimental information was very scarce, particularly about underground explosions. He became an expert, quite naturally, and often produced solutions to perplexing problems from one day's meeting to the next. He would get away for a few days rest and relaxation in the mountains, but when the problems were difficult he was always called and cheerfully came back to apply his wisdom.

Bethe also worked on the problems of re-entry of missiles and rockets into the earth's atmosphere, and with characteristic thoroughness studied the excitations and ionization of gas in the boundary layer. What counted so much in his work on these problems was his deep understanding of the fundamental atomic processes which cause the specific properties of materials under unusual conditions.

But Bethe's main interest always was nuclear physics. He returned to nuclear problems whenever he could. It is incredible how much he was able to contribute to this field when his other obligations forced him to study and reformulate physical problems of completely different character. For example, the nuclear photo-effect was always an object of great interest to him. In his work with J. Levinger, the role of the giant dipole resonance was cleared up and a number of experimental facts fell into line with the theory. Lately his interest was caught by the problem of nuclear matter. This complicated problem was opened up by some calculations of K. Brueckner which were based upon simple but daring assumptions and was then continued by S. Moszkowski. Bethe has taken this problem into his hands and applied to it his powerful gifts of synthesis by making use of all possible knowledge and experience which exists in this field. The results are correspondingly impressive.

The most striking payoff, however, of his thorough and encyclopedic knowledge of nuclear physics appeared in 1938 in the form of a paper entitled "Energy Production in Stars." Here his phenomenal knowledge of all details of nuclear reactions enabled him to find cyclic nuclear processes which take place in the interiors of stars and which produce the energy that keeps normal stars hot for billions of years. The idea itself, that nuclear reactions produce stellar energies, was not a new one. But Bethe was the first one who introduced the carbon cycle as one of the important energy sources, and who was able to estimate quantitatively the reaction rates and the energy production. With this paper he opened up a new branch of nuclear science to which he himself contributed a large number of papers. He applied nuclear physics to phenomena for which it is essential. The natural place in the universe for nuclear processes is in the interior of stars. Nuclear physics on earth is restricted to borderline phenomena such as natural radioactivity or man-made artifacts, particle accelerators, or nuclear reactors. Bethe put nuclear physics into its true place.

Bethe's contributions to physics are both important and of great breadth. The impression may have been given that they were due entirely to his power, to his encyclopedic knowledge, and his perseverence. This is not entirely true. Part at least was good fortune. Shortly after he received his Ph.D. degree at Munich, he went to Stuttgart as assistant to Ewald. Here he not only learned physics, but met the Ewald children especially Rose, now Rose Bethe. The happiness which this good fortune brought Hans Bethe has been reflected in his contributions to physics. We know that these contributions will continue and we wish him many years of satisfaction and serenity in the future.

Perspectives in Modern Physics

ROBERT OPPENHEIMER

Institute for Advanced Study

When I was asked to write on Perspectives in Modern Physics in honor of Hans Bethe, I had thought to prepare yet another evaluation, for professional colleagues, of which features of today's landscape might be expected to endure, which seemed destined to change, for what reasons, perhaps even in what way. I came to doubt whether such an appraisal, at this time, and from my hand, would bring much pleasure to the man it was intended to honor. Instead, I have decided to dedicate to him, for his sixtieth birthday, a brief account for the general intellectual community of the role of physics in this century. The first and longer part concerns the theory of relativity and quantum theory, to whose scope and power Bethe in his professional life has brought such great enlargement. The second part deals briefly with an aspect of the applications of physics which has, over the last two decades, been of profound concern to Bethe.

These remarks were made on the occasion of James Smithson's two hundredth birthday, in the city of Washington, which, both for Bethe and for me, in rather different ways, has been a city both of sorrow and of hope.

Physics has played a part in the history of the last five centuries. Closely related to astronomy, to mathematics, and to philosophy in its earlier years, it now has intimate relations with all branches of science, and plays an increasingly explicit, conscious and visible role in the changing conditions of man's life. If physics has had these extended relations with science and practice, it has still maintained a kind of central heart of its own. This is because it seeks the ideas which inform the order of nature, and of what we know of nature. Countless phenomena which, from the point of view of physics, appear calculable and explicable but not central or essential, turn out to be pivots of our

9

understanding in other sciences. No *a priori* study of physics would have been likely to explain the accidents that make the synthesis of carbon in the stars possible. Yet that has made a difference of some importance to man. Most of the miraculous findings of microbiology were not invented, and would not have been invented, by physicists, though they have played an appropriate part in helping to provide the instruments and the language for their discovery. For every science, much is accident; for every science sees its ideas and order with a sharpness and depth that comes from choice, from exclusion, from its special eyes.

These centuries, from the first inspired studies in the thirteenth century of the nature of motion, to the latest journal, or even latest newspaper, have been sensed as a time of change, often painful change, of novelty, and increasingly, of rapid growth. What is written today deploring change, or welcoming it, has its parallel in almost every decade for the last four hundred years, in Newton, in the dying Galileo, in John Donne. "'Tis all in peeces, all cohaerence gone", wrote Donne in 1611:

> And new Philosophy calls all in doubt,
> The Element of fire is quite put out;
> The Sun is lost, and th'earth, and no mans wit
> Can well direct him where to looke for it.
> And freely men confesse that this world's spent,
> When in the Planets, and the Firmament
> They seeke so many new; then see that this
> Is crumbled out againe to his Atomies.
> 'Tis all in peeces, all cohaerence gone;
> All just supply, and all Relation.

But there is one very great difference. What has happened in this century in physics rivals, I think, in its technical and intellectual imaginativeness and profundity, what has happened at any time in human history. Its effects on the way we live are even more immediate and manifest than was the use of the magnet for navigation, or of electricity for communication and power; but it has not led to so great a change in man's views, of his place in the world, his function, his nature and his destiny.

The years from the thirteenth century to the seventeenth saw the gradual acceptance of a material world no longer centered on man, or on his habitat, the gradual acceptance of an order in the heavens that could be described and comprehended, that sharply limited and circumscribed, though of course it did not eliminate the role of God, or indeed of accident. We should ask ourselves, I think, why the views of Copernicus, the discoveries of Galileo, the understanding and syntheses of Newton, should so greatly have resonated through European society, so greatly altered the words with which men spoke of themselves and their destiny. For nothing like that has happened with Hubble's discovery of a constant in nature, an interval of time of something like ten billion years, which characterizes the time in which galaxies double their distance from one another. Nothing like that happened with Einstein's theory of relativity, which tells us the meaning of velocity of light, or of quantum theory, which tells us of the meaning of the quantum. In more recent times, there is a similar contrast between the impact of the views of Darwin, and the almost total lack of general interest in Mendel's discovery of binomial coefficients in the populations of succeeding generations of peas, its rediscovery, its more recent beautiful deepening, with the great beginnings of the unraveling of its molecular basis.

To give some sharpness to my question, let me speak a little of a few of the high points of this century's physics. There are many: the discovery of new forms of order, and their very slow and gradual understanding, in the superfluid and superconducting states of matter; the discovery of the atomic nucleus itself, and the gradual unraveling of its properties, transmutations and structure; the growing insight into the properties of the ordinary materials of our world, and of special ones made to serve us. But I should like to talk of three, which at first sight seem to touch upon themes long irresistible to philosophers: the special theory of relativity, quantum theory, and particle physics. I should hasten to add that the third subject is open.

There is an analogy, long known to physicists, between the special theory of relativity and the quantum theory. Each is built about a constant of nature and has something to say about how that constant, in determining the laws of nature, restricts or enlarges our ability to learn about nature. I shall not speak of Einstein's theory of gravitation, which he called the general theory of relativity, largely because those parts of it which are assured and understood and, in part, checked by observation, were so clearly and indelibly described by Einstein that we are still not able to add much; and because those parts where Einstein felt some hesitation, or those others where no real test has so far been clearly at hand, those parts which deal with space in the very large or with truly strong gravitational fields, are still the province of the professional physicist and the astronomer.

As we all know, Einstein's first theory of relativity made clear an unexpected meaning of a constant of nature long ago determined by the astronomers, the velocity with which light propagates in empty space. It was Maxwell who showed that this constant was the same as that relating fundamental electric and magnetic units, and explained why this should be so, by showing that light is an electromagnetic wave. Einstein's role was to recognize that because of the universal validity of Maxwell's equation, and the independence of the velocity of light of the velocity of the source emitting it, this velocity must, itself, take on the role of what in earlier times was regarded as an infinite one, one which could not be surpassed. The corresponding limitations, the absence of absolute judgments of simultaneity at distant points, struck rather deep at all views of space and time ever held before. At the same time, they liberated physics to form new and consistent descriptions of nature, and by altering and refining Newtonian mechanics, to anticipate new interconnections of the most fundamental theoretical and practical import.

In some ways even more remarkable was the interpretation of Planck's constant, the quantum, that emerged from the development of the quantum theory of the atom, the work this time of many men, initiated in part by Einstein, in part by Bohr, and brought to an essential clarity by Bohr and his Copenhagen school. Here, again, physics was given a great liberation, the ability to understand the stability of atoms, the atomicity of matter, the regularities of chemistry, the atomic and molecular requirements for life, most of what physicists and chemists had known until the turn of the century. But here, again, it was discovered that the role of the quantum in the order of nature limited the traditional concepts of what we could learn about nature by experience. The quantum defines the irreducible roughness in the relations between a system being studied and the physical means—light, or beams of particles, or a gravitational field, for instance—that are used to study it. Because of this, there is an atomicity not only to the atoms and molecules, but to the traffic between them and the physical instruments of the laboratory; and, because of this, a complementary relation of mutual incompatibility between different sorts of observations on an atomic system.

From this follow all the well-known features: the ineluctable element of chance in atomic physics based, not on our laziness, but on the laws of physics; the end of the Newtonian paradigm of the certain predictions of the future from the knowledge of the present; the element of choice in the approach to atomic observation. Yet perhaps the most important lesson is that objective—and massively and beautifully successful—science could be based on a situation in which many of the traditional features of objectivity were absent, and which taught us that for scientific progress and understanding, objectivity is more closely related to our ability to describe to one another what we have done and found, to verify or refute, than to its ontological foundation.

As for particle physics, it is an unfinished story, and what we are sure of today may not yet be ready to make its contribution to the common culture. Just for the requirement that in these new domains the general principles embodied in an understanding of the quantum and the velocity of light should still apply, it follows, as has been known for more than three decades, that atoms, or particles, or the ingredients of atoms, could not themselves, as all philosophical atomists had thought, be the permanent, unchanging elements of nature. They are created, destroyed, transmuted, but do not remain unaltered. What do remain enduring are certain abstract attributes of particles, of which the electric charge is the most familiar, and of which two other examples are known: the number of protonlike particles minus the number of their antiparticles, and the same number for electronlike particles. As for the several other abstract quantities, such as strangeness or hyper-charge, and isotopic spin that do change, but remarkably slowly, we, I think, and I, I know, are not ready to tell philosophers of what we have made of it. This is not for lack of trying. But at the least, we have a rather unexpected alteration of the ancient atomists' answer to the problem of permanence and change. What lies ahead, we do not know. In the tumult of discovery and conjecture I have, myself, great hope; but whether we will be led, as has been so long speculated, to some further limits on what we can say about events in space and time on the scale of the very small, or whether the true shock will be far more shocking, I, at least, have an open mind. It may, though we hope not, and I believe not, be like *The Beast in the Jungle*.

There is at least one other relatively new set of discoveries which may teach us rather deep lessons. No one was prepared for the power of the radio galaxies, or the apparently fantastic luminosity of the quasi-stellar objects. Some have thought that we were seeing the effects of truly strong gravitational fields; but until we understand better how such effects could lead to what is observed, until we understand better why galaxies are so much more effective in converting energy to radio emission than the sun is, or than we on earth are, this had best be left in the province of the professionals.

Now these, as other discoveries of this century, past and still to be made, find their way into our schools and become part of the language and the insight of new generations, and provide new attitudes and new analogies in looking at problems outside of physics, outside of science, as has already so largely happened with classical mechanics, and with electricity. But it is clear that these discoveries, which were not easy to make, and which, to the professionals involved, brought a sense of terror as great as that which touched Newton, have clearly not changed our philosophy, either in the formal sense or in the homely one. They were unexpected and beautiful discoveries for whose general import Locke and Hume, above all Charles Peirce, and even William James, could have prepared us.

I have sometimes asked myself when a discovery in science would have a large effect on beliefs which are not, and may perhaps never be, a part of science. It has seemed clear that unless the discoveries could be made intelligible they would hardly revolutionize human attitudes. But it has also seemed likely that unless they seemed relevant to some movement of the human spirit characteristic of the day, they would hardly move the human heart or deflect the philosopher's pen. I now think that it can be put more simply. These syntheses, these new discoveries which liberated physics, have all rested on the correction of some common view which was, in fact, demonstrably in error: they have all rested on a view which could not be reconciled with the experience of physics. The shock of discovering this error, and the glory of being free of it, have meant much to the practitioners. Five centuries ago the errors that physics and astronomy and mathematics were beginning to reveal were errors common to the thought, the doctrine, the very form and hope of European culture. When they were revealed, the thought of Europe was altered. The errors that relativity and quantum theory have corrected were physicists' errors, shared a little, of course, by our colleagues in related subjects.

A recent vivid example is the discovery of the nonconservation of parity. The error which this corrected was limited to a very small part of mankind. There is a still more recent example, the nonconservation of combined parity, more limited still in the number of us who could be shocked by it, not yet understood, but with hopeful, though still unpublished and unverified, indications of its possible deeper meaning.

Thus I think it is true that only at the beginnings of a science, or only in a society in which an awareness of the problems of science is extraordinarily widespread, can its discoveries start great waves of change in human culture. Just possibly if, in years ahead, other examples, other forms, other sites of life should be discovered, we would have a valid analogy to the great shock of the last century, when the anthropologists showed us the unimagined variety of human institutions. Although the nineteenth-century discoveries in biology had gone far to relate man to other forms of life, although anthropologists had revealed the unanticipated diversity of beliefs, values and practices in different cultures, and the lack of universality of the ideals by which our own society had been nourished, although the psychologists had brought some supplement to the great religions in revealing again the universal traits of evil in all men, in fact these discoveries were to deepen and not to erode the sense of a universal human community.

If the impact of the developments in physics in this century on the general understanding of man has been restricted, quiet, and largely reserved for the young and the future, their practical consequences, along with those of all the natural and mathematical sciences, have been unrivalled in their sharpness and immediacy. I should like to speak of one, which is not isolated, in which, largely by accidents of history, the part of physics has been important: the new weaponry, the new situation of the nations and of war. It is still not clear in what way, or even whether, these developments will turn out to be important for human history. I should think it likely that they would be. These developments, and problems that they raise, cannot be lived out in isolation from all the others which characterize our time, but only concurrently. But they can be talked about in a certain isolation.

It was twenty years ago that men generally learned of the new weapons of a new order of destructiveness. At that time we knew and told our government, as no doubt experts in other countries knew and told theirs, that the bombs that cruelly, yet decisively, ended the Second World War were, from a technical point of view, very much a beginning, not an end. We thought of some ideas about using deuterium and

ordinary uranium to increase their power a thousandfold; we thought
of the probable appropriateness of delivering such objects by rocket.
We did not know too much about it; but within a decade, rather much
had been learned.

When I think back to the summer and the autumn of 1945, I
remember a number of views of the future which were formulated in
this country, and, despite preoccupation with recovery from the terrible
war, no doubt abroad. The simplest, and the only one which has been
decisively refuted, was that these weapons would remain a monopoly,
and thus either play very little part, or put to the test only the restraint,
compassion, and fortitude of our own people and government. This
was not my colleagues' view, of course, nor mine; but for a time, at
least, it was that of many, including some of the very highest officers
of our government.

Others pointed to the long history of warfare, and talked of a
defense against atomic bombs. In no meaningful sense has this characterized any period of the last two decades. As long as the armaments
race continues, we will have to ask and re-ask whether adequate new
defenses may be possible. They have not been. Thus, we have lived
these years with a complementary and opposed dependence on
preemption and deterrence.

Others, looking to past history, trying to look to the future, saw
only the certain eventuality of apocalyptic war, postponed in all likelihood by the efforts of statesmanship until it was quite total. This is one
forecast that history will never totally disprove. And still others,
looking to the past with their eyes, and trying to penetrate the future,
held, with Sir Llewellyn Woodward, that such self-defeating weapons
would be put to one side, leaving the nations to war on one another
with more limited means. There is some support for it in the wars of the
present hour.

Yet there were quite other thoughts. Colonel Stimson wrote of
the necessary government of the whole; and Mr. Grenville Clark then
as now tried to accommodate the needs of world order with the freedom, the diversity and the self-interest of the world's peoples; Einstein
said simply that world government was the only answer. To the Acting
Secretary of State, the more importunate appeals led him to suggest
that it was not always helpful to replace a difficult problem by an
insoluble one.

Most of us recognized how central the relations with the Soviet

Union would be, and, very soon, how ominous their course. Most of us recognized that with any *government of the whole* capable of serving as a vehicle for common aspirations, for expressing and advancing common interests, the extraordinary diversity of the nations and regions and peoples of the world would present hard problems. There were rich people, and there were very poor people; in any common society these inequalities would more and more become inequalities, and the inequalities more and more the source of grievance and of guilt. Even in that world which had long lived with the European heritage, with a deep—though changing—Christian sensibility, differences of history, differences of political practice, and conflicting assessments of the value and meaning of freedom, made talk of the world's community of interest rather a falsetto clarion. We did not then know, but we should have, that in vast parts of the world, in Asia, in Africa, the first, the most powerful, the most spectacular of Europe's legacy would be the lure of technology, the pleasure of privilege, and the delights of an often synthetic nationalism. We knew that the rich could not, if they would, and perhaps would not, quickly reverse the inequities in conditions of life among peoples. We knew that for the world's future the variety of historical experience, the differences of tradition, of culture, of language and the arts, should be protected and preserved. This left very little of the idea of government of the whole; but it did leave something.

In June of 1945, before the first bomb, four of us, Arthur Compton, Fermi, Lawrence, and I, wrote, in answer to questions put to us by Colonel Stimson, the Secretary of War: "To accomplish these ends, we recommend that before the weapons are used not only Britain, but also Russia, France, and China be advised that we would welcome suggestions as to how we can cooperate in making this development contribute to improved international relations." These views were endorsed by the Secretary of War's Interim Committee on Atomic Energy, though the Committee, of course, paid little attention at that moment to France, and to China.

But in fact no meaningful communication was made at all: no attempt to enlist our then allies in a common responsibility and a common concern. That would have been a moment to begin to worry about what is now called "nuclear proliferation", for we and our then allies are the five powers that today have a known nuclear military program. I think that we will not be very successful in discouraging other powers from this course unless we show, by our own example and conviction, that we regard nuclear armaments as a transitory, dangerous, and degrading phase of the world's history, that before other nations could have a competing armament, there is a good chance that armament will have become archaic.

In writing as we did in 1945, and then, of course, very much more later, we were not unaware of the diversity of condition, interest, philosophy, and political institutions even in the great powers of the world, and certainly in the world at large. But we did know one thing from our experience before and even during the war: we knew something of the universality of the practice, language, discourse, and ethos of science. Los Alamos, and other wartime laboratories, were indeed international institutions. For years before the end of the war, those responsible for the organization of the scientific effort in the United States—Vannevar Bush, James Conant, and many others—had been speaking of the hope of an international control of the new weapons, and a cooperative exploitation of the new sciences. Similar views were widely held in Britain. Sir John Anderson, who was the head of the United Kingdom Uranium Project, was persuaded of them. Most of all, Niels Bohr explored these possibilities in depth, recognizing that any such cooperation and any such control would have to rest on open access in all countries, and recognizing that this was the best guarantee against the self-delusion and the cultural and political and human abuses of societies that seal themselves off from their fellow men.

The years since the war have brought many examples of effective and fruitful international collaboration, in technology, in political economy, above all in the sciences. My own field just in the last years has been enriched by contributions of the greatest value from physicists whose countries a century ago were quite closed to the scientific tradition of Europe: Korea, Japan, China, Indochina, to name a few. We need to be grateful for the strength and beauty of this tradition, and to tremble as well as take heart in its power. These same years have also shown how modest, how fitful and inconstant, how easily overwhelmed has been the effect of these international communities on the nations and the governments.

If I recall at this time some notions of two decades ago, it is clearly because I believe them essential to our present and our future. For I see it as a crucial question of our time whether, in a world destined at best slowly to relieve the inequalities of rich and poor, the exploitation of military technology, of national pride, of privilege, will be met by the growth, in practice, in sensibility, in institutions, of a community of interest and understanding. In the discouragements of the day, good example must come to be our firmest ground for hope.

Nuclear Matter

D. J. THOULESS

University of Birmingham

Attempts to understand the properties of nuclei in terms of various "models" have been rewarded with an almost embarrassing success. Where the shell model does not work, the collective model may work, and in some cases the shell model, collective model and alpha-particle model may explain the same set of data with an equal degree of success. This wealth of models, all of which are useful for understanding certain features of nuclear data, should not obscure the fact that we still lack, and perhaps always will lack, a detailed theory of the nucleus. Calculations can be made, but if they disagree with experimental results further refinements can almost always be made to alter the answer. In particular, there has been little effort to make sure that the parameters used for calculations in different circumstances are consistent with one another.

The liquid-drop model is one of the oldest of these nuclear models. Once it was realized that the nucleus is composed of protons and neutrons, rather than protons and electrons, the fact that the binding energy per nucleon is almost constant, for all but the lightest nuclei, led naturally to the idea that a nucleus is like a small drop of "nuclear matter". The expression "nuclear matter" was used in 1933 by Majorana (1933). It was observed by Wick (1934) that there is a large contribution to the total energy of the nucleus from its surface. These ideas were systematized in the "semiempirical mass formula" of Weizsäcker (1935), and the formula was simplified and divorced from its unsound theoretical basis by Bethe and Bacher (1936). Nuclear matter is not available in bulk because the electrostatic repulsion between protons renders nuclei with mass number greater than about 250 unstable, but the theorist is at liberty to disregard the known Coulomb interaction, and consider the properties of this hypothetical bulk nuclear matter. Whether or not bulk neutron matter is bound is an open question of considerable interest to astrophysicists, but, unless gravity can hold it together, it would undergo beta decay and then spontaneous fission. The surface energy and Coulomb energy are so important that real nuclei have only half the binding energy of 16 MeV per particle that bulk nuclear matter would have in the absence of the electrostatic repulsion.

Not only does the binding energy suggest the idea of nuclear matter, but experiments on the scattering of high-energy electrons by nuclei [Hofstadter (1956)] have shown that the charge is distributed more or less uniformly over a volume proportional to the mass number. The surface region, across which the charge decreases, is quite thick, but the thickness does not depend on the mass number. The density of the central region is such that each nucleon occupies a volume $\frac{4}{3}\pi r_0^3$, where $r_0 \approx 1.08 \times 10^{-13}$ cm, and the distance over which the charge density falls from 90% to 10% of its maximum value is about 2.4×10^{-13} cm. The experiments have not been sensitive enough to determine the detailed form of the density in the surface region, or to find out if the density becomes lower in the center of the nucleus.

The neutron density cannot be measured in such a direct manner, but analysis of the absorption of high-energy nucleons by the nucleus [Elton (1961)] shows that the neutrons and protons are distributed over almost the same volume. This is slightly surprising, as it might be expected that the Coulomb field would confine the protons to a smaller region than the neutrons occupy. However, charge-exchange forces, which interchange the positions of a neutron and a proton, must help to keep their distributions similar.

It is clear that there is no inconsistency between the liquid-drop model and the shell model. The atoms or molecules in a classical liquid interact strongly, simply because it is only the short-range repulsive interaction between them that prevents them collapsing on top of one another, so that the density increases until the interaction is strong. Liquid helium is different, since the low mass of the helium atoms makes the zero-point kinetic energy important. The density is low, less than one-third of the density one would expect for a classical liquid in the case of He^3, so interactions are less important, and liquid He^3 has a spectrum similar to that of a gas of fermions. Nucleon–nucleon scattering data show that the interaction between nucleons is similar to that between atoms of an inert gas, with a short-range attraction, and a strong repulsion (repulsive core) at even shorter distances. Liquid He^3 is therefore somewhat like bulk nuclear matter, but the ratio of the interparticle spacing to the diameter of the repulsive core is almost twice as large for nuclear matter, so it is even less like a classical liquid than liquid He^3. Nucleons are able to pass some distance through nuclear matter without being scattered, and, as a first approximation, the interaction between a nucleon and a nucleus may be represented by a potential acting on the nucleon which roughly follows the nuclear density. This shell-model potential can be regarded as a very important property of nuclear matter. At higher energies the shell-model potential becomes the potential of the optical model.

The development of a microscopic theory of superconductivity by Bardeen, Cooper, and Schrieffer (1957) led to the idea that nuclear matter should also be superfluid [Bohr, Mottelson, and Pines (1958)]. If bulk nuclear matter were available this would lead to remarkable properties, but the nucleus is so small that the effects we understand as "superfluidity" do not have room to display themselves. Nucleons certainly do pair with one another similarly to electrons in a super-conductor, and various effects of this pairing are described by Belyaev (1959). The strength of this pairing seems to decrease as the mass number increases, as is shown by the analyses of Seeger (1961) and Nemirovsky and Adamchuk (1962), so it may be that pairing occurs only on the surface of nuclear matter, not deep inside.

The main interest in the properties of nuclear matter in recent years has been concentrated on the problem of calculating its properties from an interaction derived from nucleon–nucleon scattering data. High-energy scattering experiments showed that the interaction between nucleons is strongly repulsive at very short distances, and the develop-ment by Brueckner and his collaborators [see Brueckner and Gammel (1958) for refs.] of a method for calculating the energy of nuclear matter in the presence of such strong short-range forces has been of great importance. The calculation is a difficult one, and it is not always clear what is the effect of various approximations, so it has often been regarded as a test of strength—can one do the calculation so well that the experimentally determined potential leads to the measured energy and density of nuclear matter? It is more interesting to ask whether nuclear matter has properties that reveal features of the interaction between nucleons not shown up by nucleon–nucleon scattering. For example, the relative strengths of the tensor and scalar potentials affect nuclear binding and nucleon scattering differently, three-body forces cannot be observed in two-body scattering experiments, and it appears from the work of Green (1962) that nonlocal potentials fitting the scattering data will give poor results for nuclear binding. One result of a recent analysis by Wong (1964, 1965) and Bethe (1965) is that the calculated binding energy of nuclear matter is brought into better agreement with experiment by using a potential with a soft core rather than one with a hard core.

The mathematical difficulty of much of the work that Brueckner has successfully performed has sometimes obscured the simplicity of the underlying physical ideas, and many attempts have been made to remove some of these difficulties. The paper of Bethe (1956) was an important step in this direction, and a further paper by Bethe, Brandow, and Petschek (1963) embodies a great deal of work by a variety of people. The nuclear force can be divided into two parts, a strong short-range repulsion, and a relatively weak long-range attraction. With some ingenuity (Moszkowski and Scott, 1960) one can make the division into short and long range parts in such a way that the long range part is weak and can be treated by perturbation theory, while the short range part is of sufficiently short range that its effect is to produce *independent* two-particle collisions that can be treated by scattering theory; a useful refinement of this method is that attraction and repulsion can be balanced in the short-range part so as to give almost no scattering. A very simple theory based on these ideas has been published by Vagradov and Kirzhnits (1960). Unfortunately, the results of their calculations are in better argument with experiment than those of more sophisticated and careful calculations, such as those by Razavy (1963) or Brown, Schappert, and Wong (1964). Brueckner and Masterson (1962) also get poor results when they use a potential that has the correct Yukawa form at large distances.

The expansion seems to be reasonably rapidly convergent, at least for the contribution of the repulsive core. Bethe (1965) estimates that the contribution of two-particle collisions to the energy is 23 MeV, three-particle collisions contribute -1.1 MeV and four-particle collisions 0.008 MeV. It is not clear that the convergence of other contributions to the energy, those from the attractive part of the potential and from interference between the attractive and repulsive parts (modification of the wave function by the core changes the expectation value of the attractive part of the potential), is so rapid.

The most disturbing feature of these calculations is the apparent sensitivity of the results to the form of the potential that is used. Some of the uncertainty could be removed by more precise scattering experiments, to determine, for example, the strength of the tensor force more accurately. Some of the uncertainty seems to be due to a more fundamental cause, namely propagation "off the energy shell". If perturbation theory is applied to a many-body system, the terms of the series can be grouped in such a way that the series looks like a succession of scattering events of pairs of nucleons. However the energy denominators are different from those which occur in scattering theory, since the excitation energy of the whole nucleus, not just the energy of the particular pair, must be used in the energy denominator. As a result potentials that give the same scattering may give different binding energies for the many-body system. The fact that calculations using different potentials give different results is evidence for the importance of this fact, and Bhaduri and Preston (1964) and Bethe (1965) have analyzed the reasons for the dependence of nuclear binding on the form of the potential. The old argument that two-body collisions give most of the binding energy is probably correct, but the potential between nucleons is rather deep, and it is not surprising that three-body effects should contribute 10 MeV or so to the nuclear binding energy—this is not a large fraction of the total potential energy, which is something like 40 MeV. In Brueckner theory some of these three-body effects are disguised as two-body effects by the use of "self-consistent single-particle energies".

It has been emphasised by Breit (1962) that there is no reason to be sure that a potential chosen to fit scattering data should be the correct one to use in the many-body Hamiltonian, and it is not certain that it is correct to use a local potential at all at short distances. An alternative approach, the boundary condition model, is discussed by Lomon in this volume. The potential should probably be nonlocal and energy dependent, since mesons take some time to travel from one nucleon to the other, and there may be quite strong many-body forces. It seems to be impossible in principle to distinguish between two-body and many-body potentials, since a canonical transformation can turn one into the other, as Bell (1962) has shown. We cannot tell which is the correct potential, since the wave function cannot be measured. The potential model assumes that the nucleus is made up of nucleons alone, whereas, from the point of view of field theory, it is composed of nucleons and mesons. The sensitivity of nuclear-binding calculations to the form of the potential suggests that the only hope of making a calculation accurate to within 5 MeV or so is by introducing the mesons into the many-body calculation. If so, we seem to be back to the position of Brueckner and Watson (1953).

The properties of nuclear matter that have attracted most attention are its binding energy and its equilibrium density. One good reason is that these quantities are much better known experimentally, since the extrapolation from real nuclei to nuclear matter is less uncertain for these quantities than for some others. Indeed it is possible to set limits on them, since the binding energy of nuclear matter must be more than the sum of the binding energy and the Coulomb energy of a heavy nucleus, which is about 12 MeV per nucleon, and, since the surface tension of a liquid drop puts the liquid in the center of the drop under pressure, the density of nuclear matter (under no pressure) cannot be more than the observed central density of real nuclei. It is not obvious that these two quantities are the simplest to make an accurate calculation of, as they depend on a delicate balance between the attractive and repulsive parts of the nuclear force. It might be valuable to have calculations of some other properties of nuclear matter made with as much care as those of binding energy, but the results of less sophisticated calculations are of some interest, and some tentative conclusions have been drawn from them.

When the energy has been calculated as a function of density, the compressibility of nuclear matter can be deduced. Brueckner and Gammel (1958) found nuclear matter to be so incompressible that the effects which have been ascribed to the compressibility of the nucleus [Wilets, Hill, and Ford (1953)] must be due to the compressibility of the surface; if an extra neutron is added to a nucleus, it should make the charge distribution cut off more rapidly. The symmetry energy can be calculated by varying the ratio of neutrons to protons in nuclear matter. The optical-model potential in the interior of the nucleus, both real and imaginary parts, have been calculated, and the small value of the imaginary part found by Shaw (1959), Gomes (1959) and Brenig (1959) supports the suggestion that most of the absorption of incident nucleons occurs on the surface of the nucleus. Bell (1957) had calculated the polarization of nuclear matter by an added particle; the induced charge modifies the magnetic moment of the last particle. The pairing energy has been calculated by Brueckner, Soda, Anderson, and Morel (1960) and by Emery and Sessler (1960), and it is found to be rather small, perhaps 200 KeV, so that again the surface of the nucleus must be more effective than the interior.

The theory of nuclear matter has played an important part in clarifying the basis of the optical model. It has been shown by Bell and Squires (1959) that the "one-particle Green function" can be used to define a potential which, when substituted in the Schrödinger equation, gives the elastic scattering of a nucleon by the nucleus exactly. The one-particle Green function describes the response of a nucleus when a single particle is added to or taken away from the ground state, and is a function with an expansion in perturbation theory which can be expressed in quite a simple form. This, however, is far too general to serve as a basis for the optical model, since all the compound elastic scattering is included, and the optical model gives only the broad features of the scattering cross section. Approximations must be made for the Green function, in the manner described in the review article by Brown (1959). These approximations are made almost automatically if nuclear matter is considered rather than a real nucleus. The one-particle Green function for infinite nuclear matter is a function of energy, for a definite momentum, which has a pole whose position gives both the real and imaginary parts of the optical potential in the interior of the nucleus. If the surface is taken into account also, a complete basis of the optical potential can be given. This potential would not, of course, give an exact description of elastic scattering for real nuclei, but would have to be corrected for various effects due to the small size of real nuclei, such as the strong coupling of a particular excited state of the nucleus. This approach to the optical model is described in more detail in papers by the author [Thouless (1964, 1966)].

It is clear that any theory of nuclear matter that ignores the nuclear surface is only of very restricted interest. Even for the heaviest nuclei the nuclear radius is only about 7×10^{-13} cm, so that roughly half the nucleons sit in the 2.4×10^{-13} cm thick surface region. The surface energy halves the total binding energy for light nuclei and is quite important even for heavy nuclei. Absorption of bombarding nucleons and many other nuclear reactions occur mainly in the surface. Spin–orbit coupling is a surface effect, since the isotropic nature of the interior prevents the spin of a single particle from having a preferred direction there. Unfortunately calculations of the nuclear surface structure are difficult to make, since one component of momentum is not conserved, and no calculations comparable with the best calculations for uniform nuclear matter have been made. The spin–orbit coupling has been calculated by Bell and Skyrme (1956) and Kisslinger (1956), and other properties of the surface have been calculated by Skyrme (1956), Vagradov and Kirzhnits (1962), Seyler and Blanchard (1963), and Day (1964).

We have already mentioned that the pairing energy, the energy difference between nuclei with even numbers of protons and neutrons, and those with odd numbers of protons or neutrons, appears to come mainly from the nuclear surface. Emery and Sessler (1960) found that pairing is weak at the equilibrium density of nuclear matter, but would be strong at lower densities, since the repulsive core is important for nucleons with a momentum equal to the Fermi momentum at high densities, but unimportant if the momentum is less; this suggests that pairing may occur more readily in that part of the nucleus where the density is less. Kennedy, Wilets, and Henley (1964) calculated the energy gap for a slab of nuclear matter by pairing together eigenstates which are running waves in a direction parallel to the slab faces, and standing waves across the slab. The gap parameter Δ is found to be anisotropic, with a maximum when the momentum is perpendicular to the face (pure standing waves), and the general trend is in good agreement with experiment. However, there is no necessity, in a inhomogeneous medium, that the states which are paired should be the eigenstates of the shell model potential; it may happen that the gap parameter Δ and the single-particle energy cannot be diagonalized simultaneously. The gap equation is particularly simple if the interaction between two nucleons with opposite spin is separable, so that the potential is

$$\langle \mathbf{R}' + \tfrac{1}{2}\mathbf{r}', \mathbf{R}' - \tfrac{1}{2}\mathbf{r}' | V | \mathbf{R} + \tfrac{1}{2}\mathbf{r}, \mathbf{R} - \tfrac{1}{2}\mathbf{r} \rangle = -\delta(\mathbf{R} - \mathbf{R}')f^*(r')f(r). \quad (1)$$

The gap equation can be written as

$$(\varepsilon - \mu + E_\alpha)u_\alpha(\mathbf{r}) - \int \Delta(\mathbf{r}, \mathbf{r}')v_\alpha^*(\mathbf{r}')\, d^3r' = 0,$$

$$(-\varepsilon + \mu + E_\alpha)v_\alpha(\mathbf{r}') - \int \Delta(\mathbf{r}, \mathbf{r}')u_\alpha^*(\mathbf{r})\, d^3r = 0, \quad (2)$$

$$\Delta(\mathbf{R} + \tfrac{1}{2}\mathbf{r}, \mathbf{R} - \tfrac{1}{2}\mathbf{r}) = f^*(r) \int f(r') \sum_\alpha u_\alpha(\mathbf{R} + \tfrac{1}{2}\mathbf{r}')v_\alpha(\mathbf{R} - \tfrac{1}{2}\mathbf{r}')\, d^3r',$$

as was shown by Bogoliubov (1958). Here ε is the single-particle energy operator (shell-model Hamiltonian), μ is the chemical potential, E_α is an eigenvalue that gives the excitation energy of the quasi-particle α, and u_α and v_α are the eigenfunctions. This equation is obtained by minimizing

$$\sum_\alpha \int [u_\alpha^*(\mathbf{r})(\varepsilon - \mu)u_\alpha(\mathbf{r}) - v_\alpha^*(\mathbf{r})(\varepsilon - \mu)v_\alpha(\mathbf{r})] \, d^3r$$

$$- \sum_{\alpha\beta} \iiint u_\alpha^*(\mathbf{R} + \tfrac{1}{2}\mathbf{r}')v_\alpha^*(\mathbf{R} - \tfrac{1}{2}\mathbf{r}')f^*(r')f(r)$$

$$\times u_\beta(\mathbf{R} + \tfrac{1}{2}\mathbf{r})v_b(\mathbf{R} - \tfrac{1}{2}\mathbf{r}) \, d^3R \, d^3r \, d^3r'$$

subject to the restrictions

$$\int (|u_\alpha(\mathbf{r})|^2 + |v_\alpha(\mathbf{r})|^2) \, d^3r = 1.$$

If the forms of u_α and v_α are further restricted by assuming that

$$u_\alpha(\mathbf{r}) = u_k\psi_k(\mathbf{r}), \qquad v_\alpha(\mathbf{r}) = v_k\tilde{\psi}_k(\mathbf{r}),$$

where ψ_k is one of the eigenstates of ε and $\tilde{\psi}_k$ is the time-reversed state with opposite spin, the gap equation

$$\Delta_k = \iiint \psi_k^*(\mathbf{R} + \tfrac{1}{2}\mathbf{r}')\tilde{\psi}_k(\mathbf{R} - \tfrac{1}{2}\mathbf{r}')f^*(r')f(r) \sum_{k'} \psi_{k'}(\mathbf{R} + \tfrac{1}{2}\mathbf{r})\tilde{\psi}_{k'}(\mathbf{R} - \tfrac{1}{2}\mathbf{r})$$

$$\times (\Delta_{k'}/2E_{k'}) \, d^3R \, d^3r \, d^3r', \quad (3)$$

$$E_k^2 = \varepsilon_k^2 + |\Delta_k|^2$$

is obtained; this is exactly the same as the gap equation for a homogeneous medium obtained by Bardeen, Cooper, and Schrieffer (1957). In their study of the slab model, Kennedy, Wilets, and Henley (1964) solved this equation. In analogy with the usual method of solving the Hartree–Fock equations, it should be possible to use this solution of Eq. (3) as a starting point for an iterative solution of Eq. (2). The first step of this iterative process gives

$$\Delta(\mathbf{R} + \tfrac{1}{2}\mathbf{r}, \mathbf{R} - \tfrac{1}{2}\mathbf{r}) = f^*(r) \int f(r') \sum_k \psi_k(\mathbf{R} + \tfrac{1}{2}\mathbf{r}')\tilde{\psi}_k(\mathbf{R} - \tfrac{1}{2}\mathbf{r}')$$

$$\times (\Delta_k/2E_k) \, d^3r'. \quad (4)$$

If $f(r)$ is a monotonic decreasing function of r, falling close to zero when $1/r$ is of the order of the Fermi momentum, Eq. (1) represents a potential which, like the real internucleon potential, is much more attractive for low relative momenta than for high momenta. The gap found by Kennedy, Wilets, and Henley is largest for momenta normal to the slab surface, and so the main contribution to the sum over k in Eq. (4) comes from states close to the Fermi surface which are almost pure standing waves. These will give a large contribution near the surface, since $\psi_k(\mathbf{R} + \tfrac{1}{2}\mathbf{r}')$ and $\tilde{\psi}_k(\mathbf{R} - \tfrac{1}{2}\mathbf{r}')$ will have the same sign, but in the interior they will give less; those states which have a node close to **R** may even make a negative contribution to Δ. This peaking of the gap parameter near the surface might be accentuated by further iterations of the equation. If this were to happen, it would suggest that the paired state should be taken as localized close to the surface, rather than as eigenstates of the shell-model Hamiltonian.

Wilkinson (1961) has shown that there is evidence for α-particle clusters in the nuclear surface. It is hard to assess what this evidence signifies, since the formation of localized pairs in the surface already make it more probable that four nucleons are close together than it would be if there were no pairs. Also Harada (1962) has shown that clusters are present in the surface with pure shell-model wave functions, but configuration mixing greatly increases the clustering. It is difficult to construct a convincing wave function for a heavy nucleus in which α-particle clusters exist in the surface, since the different orbital angular momenta of neutrons and protons in the shell model make a permanent association between a proton and a neutron unlikely.

Since the establishment of the shell model the main effort of theoretical nuclear physicists has been directed towards the interpretation of low-lying energy levels of nuclei in terms of states of the shell model or of the collective model. In this sort of analysis angular momentum theory plays a most important part, and the success of calculations is more often due to the stringent nature of restrictions made by angular momentum theory than to a detailed understanding of nuclear dynamics. Good agreement between calculation and experiment in a particular case does not prove that the real wave function is nearly equal to the shell-model wave function. This is illustrated by the fact that the angular momenta of low-lying states of nuclei with closed neutron and proton shells plus or minus one nucleon can be explained in terms of the simple shell model, the magnetic moments deviate somewhat from the predicted values, and electric quadrupole moments are completely different from those predicted by the simple shell model. Theoretical explanations of deviations from a simple model are usually made by assuming that shell-model configurations are mixed by some sort of interaction, and finding what interaction will lead to the observed results. In most cases an interaction is chosen to fit data for only a very limited range of nuclei.

It is clear that a detailed theory of nuclear matter is needed to clear up this situation. One is never going to be able to make a detailed calculation from first principles of all the features of interest in all nuclei, and even a sophisticated shell-model calculation gives only a limited amount of reliable information. We should use whatever methods are available to systematize the properties of nuclei. Since the basic interaction between nucleons has a short range, it is reasonable to suppose that the interaction can be analyzed as the sum of a volume term and a surface term (with possibly some interference between them). This sort of analysis of a property in terms of a volume and a surface component is not usually made, except in the optical model of nuclear reactions. It is clear from work that has been done so far that some quantities of interest can be calculated from the nucleon–nucleon interaction with a fair amount of certainty, while others are very sensitive to the form of the interaction or to approximations that have to be made. On the other hand, some quantities can be determined unambiguously by an analysis of experimental data, while others are uncertain. Calculations may therefore help to remove ambiguities in the analysis of experiment. One example of this is provided by the relative importance of volume and surface absorption of nucleons by nuclei, which was mentioned earlier.

A program of this sort has been proposed by Migdal (1964) and his collaborators, although, in this paper, he rejects the possibility of calculating the properties of nuclear matter from the nucleon–nucleon interaction. The "Fermi liquid theory" of Landau (1956) is developed in such a way that it is suitable for use in nuclear physics; pairing has to be considered, and account has to be taken of the finite, small, size of nuclei. In Landau's theory, used successfully to account for the properties of liquid He^3 at very low temperatures, the parameters that enter are the effective mass, which determines the quasi-particle spectrum, and the quasi-particle interaction, a function of spin and of the angle between the momentum directions of the two quasi-particles. Because of pairing and because of the two charged states of a nucleon all these quantities have more degrees of freedom in nuclear matter than in liquid He^3. Because of the nuclear surface, momentum is not conserved and so the effective interaction depends on more variables.

It is essential to the Landau theory that the states which are observed to have the properties of single-particle states are not simple excitations of one real nucleon, but are excitations of a complicated "quasi-particle", a particle together with all the necessary distortion of the medium around it. It is not a new idea in nuclear physics that simple nucleons moving inside the nucleus cannot be observed in a low-energy experiment, since this idea is contained in a paper of Brueckner, Eden, and Francis (1955), but it is clear from discussions at conferences that this is not generally believed. A recent paper by Thouless (1965) presents further evidence for the view that only quasi-particle excitations can be observed, and the overlap of these with a bare nucleon excitation can only be seen in a high energy experiment. The situation is analogous to the problem we discussed earlier of whether the real interaction between nucleons can be found.

Migdal (1964) asserts that only a small change, of the order of the inverse of the nuclear radius, in the total momentum of two quasi-particles occurs when they interact. This is incorrect, as can be seen by examining the matrix elements of an interaction potential between eigenstates suitable for the problem of a medium with a boundary, and momentum transfers of the order of the inverse of the surface thickness occurs. The importance of the surface makes the theory in its general form almost unusable, and drastic assumptions about the form of the interaction have to be made.

The effective interaction between quasi-particles is taken to have zero range, but to have a strength that varies considerably from the uniform central region to the outside of the nucleus. On this basis a large number of calculations have been made with considerable success. Among published calculations are calculations of magnetic moments by Troitskiĭ and Khodel' (1965), of quadrupole moments by Bunatyan and Mikulinskiĭ (1965), of giant resonances and the nuclear photoeffect by Lushnikov and Zaretsky (1965), Migdal, Lushnikov, and Zaretsky (1965) and Lushnikov and Urin (1965), of the spectrum of Pb^{208} by Guman and Birbrair (1965), and of nuclear masses by Sapershtein and Troitskiĭ (1965). These calculations do not differ very much in detail from standard shell-model calculations, but a determined effort is being made to separate these effects which are characteristic of nuclear matter from those that depend on the details of the energy levels which happen to be close to the Fermi surface. It should be noticed that the discussion of nuclear pairing energy by Kennedy, Wilets, and Henley (1964) in terms of a slab model assumes that the pairing energy is not sensitive to the detailed level structure, since a slab and a spherical nucleus have very different spectra in detail; the correctness of this assumption is not self-evident.

In view of the large number of parameters which could, in principle, be introduced into Migdal's theory, it is important that some attempt should be made to relate the effective interaction to nucleon–nucleon forces. There have been recent discussions of this problem by Green and Moszkowski (1965), Kallio (1965), and Kuo and Brown (1965). It can be hoped that an extension of this approach, carefully combined with Migdal's approach, will eventually lead to a less confused theory of the nucleus.

References

Bardeen, J., L. N. Cooper, and J. R. Schrieffer (1957), *Phys. Rev.*, **108**, 1175–1204.
Bell, J. S. (1957), *Nucl. Phys.*, **4**, 295–312.
Bell, J. S. (1962), *Lecture Notes on the Many-Body Problem*, C. Fronsdal, Ed., Benjamin, New York, pp. 214–22.
Bell, J. S., and T. H. R. Skyrme (1956), *Phil. Mag.*, **1**, 1055–68.
Bell, J. S., and E. J. Squires (1959), *Phys. Rev. Letters*, **3**, 96–7.
Belyaev, S. T. (1959), *Kgl. Danske Videnskab. Selskab; Mat.-fys. Medd.*, **31**, No. 11.
Bethe, H. A. (1956), *Phys. Rev.*, **103**, 1353–90.
Bethe, H. A. (1965), *Phys. Rev.*, **138**, B804–22.
Bethe, H. A., and R. F. Bacher (1936), *Rev. Mod. Phys.*, **8**, 82–229.
Bethe, H. A., B. H. Brandow, and A. G. Petschek (1963), *Phys. Rev.*, **129**, 225–64.
Bhaduri, M. K., and M. A. Preston (1964), *Can. J. Phys.*, **42**, 696–719.
Bogoliubov, N. N. (1958), *Dokl. Akad. Nauk S.S.S.R.*, **119**, 52–5; trans. in *Soviet Physics* (*Doklady*), **3**, 292–4.
Bohr, A., B. R. Mottelson, and D. Pines (1958), *Phys. Rev.*, **110**, 936–8.
Breit, G. (1962), *Rev. Mod. Phys.*, **34**, 766–812.
Brenig, W. (1959), *Nucl. Phys.*, **13**, 333–49.
Brown, G. E. (1959), *Rev. Mod. Phys.*, **31**, 893–919.
Brown, G. E., G. T. Schappert, and C. W. Wong (1964), *Nucl. Phys.*, **56**, 191–212.
Brueckner, K. A., R. J. Eden, and N. C. Francis (1955), *Phys. Rev.*, **99**, 76–87.
Brueckner, K. A., and J. L. Gammel (1958), *Phys. Rev.*, **109**, 1023–39.
Brueckner, K. A., and K. S. Masterson (1962), *Phys. Rev.*, **128**, 2267–76.
Brueckner, K. A., T. Soda, P. W. Anderson, and P. Morel (1960), *Phys. Rev.*, **118**, 1442–6.
Brueckner, K. A., and K. M. Watson (1953), *Phys. Rev.*, **92**, 1023–35.
Bunatyan, G. G., and M. A. Mikulinskii (1965), *Yadernaya Fiz.*, **1**, 38–45; trans. in *Soviet Jour. of Nuclear Phys.*, **1**, 26–30.
Day, B. D. (1964), *Phys. Rev.*, **136**, B1594–1608.
Elton, L. R. B. (1961), *Nucl. Phys.*, **23**, 681–93.
Emery, V. J., and A. M. Sessler (1960), *Phys. Rev.*, **119**, 248–50.
Gomes, L. C. (1959), *Phys. Rev.*, **116**, 1226–9.
Green, A. M. (1962), *Phys. Rev. Letters*, **3**, 60–1.
Green, I. M., and S. A. Moszkowski (1965), *Phys. Rev.*, **139**, B790–3.

Guman, V. N., and B. L. Birbrair (1965), *Nucl. Phys.*, **70**, 545–52.

Harada, K. (1962), *Progr. Theoret. Phys.*, **27**, 430–2.

Hofstadter, R. (1956), *Rev. Mod. Phys.*, **28**, 314–54.

Kallio, A. (1965), *Phys. Rev. Letters*, **18**, 51–4.

Kennedy, R. C., L. Wilets, and E. M. Henley (1964), *Phys. Rev. Letters*, **12**, 36–39.

Kisslinger, L. S. (1956), *Phys. Rev.*, **104**, 1077–85.

Kuo, T. T. S., and G. E. Brown (1965), *Phys. Rev. Letters*, **18**, 54–8.

Landau, L. D. (1956), *Zhur. Eksp. I Theor. Fiz.*, **30**, 1038–64; trans. in *Soviet Phys.* (*JETP*), **3**, 920–5.

Lushnikov, A. A., and M. G. Urin (1965), *Yadernaya Fiz.*, **1**, 436–42: trans. in *Soviet Jour. of Nuclear Phys.*, **1**, 311–5.

Lushnikov, A. A., and D. F. Zaretsky (1965), *Nucl. Phys.*, **66**, 35–48.

Majorana, E. (1933), *Zeits. f. Physik*, **82**, 137–45.

Migdal, A. B. (1964), *Nucl. Phys.*, **57**, 29–47.

Migdal, A. B., A. A. Lushnikov, and D. F. Zaretsky (1965), *Nucl. Phys.*, **66**, 193–208.

Moszkowski, S. A., and B. L. Scott (1960), *Ann. Phys.*, **11**, 65–115.

Nernirovsky, P. E., and Yu. V. Adamchuk (1962), *Nucl. Phys.*, **39**, 551–62.

Razavy, M. (1963), *Phys. Rev.*, **130**, 1091–9.

Sapershtein, É. E., and M. A. Troitskiï (1965), *Yadernaya Fiz.*, **1**, 400–6; trans. in *Soviet Jour. Nuclear Phys.*, **1**, 284–9.

Seeger, P. A. (1961), *Nucl. Phys.*, **25**, 1–135.

Seyler, R. G., and C. H. Blanchard (1963), *Phys. Rev.*, **131**, 355–65.

Shaw, G. L. (1959), *Ann. Phys.*, **8**, 509–50.

Skyrme, T. H. R. (1956), *Phil. Mag.*, **1**, 1043–54.

Thouless, D. J. (1964), *Rept. Progr. Phys.*, **27**, 53–91.

Thouless, D. J. (1966), *Nucl. Phys.*, **75**, 128–44.

Troitskiï, M. A., and V. A. Khodel' (1965), *Yadernaya Fiz.*, **1**, 205–14; trans. in *Soviet Jour. Nuclear Phys.*, **1**, 143–8.

Vagradov, G. M., and D. A. Kirzhnits (1960), *Zhur. Eksp. Teor. Fiz.*, **38**, 1499–1506: trans. in *Soviet Phys.* (*JETP*), **11**, 1082–6.

Vagradov, G. M., and D. A. Kirzhnits (1962), *Zhur. Eksp. Teor. Fiz.*, **43**, 1301–7: trans. in *Soviet Phys.* (*JETP*), **16**, 923–7.

von Weizsäcker, C. F. (1935), *Zeits. f. Physik*, **96**, 431–58.

Wick, G. C. (1934), *Nuovo Cimento*, **11**, 227–34.

Wilets, L., D. L. Hill, and K. W. Ford (1953), *Phys. Rev.*, **91**, 1488–1500.

Wilkinson, D. H. (1961), *Proceedings of the Rutherford Jubilee International Conference*, J. B. Birks, Ed., Heywood & Co., London, pp. 339–56.

Wong, C. W. (1964), *Nucl. Phys.*, **56**, 213–23.

Wong, C. W. (1965), *Nucl. Phys.*, **71**, 385–401.

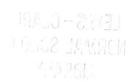

The Calculation of Nuclear Deformations

M. BARANGER

Carnegie Institute of Technology

and

K. KUMAR

Michigan State University

The fundamental problem of theoretical nuclear physics is the understanding of nuclear phenomena starting from basic two-body interactions. As one of the broadest and most versatile physicists of this century, Hans Bethe could hardly have been expected not to devote some effort to this field; in fact, he was one of its major contributors over the last ten years[1]. The field proved to be a difficult one, much of the difficulty being due to the complicated and still partly unknown nature of the two-body force. Consequently, there developed two schools of thought, which stayed rather separated until fairly recently. The "fundamental" school felt that the most important job was to learn "to do things right"; they concentrated on nuclear matter and devoted their time to finding a rapidly convergent expansion for the main nuclear properties. The "phenomenological" school was most interested in finding correlations between experimental data; they developed a hierarchy of "models" which, though only partially correct and sometimes contradictory, kept getting broader and fewer as time went on. Bethe would have felt equally comfortable in either school; by historical accident, he found himself among the fundamentalists. Now, the two schools have almost joined: the fundamental physicists have been so successful that they are beginning to be able to apply their methods to detailed properties of finite nuclei; the phenomenological physicists have essentially worked their way back to a single model, the shell model, which they are now trying to base on fundamentals. Still, the work that we shall describe in the following will be found to have a strong phenomenological flavor.

Phenomenology of Nuclear Deformations

The question we attempt to answer is: can one calculate nuclear deformations, starting from more basic quantities? We consider only quadrupole deformations, which are the most important ones, and we are interested only in heavy nuclei. We also want to describe the possible changes in deformation with time.

A phenomenological treatment of quadrupole deformations is provided by Bohr's collective Hamiltonian[2]. This is a classical Hamiltonian involving five coordinates describing both the orientation and the shape of the quadrupole. The orientation is specified by Euler angles θ, φ, and ψ, while the shape is determined by two parameters, β and γ. The three intrinsic radii R_1, R_2, and R_3, are given in terms of β and γ by

$$R_1 = R_0[1 + (5/4\pi)^{\frac{1}{2}}\beta \cos (\gamma - 120°)] \qquad (1a)$$

$$R_2 = R_0[1 + (5/4\pi)^{\frac{1}{2}}\beta \cos (\gamma + 120°)] \qquad (1b)$$

$$R_3 = R_0[1 + (5/4\pi)^{\frac{1}{2}}\beta \cos \gamma], \qquad (1c)$$

R_0 being the average radius of the nucleus. Then, Bohr's Hamiltonian is

$$\mathscr{H} = \mathscr{V}(\beta, \gamma) + \mathscr{T}_{\text{rot}} + \mathscr{T}_{\text{vib}}. \qquad (2)$$

The first term is the potential energy of deformation. The second is the rotational kinetic energy

$$\mathscr{T}_{\text{rot}} = \tfrac{1}{2}[\mathscr{I}_1(\beta, \gamma)\omega_1^2 + \mathscr{I}_2(\beta, \gamma)\omega_2^2 + \mathscr{I}_3(\beta, \gamma)\omega_3^2], \qquad (3)$$

where $\mathscr{I}_1$, $\mathscr{I}_2$, and $\mathscr{I}_3$ are the three principal moments of inertia, and ω_1, ω_2, and ω_3 are the components of the angular velocity on the intrinsic axes. The third term of $\mathscr{H}$ is the vibrational kinetic energy

$$\mathscr{T}_{\text{vib}} = \tfrac{1}{2}B_{\beta\beta}(\beta, \gamma)\dot{\beta}^2 + B_{\beta\gamma}(\beta, \gamma)\dot{\beta}\dot{\gamma} + \tfrac{1}{2}B_{\gamma\gamma}(\beta, \gamma)\dot{\gamma}^2. \qquad (4)$$

This Hamiltonian is the most general expression that can be written down, subject to the conditions of invariance under rotations, reflection, time reversal, and the condition that there be no more than two powers of the velocities. This last condition means that the motion is assumed to be slow. $\mathscr{H}$ contains seven arbitrary functions of β and γ: the potential $\mathscr{V}$, the three moments of inertia $\mathscr{I}$, and the three vibrational inertial parameters B. Invariance principles have nothing to say about these seven functions, outside of simple symmetry conditions; they are determined by the internal dynamics of the nucleus.

Once we have decided to use Bohr's Hamiltonian, we are left with two separate problems. Problem 1 is: How do we find the seven functions? Problem 2 is: Once we know the seven functions, how do we solve the Hamiltonian for energy levels, wave functions, transition probabilities, etc.? We shall first consider our solution of problem 2 briefly. Then we shall devote most of the remaining discussion to problem 1.

Solution of Bohr's Hamiltonian

First, Bohr's Hamiltonian must be quantized. Unfortunately, there is no unique way of doing this. Bohr uses the Pauli prescription[3], which is designed to give the right answer when the variables can be transformed to Cartesian coordinates, but this is not the case here and therefore the Pauli prescription loses its only justification. The correct procedure would be never to make the classical approximation, but so far this has not proved practical. Hence we follow Bohr's lead and quantize the Hamiltonian the same way he does. This yields a five-dimensional Schrödinger equation.

The next job is to take into account rotational invariance. The way to do this is well known[4]. Every stationary wave function with angular momentum I, z-component M, and other quantum numbers α, can be written

$$\psi_{\alpha IM}(\beta, \gamma, \theta, \varphi, \psi) = \sum_K A_{\alpha IK}(\beta, \gamma)\varphi^I_{MK}(\theta, \varphi, \psi). \quad (5)$$

K must be even, ≥ 0, and $\leq I$; moreover, $K = 0$ is not allowed when I is odd. The functions φ are given in terms of the usual rotation matrices $\mathscr{D}$ by

$$\varphi^I_{MK}(\theta, \varphi, \psi) = [(2I + 1)/16\pi^2(1 + \delta_{K0})]^{1/2}$$
$$\cdot [\mathscr{D}^I_{MK}(\theta, \varphi, \psi) + (-1)^I\mathscr{D}^I_{M, -K}(\theta, \varphi, \psi)]. \quad (6)$$

When expansion (5) is substituted in the Schrödinger equation, there results a set of coupled partial differential equations for the functions of two variables $A_{\alpha IK}(\beta, \gamma)$.

The big problem is to solve these coupled equations. Analytical solutions can be given only for a few very special cases of the seven arbitrary functions. This family of analytic solutions can be enlarged by perturbation theory, but the result still falls far short of the complexity and diversity encountered in Nature. At the moment, very little is known about the actual form of the six inertial coefficients $\mathscr{I}$ and B as functions of β and γ. But enough work has been done on the potential energy $\mathscr{V}(\beta, \gamma)$ to make it clear that it can have a large variety of shapes. Most of the analytic or perturbative solutions take $\mathscr{V}$ as a quadratic function of the deformation, the equilibrium point occurring either for a spherical shape or for a deformed shape. This is undoubtedly a gross oversimplification. It may be valid for a few "hard" nuclei, either spherical nuclei with almost closed shells or strongly deformed nuclei. But most nuclei are "soft", by which we mean that their deformation is not a fixed quantity, but is affected by large fluctuations, especially in the excited states and even in the ground state. This is certainly true of the "transition" nuclei at the edge of regions of deformation, such as the osmium or the light baryum isotopes, but it is also probably true of most so-called spherical nuclei, as evidenced by the fact that the assumption of harmonic vibrations does not work very well. When there are large fluctuations in the deformation, the assumption of quadratic potential energy cannot be expected to be good, one reason among many being that, with a deformed equilibrium shape, it does not satisfy the proper symmetry conditions. The correct function $\mathscr{V}(\beta, \gamma)$ is presumably considerably more complicated and may show a lot of variation from nucleus to nucleus[5]. Examples of such functions calculated with the pairing-plus-quadrupole model are given in Figs. 1 to 3.

So, we are forced to give a completely numerical solution of the system of coupled equations[6]. Since γ can be restricted to be between $0°$ and $60°$, which is obvious from Eq. (1), it is natural to choose a triangular mesh. Our mesh consists of one large equilateral triangle divided into 256 small triangles. The seven functions of β and γ are calculated (by a method to be explained later) at each point of this mesh. We solve the Schrödinger equation by the variational method, the variational parameters being the values of the components A_K of the wave function at all points of the mesh. In our most complicated case ($I = 4$) there are 392 variational parameters. By use of a two-dimensional numerical integration formula, the variational integrals are replaced by quadratic forms in the variational parameters, so that the Schrödinger equation reduces to a generalized eigenvalue problem for a very large matrix. However, the matrix has many vanishing elements, so that we are able to find the first few eigenvalues and eigenvectors by a minimization method. We shall not give the details here, but the procedure has been checked on problems whose solution is known and has been found to be good, the accuracy being of the order of a few per cent on the energy levels. Any glaring disagreement between the calculations and experiment will have to be blamed on the physics of our work, rather than the mathematics, and unfortunately the former is not nearly as good as the latter. Examples of wave functions obtained by this procedure[7] are shown in Figs. 6 to 9.

The Shell Model

Now, we return to what earlier we called problem 1: How do we find the seven functions? We must start from a more fundamental model than Bohr's, and this is the shell model. In other words, we are going to assume a certain spherically-symmetric, one-body potential, which will yield certain single-particle energies and single-particle wave functions, and we shall also need a certain residual interaction to generate corrections to this single-particle picture. But before going into the details of the special brand of shell model used, namely the pairing-plus-quadrupole model, we should give a thought to the justification of the shell model itself from higher principles. This is the "fundamental" area mentioned at the beginning and in which Bethe has made many substantial contributions.

Basically, there are two ways of treating the many-body problem so as to justify the shell model: the independent particle approximation, or Hartree–Fock approximation; and the independent-pair approximation, or Brueckner approximation. Both methods are capable of yielding a single-particle potential, a residual interaction, and a prescription for handling the latter. But the Hartree–Fock approximation is much, much easier than Brueckner's. We do not wish, and are not able, to give a detailed discussion of the relative merits of the two approximations, nor of the crossbreeds that have been or could be invented. But we can make two statements that seem to be based on fact. The first is that it is almost certain that Hartree–Fock is not strictly valid for the "true" nuclear force, whatever that may be. The second statement is that almost any theorist who works on complicated finite nuclei carries Hartree–Fock in the back of his mind, sometimes unconsciously, and if one watches carefully one will see that much of the formalism that such a person uses is not valid outside of a Hartree–Fock context. The disagreement between these two statements is unfortunate, but it is there, and it is likely that physicists (of the "phenomenological" school) will continue using Hartree–Fock until it has been shown beyond any doubt that it leads to misleading results, and this has not been shown yet. People who use Brueckner theory in shell-model calculations have to make so many additional approximations that their work ends up looking very much like Hartree–Fock, except for the fact that they have a host of hidden small assumptions where the others have a few clearly stated large ones.

We are now ready to discuss the pairing-plus-quadrupole model. It will soon become clear that we too have Hartree–Fock at the back of our heads.

The Pairing-Plus-Quadrupole Model

The Hamiltonian of the pairing-plus-quadrupole model consists of three parts

$$H = H_S + H_P + H_Q. \tag{7}$$

H_S is a spherically symmetric single-particle Hamiltonian. It is specified by giving the energies of the various shell-model levels, $3s_{1/2}$, $2d_{5/2}$, $1g_{7/2}$, etc., and by giving their wave functions, which are assumed to be harmonic oscillator's. The other two parts, H_P and H_Q, constitute the residual interaction, comprising the pairing force of BCS[8] and the quadrupole force of Elliott[9], which were brought together in Copenhagen[10] around 1958. The pairing force has matrix elements

$$\langle i\bar{i}|H_P|j\bar{j}\rangle = -g, \tag{8}$$

where i and j are any two single-particle states, in any representation, and $\bar{i}$, and $\bar{j}$ are their time-reverses. All other matrix elements of H_P vanish. Like most people working with deformed nuclei, we use different pairing constants, g_n and g_p, for neutrons and protons. The quadrupole force is

$$H_Q = -\sum_{i>j}\chi_{ij}Q(i)\cdot Q(j), \tag{9}$$

the sum being over all pairs of nucleons. In this, $Q(i)$ is the quadrupole moment of particle i, $r_i^2 Y_{2M}(\theta_i, \varphi_i)$, and $Q\cdot Q$ is the tensor product. In this case, we take the same χ for all pairs, be they neutrons, protons, or neutron and proton; otherwise, the theory of collective motion would become too complicated to manage.

Clearly, these forces do not look at all like the "real" residual interaction; the latter is very badly known, of course, but presumably it is a rather short-range affair, which may perhaps have a one-pion-exchange tail and a central repulsion. So, the pairing-plus-quadrupole model needs to be justified too. There is no doubt that it works well, if handled skillfully: it was invented expressly for the purpose of producing pairing effects and quadrupole deformations, which experiment has shown to be the two most important effects of residual interactions at low energy; this model is also much easier to use than other types of residual interactions, which explains its popularity and its wide applicability. Still, it would be nice to understand, from a theoretical point of view, why the correct residual interaction, whatever that may be, can be replaced by this obviously incorrect one.

Actually, one can get some pretty silly results if one makes this substitution without using a little caution: one should not take the pairing-plus-quadrupole model too seriously. For instance, one should not use it with a complete set of single-particle states. Suppose that we were to use the pairing force, say, with a complete set of states. Then we could use the coordinate representation and the state i of Eq. (8) could be, for instance, the state of a neutron at point x with spin up. Then the other neutron would be in the time-reversed state $\bar{i}$, i.e., it would also be at point x, but with spin down. Similarly, on the other side of the matrix element, j could be a neutron at point y with spin up and $\bar{j}$ a neutron at point y with spin down. Now, Eq. (8) says that this matrix element is $-g$, no matter what the two points x and y are. They could be one million light years apart, and it would still be $-g$. Of course, this is absurd. The cure is never to use the pairing force between a complete set of states. One should limit it to a few states near the Fermi surface, which is exactly what BCS did. Similarly ridiculous results follow if the quadrupole force is used within a complete set of states. Since the attraction is proportional to the inner product of the quadrupole moments, the tendency is for all the nucleons to line up and to recede as far as possible from the origin. The equilibrium nuclear shape is that of a needle! Here again, the quadrupole force should be restricted to a rather small set of states. What set of states is appropriate should come out of the discussion of the justification of the model.

Justification of the Pairing-plus-Quadrupole Model

In order to justify the model, we should first know how we would go about calculating nuclear deformations, given an arbitrary two-body force. We do not have to actually carry it out, but we should know how it is done in principle. This is where the Hartree–Fock approximation creeps in, or more precisely the Hartree–Bogolyubov approximation[11], which is the generalization of Hartree–Fock including pairing. Using it and other reasonable assumptions, one can write down an expression for the energy of a nucleus as a function of deformation[12]. This expression contains two types of matrix elements of the two-body force. One is the matrix element $G_0(abcd)$ between two pairs of identical nucleons (ab) and (cd), coupled to $J = 0$. This may also be called the pairing matrix element; it is that matrix element which is very simple when a pairing force is used. The other is $K_2(abcd)$, the antisymmetrized matrix element between two particle-hole pairs (ab) and (cd), coupled to $J = 2$. This is the one and only matrix element which is simple when a quadrupole force is used. What we must do now is calculate these two types of matrix elements for the "correct" residual interaction, and see if they are similar to what a pairing force would give for G_0 and what a quadrupole force would give for K_2. Naturally, we don't know the correct residual interaction, but we can try several of the most popular and the most likely candidates, and we actually find that the conclusion is always more or less the same.

We shall not discuss the pairing matrix element in very great detail, because it is the less critical of the two. People have been doing pairing calculations with conventional forces for about five years[13]. What they find is that the pairing potential, instead of being constant as in the case of the pairing force, depends on the single-particle state. But the variations are not very large, of the order of 20% or so, so that the use of the pairing force can be considered a good approximation as long as we can believe the theory on which these calculations with conventional forces are based. This is the BCS theory[8], and it holds as long as we do not include more than one single-particle state with the same charge, parity, and angular momentum quantum numbers. For instance, the latter condition would be violated if we were to mix single-particle states coming from two different major oscillator shells of the same parity. This we must not do; but it is all right to include two adjacent oscillator shells, since they have opposite parities.

For the quadrupole matrix element, the story is a little more complicated. We made a number of comparisons with what we felt were reasonably realistic two-body interactions. One of them was just a Gaussian with an exchange mixture close to Rosenfeld's. Another was a separable force acting in relative s-states and giving the right energy and density of nuclear matter[14]. Still another was the force developed by Tabakin[15] especially for doing Hartree–Fock calculations, and which fits the two-body data quite well. In all cases, the conclusion seems to be this[12]: as long as we stay inside one harmonic oscillator shell, there is quite a good correlation between the quadrupole and the realistic matrix elements, i.e., the signs are almost always the same and even the magnitudes follow each other roughly; for matrix elements involving two adjacent oscillator shells, the correlation of signs is still there, but that of magnitudes is not so good, and in particular, if the strength of the quadrupole force has been adjusted correctly for a certain shell, then that same quadrupole force is found to be too strong for matrix elements involving the shell above, and too weak for those involving the shell below; for matrix elements involving more than two adjacent oscillator shells, the signs do not correlate any more and the quadrupole force is a very bad approximation.

Considerations of this kind help to understand why the pairing-plus-quadrupole model works and why it should be restricted to a relatively small number of states, somewhere between one and two harmonic oscillator shells. The calculations of Figs. 1 to 5 use two shells. The next problem is the determination of the parameters g and χ. One possible approach is to determine them empirically by fitting the data, it being understood that they cannot jump wildly from one nucleus to the next, but must be smooth functions of the number of nucleons. However, from a theorist's point of view, it would be much nicer if their values could be predicted *a priori*, but can this be done? For the pairing force, we don't know how to do it. Everyone else in the field assumes that g is proportional to $1/A$, and we do the same, but we know of no convincing argument for it. We determine the coefficient of $1/A$ by fitting odd–even mass differences, but this is rather rough, because neither the data nor the theory are very good. The results we get, $g_n = 21$ MeV$/A$ and $g_p = 26$ MeV$/A$, agree well with the figures used by other workers for either deformed or spherical nuclei.

For the quadrupole force, on the other hand, it seems possible to predict the value of χ. One might just try to get χ out of a comparison of the quadrupole force with a realistic force, such as those mentioned earlier. But this is not correct and gives too small a χ, because the calculation is done only in two adjacent shells. The other shells do not contribute as much as if the force was really quadrupolar, but they do make a small contribution. Actually, it is possible to produce an argument to calculate χ *a priori*.

The idea is that the energy of nuclei, on the average, should be independent of their shape[16], because nuclear forces have a range much smaller than the nuclear radius. This should be true only on the average, after shell effects have been eliminated. Shell effects stabilize the spherical shape for some nuclei and the deformed one for others. But if there were no shells, if the single-particle levels were uniformly spaced, then no energy should be lost or gained by deforming the nucleus. Out of this assumption comes the value of χ. We shall give the argument for a single oscillator shell, because it is simpler; the result is the same with two shells, but it would be quite different with three or more shells, which we have seen should not be done.

Consider a nucleus with a spherical shape, in the Hartree–Fock approximation and without pairing. Call $A, B, C, \ldots$ the filled single-particle levels, and $a, b, c, \ldots$ the empty ones. The single-particle energies are $E_A, E_B, \ldots, E_a, E_b, \ldots$. The wave functions are approximated by harmonic oscillator ones. Now, the change in Hartree–Fock energy of the nucleus when we introduce a small external deformation potential DQ (Q: quadrupole moment; D: deformation parameter) is easily found by perturbation theory to be

$$D^2\left[\sum_{aA} \frac{|\langle A|Q|a\rangle|^2}{E_a - E_A} + 2 \sum_{aAbB} K_2(aAbB) \frac{\langle A|Q|a\rangle\langle B|Q|b\rangle}{(E_a - E_A)(E_b - E_B)}\right]. \quad (10)$$

The first term is the increase in single-particle energy due to the change in occupation probability of the single-particle levels; the second term is the quadrupole interaction between the particles, which is zero when the nucleus is spherical. This total energy change must be zero *on the average*. To perform the average, we take a uniform distribution of single-particle levels over energy interval $\hbar\omega$, the shell spacing, and we pick the Fermi energy at random on this interval. In the first term of Eq. (10) for instance, a given pair of levels $\alpha\beta$ will contribute only if the Fermi energy happens to fall between them, and the probability for that is $|E_\alpha - E_\beta|/\hbar\omega$. Hence, the average of the first term is

$$\frac{1}{2} \sum_{\alpha\beta} \frac{|\langle\alpha|Q|\beta\rangle|^2}{\hbar\omega}. \qquad (11)$$

Each sum runs over all states of the shell and the factor 1/2 corrects for counting each pair twice. Similarly, the average of the second term is found to be

$$\frac{1}{2(\hbar\omega)^2} \sum_{\alpha\beta\gamma\delta} K_2(\alpha\beta\gamma\delta)\langle\beta|Q|\alpha\rangle\langle\delta|Q|\gamma\rangle. \qquad (12)$$

For a quadrupole force, matrix element K_2 is

$$K_2(\alpha\beta\gamma\delta) = -\chi\langle\alpha|Q|\beta\rangle\langle\gamma|Q|\delta\rangle. \qquad (13)$$

To determine χ, we just have to write that the sum of Eqs. (11) and (12) vanishes. There comes

$$\chi = \hbar\omega/\sum_{\alpha\beta} |\langle\alpha|Q|\beta\rangle|^2. \qquad (14)$$

The evaluation of the sum inside a harmonic oscillator shell is easily done. The length parameter $b = (\hbar/m\omega)^{\frac{1}{2}}$ is determined by requiring that the nucleus have the right radius $r_0 A^{\frac{1}{3}}$. It is the quantity χb^4, rather than χ, which enters in most calculations using the quadrupole force and its value turns out to be

$$\chi b^4 = \frac{8\pi}{3} \frac{\hbar^2}{mr_0^2} A^{-5/3}. \qquad (15)$$

This is the value of χ that was used in the calculations of Figs. 1 to 5. The same expression for χ was derived by Mottelson[10] a few years ago, but his argument was more restrictive; in particular, the contribution of the closed shells to χ had to be exactly half of the total. In our derivation, this is not necessary, and we feel that in fact this contribution is probably quite a bit less than a half.

Besides g_n, g_p, and χ, the model also contains two parameters describing the effective charge and the inertia of the core. There is no a priori way to determine these; they must be fitted to the data. Finally, the single-particle spherical levels must also be chosen. We do not try to vary them and just use levels that have proved satisfactory in the past[17].

Now that we have discussed the validity of the pairing-plus-quadrupole model and the choice of parameters, we go on to the actual calculation of the seven functions in Bohr's Hamiltonian.

Calculation of the Potential Energy of Deformation

There are several, slightly different ways of calculating $\mathscr{V}(\beta, \gamma)$. We shall only explain the simplest one, which is not the one used in the calculations[18] for Figs. 1 to 5. It proceeds through the following steps:

(*I*) To the spherical shell-model Hamiltonian H_S one adds a quadrupole deformation potential, which depends on two parameters

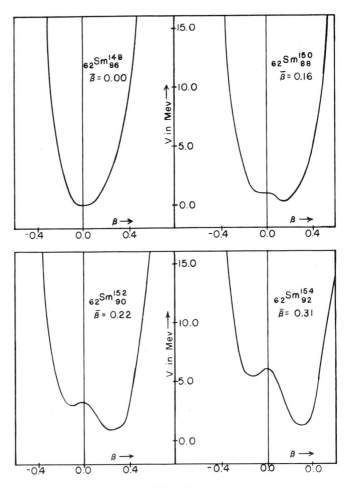

Figure 1.

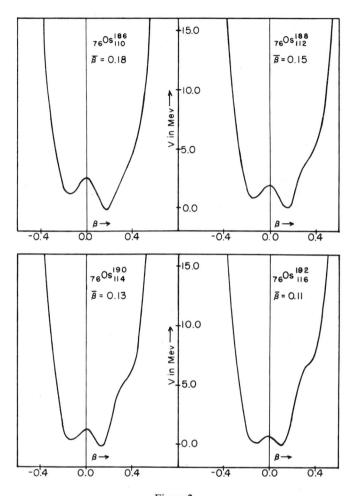

Figure 2.

β and γ. For each point of the (β, γ) mesh mentioned earlier, the energy levels and wave functions of this deformed Hamiltonian, which is essentially the Nilsson Hamiltonian[19], are calculated.

(2) For each $(\beta\gamma)$, the pairing force is used to do a BCS calculation on these Nilsson levels. Out of this come a neutron and a proton energy gap and the usual BCS occupation probabilities u^2 and v^2.

(3) The expectation value of the original pairing-plus-quadrupole Hamiltonian (Eq. (7)) is taken for the BCS wave function thus obtained. The result is $\mathscr{V}(\beta, \gamma)$.

If $\mathscr{V}(\beta, \gamma)$ has a sharp minimum, the nucleus is "hard" and its permanent deformation may be taken to be that which minimizes $\mathscr{V}$. The various characteristics of the nucleus, odd-even mass difference, intrinsic quadrupole moment, moment of inertia, gyromagnetic ratio, ..., may then be calculated at this equilibrium deformation. If $\mathscr{V}(\beta, \gamma)$ only has a shallow minimum, then fluctuations or collective motion are quite important; the nucleus is "soft" and the deformation that minimizes $\mathscr{V}$ has no great significance.

Figures 1 and 2 are plots of $\mathscr{V}$ vs. β for $\gamma = 0$, for two series of isotopes. In the Sm isotopes, one can see the sudden onset of deforma-

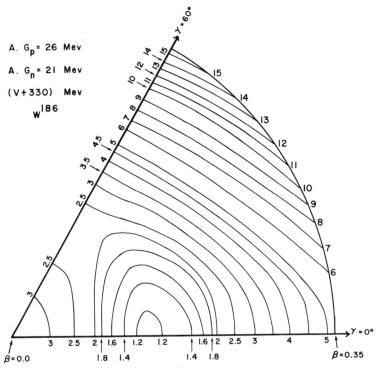

Figure 3a.

tion as the neutron number reaches 90. For $N = 88$, there is a deformed minimum, but it is very shallow and should be washed out by the fluctuations; in other words, this is a very soft spherical nucleus. For $N = 90$, the minimum is already several MeV deep, so that this nucleus should be well-deformed. One can also see how prolate deformations ($\beta > 0$) are much preferred over oblate ($\beta < 0$). In the Os isotopes, on the other hand, the change with neutron number is very gradual and the difference between prolate and oblate is also almost gone. These nuclei tend to be γ-unstable and should have low γ-vibrations.

Figures 3a, b, and c are examples of contour plots of $\mathscr{V}$ vs. both β and γ. The point is to show the effect of the pairing force. In Fig. 3a, the strength of the pairing force is at its normal value and the minimum comes for a prolate deformation. In Fig. 3b, the pairing strength has

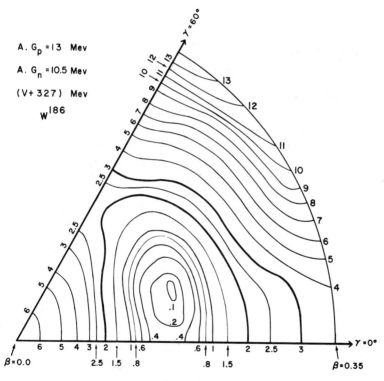

Figure 3b.

been decreased by a factor 2; the energy surface is much less smooth than before and has a shallow minimum for an asymmetric shape. In Fig. 3c, the pairing is 50% greater than in Fig. 3a; now, the deformation energy is essentially proportional to β^2. The pairing force acts as a great symmetrizing agent, smoothing out the energy surface more and more as its strength is increased. In particular, we found that a reasonable amount of pairing will always wash out an asymmetric minimum such as that of Fig. 3b, especially since such minima are always very shallow in the first place.

Figures 4 and 5 show comparisons with experiment of the intrinsic quadrupole moments and moments of inertia, calculated at the potential minimum, for nuclei of the rare earth region. There is considerable detailed agreement. The sharp rise in deformation at the beginning of

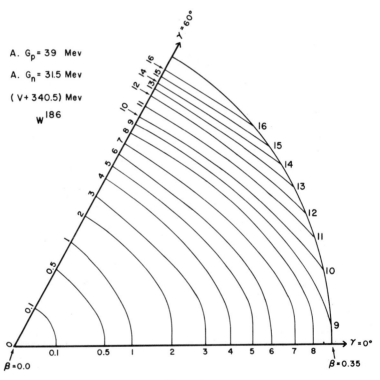

Figure 3c.

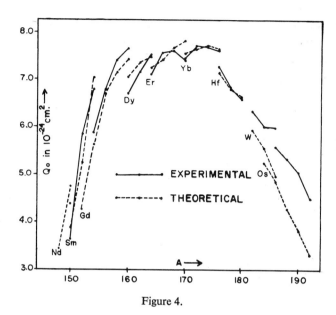

Figure 4.

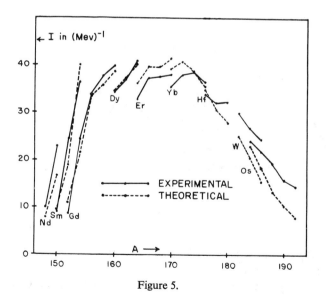

Figure 5.

the region is well reproduced. At the other end, the W and Os nuclei are soft and good agreement should not be expected. For soft nuclei, it is necessary to solve the problem of collective motion completely, which means finding the six inertial functions of Bohr's Hamiltonian.

Calculation of the Inertial Functions

These functions are calculated with a theory of collective motion[12] in which the main assumption, over and above the pairing-plus-quadrupole model, is the adiabatic approximation. This is appropriate

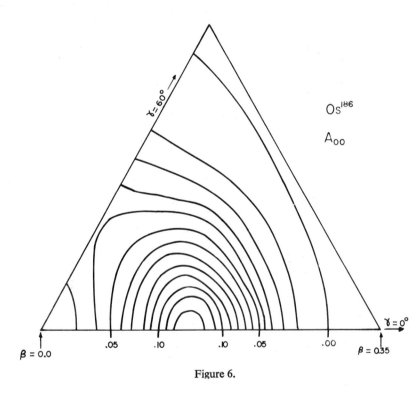

Figure 6.

since soft nuclei are those in which collective motion is slow. It is not a linearized theory, such as the random phase approximation; the latter would be very bad since we are dealing with potential surfaces whose shape is very far from parabolic. It is closer to the cranking model, but it is more satisfactory because it is based on the time-dependent Hartree–Fock picture and is fully self-consistent. Before ending, we shall present a few wave functions that have been calculated[7] by this method, followed by the numerical solution outlined earlier for Bohr's Hamiltonian.

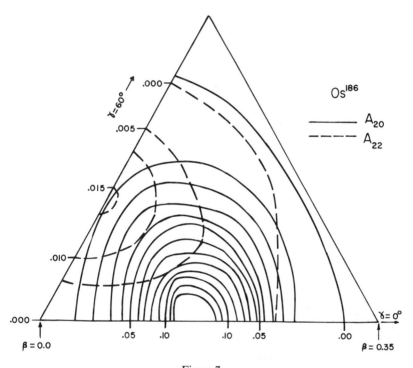

Figure 7.

Figure 6 shows the ground state wave function $A_{00}(\beta, \gamma)$ of Os^{186}, again as a contour plot. It is fairly well concentrated around $\beta = 0.15$, $\gamma = 0$, which seems to indicate that Os^{186} is a soft, but well-deformed nucleus. This indication is confirmed when we look at the first excited state wave function, $A_{2K}(\beta, \gamma)$, Fig. 7. The $K = 0$ component, given by the solid lines, is essentially the same as that of the ground state; the $K = 2$ component, given by the dotted lines, is very small. Hence K is a

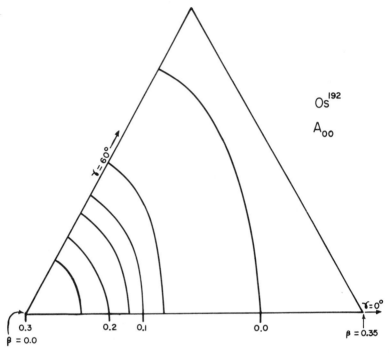

Figure 8.

fairly good quantum number, as befits a rotational nucleus. Figures 8 and 9 show the corresponding wave functions for Os^{192}; they are completely different. Now, the ground wave function has its maximum at $\beta = 0$; the two wave functions of the first excited state differ from the ground, and from each other, and have about equal intensity, all of which agrees qualitatively with the picture of a vibrational nucleus.

In conclusion, there seems to be no insurmountable difficulties associated with nuclear deformation and collective motion themselves. The serious problems are still in the foundations on which one has to build: how good is the shell model, and what parameters should be used in it?

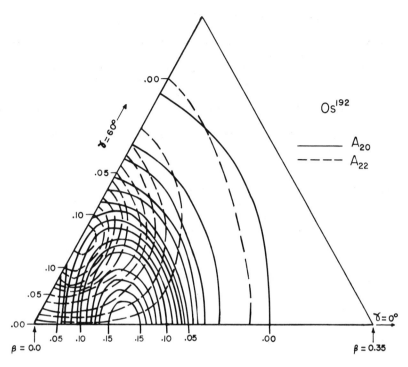

Figure 9.

References

1. Bethe, H. A., *Phys. Rev.*, **103**, 1353 (1956); **138**, 804 (1965).
2. Bohr, A., *Mat. Fys. Medd. Dan. Vid. Selsk.*, **26**, No. 14 (1952).
3. Pauli, W., Handbuch der Physik, 2nd ed., Springer, Berlin, 1933, Vol. XXIV/I.
4. Van Winter, C., *Physica*, **20**, 274 (1954).
5. For instance, a discussion of some possible forms of this function is given by W. D. Myers and W. J. Swiatecki, *Nuclear Masses and Deformations*, UCRL-11980, to be published. The numerical solution of Bohr's Hamiltonian with their potential has been given by K. Kumar, *Bull. Am. Phys. Soc.*, **10**, 1106 (1965), and to be published.
6. Kumar, K., and M. Baranger, to be published.
7. Kumar, K., Doctoral Dissertation, Carnegie Institute of Technology, December, 1963, unpublished.

8. Bardeen, J., L. N. Cooper, and J. R. Schrieffer, *Phys. Rev.*, **108**, 1175 (1957).
9. Elliott, J. P., *Proc. Roy. Soc. (London)*, **A245**, 128, 562 (1958).
10. Mottelson, B. R., in The Many-body Problem, lectures given at the summer school in Les Houches 1958, Wiley, New York, 1959; S. T. Belyaev, *Mat. Fys. Medd. Dan. Vid. Selsk.*, **31**, No. 11 (1959); B. R. Mottelson, in *Proc. Int. School of Physics "Enrico Fermi"*, Course 15, Varenna 1960, Academic Press, New York, 1962; L. S. Kisslinger and R. A. Sorensen, *Mat. Fys. Medd. Dan. Vid. Selsk.*, **32**, No. 9 (1960); D. R. Bès, *Mat. Fys. Medd. Dan. Vid. Selsk.*, **33**, No. 2 (1961); M. Baranger and K. Kumar, *Nucl. Phys.*, **62**, 113 (1965).
11. Bogolyubov, N. N., *Uspekhi Fiz. Nauk*, **67**, 549 (1959); English trans., *Soviet Phys.-Uspekhi*, **67** (2), 236 (1959).
12. Baranger, M., and K. Kumar, to be published.
13. For instance, see R. Arvieu et al., *Phys. Letters*, **4**, 119 (1963).
14. Muthukrishnan, R., and M. Baranger, *Phys. Letters*, **18**, 160 (1965).
15. Tabakin, F., *Ann. Phys. (New York)*, **30**, 51 (1964). The matrix elements of this interaction were calculated by T. T. S. Kuo, to whom we are very grateful.
16. It is also possible to take into account the changes in surface energy and Coulomb energy with deformation.
17. Mottelson, B. R., and S. G. Nilsson, *Mat. Fys. Skr. Dan. Vid. Selsk.*, **1**, No. 8 (1959); L. S. Kisslinger and R. A. Sorensen, *Revs. Mod. Phys.*, **35**, 853 (1963); J. Blomqvist and S. Wahlborn, *Arkiv Fysik*, **16**, 545 (1960).
18. The latter method is given in refs. 7 or 12.
19. Nilsson, S. G., *Mat. Fys. Medd. Dan. Vid. Selsk.*, **29**, No. 16 (1955).

A Model for the Study of the Interference of Nuclear Reaction Mechanisms*

N. AUSTERN and K. F. RATCLIFF†

University of Pittsburgh

1. Introduction

Bethe's great review of nuclear physics incorporated as one major section (Be37) a quantitative study of nuclear reactions as processes of many-body systems. It came only one year after Bohr (Bo36) had emphasized the necessity of a many-body approach, and had shown that more simplified models of nuclear reactions were not correct. However, Bethe's theory soon was superseded: Although it did yield an important generalization of the Breit–Wigner resonance formula (Br36), subsequent theories (Ka38, Wi47) yielded this same kind of result more clearly and rigorously. Nevertheless, Bethe's basic approach is both heuristic and flexible, and is very much in the spirit of current work with nuclear reactions (for example, see Fe58 and Fe62). It is used as the starting point of the present article.‡

An inelastic scattering reaction entails a transition between two states of the target nucleus, φ_1 and φ_2. It is often interesting to disregard the existence of other states of the target nucleus and to consider as a crude approximation to the stationary-state wave function for the system the linear combination

$$\Psi^{(+)} \approx \xi_1(\mathbf{r})\varphi_1 + \xi_2(\mathbf{r})\varphi_2, \tag{1}$$

where $\xi_1(\mathbf{r})$ and $\xi_2(\mathbf{r})$ describe the motion of the incident nucleon with respect to the center of mass of the target nucleus. The approximation

---

* Supported in part by the National Science Foundation.
† NSF Fellow, 1963–1965, now at the University of Rochester.
‡ The present article is limited to a study of the inelastic scattering of spinless "nucleons". Furthermore, no explicit account is taken of the Pauli principle.

of Eq. (1) may be useful for studies of direct reactions, because in such reactions the incident and exit channels are not coupled strongly to more complicated modes of excitation. Equation (1) is most readily employed quantitatively if it is regarded as a trial wave function, to be inserted into variational expressions for $\Psi^{(+)}$. The coupled Euler–Lagrange equations for $\xi_1(\mathbf{r})$ and $\xi_2(\mathbf{r})$ that are obtained may be solved by more or less accurate theoretical methods. For example, exact solutions may be obtained by numerical integration of the equations, using fast computing machines. This is known as the "method of coupled channels", or the "Tamm–Dancoff method". In any case, no matter how its consequences may be developed, because Eq. (1) disregards the existence of other excited states of the target nucleus than φ_1 and φ_2, it is clear that theories based on this model of the wave function take little account of the nuclear reaction as a many-body process.

Bethe's theory is obtained by adding in to Eq. (1) an additional term, to represent the complicated many-body excitations that appear in $\Psi^{(+)}$ when all the nucleons are close together and in interaction with each other. The extended trial wave function is

$$\Psi^{(+)} \approx \xi_1(\mathbf{r})\varphi_1 + \xi_2(\mathbf{r})\varphi_2 + c\Phi. \tag{2}$$

Here Φ must only be nonvanishing when all the nucleons are close together. It must go to zero asymptotically as the system breaks apart into fragments in any manner. Therefore Φ is normalizable. It will be understood to be normalized to unity. Evidently a variational problem based on Eq. (2) must lead to Euler–Lagrange equations for $\xi_1(\mathbf{r})$ and $\xi_2(\mathbf{r})$, together with an algebraic equation for the coefficient c.

The function Φ is the "compound nucleus" wave function. Let us suppose the compound nucleus is long lived. In this case Φ, by itself, is very nearly an eigenfunction of the same Hamiltonian H that governs the exact $\Psi^{(+)}$. Thus

$$H\Psi^{(+)} = E\Psi^{(+)}, \tag{3}$$

and

$$H\Phi \approx E\Phi. \tag{4}$$

In fact Φ generally is obtained as a bound eigenfunction of some model Hamiltonian, H_0, that is related closely to H of Eq. (3):

$$H_0\Phi = E'\Phi, \tag{5}$$

where

$$E' \approx E. \tag{6}$$

Although Φ is bound with respect to H_0, it evidently is a "bound state in the continuum". The state Φ has enough energy for particle emission, but H_0 does not couple in to Φ any terms that are not bound. On the other hand, Φ is not an eigenfunction of the full H of Eq. (3). It is $\Psi^{(+)}$ of Eq. (2) that we have assumed to be a good approximate eigenfunction of H, and the first two terms of $\Psi^{(+)}$, the wave functions of the entrance and exit channels, are not bound. The Hamiltonian H must couple these two terms to the function Φ, and it is by means of this coupling the compound nucleus is able to decay. This coupling must be weak if the compound nucleus is to be long lived.

As an example of these ideas we may consider that H_0 is the Hamiltonian for an independent particle model (IPM) of the compound nucleus. Then Φ may be an IPM eigenstate that has several particles excited, such that the sum of their excitation energies is $E' \approx E$, as in Eq. (6). This Φ would be a bound eigenfunction, if no one of the excited particles would have enough energy to lie in the single-particle continuum. Nowadays, just such IPM models of Φ are being explored by many authors (for example, see Da65, Fe58, Fe62, Ma64, and Ro61).

However, it is not always necessary to consider models for Φ that are as explicit as the one just mentioned. Nuclear reaction calculations utilize the matrix elements that connect Φ to the first two terms of Eq. (2). Instead of attempting to calculate these matrix elements it is possible to regard them as phenomenological parameters, to be fitted to experiment. Then we would carry through only such calculations with Eq. (2) as would be required to exhibit the mathematical expressions in which these phenomenological parameters would be used. Such an approach was taken in Bethe's work (Be37) and is taken again in the present article.

Further generalization of the wave function can be achieved by adding in to Eq. (2) terms to represent other open channels (i.e., other excited states of the target nucleus), as well as terms to represent additional compound nucleus states. The generalized trial wave function would be

$$\Psi^{(+)} \approx \sum_i \xi_i(\mathbf{r})\varphi_i + \sum_j c_j\Phi_j. \tag{7}$$

The various Φ_j would be eigenstates of the model problem, governed by H_0, with a variety of different eigenenergies E'_j. At energies $E \approx E'_j$ each of the Φ_j would be very nearly an eigenfunction of H. Presumably an exact representation of $\Psi^{(+)}$ could be obtained if enough terms were taken in Eq (7).

Equation (7) now illustrates a weakness of Bethe's method. Not only are $\Psi^{(+)}$ and Φ_j in Eq. (7) governed by different Hamiltonians, H and H_0, but it is not clear that ξ_i and φ_i are related simply to either of these Hamiltonians. Thus there is some confusion about questions of orthogonality. Furthermore, the expansion of Eq. (7) probably is over-complete, in that the terms of the first summation extend into the nuclear interior and may well incorporate some of the properties of the Φ_j. It is understandable that compound nucleus theories that stressed questions of completeness and orthogonality (Ka38, Wi47) abandoned such expansions as Eq. (7). More recently Feshbach (Fe58, Fe62) has returned to the use of such expressions as Eq. (7) to represent $\Psi^{(+)}$, but has introduced *projection operators* to guarantee orthogonality of the bound-state and channel wave functions.

However, it is possible to ignore such questions, and to continue with the simple point of view described earlier: either Eq. (7) or Eq. (2) may be regarded as trial wave functions, to be used in variational calculations of $\Psi^{(+)}$. The construction of such trial wave functions would be motivated heuristically, by the insight that in some reaction of interest only certain channels or only certain Φ_j are important enough to take into account. Such a variational point of view is equivalent to the diagonalization of H within the limited part of Hilbert space that is spanned by the particular terms that are carried in the trial wave function. Much recent work follows this pattern of calculation. We will follow this procedure here.

In the present article a surface reaction model of the coupling between the incident nucleon and the bound wave functions is studied. Using this model it is possible to diagonalize H exactly, either within the space spanned by Eq. (2) or within the space spanned by Eq. (7). These exact diagonalizations therefore incorporate on equal terms both the compound nucleus (CN) couplings between the channels and the Φ_j, which were studied by Bethe (Be37), and the direct (DI) couplings among the channels. In this manner a fully quantum-mechanical theory of DI-CN interference is obtained. Section 2 traces out the consequences of Eq. (2), in which we carry two channels and one CN state. In Sec. 3 we remark on some of the consequences of the generalizations introduced in Eq. (7). Further details of this work are given elsewhere (Ra65, Ra66).

2. One Compound State, Two Channels

The amplitude for inelastic scattering in the presence of one compound state is obtained by diagonalizing H in the space spanned by the trial wave function of Eq. (2). The diagonalization leads to an eigenvalue equation that is basically a 3×3 matrix equation, its rows and columns being labelled by φ_1, φ_2, and Φ. This matrix equation thus may be written in the form of three coupled equations in the components,

$$(\varphi_1(y), (H - E)[\xi_1(\mathbf{r})\varphi_1(y) + \xi_2(\mathbf{r})\varphi_2(y) + c\Phi(\mathbf{r}, y)]) = 0, \quad (8)$$

$$(\varphi_2(y), (H - E)[\xi_1(\mathbf{r})\varphi_1(y) + \xi_2(\mathbf{r})\varphi_2(y) + c\Phi(\mathbf{r}, y)]) = 0, \quad (9)$$

$$(\Phi(\mathbf{r}, y), (H - E)[\xi_1(\mathbf{r})\varphi_1(y) + \xi_2(\mathbf{r})\varphi_2(y) + c\Phi(\mathbf{r}, y)]) = 0. \quad (10)$$

The internal variables of the target nucleus here are indicated by the symbol y. The scalar products of Eqs. (8) and (9) indicate integration over y, whereas the scalar product of Eq. (10) indicates integration over $\mathbf{r}$ and y.

Equations (8)–(10) simplify greatly because of the orthogonality of φ_1 and φ_2. We shall also assume that Φ is orthogonal to φ_1 and φ_2, with respect to integration over y. This assumption is based on the recognition that to construct a bound Φ that lies in the continuum it probably is necessary to use rather high excited states of the target nucleus. To write the simplified equations we introduce some additional notation:

$$H = H_t(y) + T(\mathbf{r}) + V(\mathbf{r}, y), \quad (11)$$

$$H_t(y)\varphi_i(y) = \epsilon_i\varphi_i(y), \quad (12)$$

$$V_{ii'}(\mathbf{r}) = \int dy\varphi_i^*(y)V(\mathbf{r}, y)\varphi_{i'}(y), \quad (13)$$

$$\mathscr{V}_i(\mathbf{r}) = \int dy\varphi_i^*(y)V(\mathbf{r}, y)\Phi(\mathbf{r}, y). \quad (14)$$

Here H_t is the Hamiltonian that governs the target nucleus, $T(\mathbf{r})$ is the kinetic energy operator for the relative motion of the incident nucleon and the target nucleus, and $V(\mathbf{r}, y)$ denotes all the interactions between this nucleon and the target nucleus. Then the simplified versions of Eqs. (8)–(10) are found to be

$$[T + V_{11} - (E - \epsilon_1)]\xi_1 = -V_{12}\xi_2 - c\mathscr{V}_1, \quad (15)$$

$$[T + V_{22} - (E - \epsilon_2)]\xi_2 = -V_{21}\xi_1 - c\mathscr{V}_2, \quad (16)$$

$$c = (E - E')^{-1} \int d^3r(\mathscr{V}_1^*\xi_1 + \mathscr{V}_2^*\xi_2), \quad (17)$$

where

$$E' \equiv \int dy \, d^3 r \Phi^* H \Phi. \tag{18}$$

It is particularly to be noted that E' is an *expectation value* and not an eigenvalue. Therefore Eq. (18) makes no explicit reference to the method by which Φ was constructed.

To compute ξ_1 and ξ_2, the functions from which the reaction amplitudes will be obtained, we substitute Eq. (17) into Eqs. (15) and (16), so as to eliminate c. The coupled integro-differential equations for ξ_1 and ξ_2 that thus result are solved readily in the special case of a "surface transition model". This model is defined by the property that all the off-diagonal matrix elements, V_{12}, V_{21}, $\mathscr{V}_1$, and $\mathscr{V}_2$, are assumed to be proportional to $\delta(r - r_0)$, where r_0 is some characteristic "nuclear radius". While such a model does give an oversimplified picture of nuclear structure, it is not altogether unrealistic. A localization of interactions at the nuclear surface was suggested long ago by Bohr and Mottelson as a convenience for reaction calculations (Bo53), and in many recent studies of direct reactions the coupling between channels does largely seem to be concentrated near the nuclear surface (Au63, Go63, and Sa65). Furthermore, Green and Moszkowski recently suggested that much that is known about nuclear spectroscopy could be described in terms of surface interactions (Gr65). In any case, whether a surface transition model is considered to be well or poorly justified, its use to solve the coupled equations is straightforward: Because the coupling occurs at only one radius the functions ξ_1 and ξ_2 everywhere are linear combinations of the solutions found in the absence of coupling. The coefficients in these linear combinations are determined by boundary matching at the radius r_0. The coupling terms are introduced as "jump conditions" in the boundary-matching calculation.

Let us now introduce the surface-transition model into the integro-differential equations, and evaluate their solutions, as just described. For simplicity only s-wave scattering will be considered, with φ_1, φ_2, and Φ having zero angular momentum. (For considerations of other angular momenta see Ra65, Ra66.) The coupled equations are found to reduce to the forms,

$$\left[\frac{d^2}{dr^2} - \frac{2M}{\hbar^2} V_{11}(r) + k_1^2 \right] \chi_1(r)$$
$$= r_0^{-1} \delta(r - r_0) \left[D_{12} \chi_2(r) + \sum_{i=1,2} R_{1i} \chi_i(r) \right], \tag{19}$$

$$\left[\frac{d^2}{dr^2} - \frac{2M}{\hbar^2} V_{22}(r) + k_2^2\right]\chi_2(r)$$
$$= r_0^{-1}\delta(r - r_0)\left[D_{21}\chi_1(r) + \sum_{i=1,2} R_{2i}\chi_i(r)\right], \quad (20)$$

where $(\hbar^2/k_i^2/2M) = E - \epsilon_i$. The functions χ_1 and χ_2 are the s-wave radial-wave-function parts of ξ_1 and ξ_2. The matrices $D_{ii'}$ and $R_{ii'}$ of Eqs. (19) and (20) are derived from the off-diagonal terms of Eqs.(15) and (16). These matrices are real and symmetric and are, respectively, measures of the strengths of coupling of channels i and i' by the DI and CN reaction mechanisms. The matrix $R_{ii'}$ is strongly energy dependent. It has the form

$$R_{ii'} = \gamma_i\gamma_{i'}/(E - E'), \quad (21)$$

and has properties that are rather similar to those of Wigner's R-matrix (Wi47, La58). The parameters of $D_{ii'}$ and $R_{ii'}$ may be regarded as phenomenological parameters in terms of which experiments are to be described. The introduction of such parameters was mentioned in Section 1.

From the solutions of Eqs. (19) and (20) we compute U_{21}, that matrix element of the scattering matrix that describes the transition from φ_1 to φ_2. It is found to be

$$U_{21} = -2i\Omega_1\Omega_2 P_1^{1/2}P_2^{1/2}\left[\frac{D_{21} + R_{21}}{(\lambda_1 - R_{11})(\lambda_2 - R_{22}) - (D_{21} + R_{21})^2}\right]. \quad (22)$$

The new symbols in this equation are Ω_1, Ω_2, P_1, P_2, λ_1, and λ_2. These all describe properties, evaluated at r_0, of those solutions of Eqs. (19) and (20) that are obtained in the absence of the interaction terms. Two such sets of solutions that must be considered are I_i and O_i, where

$$\left[\frac{d^2}{dr^2} - \frac{2M}{\hbar^2} V_{ii} + k_i^2\right]I_i = 0, \quad (23)$$

and

$$\left[\frac{d^2}{dr^2} - \frac{2M}{\hbar^2} V_{ii} + k_i^2\right]O_i = 0. \quad (24)$$

These solutions obey the familiar boundary conditions that I_i are asymptotically radially-ingoing traveling waves and O_i are asymptotically radially-outgoing traveling waves. In terms of these solution functions we are able to define, as usual (La58),

$$L_i \equiv \left(r\frac{dO_i}{dr} \middle/ O_i \right)_{r_0}, \tag{25}$$

$$P_i \equiv \operatorname{Im} L_i, \tag{26}$$

$$\Omega_i \equiv I_i^{1/2}(r_0)/O_i^{1/2}(r_0). \tag{27}$$

The quantities λ_i are defined to be

$$\lambda_i \equiv L_i - F_i, \tag{28}$$

where F_i is the logarithmic derivative of the physical solution function χ_i, evaluated just inside the nuclear radius. Thus

$$F_i \equiv \left(r\frac{d\chi_i}{dr} \middle/ \chi_i \right)_{r_0 - \varepsilon}, \tag{29}$$

where $\epsilon > 0$. We now consider what physical effects are described by Eq. (22).

First of all it must be remarked* that Eq. (22) contains explicitly and exactly both the effects of the direct (DI) coupling between channels 1 and 2, and the effects of indirect coupling (CN) through the compound state Φ. Therefore, by inspection of Eq. (22) it is possible to determine the influence these two reaction mechanisms may have on each other. For example, we could attempt to associate individual amplitudes with each of the two reaction mechanisms. A purely DI amplitude, U_{21}^{DI}, could be obtained from Eq. (22) by setting $R_{ii'}$ equal to zero. (This DI amplitude is not linear in D_{21}, because of coupled-channel effects.) A purely CN amplitude U_{21}^{CN}, could be obtained from Eq. (22) by setting D_{21}, equal to zero. However, it is clear that U_{21} would not be simply a sum of these two partial amplitudes, and that therefore the interference between DI and CN reaction mechanisms is more than just the "trivial interference" that is obtained when a sum of DI and CN amplitudes is squared for the computation of the cross section. Although a simple linear combination of DI and CN amplitudes often is used as a model for DI-CN interference (Al65, Bu59, Ma56, Pe65, and Ta65), Eq. (22) does not substantiate that model. This is hardly surprising. Equation (22) is derived from a unitary theory. However, unitarity of the scattering matrix could not be preserved by a model that would simply add two independently-calculated amplitudes.

---

* Bethe (Be37) did not use the surface transition model. As a result he was compelled to drop the direct coupling in order to solve the coupled integro-differential equations.

To display more clearly those effects in U_{21} that are caused by its nonlinear dependence on the two reaction mechanisms, we substitute into Eq. (22) the explicit form of the matrix $R_{ii'}$, as given by Eq. (21). After some manipulation there results

$$U_{21} = \frac{-2i\Omega_1\Omega_2 P_1^{1/2} P_2^{1/2}}{\lambda_1\lambda_2 - D_{21}^2} \left[D_{21} + \frac{\gamma_1\gamma_2 + D_{21}Q}{E - E' - Q} \right], \qquad (30)$$

where

$$Q \equiv \frac{\lambda_2\gamma_1^2 + \lambda_1\gamma_2^2 + 2D_{21}\gamma_1\gamma_2}{\lambda_1\lambda_2 - D_{21}^2}. \qquad (31)$$

The first term of Eq. (30), the term that is proportional to D_{21} in the brackets, is the exact DI result that would appear in the absence of the CN mechanism. The denominator $(\lambda_1\lambda_2 - D_{21}^2)$ expresses strong-coupling effects, namely D_{21}^2 in this denominator expresses the influence that the direct coupling between channels has on the forms of the wave functions in the individual channels. Numerical estimates make it clear that these effects generally can be expected to be weak, so that

$$D_{21}^2 \ll |\lambda_1\lambda_2|. \qquad (32)$$

The condition that strong-coupling effects be weak also is helpful for the simplification of Q. Upon omission of all small terms of this nature, Q reduces to

$$Q \approx \gamma_1^2/\lambda_1 + \gamma_2^2/\lambda_2. \qquad (33)$$

It is seen that Q is complex, because λ_1 and λ_2 are complex, and that it has no particularly rapid energy dependence. Its presence in the denominator of the resonance term of Eq. (30) gives the level width and level shift, as usual. In its appearance in the numerator of the resonance term, however, it is multiplied by D_{21}. The term, $D_{21}Q$, appears to be the principal nonlinear DI-CN effect in U_{21}. Still another effect caused by the presence of this nonlinear term in the resonance numerator is that the numerator does not have Breit–Wigner form; it is not a product of factors that refer separately to the two channels. In view of these interesting effects it is worthwhile to estimate the magnitude of the nonlinear term. From Eq. (33) this magnitude may be seen to be roughly of order $D_{21}|\lambda_1\lambda_2|^{-1/2}$, relative to the first term of the resonance numerator. Further remarks about this magnitude are given elsewhere (Ra65, Ra66).

If the real and imaginary parts of Q are indicated separately,

$$Q \equiv \text{Re } Q - \frac{i}{2} \Gamma, \tag{34}$$

then

$$U_{21} = \frac{-2i\Omega_1\Omega_2 P_1^{\frac{1}{2}} P_2^{\frac{1}{2}}}{\lambda_1\lambda_2 - D_{21}^2} \left[D_{21} + \frac{(\gamma_1\gamma_2 + D_{21}\text{ Re } Q) - \frac{i}{2}\Gamma D_{21}}{E - (E' + \text{Re } Q) + \frac{i}{2}\Gamma} \right]. \tag{35}$$

It is seen that the expression in brackets in Eq. (35) may be para-meterized in terms of four real quantities: D_{21}, Γ, $(E' + \text{Re } Q)$, and $(\gamma_1\gamma_2 + D_{21}\text{ Re } Q)$. These may be regarded as phenomenological parameters, to be determined by fitting to experimental cross sections. It is interesting that the relative phase of the DI and resonance terms is not an independent parameter. Instead, this phase is determined uniquely by the form of the nonlinear imaginary term in the resonance numerator. This nonlinear imaginary term may be responsible for some of the strange phases found when phenomenological fits to DI-CN interference have been attempted (Ma56). Perhaps this term can be carried in practical calculations.

However, in order to fit the parameters of Eq. (35) to experimental cross sections, it is necessary to make theoretical estimates of P_i and λ_i. It is necessary to remark, therefore, that the quantity λ_i tends to be strongly model dependent. From Eqs. (28) and (29) it is seen that λ_i depends on F_i, which, in turn, depends on the potential $V_{ii}(r)$ in the nuclear interior. This strong model dependence of λ_i would be alleviated if the physical model were generalized, such that $V_{ii}(r)$ would be treated as complex. A further discussion of these questions is given elsewhere (Ra65, Ra66).

One additional observation about our expression for U_{21} is of interest. At the unshifted resonance energy, $E = E'$, the nonlinear DI-CN term in Eq. (30) exactly cancels the amplitude that would be contributed by DI alone. It is further found that at $E = E'$ the radial wave functions $\chi_1(r)$ and $\chi_2(r)$ vanish at r_0, the coupling radius. These two effects, which are related, appear to provide an elementary example of the reason why the averaged influence of CN levels on a DI calculation must be represented by an absorbing potential.

3. Generalizations

Considerable generalization of the results of Sec. 2 is possible (Ra65, Ra66), within the basic context of the surface transition model. A few of the generalized results may be mentioned here.

By diagonalization of H in the space spanned by the trial wave function of Eq. (7) it is possible to study inelastic scattering in the presence of many open channels and many compound states. The result that is found for the scattering matrix is an algebraic expression that involves matrices whose rows and columns are labelled by the open channels:

$$\mathbf{U} = \mathbf{\Omega}[\mathbf{1} - 2i\mathbf{P}^{\frac{1}{2}}(\mathbf{L} - \mathbf{Z})^{-1}\mathbf{P}^{\frac{1}{2}}]\mathbf{\Omega}. \qquad (36)$$

Here the matrices $\mathbf{1}$, $\mathbf{L}$, $\mathbf{P}$, and $\mathbf{\Omega}$ are diagonal, and have as their diagonal matrix elements 1, and the L_i, P_i, and Ω_i of Eqs. (25)–(27). The matrix $\mathbf{Z}$ is defined by

$$\mathbf{Z} = \mathbf{F} + \mathbf{D} + \mathbf{R}, \qquad (37)$$

where $\mathbf{F}$ is diagonal, and has as its diagonal matrix elements the F_i of Eq. (29). The matrices $\mathbf{D}$ and $\mathbf{R}$ were discussed already in connection with Eqs. (19) and (20). However it is necessary to introduce now a multiresonance generalization of Eq. (21), so that

$$R_{ii'} = \sum_j \frac{\gamma_{ji}\gamma_{ji'}}{E - E_j}, \qquad (38)$$

where the index j labels the various compound states of Eq. (7). The expressions just given are familiar from the usual R-matrix theory (Wi47, La58).

One simple result that is found from Eq. (36) is that the basic structure of the expressions obtained in the case of one resonance and two open channels is preserved as the number of open channels is increased. It certainly is preserved as we go from two to three open channels.

It is of particular interest to introduce into Eq. (36) a statistical distribution of CN states, and to average the transition amplitude with respect to bombarding energy. The energy-averaged amplitude that is thus obtained is found to have the structure of a purely DI amplitude, as in Eq. (30), as if no CN couplings were present. Such a result often is assumed (for example, see Br59, Sa58). However the parameters λ_i

that appear in the DI amplitude, are modified by the coupling to the CN states. The modification is

$$\lambda_i \rightarrow \lambda_i + \frac{i\pi}{d} \langle \gamma_i^2 \rangle, \tag{39}$$

where d is the average spacing of CN states, and $\langle \gamma_i^2 \rangle$ is the average square of their reduced-width amplitudes for transitions to the channel i. This is the same kind of modification that would be introduced if the wave functions used to compute the DI amplitude were eigenfunctions of complex potentials.

A fundamental generalization of the surface transition model is made by the introduction of delta-function coupling terms at *more than one coupling radius*. Such a use of more than one radius for the DI coupling is found not to change the basic structure of the scattering matrix, as given by Eq. (36), provided the coupling to the CN states takes place at only one radius. The phase relation between the DI and CN amplitudes, which was discussed in connection with Eq. (35), does seem to be altered if a variety of radii are involved in the CN coupling.

4. Summary

By introduction of a surface transition model it is possible to obtain exact solutions in the context of Bethe's nuclear reaction theory. In these solutions it is easy to trace the effects of DI and CN reaction mechanisms. The nonlinear influence of one mechanism upon the other is of particular interest. Our investigation is related closely to a number of "unified theories" that are being considered by other authors (Da65, Fe58, Fe62, Ma64, Ro61).

5. Acknowledgments

We are grateful to Dr. Peter Moldauer for some discussion of this work.

References

Al65. Alford, W. P., L. M. Blau, and D. Cline, *Nucl. Phys.*, **61**, 368 (1965).
Au63. Austern, N., in *Selected Topics in Nuclear Theory*, edited by F. Janouch, IAEA, Vienna, 1963.

Be37. Bethe, H. A., *Rev. Mod. Phys.*, **9**, 69 (1937).
Bo36. Bohr, N., *Nature*, **137**, 344 (1936).
Bo53. Bohr, A., and B. R. Mottelson, *Kgl. Danske Videnskab. Selskab, Mat.-Fys. Medd.*, **27**, No. 16 (1953).
Br36. Breit, G., and E. P. Wigner, *Phys. Rev.*, **49**, 519 (1936).
Br59. Brown, G. E., *Rev. Mod. Phys.*, **31**, 893 (1959).
Bu59. Buck, B., Ph.D. Thesis, Oxford University, 1959, unpublished.
Da65. Danos, M., and W. Greiner, *Phys. Rev.*, **138**, B93 (1965).
Fe58. Feshbach, H., *Ann. Phys. (N.Y.)*, **5**, 357 (1958).
Fe62. Feshbach, H., *Ann. Phys. (N.Y.)*, **19**, 287 (1962).
Go63. Goldfarb, L. J. B., and M. B. Hooper, *Phys. Rev. Letters*, **4**, 148 (1963).
Gr65. Green, I. M., and S. A. Moszkowski, *Phys. Rev.*, **139**, B790 (1965).
Ka38. Kapur, P. L., and R. E. Peierls, *Proc. Phys. Soc. (London)*, **A166**, 277 (1938).
La58. Lane, A. M., and R. G. Thomas, *Rev. Mod. Phys.*, **30**, 257 (1958).
Ma56. Marion, J. B., and G. Weber, *Phys. Rev.*, **102**, 1355 (1956).
Ma64. MacDonald, W. M., *Nucl. Phys.*, **54**, 393 (1964).
Pe65. Pessoa, E. F., et al., *Nucl. Phys.*, **68**, 337 (1965).
Ra65. Ratcliff, K. F., Ph.D. Thesis, Univ. of Pittsburgh, 1965, unpublished.
Ra66. Ratcliff, K. F., and N. Austern, to be published.
Ro61. Rodberg, L. S., *Phys. Rev.*, **124**, 210 (1961).
Sa58. Sano, M., S. Yoshida, and T. Terasawa, *Nucl. Phys.*, **6**, 20 (1958).
Sa65. Satchler, G. R., *Lecture Notes for the 1965 Summer Institute for Theoretical Physics*, Univ. of Colorado, to be published.
Ta64. Tamura, T., and T. Terasawa, *Phys. Rev. Letters*, **8**, 41 (1964).
Wi47. Wigner, E. P., and L. Eisenbud, *Phys. Rev.*, **72**, 29 (1947).

Direct Nuclear Reactions: Deuteron Stripping

S. T. BUTLER

University of Sydney

Introduction

As is well known, direct nuclear reactions are in principle capable of yielding significant information regarding nuclear energy levels and nuclear structure. If we follow the definition used by Austern[1], direct reactions may be considered to be those whose analysis requires only the consideration of a small number of degrees of freedom of the nuclear system—usually only of those degrees of freedom which are already required simply to describe the incident and outgoing wave functions in channel regions of configuration space.

Of all types of direct nuclear reactions perhaps the most well known are the so-called deuteron stripping reactions, a simple theory for which was proposed many years ago by the present author[2]. In this article I will confine my attention to the theory of (d, p) reactions, with much of the discussion also probably being applicable to (d, n) reactions.

The interpretation of a (d, p) reaction should be capable of yielding quite "clear-cut" information. The shape of the differential cross-section should be able to give a unique determination of the orbital angular momentum—or l value—with which the neutron is captured into its final state, thus determining the parity and very often the spin of the final nuclear level. Moreover, the absolute magnitude of the cross section should determine how much the final state "likes" to be in the configuration of ground state initial nucleus plus neutron. This latter information is contained in the co-called spectroscopic factor, discussed in detail by Macfarlane and French[3]. The original simple theory[2] has proved useful for determining spins and parities of nuclear states in many cases. It suffers the disadvantage, however, that it over-estimates absolute cross sections, so that it may reasonably be expected

71

to yield information only of the ratios of reduced widths[3,4]. Moreover, experimental angular distributions of reactions involving medium and heavy nuclei sometimes show little relationship to the results of the simple theory and for such cases no determination of spins and parities can be made on the basis of this theory.

Attempts to improve the theory have generated the so-called distorted-wave Born approximation (DWBA) theory[5,6]. The usual DWBA approach, however, is based on a premise which is quite difficult to justify and its status has still not been satisfactorily established. The aim of the present article is to describe a new approach, first proposed independently by the present author[7] and Tanifuji[8], and for which preliminary results have proved very encouraging.

Basic Theory

We consider a (d, p) stripping reaction in which the incident and outgoing wave vectors are $\mathbf{k}_d$ and $\mathbf{k}_p$, respectively, and where the spins of the initial and final nuclei are J_i and J_f, respectively. The theoretical cross section, in terms of optical model wave functions, is[2,6]

$$\frac{d\sigma}{d\Omega} = \frac{\frac{1}{2}m_p m_d}{(2\pi\hbar^2)^2} \frac{k_p}{k_d} \frac{(2J_f + 1)}{(2J_i + 1)} \sum_{l,m} \frac{1}{2l + 1}\, S(l, J_i, J_f)\, |M|^2, \qquad (1)$$

where the matrix element M is given as

$$M(k_p, k_d) = \langle \psi_d^+, \mathbf{k}_d, \mathbf{r}_p, r_n) | V_{np} | F_l^m(\mathbf{r}_n)\psi_p^-(\mathbf{k}_p, \mathbf{r}_p)\rangle. \qquad (2)$$

Here $\mathbf{r}_p$ and $\mathbf{r}_n$ are the proton and neutron coordinates, respectively. The wave function ψ_d^+ describes elastically scattered deuterons with outgoing spherical waves, ψ_p describes elastically scattered protons with incoming spherical waves, and F_l^m is the wave function of the final bound neutron with orbital angular momentum l and projection m, normalized to unity. The normal neutron–proton interaction is represented by V_{np}. In the form of Eq. (1) all other nuclear coordinates have been integrated out so that ψ_p^- may be considered to be a known optical-model wave function. The factor $S(l, J_i, J_f)$ is the so-called spectroscopic factor which is a real, positive number. It is unity if the final state exhausts the single-particle strength, as would occur in capture by a closed-shell nucleus into a pure, single-particle state.

In the usual evaluation of the matrix element M associated with DWBA calculations the interaction V_{np} is taken to be of zero range, that is it is written

$$V_{np}\chi(|\mathbf{r}_p - \mathbf{r}_n|) = \frac{-\hbar^2 \sqrt{8\pi\gamma}}{m} \delta(\mathbf{r}_p - \mathbf{r}_n), \tag{3}$$

where χ is the internal deuteron wave function and $\hbar^2\gamma^2/m$ is the deuteron binding energy with m being the nucleon mass.

In addition the wave function ψ_d^+ is assumed to have no internal distortion or polarization of the deuteron; thus ψ_d^+ is taken as a product wave function involving the undistorted internal wave function χ together with the center-of-mass motion of the deuteron described by an optical-model wave function.

Extensive exploration of this DWBA approach over the past decade has still left its status somewhat obscure. There are always ambiguities in the deuteron optical parameters, and until recently it was considered usually necessary to employ optical parameters different from those required to fit elastic scattering[5]. However, as emphasized by Satchler[9], a satisfactory theory should, with no adjustable parameters, be able to fit data such that l values can be determined unambiguously and spectroscopic factors given accurately. A recent DWBA study[5] of (d, p) reactions on Ca^{40}, involving careful selection of deuteron optical parameters from among those consistent with elastic scattering data, has yielded satisfactory results. Yet there still remain large numbers of cross sections reported in the literature which would seem to require optical parameters not in agreement with elastic scattering data.

In the new method no such difficulties appear to arise. The difference in approach lies in the evaluation of the matrix element M, specifically in the treatment of the wave function ψ_d^+ by a method which also incidentally does not require the use of the zero-range approximation of Eq. (3).

Suppose we assume that ψ_d^+ satisfies the equation

$$(T_n + T_p + V_{np} + V_n + V_p)\psi_d^+ = E\psi_d^+, \tag{4}$$

where T_n and T_p are kinetic-energy operators, and where V_n and V_p are optical potentials for neutron and proton, respectively, incident on the initial nucleus. Strictly, these are energy dependent and should be considered as operators dependent on the square of the momenta of the particles.

We know that a plane-wave deuteron has the following transform:

$$\exp{(i\mathbf{k}_d\mathbf{R})}\chi(r) = \frac{N}{2\pi^2}\int d\mathbf{k}_p' G(\mathbf{k}_p', \mathbf{k}_d) \exp{(i\mathbf{Q}'\mathbf{r}_n)} \exp{(i\mathbf{k}_p'\mathbf{r}_p)}, \qquad (5)$$

where $\mathbf{Q}' = \mathbf{k}_d - (M_i/M_f)\mathbf{k}_p'$ with M_i and M_f the respective masses of the initial and final nuclei; the ratio M_i/M_f arises when $\mathbf{r}_n$ and $\mathbf{r}_p$ are appropriate center-of-mass coordinates for the (d, p) reaction[2]. For Eq. (5) the internal deuteron wave function has been written

$$\chi(r) = N(e^{-\gamma r}/r - e^{-\zeta r}/r),$$

where N normalizes χ to unity[2]. The form factor G is simply

$$G(\mathbf{k}_p', \mathbf{k}_d) = \left\{ \frac{1}{[(\mathbf{k}_d/2) - \mathbf{k}_p']^2 + \gamma^2} - \frac{1}{[(\mathbf{k}_d/2) - \mathbf{k}_p']^2 + \zeta^2} \right\} \qquad (6)$$

Equation (5) may be discussed in time-dependent terminology in a way which can be instructive. If a "snap shot" is taken of a moving deuteron wave packet with an "exposure time" short compared to the natural period of the deuteron the neutron and proton would appear to be described by independent wave packets with momenta $\mathbf{k}_p'$ and $\mathbf{Q}'$. The probability for finding given momenta is described by G^2.

For deuterons with a sufficiently high momentum involved in a stripping reaction it would seem plausible that any interaction of the neutrons and protons with the initial nuclei might occur in a period small compared to the natural period of the deuteron; this might be particularly the case if the reaction tends to be confined to a surface volume. It could then be a reasonable approach to use a "sudden" approximation for ψ_d^+ in Eq. (2) and to write it

$$\psi_d^+ = \frac{N}{2\pi^2}\int d\mathbf{k}_p' G(\mathbf{k}_p', \mathbf{k}_d)\psi_n^+(\mathbf{Q}', \mathbf{r}_n)\psi_p^+(\mathbf{k}_p', \mathbf{r}_p) \qquad (7)$$

where ψ_n^+ and ψ_p^+ are optical-model wave functions for neutron and proton, respectively, with the appropriate momenta. Thus ψ_n^+ and ψ_p^+ satisfy wave equations

$$(T_n + V_n)\psi_n^+ = E_n\psi_n^+$$

and

$$(T_d + V_d)\psi_p^+ = E_d\psi_p^+ \qquad (8)$$

with E_n and E_d being energies appropriate to the momenta k_p' and Q', respectively.

We use Eq. (4) to reexpress the quantity $V_{nd}\psi_d^+$ of the matrix element [Eq. (2)] as follows:

$$V_{np}\psi_d^+ = \{E - (T_n + T_p + V_n + V_p)\}\psi_d^+ \tag{9}$$

On substituting the approximation [Eq. (7)] for ψ_d^+, and making use of the wave equations [Eq. (8)], the matrix element [Eq. (2)] takes the form

$$M(\mathbf{k}_p, \mathbf{k}_d) =$$

$$-\frac{\hbar^2 N}{2\pi^2 m}\int d\mathbf{k}_p' g(\mathbf{k}_d, \mathbf{k}_p')\langle\psi_p^+(\mathbf{k}_p', \mathbf{r}_p)|\psi_p^-(\mathbf{k}_p, \mathbf{r}_p)\rangle\langle\psi_n^+(\mathbf{Q}', \mathbf{r}_n)|F(\mathbf{r}_n)\rangle \tag{10}$$

where

$$g(\mathbf{k}_d, \mathbf{k}_p') = \{[(\mathbf{k}_d - (k_p'/2)]^2 + \gamma^2\}G(\mathbf{k}_d, \mathbf{k}_p') \tag{11}$$

The quantity $\langle\psi_p^+|\psi_p^-\rangle$ is determinable[10]; it is

$$\langle\psi_p^+(\mathbf{k}_p', \mathbf{r}_p)|\psi_p^-(\mathbf{k}_p, \mathbf{r}_p)\rangle = (2\pi)^3\left[\delta(\mathbf{k}_p - \mathbf{k}_p') + \frac{i}{\pi}\delta(k_p^2 - k_p'^2)f(\mathbf{k}_p, \mathbf{k}_p')\right] \tag{12}$$

where f is the proton elastic-scattering amplitude so normalized that $|f|^2$ is directly the differential cross section.

The first term in Eq. (12) by itself yields a cross section sharply peaked at some forward angle, and rapidly becoming negligibly small beyond the peak. The second term is strongly coupled to the proton elastic scattering; in many cases it is completely swamped by the first term in the vicinity of the forward peak, but rapidly takes over and dominates at larger angles[11]. For reactions involving heavy nuclei the second term can also be of importance at small angles of scattering, tending to eliminate the appearance of a characteristic forward stripping structure; for light and medium-heavy nuclei this seldom if ever occurs.

Insertion of Eq. (12) into the matrix element [Eq. (10)] yields a final cross section which may be coded for computing. In an initial investigation by Hewitt, May and myself[12], we chose reactions for which the first term of Eq. (12) does completely dominate at the main structural peak. Reliable criteria for this may readily be found[13].

We then computed a cross section yielded by the first term of Eq. (12), assuming a square well of radius r_0 rather than the usual Saxon-Wood potential for determining the neutron optical and bound wave functions. The disadvantages of a square well are well recognized; it is, however, sufficient for the aim of the present discussion.

An optical, square-well potential of depth $V_0 + iW$ is chosen for determining ψ_n, and a real square-well of depth U_0, with the same radius, is chosen for determining F_n. The element $\langle \psi_n | F_n \rangle$ may then be represented analytically[14]. It is

$$\langle \psi_n | F_n \rangle = \delta_{m0} \frac{\{4\pi(2l+1)\}^{1/2} r_0^2}{Q^2 + \kappa^2} \left\{ \frac{\Delta V - iW}{(E_Q + E_B + \Delta V) - iW} \right\}.$$
$$A_l e^{i\delta_l} \cos \delta_l [\underline{W}\{j_l(Qr_0), h_l(i\kappa r_0)\} - \tan \delta_l \underline{W}\{\eta_l(Qr_0), h_l(i\kappa r_0)\}], \quad (13)$$

where $E_Q = \hbar^2 Q^2 / 2m$, $E_B = \hbar^2 \kappa^2 / 2m$ is the neutron binding energy, $\delta_l(Q)$ is the complex phase shift for the lth partial wave of ψ_n, h_l is the Hankel function of the first kind, and j_l and η_l are the spherical Bessel functions of the first and second kinds, respectively. Moreover, $\Delta V = |V_0| - |U_0|$ and $\underline{W}$ denotes a Wronksian with derivatives taken with respect to r_0. We have also written $F_n = R_l(r_n) Y_{lm}(\theta_n \varphi_n)$ and A_l is defined in terms of R_l by the equation $R_l(r_0) = A_l h_l(i\kappa r_0)$. This expression for the cross section reduces to the familiar Butler-Born result[15] if we put $\delta_l = 0$ and replace the factor inside the braces by unity.

The depth U_0 is chosen to fit the observed binding energy. For the neutron optical potential we take *one* potential which gives a good fit to neutron scattering at all energies E_Q of relevance and on all target nuclei[16,17]:

$$V_0(Q) = -(52.6 - 0.6E_Q); \quad E_Q < 21$$
$$= -(40 - 10.8 \ln E_Q/21); \quad E_Q > 21$$
$$W(Q) = -(2.5 + 0.3E_Q); \quad E_Q < 21 \quad (14)$$
$$= -(8.8 + 2.25 \ln E_Q/21); \quad E_Q > 21$$
$$r_0 = (1.33 A^{1/3} + 0.30) f.$$

(V_0, W, and E_Q are expressed in MeV units.) Notice that, unlike Butler-Born theory, the nuclear radius is *not* treated as an adjustable parameter.

Preliminary Results

Cross sections obtained in the manner discussed above using the first term of Eq. (12), both as regards absolute magnitude and angular distribution, are displayed in Figs. 1 and 2. In each case the spectroscopic

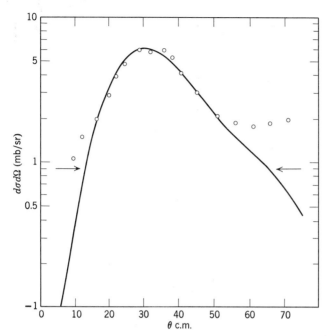

Fig. 1. Experimental points (5) and theoretical curve for Ca^{40} (d, p) Ca^{41} g.s. (E_d = 12 MeV; Q = 6.14 MeV; l = 3; S = 1). The arrows indicate roughly the point at which the second term in Eq. (12) becomes important[13].

factor S was taken to be unity. The arrows on the curves label the regions where we expect the second term in Eq. (12) to assume significance[11]. The reactions $O^{16}(d, p)O^{17}$ and $Ca^{40}(d, p)Ca^{41}$ were chosen because the initial nuclei are doubly magic and the assignment S = 1 should be reliable. The experimental[6,18] absolute magnitudes are subject to overall systematic errors of $\pm 25\%$ for O^{16} and $\pm 10\%$ for Ca^{40}. Equally good fits have been obtained (with the same potential) for the peaks in Ca^{40} $(d, p)Ca^{41}$ at other deuteron energies and for excited states, and also for $C^{12}(d, p)C^{13}$ g.s. (S = 0.5)[19,20], $K^{39}(d, p)$ K^{40} g.s. (S = 0.45)[21], and the set[22] of reactions $Kr^{86}(d, p)Kr^{87}$ g.s. (S = 0.4), $Sr^{88}(d, p)Sr^{89}$ g.s. (S = 0.5), $Zr^{90}(d, p)Zr^{91}$ g.s. (S = 0.6). The spectroscopic factors in brackets are those which achieve exact agreement between experimental peak magnitudes and our theory; they are consistent with shell-model theory.

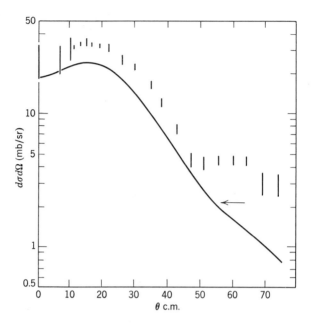

Fig. 2. Experimental points[18] and theoretical curve for O^{16} (d, p) O^{17} g.s. $(E_d = 15$ MeV; $Q = 1.92$ MeV; $l = 2$; $S = 1)$. The error bars represent relative errors; the overall experimental cross section is $\pm 25\%$

The second term of Eq. (12) has also been investigated by Pearson and Coz[23], although quite approximately and only for $l = 0$ reactions.

Let us denote the first term of the matrix element M by $M_1(l, \theta)$ and the second term by $M_2(l, \theta)$. Then it may readily be seen that

$$M_2(l, \theta) = \frac{ik_p}{2\pi} \int d\Omega' M_1(l, \theta') f(\mathbf{k}_p, \mathbf{k}'_p) \qquad (15)$$

where $d\Omega'$ represents the solid angle of the vector $\mathbf{k}'_p$ and θ' is the polar angle of $\mathbf{k}'_p$.

The argument used by Pearson and Coz is that when $l = 0$ the amplitude M_1 is quite sharply peaked around the zero angle of scattering, that is, the vector $\mathbf{k}'_p$ is close to the direction of $\mathbf{k}_d$ for maximum contribution to the integral. If this is accepted the amplitude f may be taken outside the integral and simply be written as $f(\theta)$ where

θ is the angle of scattering in the (d, p) reaction. Thus for $l = 0$ an approximation to the amplitude M_2 is given as

$$M_2(\theta) = (ik_p)f(\theta) \int \sin \theta' \, d\theta' M_1(\theta').$$ (16)

With no more calculation Pearson and Coz can thus conclude that for sufficiently large angles of scattering the following approximate connection should exist between an $l = 0$, (d, p) differential cross section and the corresponding proton elastic-scattering cross section:

$$\sigma_{d,p}(\theta) = \Lambda\sigma_{p,p}(\theta)$$ (17)

where Λ is an angle-independent constant.

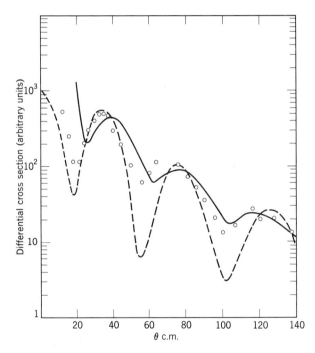

Fig. 3. Angular distribution from elastic proton scattering (solid line), compared with experimental points, and with the DWBA best fit (dashed line), for reaction. Zr^{90} (d, p) Zr^{91}. The deuteron energy is 10.85 MeV and $l = 0$, $Q = 3.8$ MeV. The proton scattering cross section from Zr^{90} was calculated using the parameters of Rosen et al.[25]. The DWBA best fit is taken from ref. 26 and the experimental points from ref. 27.

Such a comparison is shown in Figs. 3 and 4 which are essentially replicas of examples quoted by Pearson and Coz. In each case use of the simple criteria[11] shows that for the reactions here considered the M_2 term should be predominant at angles greater than about 60°; at angles less than this, the M_1 and M_2 terms are of comparable magnitude. It is to be observed that there does appear to be a strong correlation in the oscillations of the two cross sections.

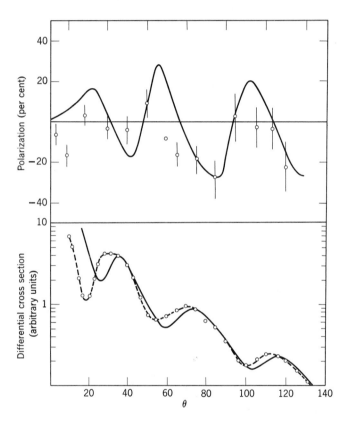

Fig. 4. Angular distribution and polarization from elastic proton scattering compared with experimental measurements for the reaction Sr^{88} (d, p) Sr^{89}. The deuteron energy is 11 MeV, $l = 0$, $Q = 3.11$ MeV. The experimental points are those of Ludwig and Miller[28]. The proton elastic scattering cross section and polarization from Sr^{88} was calculated for a proton energy of 14 MeV, using the parameters of Rosen et al.[25].

Also from Eq. (17) an interesting conclusion emerges; this is that the polarization of the (d, p) reaction should, at sufficiently large angles, be the same as the polarization observed in the proton elastic scattering. Such a comparison is also shown in Fig. 4.[24]

It is interesting that polarization for $l = 0$ cases most clearly arises in the present method and is indeed strongly coupled to the (p, p) polarization; in the opinion of the present author, however, the approximation used by Pearson and Coz is relatively crude and the comparisons shown in Figs. 3 and 4 should simply be interpreted as indications that the second term in Eq. (12) also yields results which are behaving in an appropriate fashion. Actual numerical investigation shows that even for $l = 0$, contributions in Eq. (15) arise from a relatively large spread of angles of the vector $\mathbf{k}_{p'}$ and not simply from directions close to $\mathbf{k}_d$.

A quite basic and searching test of the full sudden approximation method would be, of course, to explore the approximate wave function ψ_d^+ represented by Eq. (7) and to see how well this predicts elastic deuteron scattering from known nuclear optical parameters. An investigation along these lines has been reported by May[29]. Although the method used by May to extract elastic-scattering cross sections is also quite approximate, and intended only to be of a preliminary nature, it clearly demonstrates that all the main features of deuteron elastic scattering appear to be yielded automatically if Eq. (7) be taken as the deuteron wave function.

Conclusions

On the basis of the above preliminary results it is my belief that there is ample evidence for the new approach discussed to be thoroughly explored numerically. A complete computer code would be no more complex, and perhaps somewhat less so, than the usual DWBA code, and complete (d, p) cross sections using both terms of Eq. (12) and and standard Saxon-Wood potentials throughout should provide very interesting results. I hope that this may be done in the near future. In any case, however, the simple square-well cross section presented in the previous section, which involves no adjustable parameters and whose coding for a computer is trivial, would seem to provide a satisfactory basis for analyzing many experimental results.

In conclusion I would like to acknowledge the cooperation of my colleagues, Drs. R. M. May and B. H. J. McKellar, and Mr. R. G.

Hewitt; it is also a pleasure to acknowledge the interest and support of Professor H. Messel.

References

1. Austern, N., *Fast Neutron Physics, Part II*, Interscience, New York, 1962.
2. Butler, S. T., *Phys. Rev.*, **80**, 1095 (1950); *Proc. Roy. Soc. (London)*, **A208**, 559 (1951); *Phys. Rev.*, **88**, 685 (1952); S. T. Butler and O. Hittmair, *Nuclear Stripping Reactions*, John Wiley, New York, 1959.
3. Macfarlane, M. H., and J. B. French, *Rev. Mod. Phys.*, **32**, 567 (1960).
4. Bethe, H. A., and S. T. Butler, *Phys. Rev.*, **85**, 1045 (1952).
5. Lee, L. L., Jr., J. P. Schiffer, B. Zeidman, G. R. Satchler, R. M. Drisko, and R. H. Bassel, *Phys. Rev.*, **136**, B971 (1964).
6. See, for example, W. Tobocman, *Phys. Rev.*, **115**, 98 (1959); B. Buck and P. E. Hodgson, *Nucl. Phys.*, **29**, 496 (1962); H. E. Gove, *Proceedings of the Rutherford Jubilee Conference*, Heywood and Co., London, 1961, pp. 437–478.
7. Butler, S. T., *Australian J. Sci.*, **26**, 236 (1964); *Nature*, **207**, 1346 (1965).
8. Tanifuji, M., *Nucl. Phys.*, **58**, 81 (1964). The approach adopted here is more formal than that of ref. 7.
9. Satchler, G. R., *Direct Interactions and Nuclear Reaction Mechanisms*, E. Clementel and C. Villi, Eds., Gordon and Breach, New York, 1963, p. 80.
10. Goldberger, M. L., and K. M. Watson, *Collision Theory*, John Wiley, New York, 1964, p. 194.
11. The Coulomb singularity in f at zero angle causes no trouble. The Coulomb scattering amplitude at very small angles is violently oscillatory; the integration over small angles can be carried out analytically and the contributions found to be essentially zero. Thus large spurious contributions from large proton impact parameters do not arise.
12. Butler, S. T., R. G. Hewitt, and R. M. May, *Phys. Rev. Letters*, Dec. 27 (1965).
13. For $l = 0$, for example, one can estimate that the second term of Eq. (12) becomes significant only at those angles for which

$$\frac{d\sigma_1(\theta)}{d\Omega} < \left[k_p^2 \frac{d\sigma_1(0)}{d\Omega} \frac{(\varDelta\theta)^4}{4} \right] \frac{d\sigma_p(\theta)}{d\Omega} .$$

Here $\varDelta\theta$ is the half-width of the forward stripping peak yielded by the first term, $d\sigma_1/d\Omega$ is the cross section yielded by the first term and $d\sigma_p/d\Omega$ is the proton elastic scattering cross section. Similar estimates are available for $l \neq 0$.
14. May, R. M., *Nature*, **207**, 1348 (1965).
15. Lubnitz, C. R., Univ. of Michigan Report, unpublished, 1957.
16. Green, A. E. S., *International Conference on the Nuclear Optical Model*, Tallahassee, 244, Florida State Univ. Press, 1959, p. 44; P. E. Hodgson, *Optical Model of Elastic Scattering*, Oxford Univ. Press, 1963.
17. For a discussion of the correspondence between the parameters for square-well and Saxon-Wood potentials, see W. S. Emmerich, *Fast Neutron Physics, Part II*, Interscience, New York, 1963, pp. 1060 1065.

18. Keller, E. L., *Phys.*, **121**, 820 (1961).
19. Green, T. S., and R. Middleton, *Proc. Phys. Soc.*, **A69**, 28 (1956).
20. McGruer, J. N., E. K. Warburton, and R. S. Bender, *Phys. Rev.*, **100**, 235 (1955).
21. Enge, H. A., E. J. Irwin, Jr., and D. H. Weaner, *Phys. Rev.*, **115**, 949 (1959).
22. Sass, R. E., B. Rosner, and E. J. Schneid, *Phys. Rev.*, **138**, B399 (1965) and references therein.
23. Pearson, C. A., and M. Coz, *Nucl. Physics.*, in press.
24. Actually, the authors of ref. 23 attempt to generalize the sudden approximation method by taking the viewpoint that Eq. (7) is an expansion of ψ_d^+ in terms of the set of wave functions ψ_p^+. Thus ψ_N^+ emerges as a generalized neutron wave function, rather than the optical wave function of Eq. (8). The solution of the appropriate equation for this generalized function of course presents difficulties of the same order of magnitude as solving exactly for ψ_d^+ in the first place. However, Pearson and Coz point out that, within the framework of the approximation of taking f in Eq. (15) outside the integral, their general conclusions do not depend on the amplitude M_1 being evaluated.

These authors also go one step further than the present text as regards polarization. They suggest that for $l = 0$ the contributions from interference between M_1 and M_2 are very small, while the amplitude M_1 itself leads to zero polarization for $l = 0$. They thus express the (d, p) polarization as equal to the (p, p) polarization multiplied by a ratio of cross sections. In the opinion of the present author, however, the whole approach is sufficiently approximate as not to warrant it being carried too far.
25. Rosen, L., J. G. Beery, A. S. Goldhaber, and E. J. Auerbach, *Ann. Phys.*, **34**, 96 (1965).
26. Smith, W. R., *Phys. Rev.*, **137**, B913 (1965).
27. Preston, R. L., H. J. Martin, and M. B. Sampson, *Phys. Rev.*, **121**, 1741 (1961).
28. Ludwig, E. J., and D. W. Miller, *Phys. Rev.*, **138**, B364 (1965).
29. May, R. M., *Phys. Rev. Letters*, January 15 (1966).

Electroexcitation of Nuclei*

M. E. ROSE

University of Virginia

Introduction

When, in 1930, Bethe's definitive article[1] on electron scattering was published, the emphasis was on stopping power of electrons, and eventually, other charged particles. The inelastic processes considered then were, of course, atomic excitation and ionization. Since that time, and especially, in recent years, the emphasis has shifted radically toward the end of using high energy electron beams as probes of nucleon and nuclear structure.

Essentially the same problems confront the theoretical description of the atomic and nuclear processes. These problems are broadly classified as follows: (1) the inclusion of distortion of the electron motion by the Coulomb field and (2) the requirement of an adequate representation of the wave functions of the target system. The first of these is, no doubt, the less formidable of the two since partial-wave expansions in terms of known eigenfunctions in the angular momentum representation are feasible. However, the second problem is far more acute in the nuclear than in the atomic collision. Moreover, degree of sensitivity of the calculated results for the scattering to certain features of the model description is a more crucial question when nuclear excitations are involved. Therefore, the major purpose of the electro-excitation studies is to provide a means of testing the nuclear models used to describe excited states.

The fact that nuclear interactions are not known with any great degree of certainty and the difficulties associated with the solution of the many-body nuclear problem make it clear that high-energy electron scattering (say, from 50 to 250 MeV) is essential and can provide

* Partially supported by the U.S. Atomic Energy Commission.

valuable nuclear information. This program has only begun to bear fruit and the results described here should be regarded as preliminary.

Excitation Cross-Section and Form Factors

As the foregoing remarks indicate, there are two steps in obtaining theoretical results for the excitation cross sections. One is to adequately treat the electron part of the problem and the second is to evaluate appropriate nuclear form factors which enter. The separation of these two parts of the problem is most easily illustrated when the electrons are treated as plane waves. This Born approximation then allows one to perform the integration over electron coordinates in the matrix element

$$\iint d\tau \, d\tau_e j_\mu J_\mu \exp(ik_o R)/R \tag{1}$$

which describes the scattering to lowest order in $e^2 = \alpha \cong 1/137$. In Eq. (1), j_μ is the transition 4-current for the electrons and J_μ is the corresponding 4-vector for the nuclear transition. Also $\hbar c k_0$ is the energy transfer and R is the nucleon–electron separation. Of course, $j_\mu = e\bar{\psi}_f\gamma_\mu\psi_i$ while the structure of J_μ is less well known. After the electron-coordinate integration is performed, leading to Møller potentials, it is clear that what remains in the matrix element [Eq. (1)] are Fourier transforms of J_μ which will lead to the form factors appearing in the Born approximation cross section. For scattering an angle ϑ with the nucleus excited from state i to state f, the angular distribution is (in units with $m_e = c = \hbar = 1$)

$$\frac{d\sigma}{d\Omega} = 8\pi e^2 \frac{2J_f + 1}{2J_i + 1} \frac{p'}{p} \sum_L \{K_c|F_L(c)|^2 + K_t[|F_L(e)|^2 + |F_L(m)|^2]\} \tag{2}$$

In Eq. (1), $\mathbf{p}'$ and $\mathbf{p}$ are the moments of scattered and incident electrons. The corresponding energies are E' and E. The 4-momentum transfer is given in terms of $(\mathbf{k}, k_0) = (\mathbf{p} - \mathbf{p}', E - E')$. The kinematic factors are

$$K_c = \frac{EE' + \mathbf{p}\cdot\mathbf{p}' + 1}{k^4} \tag{2a}$$

for Coulomb modes of the virtual electromagnetic field and

$$K_t = \frac{EE' - (\mathbf{p}\cdot\hat{\mathbf{k}})(\mathbf{p}'\cdot\hat{\mathbf{k}}) - 1}{(k^2 - k_0^2)^2} \tag{2b}$$

for the transverse modes, electric (e) and magnetic (m). Here $\hat{k} = \mathbf{k}/k$.

The important quantities in Eq. (2) are the form factors $F_L(x)$ which are the reduced matrix elements of the nuclear 4-current transforms. Thus, writing

$$F_L(x)C(J_iLJ_f; M_iM_f - M_i) = \langle f|\Phi_L^M|i\rangle \qquad (3)$$

with $M = M_f - M_i$, we have

$$\Phi_L^M = j_L(kr)Y_L^M(\hat{\mathbf{r}})\rho_{op} \qquad (3a)$$

for $x = c$, and

$$\Phi_L^M = \pm i\mathbf{A}_L^M \cdot \mathbf{J}_{op} \qquad (3b)$$

for the transverse fields with the upper (lower) sign referring to $x = e(m)$. The vector potential normalization is implied by Eq. (3a) and the continuity equation[2]. Obviously J_i, J_f, and L form a triangle and the parity selection rule is $\pi_i\pi_f = (-)^{L+\eta}$, where $\eta = 0$ for $x = c$ and e and 1 for $x = m$.

For most experimental conditions ($E, E' \gg k_0 \sim 1$) the cross section reduces to

$$\frac{d\sigma}{d\Omega} = \frac{4\pi\sigma_0}{(Ze)^2}\frac{2J_f + 1}{2J_i + 1}\sum_L \left\{|F_L(c)|^2 + \left(\frac{1}{2} + \tan^2\frac{\vartheta}{2}\right)[|F_L(e)|^2 + |F_L(m)|^2]\right\},$$
$$(4)$$

where

$$\sigma_0 = \left(\frac{Ze^2}{2E}\right)^2\frac{\cos^2\vartheta/2}{\sin^4\vartheta/2}$$

is the high-energy limit of the Mott scattering.

It is important to recognize that at $\vartheta = \pi$ only transverse scattering is expected, although to what extent this conclusion would be modified in a non-Born approximation calculation is a somewhat open question. In any event, back-scattering is measured with the aid of a magnetic field, and is generally used to extract the transverse part of the scattering.* Since the form factors depend only on k among the kinematic variables, it follows that more generally, a program involving measurements at fixed j and various ϑ and E would, in principle, permit a separation between Coulomb and transverse contributions. The fact that the Coulomb scattering is often larger than the transverse part by as much

* For elastic scattering at $\vartheta = \pi$ one would expect only magnetic contributions. This has been shown by Pratt, Walecka, and Griffy, [*Nucl. Phys.*, **64**, 677 (1965)] on the basis of time-reversal invariance and simple parity arguments.

as two orders of magnitude obviously does not impugn the validity of this remark although in such cases it may be unnecessary to carry through the separation procedure since it can be known *a priori* that $|F_{L(e)}^{(c)}| \gg |F_L(e \text{ or } m)|$.

It is important to note that while more accurate treatments of the scattering problem do exist, these are always quite laborious being based on distorted wave methods with a very large number of partial waves included. Aside from the loss of clarity involved in such machine computations and despite the somewhat indecisive conclusions derived from them as to the validity of the Born approximation, the latter has been used extensively for excitation of light nuclei (up to Ca). Although care must be taken to avoid spurious zeroes* of the form factors in the Born approximation and despite some indications that beyond the first zero the plane wave results may be quantitatively faulty, a considerable amount of progress has been made using this approximation.

The Nuclear Structure Problem

Much of the experimental and theoretical effort has been concerned with excitation of the giant resonance. For reasons connected with the limited applicability of the shell-model calculations, only data for closed-shell or closed-subshell nuclei are of great interest at present. Figs. 1 and 2 show the comparison of quantities proportional to $|F_1(e)|^2$ versus k for C^{12} and O^{16}, respectively. The measurements[3,4] were made for backward scattering. The hydrodynamical models in Figs. 1 and 2 are in clear disagreement with the observations. The results of the Brown model[5] or, as we shall refer to it, the particle-hole model are in much better agreement with the measured points. In particular, the dip at intermediate values of momentum transfer, more clearly indicated for C^{12}, is reproduced. In this connection it must be observed that what is plotted as ordinate in Figs. 1 and 2 is a sum of $|F_1(e)|^2$ over two or more closely-spaced levels. This procedure is in accord with the limited resolution in the measurements. The aforementioned dip arises mainly from two constituents: the main peak in the giant resonance and a so-called spin-flip contribution. The former decreases with increasing k while the latter exhibits the opposite behavior.

* These do not, generally speaking, occur at the same moment transfer for the Coulomb and transverse parts.

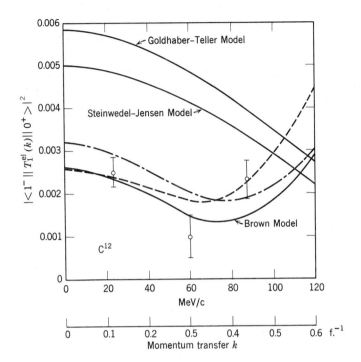

Fig. 1. The square of the transverse electric-dipole form factor for the giant dipole resonance in C^{12} as a function of momentum transfer k, taken from ref. 3. The units for the ordinate are indirectly defined in this reference. The dashed line is obtained by omitting a high-lying unperturbed state: $(1s_{1\,2})^{-1}\,1p_{1/2}$ coupled to
$$J^\pi = 1^-, T = 1.$$

In the particle-hole model without ground state correlations (see below) the ground state corresponds to filled $1s_{1/2}$, $1p_{3/2}$, and (for O^{16}) $1p_{1/2}$ subshells. Excited states are produced by promoting nucleons from the $1p$ to the $2s$ or $1d$ shell. These shell-model states, with particle and hole appropriately coupled, form the basis for the calculation of energy levels of the excited states with a two-nucleon residual interaction. This interaction is here taken to be a zero-range Soper mixture:

$$V_{ij} = -V_0[1 - \eta' + \eta'\boldsymbol{\sigma}_i\cdot\boldsymbol{\sigma}_j]\delta(\mathbf{r}_i - \mathbf{r}_j),$$

with $\eta' = 0.135$. The single-particle wave functions are harmonic-oscillator states characterized by a reciprocal-length parameter $a = (M\omega/\hbar)^{1/2}$, with ω the oscillator frequency. It is fairly evident that the only parameters entering, aside from single-particle unperturbed energies, are η' and $\beta \equiv V_0 a^3/4\pi$. The single-particle energies are obtained empirically from neighboring isotope level data. The main peak and spin-flip levels referred to above correspond to levels which are primarily $(1p_{3/2})^{-1} 1d_{5/2}$ and $(1p_{3/2})^{-1} 1d_{3/2}$, respectively.

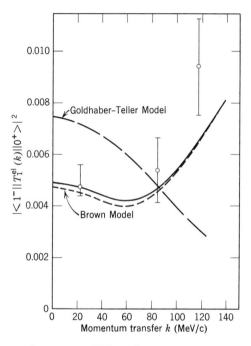

Fig. 2. The squared transverse $E1$ form factor versus momentum transfer for the giant dipole resonance in O^{16} (see ref. 4) the ordinate is the same as in Fig. 1. The solid curve is calculated with a Serber mixture and a Yakawa potential for the residual interaction while the dashed curve marked "Brown model" is obtained with an ordinary ($\eta' = 0$) zero range force. The experimental points are discussed in ref. 4.

Here and in the following, the current density is a sum of convective and magnetization contributions. The latter contributes only to the transverse form-factors. The result that these are usually small compared to the Coulomb form-factor is simply an expression of the non-relativistic state of motion of the nucleons.

The particle-hole model has also been used with considerable success in the discussion of electroexcitation of levels below the giant resonance. Gillet and Melkanoff[6] have calculated form factors for a number of levels in C^{12} and Ca^{40}. Some of their results are shown in Figs. 3–5. The dotted curves in each figure give results of the in-

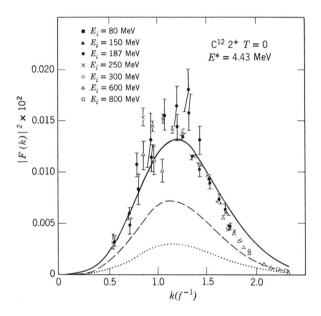

Fig. 3. The squared form factor for the indicated resonance in C^{12}, taken from ref. 6. The three curves correspond to three different models as explained in the text.

dependent-particle model, the dashed curves result from the particle-hole model as described above, while the full curves contain the ground state correlations as given by the random-phase approximation[7]. The agreement between the calculated and measured form factors is quite gratifying. For the 4.48 MeV 5^-, $T = 0$ level in Ca^{40} (not shown), the agreement is not quite as good.

So far, all the calculations based on the harmonic oscillator model have been truncated so that only the minimum number of particle-hole pairs (namely one) are included. For odd-parity levels this involves excitations of the $\hbar\omega$ and for even-parity levels excitations of $0\hbar\omega$ only are considered. In a closed-shell nucleus, 0^{16} say, the even-parity levels must involve $2\hbar\omega$ excitations with one particle-hole pair and two particle-hole pairs, each involving excitation of one oscillator quantum. A calculation[8] of form factors leads to disappointing results although the calculated level spectrum is reasonable. The residual interaction

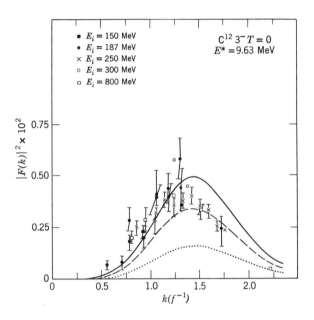

Fig. 4.   The same as Fig. 3 for the indicated level in C^{12}.

described above is used, with $\beta = 4.41$ MeV, and no ground-state correlations are taken into account. In the best case, the calculated form factor is too small by a factor of about 40, almost independent of the momentum transfer. Hence, the shape but not the magnitude of $|F|^2$ is given correctly. The same large discrepancy afflicts gamma-ray transition rates between excited states[9]. The pair rate for $0^+ \rightarrow 0^+$ ground state as calculated is too small by a factor 10^3. Some corrections for spurious states may be made but present indications are that the large discrepancies cited will not be removed[10].*

The conclusion from the foregoing would appear to be that the nuclear model used is somehow satisfactory if one truncates as drastically as possible in the Tamm-Dancoff procedure but is otherwise entirely inadequate. One may use more realistic radial functions—the harmonic oscillator, while simple, misrepresents the tail of the wave functions.

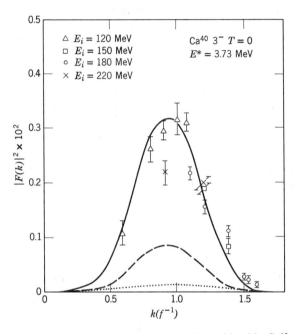

Fig. 5.   The same as Fig. 3 for the indicated level in Ca⁴⁰.

* A very closely analogous situation arises in the calculation of the absolute β-transition rate in the decay of $B^{12} \rightarrow C^{12}$ (ground state) and the decay of $N^{16} \rightarrow O^{16}$ (ground state). These involve the static limit of the $M1$ and $M2$ transition operators, respectively. Using $0\hbar\omega$ and $1\hbar\omega$ one particle-one hole excitations the matrix elements turn out to be too large by a factor 2 and $\sqrt{2}$, respectively. Such factors are serious from the point of view of checking weak interaction models but are, of course, not so drastic as compared to the discrepancies encountered between calculated and observed electromagnetic transition rates.

Alternatively, one may use more realistic residual interactions between pairs of nucleons. The latter, at least, does not seem to alter β-transition rates appreciably[11]. It may very well be that in some way the deformation which is probably present in many of the excited states must be taken into account and that the n-particle-hole model with $n \geqslant 2$ does not form a sufficiently good basis for doing this*.

Other approaches in which the nuclear model undergoes some refinement have been attempted. A noteworthy example is the work of da Providência and Shakin[12] in which the effect of a hard core is introduced. This has the effect of reducing the form factors at large momentum transfer. The comparison with experimental data[13] for Li^6 leaves room for further improvement in the theory.

The effect on the inelastic scattering of correlations between nucleons is, to some extent, taken into account by da Providência and Shakin[12]. This problem had also been discussed by Czyz and Gottfried[14] who recognized the possibility of a direct study of such correlations in nuclear matter by measurement of inelastic form factors. This type of study would no doubt profit from a more exact treatment of the problem of nuclear matter. In this context attention should also be called to the work of Reiner[15].

Coulomb Distortion Effects

The first serious attempt to replace the Born approximation treatment of the scattering by something better was made by Schiff[16] who made an approximate evaluation of the entire Born series by using the stationary phase assumption. As pointed out by Czyz and Gottfried[14] it may be further argued that this equivalent to the replacement, in the Born approximation, of the actual momentum transfer by an effective momentum transfer†

$$k_{\mathrm{eff}} = k(1 + 3\alpha Z/pR_n) \tag{5}$$

where R_n is the nuclear radius. For $Z = 82$, $R_n \approx 7f$, and $p = 400$ MeV/c this amounts to a 6% correction. Of course, considering only Coulomb or transverse scattering, the Born zeroes are simply shifted.

* Indications are that $3\hbar\omega$ excitations for odd-parity states make non-negligible contributions. This emerges from perturbation calculations of S. Fujii (to appear in *Nuclear Physics*).

† There is a sign error in Eq. (2.10′) of ref. 14.

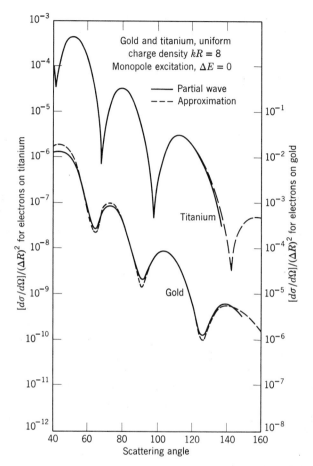

Fig. 6.   Electric monopole scattering in Ti and Au as a function of scattering angle, taken from ref. 17. The approximation referred to by the dashed curve is based on the eikonal wave function described in this reference.

Since the Born approximation always falsifies the calculated scattering near the zeroes, this procedure is a palliative. Nevertheless, this semi-classical approach is capable of further refinement as Yennie et al.[17] have shown. Their three dimensional WKB (eikonal) approximation gives results which compare very well indeed with partial-wave calculations for elastic scattering[18] in Ti and Au. Figure 6 shows the comparison for monopole excitations. Similar results are obtained for quadrupole excitation (their Fig. 10).

Since the standard of comparison is the partial-wave expansion it may well be questioned inasmuch as partial-wave expansions are always possible. If these are carried out with sufficient care, and one must recognize that a very large number of partial waves must be taken into account[19], it would then appear that the Coulomb distortion effects have been properly taken into account and the only possibility for a discrepancy between theory and experiment would be shortcomings in the nuclear model. Nevertheless, there are two reasons for seeking accurate but relatively simple analytic procedures. First, the numerical computations are simplified and presumably more trustworthy from that restricted point of view. Comparison of Born approximation and partial-wave calculations of the scattering by different authors leads to somewhat discordant conclusions[20]. A test of the partial-wave expansion has been exhibited by Scheck* who calculated the non-retarded Coulomb ($L = 1$) Born cross section for Er and compared it with the partial-wave expansion for $Z = 0$ (see Fig. 7). Of course, when the calculation is made with $Z = 68$ the difference between Born and partial-wave results is very much enhanced[20]. A second reason for attempting to construct analytical procedures is, of course, the greater insight one may hope to obtain as to the reasons for the particular shape that any given calculated cross section does exhibit. It is especially desirable to be able to ascertain what particular features of the cross section are characteristic of a given nuclear model.

The work of Biedenharn and his collaborators was basic for the partial-wave calculations which have appeared. The method is based on a division of the partial waves into three groups which are roughly and schematically designated as follows: (a) $|\kappa| = j + 1/2 < 10$, say; (b) $10 < |\kappa| <$ about 1000; (c) $|\kappa| > 1000$. In the first region (low $|\kappa|$) an essentially exact calculation is carried out. In the second, nuclear penetration effects are neglected and the energy loss is set equal to zero. The third, or so-called adiabatic region, makes a small contribution and is discarded. The Duke group has exhibited results for $E2$ Coulomb excitation from which the conclusion is drawn that if the radius of the nuclear charge distribution is appropriately increased in the Born

---

* The nuclear model used by Scheck is of interest. His work is concerned with the giant dipole resonance and the nuclear states are described by the Danos-Greiner extension of the hydrodynamical model of Jensen and Steinwedel.

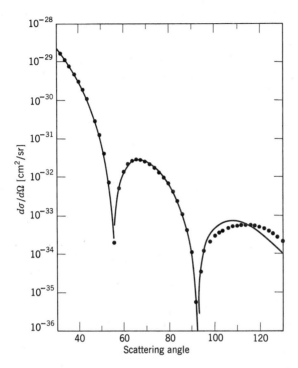

Fig. 7. A comparison of the partial-wave analysis for $Z = 0$ (dots) and the Born approximation (full curve) for the cross section for Coulomb excitation with $L = 1$, taken from ref. 20. This reference should be consulted for a definition of the parameters for which the results apply.

approximation the calculated scattering compares well with the partial-wave expansion results at least up to the first Born zero. The increase in radius is not the same for electrons as it is for positrons but is linear for small Z. For large Z, $\Delta R_n/R_n \sim 0.08$. This may be compared with the effective increase of momentum transfer involved in Eq. (5) and, at least in a qualitative sense, the two suggested procedures for correcting the Born approximation would appear to be consistent.

In conclusion it appears at the time of writing that electroexcitation of nuclei is a promising field for the study of nuclear structure. Extensive work has been carried out only during the past few years and there is every reason to believe that the next few years will be marked by even more rapid progress. To achieve this progress, considerable effort will have to be concentrated on the problem of constructing more realistic nuclear models. It is especially important to discover those features of the model to which the scattering is sensitive. In any event, the theoretical activity in this field involves a difficult but challenging problem.

References

1. Bethe, H. A., *Ann. Phys.*, **5**, 325 (1930).
2. For explicit forms see M. E. Rose, *Elementary Theory of Angular Momentum*, John Wiley, New York, 1957.
3. Lewis, Walecka, Goldemberg, and Barber, *Phys. Rev. Letters*, **10**, 493 (1963); **11**, 105 (1963).
4. The data for O^{16} is discussed by F. H. Lewis, Jr., *Phys. Rev.*, **134**, B331 (1964).
5. Brown, Castillejo, and Evans, *Nucl. Phys.*, **22**, 1 (1961); V. Gillet, *Nucl. Phys.*, **51**, 410 (1964); V. Gillet, and N. Vinh Mau, *Nucl. Physics.*, **54**, 321 (1964).
6. Gillet, V., and M. A. Melkanoff, *Phys. Rev.*, **133**, B1190 (1964).
7. Brown, G. E., *Unified Theory of Nuclear Models*, North-Holland Publ. Co., Amsterdam, 1964.
8. Eisenberg, Spicer, and Rose, to appear in *Nucl. Phys.*
9. Rose, M. E., and S. Fujii, to be published.
10. Eisenberg, J. M., and J. B. Seaborn, private communication.
11. This conclusion is based on wave functions obtained by A. Green, private communication.
12. Da Providência, J., and C. M. Shakin, *Ann. Phys.* (*NY*), **30**, 95 (1964); *Nucl. Phys.*, **65**, 54 (1965).
13. Bernheim, M., and G. R. Bishop, *Phys. Rev. Letters*, **5**, 270 (1963).
14. Czyz, W., and K. Gottfried, *Ann. Phys.* (*NY*), **21**, 47 (1963); W. Czyz, *Phys. Rev.*, **131**, 2141 (1963).
15. Reiner, A. S., *Phys. Rev.*, **138**, B389 (1965).
16. Schiff, L. I., *Phys. Rev.*, **103**, 443 (1956).
17. Yennie, Boos, and Ravenhall, *Phys. Rev.*, **137**, B882 (1965).
18. See also A. Baker, *Phys. Rev.*, **134**, B240 (1964).
19. Griffy, Onley, Reynolds, and Biedenharn, *Phys. Rev.*, **128**, 833 (1962); Onley, Griffy, and Reynolds, *Phys. Rev.*, **129**, 1689 (1963).
20. For example, see F. Scheck (to be published) and results of reference 18.
21. A convenient summary is given by L. C. Biedenharn in, *Proceedings of the 1962 Eastern Theoretical Physics Conference*, Gordon-Breach, New York (1963), p. 87.

Ingoing Waves in β-Emissions

E. J. KONOPINSKI

Indiana University

Anyone who has worked with Hans Bethe knows his gift for making formal results also seem reasonable, adding to confidence that the formulation is not somehow defective. An example is exhibited by his paper[1] with Breit, on the role of ingoing wave final states in describing outgoing products of scattering processes.

The aim of that paper was to elucidate why, when forming matrix elements for transitions to final states containing outgoing products, and when the outgoing particles are to be described by distorted plane waves, then these must be taken to have *ingoing* components. The paper discusses processes which, like Bremsstrahlung, are initiated by incident waves. A like situation develops in β-emissions, and here it may seem even more paradoxical, since there is no incident wave to be represented. The β-particles may be described as forming *purely outgoing* waves, yet, to derive expectations for detecting a definite electron momentum, it is necessary to calculate the formation probability of a final state which has only ingoing wave components superposed on the plane wave of definite momentum.

A comparison of the phenomenon as it occurs in β-emission, and in simple, nonrelativistic elastic scattering, is undertaken here. It then becomes particularly easy to understand that the phenomenon has to do with any attempt to detect a plane wave at infinity, and should arise however the process is initiated. The discussion will owe much to instruction by the Bethe-Breit paper.

1. Distorted Plane Waves

A principal part in the discussion is played by the familiar modified plane waves having the asymptotic forms

$$\psi_{\mathbf{k}}^{\pm}(\mathbf{r} \to \infty) = e^{i\mathbf{k}\cdot\mathbf{r}} + \frac{f_{\pm}\, e^{\pm ikr}}{r}, \tag{1.1}$$

where $f_\pm$ are amplitudes independent of the radial separation r between a particle and a distorting force center. The outgoing-wave modification in ψ_k^+ is best known as a description of a steady, elastically-scattered wave, in time-independent treatments of scattering. Inclusion of the modifications is needed whenever an improvement on the Born (plane wave) approximation is sought because of the presence of some distorting field, like the Coulomb field of a nucleus. In the case of Bremsstrahlung, the distortion provides for essential momentum absorptions. In β-decay, the momentum of the emissions is primarily absorbed in a recoil of the source nucleon, but the coulomb field modifies the electron wave densities available for excitation at the nucleus.

Bethe and Breit's method of elucidation is to consider "temporal sequences" in the processes, starting with an initial scattering state. To avoid mere repetition here, a simple example will be presented of a construction which Bethe and Breit discussed in more general terms.

Discussion in terms of a temporal sequence requires separating steady states like Eq. (1.1) into phases before, during, and after scattering by the distorting field. There must then be some restriction of the wave to a packet which, for example, does not yet overlap on the effective range of the distorting field during the earliest phases of a scattering. Bethe and Breit discussed packets of the form

$$\Psi_0(\mathbf{r}, t) = \oint (d\mathbf{k}) C_\mathbf{k} \psi_\mathbf{k} \exp\left[-iE(\mathbf{k})t/\hbar\right], \qquad (1.2)$$

where $E(\mathbf{k})$ is the energy corresponding to the momentum $\hbar\mathbf{k}$. They pointed out that the weights $C_\mathbf{k}$ given to the various solutions $\psi_\mathbf{k}$, which are ones subject to boundary conditions like Eq. (1.1), must be such as to provide constructive or destructive interferences of their plane-wave parts in appropriate relation to interferences among the spherical-wave parts. Thus, to represent elastic scattering of an incident plane wave, they argue that the necessity of using the boundary condition ψ_k^+ for it follows from the fact that this provides in the earliest phases ($t \leq 0$) a destructive interference of the spherical wave parts concurrently with the constructive interference of the plane wave parts:

$$(f_+/r) \oint (d\mathbf{k}) C_\mathbf{k} \exp\left[i(kr - Et/\hbar)\right] = 0 \qquad (1.3a)$$

occurs for $t \leq 0$ when

$$\oint (d\mathbf{k}) C_\mathbf{k} \exp \left[i(\mathbf{k} \cdot \mathbf{r} - Et/\hbar) \right] \neq 0. \tag{1.3b}$$

A simple explicit example will be given.

Let an incident plane wave approaching a scattering center at $\mathbf{r} = 0$, but at $t = 0$ still confined to positions $z < -a$ outside the force range, be represented by (see Fig. 1):

$$
\begin{aligned}
\Psi_0(\mathbf{r}, 0) &= e^{ik_0 z} \qquad \text{for} \qquad z < -a, \\
&= 0 \qquad\quad \text{for} \qquad z > -a.
\end{aligned} \left.\vphantom{\begin{aligned}e\\0\end{aligned}}\right\} \tag{1.4}
$$

No confinement of the packet in directions normal to the incidence direction need be introduced, since edge effects of any finite beam will be negligible. The restriction to $z < -a$ introduces uncertainty of momentum in a way obtainable by fourier analysis:

$$\Psi_0(\mathbf{r}, 0) = \oint (d\mathbf{k}) C_\mathbf{k} \, e^{i\mathbf{k}\cdot\mathbf{r}}, \tag{1.5}$$

if

$$
\begin{aligned}
C_\mathbf{k} &= \oint \frac{(d\mathbf{r})}{(2\pi)^3} \, e^{-i\mathbf{k}\cdot\mathbf{r}} \, \Psi_0(\mathbf{r}, 0), \\
&= \delta(k_x)\delta(k_y) \frac{e^{i(k_z - k_0)a}}{-2\pi i(k_z - k_0)}.
\end{aligned} \tag{1.6}
$$

There is omitted here a rapidly oscillating exponential which arises from the lower limit ($z \to -\infty$) of the integration along the incidence direction z, having a zero average even in intervals $\Delta k_z \to 0$. The omission is finally justified if the integration over k_z in (1.5) is carried out in the complex plane of k_z, along a line $\mathrm{Re}\,(k_z) + i\varepsilon$ with $\varepsilon > 0$, or

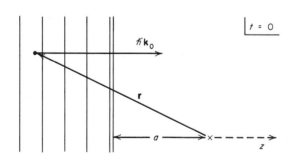

Figure 1.

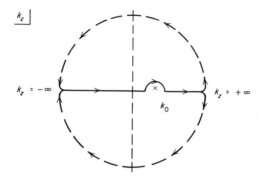

Figure 2.

as indicated in Fig. 2. Then, after substitution of (1.6) into (1.5), the integration over k_z for $z + a > 0$ becomes equivalent to one which follows the closed path including the upper half-circle of infinite radius and not enclosing the pole at $k_z = k_0$. As a consequence, $\Psi_0(z > -a) = 0$, properly. When $z + a < 0$, the lower half-circle must be taken to complete the path, the pole is enclosed, and the remainder of the desired result (1.4) is obtained.

Next, the results of using the fourier coefficients (1.6) as the weights C_k in the wave packet (1.2) may be examined. When this is done for $\psi_k \rightarrow \psi_k^+(\infty)$, evaluations on the integration paths of Fig. 2 show that the plane-wave parts (1.3b) of the resultant packet add up to

$$
\left.\begin{array}{ll}
\exp\left[i(k_0 z - E_0 t/\hbar)\right] & \text{for} \quad z < -a + v_0 t, \\
0 & \text{for} \quad z > -a + v_0 t,
\end{array}\right\} \quad (1.7a)
$$

where $E_0 \equiv E(\mathbf{k}_0)$, while $v_0 = (\partial E/\hbar\, \partial k_z)_0$ is the "group velocity" corresponding to the momentum $\hbar\mathbf{k}_0$. Concurrently, the interferences among the spherical wave parts of $\Psi_0(\infty, t)$ yield for positions $r \rightarrow \infty$:

$$
\left.\begin{array}{ll}
0 & \text{for} \quad t < (a + r)/v_0, \\
(f_+/r) \exp\left[i(k_0 r - E_0 t/\hbar)\right] & \text{for} \quad t > (a + r)/v_0.
\end{array}\right\} \quad (1.7b)
$$

These are obviously just the properties needed to fit the boundary conditions characterizing the elastic scattering of an incident plane wave. The first of the lines (1.7b) exhibits the conformity to the Bethe–Breit dictum (1.3a).

The example illustrates the kind of criteria Bethe and Breit also used for the suitability of final states proportional to ψ_k^- in describing inelastically scattered particles, forming waves without parts interpretable as "incident." Rather than just repeating that phase of the Bethe–Breit analysis here, two contrasting examples will be discussed and conclusions from them drawn.

2. The Outgoing Wave Generated by β-Emission

One way to construct a wave picture of the electrons emitted in β-decay is guided by analogy to the generation of Maxwell field from a given electromagnetic source current vector. A source of Dirac spinor field $\Psi(\mathbf{r}, t)$ must be represented by some spinor $S(\mathbf{r}, t)$ in the equation[2]

$$ i\hbar \frac{\partial}{\partial t} \Psi = [-i\hbar c\boldsymbol{\alpha}\cdot\nabla + \beta mc^2 + V]\Psi + S(\mathbf{r}, t). \qquad (2.1) $$

Just as it is sufficient to deal with a Fourier component of definite frequency in electromagnetic theory, so here a stationary energy eigenstate $\psi(r)$, of definite positive energy W, may be considered:

$$ W\psi(\mathbf{r}) = [-i\hbar c\boldsymbol{\alpha}\cdot\nabla + \beta mc^2 + V(r)]\psi + s(\mathbf{r}), \qquad (2.2) $$

where $s(\mathbf{r})$ is a suitable fourier transform of $S(\mathbf{r}, t)$. The potential $V(r)$ represents, for nuclear β-decay, the wave-distorting coulomb field of the nucleus, being $V = -Ze^2/r$ in the point-charge approximation. Details of the source spinor $s(\mathbf{r})$ are not germane to issues here, but it may be recognized that

$$ s(\mathbf{r}) \equiv 8^{1/2}g\beta\gamma_\alpha\tfrac{1}{2}(1 + \gamma_5)\psi_\nu^C(\mathbf{r})\langle f| \sum_a \delta(\mathbf{r} - \mathbf{r}^a)\tfrac{1}{2}(C_V - C_A\gamma_5^a)\beta^a\gamma_\alpha^a\tau_+^a |i\rangle \qquad (2.3) $$

leads to a contribution,

$$ mc^2 \oint (d\mathbf{r}')\psi^\dagger s(\mathbf{r}') \equiv \langle f| H_\beta |i\rangle, \qquad (2.4) $$

to the field energy which is identical with the usual transition matrix element following from the "V-A law" of β^- decay. The symbols $|i\rangle$ and $|f\rangle$ refer to states of nuclear structures containing source nucleons labeled a and $\psi_\nu^C(\mathbf{r})$ is a charge-conjugate spinor describing the antineutrino to be emitted.

An outgoing wave solution of Eq. (2.2) is needed to get a positive decay rate proportional to the outward Dirac current density $c(\psi^\dagger \alpha_r \psi)$, where $c\alpha_r \equiv c\hat{r} \cdot \alpha$ is the radial component of the "instantaneous velocity operator," $c\alpha$. The decay rate yielding electrons in the energy range dW, and headed into the solid-angle element $d\Omega \equiv (d\hat{r})$, is given by[2]

$$d\lambda/dW \, d\Omega = cr^2(\psi^\dagger \alpha_r \psi)_{r \to \infty}, \qquad (2.5)$$

when the states given in the source spinor are suitably normalized (the nuclear states to unity in all space and the lepton states "per unit energy"). A similar outward current was exhibited by Rose, Biedenharn, and Arfken[3], to represent conversion electrons ejected from atomic orbits during electromagnetic transitions in nuclei.

The requisite outgoing wave solution of Eq. (2.2) may be expressed with the help of a propagator G from source points to detector. The solution may be written

$$\psi(\mathbf{r}) = \oint G(|\mathbf{r} - \mathbf{r}'|)s(\mathbf{r}')(d\mathbf{r}') \qquad (2.6a)$$

if G obeys the "unit point-source" equation

$$[W + i\hbar c\alpha \cdot \nabla - \beta mc^2 - V]G = \rho_0 \, \delta(\mathbf{r} - \mathbf{r}'), \qquad (2.6b)$$

where ρ_0 is the Dirac unit matrix. The propagator itself may be expressed with the help of spherical wave solutions $\psi_{\kappa\mu}(\mathbf{r})$ of the homogeneous Dirac equation (2.2) with $s \equiv 0$, since this is equivalent to Eq. (2.6b) at $\mathbf{r} \neq \mathbf{r}'$. The subscript $\kappa = \pm(j + \frac{1}{2})$, with j the total angular momentum quantum number of the electron, is the "spin–orbit" quantum number corresponding to $l = j \pm \frac{1}{2}$, while μ is the projection of j. There is available not only a set of "standing wave" spherical wave solutions $\psi_{\kappa\mu}$, which are regular at the origin, but also a set $\psi^0_{\kappa\mu}$ which are singular at the origin and each forming a purely outgoing wave at infinity. Then the propagator having the requisite boundary $(r \to \infty)$ properties is[3]

$$G = -i2^{1/2}\pi \sum_{\kappa\mu} \psi^0_{\kappa\mu}(\mathbf{r})\psi^\dagger_{\kappa\mu}(\mathbf{r}'), \qquad (2.7)$$

with $\mathbf{r}$ and $\mathbf{r}'$ to be interchanged for $r < r'$. The latter circumstance is what makes the operation (2.6b) on G yield the singularity at $\mathbf{r} = \mathbf{r}'$, while giving zero at every other point. The result (2.7) is unsurprising if it is recognized as an appropriate generalization, taking into account distorting field and relativistic effects, of the well-known representation of the "Huyghen's wavelet" in free space:

$$\frac{\exp{(ik|\mathbf{r} - \mathbf{r}'|)}}{4\pi|\mathbf{r} - \mathbf{r}'|} = ik \sum_{lm} h_l(kr) Y_{lm}(\hat{\mathbf{r}}) \cdot j_l(kr') Y^*_{lm}(\hat{\mathbf{r}}'), \qquad (2.8)$$

where j_l is the regular spherical Bessel function while h_l is the outgoing spherical wave Hankel function, when $r > r'$.

The function $h_l(kr)$ also helps express the relativistic outgoing wave $\psi^0_{\kappa\mu}$ when no distorting field is present,

$$\psi^0_{\kappa\mu}(\mathbf{r}) = \left[\frac{k(W + mc^2)}{2\pi c^2 \hbar^2}\right]^{1/2} \left(\begin{array}{c} e^{-i\delta^0_\kappa} h_{l(\kappa)}(kr) \\ e^{-i\delta^0_\kappa} h_{l(-\kappa)}(W + mc^2)^{-1} c\hbar k\sigma_r \end{array}\right) \chi_{\kappa\mu}(\hat{\mathbf{r}}) \qquad (2.9)$$

for $V = 0$. Here $l(-\kappa) = l(\kappa) \pm 1$ for $\kappa = \mp(j + \frac{1}{2})$, respectively, and $\sigma_r \equiv \boldsymbol{\sigma} \cdot \hat{\mathbf{r}}$ is the radial component of the Pauli spin operator. The directional dependence is given by the two-component "spinor spherical harmonic,"

$$\chi_{\kappa\mu}(\hat{\mathbf{r}}) = \sum_{\sigma = \pm 1/2} \langle l(\mu - \sigma)\tfrac{1}{2}(\sigma)|j(\mu)\rangle \chi_\sigma Y_{l,\mu-\sigma}(\hat{\mathbf{r}}), \qquad (2.10)$$

where $l = \kappa$ or $-(\kappa + 1)$, $\chi_{\pm 1/2}$ are the Pauli eigenspinors, and the angular bracket stands for a conventional vector-addition coefficient. It is noteworthy that $\sigma_r \chi_{\kappa\mu} = -\chi_{-\kappa\mu}$ and $\chi_{-1\mu} = (4\pi)^{-1/2}\chi_\mu$. The phase shift $\delta^0_\kappa \equiv -(l + 1)\pi/2$ is just the one which characterizes the asymptotic behavior

$$h_l(\infty) = \exp{[i(kr + \delta^0_\kappa)]}/kr. \qquad (2.11)$$

The standing spherical wave $\psi_{\kappa\mu}$ (in free space) differs from (2.9) only in that $2^{1/2}j_l = 2^{-1/2}(h_l + h_l^*)$ replaces h_l; for $j_l(\infty)$, the cosine replaces the exponential in (2.11).

In the presence of a distorting field $V(r) \neq 0$, the radial waves h_l and j_l are replaced by much more complicated irregular and regular functions (respectively). However, the change in asymptotic behavior is simple; there is merely a replacement of δ^0_κ by a new phase shift δ_κ characteristic of the distorting field. In the case $V = -Ze^2/r$,

$$\delta_\kappa = \nu \ln{(2kr)} - \arg{\Gamma(\gamma + i\nu)} + \eta - \tfrac{1}{2}\pi\gamma, \qquad (2.12a)$$

where

$$\nu = \alpha ZW/c\hbar k,$$

$$\gamma = (\kappa^2 - \alpha^2 Z^2)^{1/2}$$

and

$$e^{2i\eta} = -[\kappa - i\nu(mc^2/W)]/(\gamma + i\nu). \qquad (2.12b)$$

The expression (2.12a) properly reduces to δ_κ^0 for $Z = 0$. Thus the asymptotic behavior of the relativistic outgoing wave, in the presence of a distorting field which leads to the phase-shift δ_κ, is:

$$\psi_{\kappa\mu}^0(\infty) = \left(\frac{W + mc^2}{2\pi c^2\hbar^2 k}\right)^{\frac{1}{2}} \frac{\exp\left[i(kr + \delta_\kappa - \delta_\kappa^0)\right]}{r} \left(\begin{array}{c} 1 \\ [c\hbar k/(W + mc^2)]\sigma_r \end{array}\right)$$
$$\times \chi_{\kappa\mu}(\hat{\mathbf{r}}). \quad (2.13)$$

Simple substitution of this into Eqs. (2.7) and (2.6a) makes explicit the outgoing wave character of the total wave emitted by a β-source.

It may immediately be noticed that the spherical wave (2.13) takes on, in any given direction $\hat{\mathbf{r}}$, the characteristics of a plane wave of momentum $\hbar\mathbf{k} = \hbar k\hat{\mathbf{r}}$. The well-known representation of a Dirac plane wave is

$$u_{\mathbf{k}\sigma}(\mathbf{r}) = \left(\frac{W + mc^2}{2W}\right)^{\frac{1}{2}} \left(\begin{array}{c} 1 \\ (W + mc^2)^{-1}\hbar\mathbf{k}\cdot\boldsymbol{\sigma} \end{array}\right)\chi_\sigma \frac{\exp[i\mathbf{k}\cdot\mathbf{r}]}{(2\pi)^{3/2}}, \quad (2.14)$$

hence Eq. (2.13) may be rewritten as

$$\psi_{\kappa\mu}^0(\infty) = \frac{\exp\left[i(\delta_\kappa - \delta_\kappa^0)\right]}{r}\left(\frac{8\pi^2 W}{c^2\hbar^2 k}\right)^{\frac{1}{2}} \sum_\sigma [\chi_\sigma^\dagger\cdot\chi_{\kappa\mu}(\hat{\mathbf{k}})]u_{\mathbf{k}\sigma}(\mathbf{r}), \quad (2.15)$$

if the identification $\hat{\mathbf{r}} \equiv \hat{\mathbf{k}}$ is made. It can be argued that $e^{i\delta_\kappa}/r$ is a constant over many wave lengths as $r \to \infty$. A proper analysis into plane waves (with more careful attention to the incompatibility of knowing $\mathbf{k}$ and $\mathbf{r}$ simultaneously) will be carried out in Sec. 4.

The inelastically scattered particles given primary attention by Breit and Bethe might also have been described as forming a purely outgoing wave. Such a description was not explicitly constructed by those authors because they introduced the analysis into distorted plane waves, here being reserved for Sec. 4, right at the outset of their considerations. Thus, the phenomenon to be exhibited, the role of the ingoing-wave distortions in a purely-outgoing total wave, could also be carried out for that case. However, one of the objectives here is to demonstrate the phenomenon explicitly for β-emissions.

The formal part of the β-emission description here is practically the same as the treatment of conversion electrons by Rose, Biedenharn and Arfken[3], in a paper preceding that of Bethe and Breit. Indeed, demonstrations of the formal necessity of using ingoing-wave distortions in final states have a long history[4]. Besides demonstrating the recurrence of the formal necessity in β-emissions, it is hoped here to achieve an elucidation comparable to that of Bethe and Breit, with the help of a comparison to simple elastic scattering, as introduced in the next section.

3. A Non-Relativistic Spherical Wave Emission

The phenomenon of interest is much more transparent in an analogous treatment of nonrelativistic elastic scattering by a central potential. The relativistic propagations of the β-emission case are complicated by the fact that even in free space they couple orbital motions with spin.

The comparability is made more complete by dividing the scattering potential into two parts, $V(r) + V'(r)$. The part $V'(r)$ may be some perturbation as localized as a β-source and providing an outgoing scattered wave to be compared with the β-emission. The part $V(r)$ is to play the role of the longer-range distorting field; the result will be a treatment of elastic scattering which improves on the Born approximation by taking into account the exact distortion of incident and scattered waves by $V(r)$. The analog of the Fourier-component field equation (2.2) becomes

$$E\psi(\mathbf{r}) = H_0\psi + V'(r)\psi, \qquad (3.1a)$$

where

$$H_0 = -\frac{\hbar^2}{2m}\nabla^2 + V(r). \qquad (3.1b)$$

The term $V'\psi$ is to be given the role of the "source," analogous to $s(\mathbf{r})$ in Eq. (2.2). Both H_0 and $H_0 + V'$ can have in common the energy eigenvalue $E = \hbar^2k^2/2m$, since it is the continuous spectrum that is to be involved. Then the energy eigenstate may be written

$$\psi(\mathbf{r}) = \psi_{\mathbf{k}_0}^+(\mathbf{r}) + \oint g(|\mathbf{r} - \mathbf{r}'|)V'\psi(\mathbf{r}')(d\mathbf{r}') \qquad (3.2a)$$

if the propagator g satisfies

$$\left[E + \frac{\hbar^2}{2m}\nabla^2 - V(r)\right]g = \delta(\mathbf{r} - \mathbf{r}'). \qquad (3.2b)$$

The term $\psi_{\mathbf{k}_0}^+$ describes the distorted incident plane wave as discussed in Sec. 1, with $\mathbf{k}_0$ in the incidence direction and having the magnitude $k_0 = k$. It is important to include because it makes the most essential contribution to the "source strength" $V'\psi$. Equation (3.2a), as it stands, amounts to an integral equation for ψ; it may be recognized as an example of the symbolic Lippmann–Schwinger equation

$$\psi = \psi_0^+ + (E - H_0)^{-1}V'\psi.$$

The equation may be made an explicit solution for ψ by approximating the source strength within the integral as $V'\psi \approx V'\psi_{k_0}^+$; corresponding approximations were made for the β-emission and also in the Bethe–Breit treatment of the inelastic scattering. The distorted plane wave $\psi_{k_0}^+$ is itself a solution of an integral equation like (3.2a) but having $\psi \to \psi_{0k}^+$, $\psi_{k_0}^+ \to \exp[i\mathbf{k}_0 \cdot \mathbf{r}]$, $V'\psi \to V\psi_{k_0}^+$ and $g \to g_0$. Here g_0 represents a propagator in free space, obeying Eq. (3.2b) with $V \equiv 0$; it is well known to be just the "Huyghen's wavelet" (2.8) multiplied by $(-2m/\hbar^2)$.

Again it is an outgoing solution for the emitted wave (scattered from V'),

$$\psi_s \equiv \psi - \psi_{k_0}^+ \approx \oint g(|\mathbf{r} - \mathbf{r}'|)V'\psi_{k_0}^+(\mathbf{r}')(d\mathbf{r}') \qquad (3.3)$$

which is of interest since a positive outward radial current is needed for evaluating the cross section

$$d\sigma'/d\Omega = r^2(\hbar/2imv)[\psi_s^*(\partial\psi_s/\partial r) - (\partial\psi_s^*/\partial r)\psi_s], \qquad (3.4)$$

arising from the scattering by $V'(r)$. The velocity $v = \hbar|\mathbf{k}_0|/m$ enters thus if the incident wave $\psi_{k_0}^+$ is normalized to unit average density (flux $= v$), as in (1.1). The expression (3.4) represents only a part of the total elastic scattering, the part analogous to the β-emission through a distorting field.

The requisite outward propagator may be written

$$g = -i2^{1/2}\pi \sum_{lm} R_l^0(kr)Y_{lm}(\hat{\mathbf{r}}) \cdot R_l^*(kr')Y_{lm}^*(\hat{\mathbf{r}}') \qquad (3.5)$$

for $r > r'$, quite in analogy to the relativistic case (2.7). Here, R_l and R_l^0 are respectively the regular (standing) and irregular (outgoing) radial waves in the distorting field $V(r)$. As in Eq. (2.7), normalization per unit energy is presumed, so that in the absence of distortion

$$R_l \to (2mk/\pi\hbar^2)^{1/2}j_l \quad \text{and} \quad R_l^0 \to (mk/\pi\hbar^2)^{1/2}h_l. \qquad (3.6)$$

This can be easily seen to check with the $g \to g_0$ mentioned in a preceding paragraph.

Whatever the distortion by $V(r)$, the outgoing radial wave has the asymptotic behavior

$$R_l^0(\infty) = (m/\pi\hbar^2 k)^{1/2} \exp[i(kr + \delta_l)]/r, \qquad (3.7)$$

with the phase shift δ_l characterizing the distortion and reducing to $\delta_l^0 = -(l + 1)\pi/2$ for a vanishing distortion, as in Eq. (3.6). This result, multiplied with $(-i)^{l+1}Y_{lm}(\hat{\mathbf{r}})$, is the nonrelativistic analog of Eq. (2.13). It can now be seen that the outgoing wave (3.3) arising in the scattering by $V'(r)$ is

$$\psi_s(\infty) = -i\left(\frac{2\pi m}{\hbar^2 k}\right)^{1/2} \frac{e^{ikr}}{r} \sum_{lm} e^{i\delta_l} Y_{lm}(\hat{\mathbf{r}}) \oint (d\mathbf{r}') R_l^* Y_{lm}^* V' \psi_{\mathbf{k}_0}^+. \qquad (3.8)$$

This can be adapted to yield a familiar result for the scattering amplitude f_+ in $\psi_{\mathbf{k}}^+$ of (1.1), as to be expected from discussion above:

$$f_+ \approx -\frac{2m}{\hbar^2} \sum_{lm} i^{-l} Y_{lm}(\hat{\mathbf{r}}) \oint (d\mathbf{r}') j_l Y_{lm}^* V \exp(i\mathbf{k}_0 \cdot \mathbf{r}'). \qquad (3.9)$$

With (3.8), the formulation of the elastic scattering has been brought to the same stage as was the β-emission in the preceding section.

4. Analysis into Distorted Plane Waves

The analyses into the spherical-wave constitution of the emissions, in Eqs. (2.7) and (3.8), are suited for finding expectations about the angular momenta which are carried off. Thus, evaluation of the outward current in the rate expression (2.5), for the emitted β-wave as analyzed in (2.7), leads to

$$d\lambda/dW\,d\Omega = (2\pi/\hbar)\left|\sum_{\kappa\mu} e^{i\delta\kappa} \chi_{\kappa\mu}(\hat{\mathbf{r}}) \oint (d\mathbf{r}')\psi_{\kappa\mu}^+(\mathbf{r}')s(\mathbf{r}')\right|^2, \qquad (4.1a)$$

and

$$d\lambda/dW = (2\pi/\hbar)\sum_{\kappa\mu}\left|\oint (d\mathbf{r}')\psi_{\kappa\mu}^+ s\right|^2 \qquad (4.1b)$$

after integration over all directions of emission $\left(\oint d\Omega \equiv \oint (d\hat{\mathbf{r}})\right)$. The individual terms of the last sum give the chances for producing a β-particle with a specific angular momentum j, μ and relative spin–orbit orientation $(j = l \pm \frac{1}{2})$. The antineutrino and nuclear states which accompany such an electron depend on what has been "given" for those states when constructing the source description $s(\mathbf{r}')$. Similarly, evaluation of the outward current in the cross section (3.4) for the outgoing wave (3.8) of elastically scattered particles yields

$$d\sigma'/d\Omega = (2\pi/\hbar v)\left|\sum_{lm} e^{i\delta_l}\, Y_{lm}(\hat{\mathbf{r}})\oint (d\mathbf{r}')R_l^*\, Y_{lm}^*\, V'\psi_{\mathbf{k}_0}^+\right|^2 \tag{4.2a}$$

and

$$\sigma' = (2\pi/\hbar v)\sum_{lm}\left|\oint (d\mathbf{r}')R_l^*\, Y_{lm}^*\, V'\psi_{\mathbf{k}_0}^+\right|^2. \tag{4.2b}$$

The form (4.2a) is more familiar for the case in which the scattering potential is the entire one, $V + V'$, with none of it more precisely treated as distorting the initial and final waves:

$$\left. \begin{aligned} d\sigma/d\Omega &= (2m/\hbar^2)^2\left|\sum_{lm} i^{-l}Y_{lm}(\hat{\mathbf{r}})\oint (d\mathbf{r}')j_l Y_{lm}^*(V + V')\exp(i\mathbf{k}_0\cdot\mathbf{r}')\right|^2 \\ &\to |f_+|^2 \quad \text{for} \quad V' \equiv 0, \end{aligned} \right\} \tag{4.3}$$

as follows from (3.9).

It is often important to find the chances for producing a definitely directed *linear* momentum, $\hbar\mathbf{k}$, as when directional correlations of some type are in question. Even in the study of elastic scattering by a central potential, the detector usually measures a definite direction and magnitude of momentum. This calls for a reanalysis of the propagator into plane waves of definite momentum, having this character at least "at infinity" (at the detector). It is the regular, standing wave factors in each propagator which must be reanalyzed, for it is the transition matrix elements to the standing waves which determine the proportions of what is detected, just as in Eqs. (4.1b) and (4.2b). What is finally detected is generated at the source, through the matching of the source distribution, $s(\mathbf{r}')$ or $V'\psi(\mathbf{r}')$, to the wave factors regular in the source. The irregular, outgoing wave factors furnish the propagation connection between source and detector.

Provision for distinguishing linear momenta may be made from the outset when there is no distorting field to alter them on the way from source to detector. Already in the discussion of (3.2), it was pointed out that the nonrelativistic propagator in the absence of distorting field, g_0, is just the "Huyghen's wavelet" (2.8) within a factor $-2m/\hbar^2$, and

$$g_0(r \to \infty) \approx -(m/2\pi\hbar^2)(e^{ikr}/r)\exp(-ik\hat{\mathbf{r}}\cdot\mathbf{r}'). \tag{4.4}$$

This is appropriate to use for the scattering from the entire potential, $V + V'$, and replaces the scattered wave (3.8) with

$$\psi_s(\infty) = -(m/2\pi\hbar^2)(e^{ikr}/r) \oint (d\mathbf{r}') \exp(-ik\hat{\mathbf{r}} \cdot \mathbf{r}')(V + V') \exp(i\mathbf{k}_0 \cdot \mathbf{r}')$$

$$\rightarrow f_+(e^{ikr}/r) \quad \text{when} \quad V' \equiv 0. \tag{4.5}$$

The cross section (4.3) is replaced by the form

$$d\sigma/d\Omega = (m/2\pi\hbar^2)^2 \left| \oint (d\mathbf{r}') \exp(-i\mathbf{k} \cdot \mathbf{r}')(V + V') \exp(i\mathbf{k}_0 \cdot \mathbf{r}') \right|^2, \tag{4.6}$$

giving the chances for detecting the momentum $\hbar\mathbf{k} = \hbar k\hat{\mathbf{r}}$. In the relativistic case, the propagator solution of the equation (2.2) with distortion absent ($V = 0$) may be written

$$G_0 = -(c\hbar)^{-2}(W - i\hbar c\, \boldsymbol{\alpha} \cdot \nabla + \beta mc^2) \exp(ik|\mathbf{r} - \mathbf{r}'|)/4\pi|\mathbf{r} - \mathbf{r}'|, \tag{4.7a}$$

and this becomes

$$G_0 \rightarrow -(c\hbar)^{-2}(W + c\hbar k\, \boldsymbol{\alpha} \cdot \hat{\mathbf{r}} + \beta mc^2) \exp[ik\hat{\mathbf{r}} \cdot (\mathbf{r} - \mathbf{r}')]/4\pi r \tag{4.7b}$$

as $r \rightarrow \infty$. The operator in front of this, divided by $2W$, is an idempotent projection operator which selects positive energy eigenvalues out of the two relativistic possibilities $\pm W = \pm c\hbar[k^2 + (mc/\hbar)^2]^{1/2}$. The asymptotic form (4.7b) is readily shown to be equivalent to the projection operator

$$G_0(r \rightarrow \infty) = -\frac{4\pi^2 W}{c^2\hbar^2 r} \sum_{\sigma} u_{\mathbf{k}\sigma}(\mathbf{r}) u_{\mathbf{k}\sigma}^{\dagger}(\mathbf{r}'), \tag{4.8}$$

in terms of relativistic plane waves like Eq. (2.14), with $\mathbf{k} \equiv k\hat{\mathbf{r}}$. It is essentially the modification of this form by the distorting field that is of interest here.

The modifications caused by a distorting field are properly included in the spherical wave forms (2.7), (3.5), and (3.8), hence the problem is one of unitary transformation from the spherical waves to properly modified plane waves. Transformations exist to either of two sets of modified plane waves, $\psi_{\mathbf{k}}^{\pm}$ as in Eq. (1.1). The point is to find which of the two sets *must* be used; it should follow from the spherical waves already found proper.

The nonrelativistic distorted plane waves, $\psi_{\mathbf{k}}^{\pm}$ of Eq. (1.1), each have an undistorted plane wave part $\exp(i\mathbf{k} \cdot \mathbf{r})$, hence the transformation should be obtainable from the field-free case in which Eqs. (3.9) and

(4.3) are replaced by Eqs. (4.5) and (4.6). Clearly the connection in free-space is the well-known relation

$$\exp(i\mathbf{k}\cdot\mathbf{r}') = 4\pi \sum_{lm} i^l j_l(kr') Y_{lm}(\hat{\mathbf{r}}') Y_{lm}^*(\hat{\mathbf{k}}), \tag{4.9}$$

in which the identification $[\mathbf{k} = \mathbf{r}]$ must be made. That this is not inconsistent with the uncertainty principle follows from first inverting Eq. (4.9) to

$$\oint \frac{(d\hat{\mathbf{k}})}{4\pi} Y_{lm}^*(\hat{\mathbf{k}}) \exp(-i\mathbf{k}\cdot\mathbf{r}') = i^{-l} j_l(kr') Y_{lm}^*(\hat{\mathbf{r}}'),$$

substituting this into Eq. (3.9), for example, to get

$$f_+ \approx -\frac{m}{2\pi\hbar^2} \sum_{lm} Y_{lm}(\hat{\mathbf{r}}) \oint (d\hat{\mathbf{k}}) Y_{lm}^*(\hat{\mathbf{k}}) \oint (d\mathbf{r}') \exp(-i\mathbf{k}\cdot\mathbf{r}') V \exp(i\mathbf{k}_0\cdot\mathbf{r}'),$$

then using the completeness relation

$$\sum_{lm} Y_{lm}(\hat{\mathbf{r}}) Y_{lm}^*(\hat{\mathbf{k}}) = \delta(\hat{\mathbf{r}} - \hat{\mathbf{k}})$$

to arrive at Eq. (4.5). The identification $\hbar k \mathbf{r} = \hbar \mathbf{k}$, which first came into question when the outgoing β-emitted wave (2.15) was written, is thus justified.

When the effect of the distorting field is now taken into account, the regular spherical waves in Eqs. (3.9) and (4.3) are replaced by those in Eqs. (3.8) and (4.2a), hence the undistorted plane wave (4.9) must be replaced by the distorted one having the definition

$$\psi_{\mathbf{k}} = -4\pi i(\pi\hbar^2/2mk)^{1/2} \sum_{lm} e^{-i\delta_l} R_l(kr') Y_{lm}(\hat{\mathbf{r}}') Y_{lm}^*(\hat{\mathbf{k}}). \tag{4.10}$$

That this reduces to (4.9) for $V \to 0$ can be seen from (3.6) and $\delta_l^0 = -(l+1)\pi/2$. With it, the outgoing scattered wave (3.8) becomes

$$\psi_s(\infty) = -(m/2\pi\hbar^2)(e^{ikr}/r) \oint (d\mathbf{r}') \psi_{\mathbf{k}}^* V' \psi_{\mathbf{k}_0}^+, \tag{4.11}$$

and the elastic cross section (4.2) becomes

$$\left. \begin{aligned} \sigma' &= (m/2\pi\hbar^2)^2 \oint (d\hat{\mathbf{k}}) \left| \oint (d\mathbf{r}') \psi_{\mathbf{k}}^* V' \psi_{\mathbf{k}_0}^+ \right|^2, \\ &= (m/\pi\hbar^2)^2 \oint (d\mathbf{k}) k^{-1} \delta(k^2 - k_0^2) \left| \oint (d\mathbf{r}') \psi_{\mathbf{k}}^* V' \psi_{\mathbf{k}_0}^+ \right|^2. \end{aligned} \right\} \tag{4.12}$$

The last form is written merely to indicate that an analysis into linear momenta, $\hbar\mathbf{k}$, has indeed been carried out (their magnitudes are naturally restricted to the incident magnitude of $\hbar\mathbf{k}_0$).

The relativistic case can be clarified in the same manner, i.e., by examining the spherical-to-plane wave transformation when $V = 0$, then seeing how this must be modified when $V \neq 0$. The spherical wave analysis can be written in the same form for both $V = 0$ and $V \neq 0$. As follows from Eqs. (2.6a), (2.7), and (2.15), the outgoing β-emitted wave is

$$\psi(\infty) = -i\frac{4\pi^2}{c\hbar r}\left(\frac{W}{k}\right)^{1/2}\sum_\sigma u_{\mathbf{k}\sigma}(\mathbf{r})$$

$$\times \sum_{\kappa\mu}[\chi_\sigma^\dagger\cdot\chi_{\kappa\mu}(\hat{\mathbf{k}})]\exp[i(\delta_\kappa - \delta_\kappa^0)]\oint\psi_{\kappa\mu}^\dagger s(d\mathbf{r}'), \quad (4.13)$$

with $\delta_\kappa \to \delta_\kappa^0$, and $\psi_{\kappa\mu}$ the $V = 0$ standing wave, when $V = 0$. The plane wave analysis of the standing wave follows from the propagator G_0 of (4.8) *when* $V = 0$,

$$\psi(\infty) = -\frac{4\pi^2 W}{c^2\hbar^2 r}\sum_\sigma u_{\mathbf{k}\sigma}(\mathbf{r})\oint u_{\mathbf{k}\sigma}^\dagger s(d\mathbf{r}'). \quad (4.14)$$

The relativistic generalization of the relation (4.9), in free space, is known[2] to be

$$u_{\mathbf{k}\sigma}(\mathbf{r}') = -i\hbar c(kW)^{-1/2}\sum_{\kappa\mu}[\chi_{\kappa\mu}^\dagger(\hat{\mathbf{k}})\cdot\chi_\sigma]\psi_{\kappa\mu}(\mathbf{r}), \quad (4.15)$$

and this is just what is needed for the compatibility of (4.13) and (4.14) when $V = 0$. It is now clear that in the $V \neq 0$ case, the undistorted plane wave (4.15) must be replaced by

$$\psi_{\mathbf{k}\sigma}(\mathbf{r}') = -i\hbar c(kW)^{-1/2}\sum_{\kappa\mu}[\chi_{\kappa\mu}^\dagger(\hat{\mathbf{k}})\cdot\chi_\sigma]\,e^{-i(\delta_\kappa - \delta_\kappa^0)}\,\psi_{\kappa\mu}(\mathbf{r}), \quad (4.16)$$

where $\psi_{\kappa\mu}$ is now the standing spherical wave in the distorting field. With this inserted into Eq. (4.13) [$\equiv$ replacing $u_{\mathbf{k}\sigma}^\dagger(\mathbf{r}')$ in Eq. (4.14)], the decay rate (2.5) becomes

$$d\lambda/dW = (2\pi/\hbar^3 c^2)kW\oint(d\hat{\mathbf{k}})\sum_\sigma\left|\oint\psi_{\mathbf{k}\sigma}^\dagger s(d\mathbf{r}')\right|^2 \quad (4.17a)$$

in place of Eq. (4.1b). This may be rewritten

$$d\lambda/(d\mathbf{k}) = (2\pi/\hbar)\sum_\sigma\left|\oint\psi_{\mathbf{k}\sigma}^\dagger s(d\mathbf{r}')\right|^2, \quad (4.17b)$$

to make particularly explicit the analysis into linear momenta which has been sought.

The particular plane wave modifications describing the emergence of definite linear momenta, $\hbar\mathbf{k}$, at infinity have now been found: $\psi_\mathbf{k}$ of Eq. (4.10) for the elastic scattering and of Eq. (4.16) for the β-emissions. The character of these distorted waves will be explored in the final section.

5. Plane Waves Emerging from a Distorting Field

The character of the spherical wave combinations, $\psi_\mathbf{k}$ of Eq. (4.10) and $\psi_{\mathbf{k}\sigma}$ of Eq. (4.16), is best revealed when their behavior at infinity is examined. The standing radial wave R_l in Eq. (4.10) differs asymptotically from the outgoing wave R_l^0 of Eq. (3.7) in that the exponential is replaced by a cosine, hence

$$R_l(\infty) = (2mk/\pi\hbar^2)^{\frac{1}{2}} \left[\exp\left[i(kr' + \delta_l)\right] + \exp\left[-i(kr' + \delta_l)\right]\right]/2kr',$$
$$(5.1)$$

a sum of outgoing and ingoing "running" waves. The important point is that forming the combination (4.10) requires cancelling the phase shift δ_l out of just the outgoing part. The consequence is that the outgoing parts of $\psi_\mathbf{k}(\infty)$ are independent of the distorting field and match exactly the behavior of just the outgoing spherical wave parts in the undistorted plane wave (4.9). Indeed, it follows in a familiar way that the necessary combination has the behavior of

$$\psi_\mathbf{k}^-(\infty) = \exp(i\mathbf{k}\cdot\mathbf{r}') + f_- \exp(-ikr')/r', \qquad (5.2)$$

where

$$f_- = k^{-1} \sum_l (-)^l (2l + 1) P_l \exp\left[-i(\delta_l - \delta_l^0)\right] \sin(\delta_l - \delta_l^0), (5.3)$$

with

$$P_l(\hat{\mathbf{k}}\cdot\hat{\mathbf{r}}') \equiv (4\pi/2l + 1) \sum_m Y_{lm}^*(\mathbf{k}) Y_{lm}(\hat{\mathbf{r}}').$$

Thus, the elastic scattering transitions in Eq. (4.12) go from the incident wave $\psi_{\mathbf{k}0}^+$ to a final state, $\psi_\mathbf{k}^-$, which is a plane wave distorted by an *ingoing* wave component. This transpires despite the purely outgoing wave character of the scattered wave (4.11).

The demonstration for the relativistic case (4.16) is more intricate (being equally simple only for the "large component") but can be carried through to a like conclusion. The important point is that $+ \delta_{\mathbf{k}}$ is the phase shift caused by the distorting field in the outgoing part of the standing wave $\psi_{\kappa\mu}$, hence is cancelled out of just that when the combination (4.16) is formed. The consequence is that the resultant $\psi_{\mathbf{k}0}$ differs from the undistorted plane wave $u_{\mathbf{k}0}$ only by an *ingoing* wave, suitably denoted in

$$\psi_{\mathbf{k}\sigma}^{-} = u_{\mathbf{k}\sigma} + f_{\sigma} \exp\left(-ikr\right)/r. \tag{5.4}$$

It may still be mentioned that slight modifications of this, and of the nonrelativistic result (5.2), are necessary in the important special case of distortion by the coulomb field $V = -Ze^2/r$. As reference to Eq. (2.12) shows, δ_{κ} varies slowly with position because of the term $\nu \ln (2kr)$, hence the superposition (4.16) cannot be an energy eigenstate when $\psi_{\kappa\mu}$ is. The remedy is simple because the variable factor is the same in every term of the superposition; the latter can be made an energy eigenstate by using phase shifts $\delta_{\kappa} - \nu \ln (2kr)$ in place of δ_{κ}. Then Eq. (5.4) is replaced by

$$\psi_{\mathbf{k}\sigma}^{-} = \exp\left[i\nu \ln (2kr)\right] u_{\mathbf{k}\sigma} + f_{\sigma}' \exp\left(-ikr\right)/r$$

with f_{σ}' also containing the slowly varying phase shift $\nu \ln (2kr)$. This will be recognized as expressing a well-known property of the ideal coulomb field; slight variations of the momentum take place even in regions remote from the charge. The variations are of order ν/kr and completely negligible over any practical range of momentum measurement at $r \to \infty$.

The formal demonstration of the necessity for calculating formation probabilities of $\psi_{\mathbf{k}}^{-}$ and $\psi_{\mathbf{k}\sigma}^{-}$, in the examples here, is now complete. It is now plain that such stationary states have to be discriminated out of the total radiated outgoing wave, as in Eq. (4.11) or in

$$\psi(\infty) = \frac{-4\pi^2 W}{c^2\hbar^2} \sum_{\sigma} \frac{u_{\mathbf{k}\sigma}(\mathbf{r})}{r} \oint \left[\psi_{\mathbf{k}\sigma}^{-}(\mathbf{r}')\right]^{\dagger} s(\mathbf{r}')(d\mathbf{r}')$$

for the β-emission, if preparation for detecting an outgoing linear momentum $\hbar\mathbf{k} = \hbar k\hat{\mathbf{r}}$ is desired. The occurrence of an ingoing-wave superposition on the plane wave of $\psi_{\mathbf{k}}^{-}$ or $\psi_{\mathbf{k}\sigma}^{-}$ could be understood informally from an elementary fact of wave mechanics; a wave meeting any variation of potential, like that of the distorting field, is always partially reflected at any point where such a variation is met. Thus a wave which arrives at infinity as a plane wave must be expected to have had reflections back toward the origin superposed on it during its propagation through the distorting field.

Another rationalization comes from viewing the distorting field as a scatterer. When a plane wave $\exp(i\mathbf{k}_0 \cdot \mathbf{r})$ is incident, then an outgoing scattered wave as in $\psi_{\mathbf{k}_0}^+$ must be generated in the presence of the scattering center, before there can be a settling into a stationary energy eigenstate. To have a steady *plane* wave scattered instead, such as is detected when a specific emerging momentum $\hbar\mathbf{k} = \hbar k\hat{\mathbf{r}}$ is measured, there must be an equivalent of sending in a spherical wave of particles *converging* on the scattering center, as in $\psi_{\mathbf{k}}^-$. The converging "incident" wave must be part of any energy eigenstate (i.e., a steady state) having the plane wave emerging at infinity, and such must be discriminated out of whatever total "radiation" is emitted.

The Bethe–Breit line of argument requires thinking about a packet like Eq. (1.2) being detected at infinity. With a specific momentum direction detected, the packet must add up to a plane wave train. Moreover it must be formed of components $\psi_{\mathbf{k}}^+$ or $\psi_{\mathbf{k}}^-$ when a distorting field is present. The plane wave parts of these components must add up to the detected plane wave train by themselves, and *concurrently* their spherical wave parts must cancel each other out. It was packets of $\psi_{\mathbf{k}}^+$ which were found in Sec. 1 to have those properties (1.3), when it was an *incident* plane wave train which was to be represented. It is a packet of $\psi_{\mathbf{k}}^-$ that will have the requisite properties when the plane wave train is to represent particles of definite *emergent* momentum, $\hbar\mathbf{k} = \hbar k\hat{\mathbf{r}}$. Bethe and Breit's argument will be illustrated here by the following specific example of a packet.

Let the plane-wave train detected at some very large radius R be

$$\left.\begin{aligned}\Psi_0(\mathbf{r}, 0) &= \exp(i\mathbf{k}_0 \cdot \mathbf{r}) \quad \text{for} \quad R - \tfrac{1}{2}\Delta < r < R + \tfrac{1}{2}\Delta, \\ &= 0 \quad \text{elsewhere,}\end{aligned}\right\} \quad (5.5)$$

with $t = 0$ being taken as the detection time. If the detected momentum direction $\hat{\mathbf{r}} \equiv \hbar\mathbf{k}_0/k_0$ is taken as the z-axis ($r \equiv z$), then the weights needed for the packet (1.2) are readily found to be expressible as

$$C_{\mathbf{k}} = \delta(k_x)\,\delta(k_y) \exp\left[-i(k_z - k_0)R\right] \frac{\sin(k_z - k_0)\Delta/2}{\pi(k_z - k_0)}. \quad (5.6)$$

With these, the plane wave parts of the packet

$$\Psi_0(\infty, 0) = \oint (d\mathbf{k})C_\mathbf{k}[\exp(i\mathbf{k}\cdot\mathbf{r}) + (f_-/r)\exp(-ikr)] \quad (5.7)$$

add up to Eq. (5.5) by themselves. In those parts $\exp(i\mathbf{k}\cdot\mathbf{r}) \equiv \exp(+ikr)$ while the phases are opposite in the ingoing wave parts $\sim \exp(-ikr)/r$, taken here as modifying the plane waves. That will lead to a destructive interference of the spherical-wave parts with the weights $C_\mathbf{k}$ being such (5.6) as to give the constructive interference of the plane wave parts. That is demonstrated specifically by the evaluation

$$(f_-/r) \oint (d\mathbf{k})C_\mathbf{k} \exp(-ikr) = \frac{f_-}{r} \exp\frac{(-ik_0r)}{2\pi} \int_{-\infty}^{\infty} \frac{dK}{K}$$

$$[\sin K(R + r + \tfrac{1}{2}\Delta) - \sin K(R + r - \tfrac{1}{2}\Delta)], \quad (5.8)$$

where the substitution $K \equiv k_z - k_0$ has been made. The same integral, except with $r \leftrightarrow -r$ in it, arises from the plane-wave parts. Whereas the latter integral adds up to 2π for $R - \tfrac{1}{2}\Delta < r < R + \tfrac{1}{2}\Delta$, the two parts of the integral in Eq. (5.8) cancel everywhere because of the opposite sign given to r. The spherical-wave contribution would have persisted instead, if the outgoing wave, as in $\psi_\mathbf{k}^+$, had been used.

References

1. Breit, G., and H. A. Bethe, *Phys. Rev.*, **93**, 888 (1954).
2. Konopinski, E. J., *Theory of β-Radioactivity*, Clarendon Press, Oxford, 1965, Eq. (6.1).
3. Rose, M. E., L. C. Biedenharn, and G. B. Arfken, *Phys. Rev.*, **85**, 5 (1952), formula (2a). These authors retain Dirac's original definition, $-c\alpha$ rather than $+c\alpha$, for the velocity operator.
4. Mott, N. F., and H. S. W. Massey, *Atomic Collisions*, Clarendon Press, Oxford, 1933; A. Sommerfeld, *Atombau und Spektrallinien*, Vieweg and Son, Braunschweig, 1939; W. Rarita and J. S. Schwinger, *Phys. Rev.*, **59**, 556 (1941); K. M. Watson, *Phys. Rev.*, **88**, 1163 (1952); M. Gell–Mann and M. L. Goldberger, *Phys. Rev.*, **91**, 398 (1953); M. L. Goldberger and K. M. Watson, *Collision Theory*, Wiley, New York, 1964.

Two-Nucleon Interactions*

GREGORY BREIT

Yale University

I. Introductory

In the twenties and early thirties there were few subjects more exciting to speculate about than what would happen and what one would learn if experiments were made on the collisions of protons with protons at energies high enough to overcome the repulsive electric forces caused by the Coulomb potential. The discovery of the neutron and the evidence concerning the presence of large neutron–proton interactions in neutron–proton scattering and in the deuteron have made the general subject of nucleon–nucleon scattering even more enticing.

II. Early History

In many respects nature lived up to the expectations. Approximately valid pictures of nucleon–nucleon interactions have been formed. Indications have soon been found for the approximate equality of the proton–proton (p–p), neutron–neutron (n–n), and neutron–proton (n–p) interactions provided the influence of electrostatic forces was properly discounted. The binding energies of nuclei of mass 3 and 4 appeared to fall into line with the simple potential-well models that also appeared to provide adequate explanations of n–p and p–p scattering. This period owes its development to the efforts of many people. Without any attempt at exhaustiveness or exact chronology one might mention among the experimenters Chadwick in connection with the discovery of the neutron, Urey in connection with the discovery of the deuteron,

* This work was partially supported by the U.S. Atomic Energy Commission.

119

Rabi in connection with ascertaining that the deuteron has an electric quadrupole moment, Fermi and Amaldi in connection with studies of n–p interactions as evidenced in scattering and in their recombination, Tuve, Hafstad, and Heydenburg as well as Herb and Kerst in connection with p–p scattering. Among the theorists there come to mind the names of Heisenberg regarding the formulation of a general picture of nuclear structure; Wigner regarding n–p interactions, saturation of nuclear forces, binding energies of light nuclei and the super-multiplet theory; Bethe in connection with nucleon–nucleon ($\mathcal{N}$–$\mathcal{N}$) scattering and interactions, nuclear structure, nuclear models and reactions; Fermi regarding n–p recombination, the scattering of neutrons by bound protons; Feenberg regarding binding energies of light nuclei; Teller and Schwinger regarding the suggestion of important experiments distinguishing between the possibilities of the $^1S_0$ interaction corresponding to a real or a virtual level, Schwinger and Rarita in connection with the first concrete employment of the tensor force in n–p scattering theory. It appeared temporarily that perhaps nucleon–nucleon scattering and properties of nuclei would before long be consistently described in terms of rather simple and essentially nonrelativistic pictures.

The explanation for the $\mathcal{N}$–$\mathcal{N}$ interactions was, of course, still lacking. To be sure there was the idea of Yukawa, proposed in the mid-thirties, according to which nucleon–nucleon interactions could be pictured in terms of an exchange of heavy electrons. Although the idea was highly thought of by many almost from the time of the appearance of Yukawa's paper, its application was slow in coming. There have been many papers in the late thirties and early forties on the meson theory of nuclear forces and especially those of Møller, Rosenfeld, Bethe, and Kemmer. Such applications of theory to experiment as could be made suffered from the insufficiency of experimental material both regarding the nature of the participating meson and regarding the dependence of the scattering properties on energy. For some time mesons of mass $\approx 200\ m_e$, where m_e is the electron mass, which are relatively abundant in cosmic rays were held responsible for the $\mathcal{N}$–$\mathcal{N}$ interaction. It is not too surprising therefore, that an early attempt to fit the energy dependence of the $^1S_0$ phase shift by a Yukawa potential gave an appreciably higher mass than that of the μ meson which was the principal constituent in the cosmic ray experiments. The discovery of the π meson has changed the situation, since the μ meson does not participate in $\mathcal{N}$–$\mathcal{N}$ interactions appreciably. In the same period marked progress has been made in the art of construction of high-energy accelerators leading to p–p and n–p scattering experiments in the 100 MeV energy region. One of the first surprises was the relative constancy of the p–p scattering cross section with angle, provided a small range of angles in which Coulomb effects are dominant is excluded. At the same time experimental techniques of measuring polarization scattering parameters have been developed to a considerable extent under the stimulus of the theoretical work of Wolfenstein[1] and of Wolfenstein and Ashkin[2].

The relative importance of different questions changed as a result of these developments. In the earlier period it appeared important to obtain the highest possible precision in measurements of the differential cross section so as to attempt to draw some inference regarding the magnitude of p- and d-waves, partly for their own sake and also because the correctness of conclusions regarding the energy dependence of the $^1S_0$ phase shift K_0 depends on the knowledge of p- and d-wave contributions. Since the spin-polarization measurements offered ways of determining higher L-waves at higher energies, for which the $L = 1$ and $L = 2$ waves are no longer small, the emphasis shifted toward phase-shift analyses at the higher energies. The attainment of extreme accuracy at low energies became less important since knowledge regarding the low-energy region would eventually be obtained as a by-product through an extrapolation combined with the rather safe theoretical predictions of the asymptotic $E^{L + (1/2)}$ dependence of phase shifts on energy.

The early analyses of the data by Christian and Hart[3] and Christian and Noyes[4] appeared to lead to the necessity of abandoning the hypothesis of charge independence of nuclear forces but the work of Case and Pais[5] showed that the employment of the spin–orbit interaction was capable of restoring this simplifying principle while Jastrow[6] showed that through the use of a hard core potential the same objective could be attained. Reliance was placed in all of this work on the validity of static local potentials.

Pion physics has been developing in the meanwhile. The pion has been ascertained to be pseudoscalar, the masses of charged and neutral pions became known and the coupling of pions to nucleons was formulated in the $PS(ps)$ and $PS(pv)$ forms. Furthermore, much work on the data analysis of pion–nucleon scattering has been done notably by Fermi, Yang, Brueckner, and Bethe[7]. Through the latter's efforts the ambiguities in earlier analyses have been removed and further analyses could then be undertaken. These developments have led, in their preliminary stages to the formulation of a view by Taketani, Nakamura, and Sasaki[8] regarding the relative participation of one-pion-, two-pion-, and many-pion-exchange phenomena at various distances between the nucleons.

III. Phase Shift Analysis

The one-pion-exchange (OPE) region deserves perhaps the largest attention, because it is more definitely and clearly distinguishable from the others and can be used reasonably unambiguously in the phase-shift analysis of scattering data. Evidence to the effect that this application is possible has been given in the work quoted in reference[8]. A particularly striking application has been made by Moravcsik et al. and by Cziffra et al.[9] in eliminating many possibilities of fitting the 310 MeV group of Berkeley data that resulted in the work of Stapp, Ypsilantis, and Metropolis[10]. A general understanding of the OPE interaction has been available for some time[11] and a preliminary idea of the two-pion-exchange (TPE) effective potential was obtained by Taketani, Machida, and Ohnuma[12] rather early. The employment of the OPE interaction in $\mathcal{N}-\mathcal{N}$ data analysis is helpful in two ways. In the first place, when the phase parameters[13] for L greater than a certain value L_m are used in accordance with the theoretical formulas for the OPE the value of the pion–nucleon coupling constant g may be varied so as to make the weighted sum of squares of deviations of the calculated values of the experimental quantities from their measured values, the chi squared, a minimum. The best fit of g to experiment is produced and this constant is thus determined. The values obtained are in fair agreement with those obtained in more direct studies of the pion–nucleon interaction. It is also very useful in data analysis to reduce the number of free parameters available for fitting data thus eliminating some of the freedom which is present when the infinite number of phase-parameters for $L > L_{min}$ is added to the finite number corresponding to $L < L_{min}$, with L_{min} standing for the minimum L in the OPE set. Employment of many parameters lowers the accuracy of the determination of any one of them. If a high L_{min} is used without adding the effect of the OPE set of phases many alternative ways of fitting the data become possible. Wiggly angular distribution curves for experimental quantities are then often found, the presence of the wiggles being related to the absence of the wiggly contribution of the OPE set of phase parameters. The advent of high-speed computing machines has made it possible to make fits to many data adjusting values of phase parameters so as to secure a minimum chi squared.

The determination of phase parameters is subject to the difficulties of lack of uniqueness even if the OPE phases are used for high L. There are various degrees of systematization that can be used in dealing with the problem of phase-parameter determination. The ideal way is to ascertain the scattering matrix (often called M) at a given energy and angle. It is necessary to perform nine measurements to do so but in general there is a lack of uniqueness in the answer. According to Pusikov, Ryndin, and Smorondinskii[14] one could measure only five quantities at all angles instead. It has been shown by Bethe and Schumacher[15] how, by measuring proper quantities, it should be possible to determine the elements of M at one energy and angle unambiguously except for a common phase factor making use of polarized targets. On this general plan the values of M would be determined at a sufficient number of angles to make it possible to ascertain the phase parameters at each energy or else M would be used for theoretical considerations directly without going through the phase-parameters. When such measurements will be performed the certainty of phase-shift analyses may be expected to be appreciably increased. The procedures of reference[14] require modification if OPE phases are used in the analysis. The specification of the phase parameters by the OPE leaves a relatively small number of phases to be determined which may be of the order of 10 in the p–p case and of 13 in the n–p case, assuming that the $I = 1$ phase-parameters for the n–p case are inferred from those for p–p scattering. It is not necessary therefore to be making measurements at all angles. Nevertheless, there remains a lack of uniqueness unless the choice of quantities to be measured is properly made. In practice the limited accuracy of measurements is a serious factor not only in its influence on the accuracy of the phase-parameters but also because it can be responsible for the introduction of wrong types of phase-parameter fits. The chance of obtaining a wrong type of phase-parameter fit is decreased[16] through the employment of data at many energies and the requirement of an energy dependence of the phases which is plausible from physical considerations. The gain in using data at many energies in the same phase-parameter search is partly that of employing more data and thus decreasing the chance of a low chi squared for a wrong fit, partly the direct introduction of the correct limits of the phases at low energies. In principle it should also be possible to make use of the asymptotic forms of scattering amplitudes at the meson production thresholds. The latter is done to some extent in the Scotti-Wong[17] dispersion theoretical fit, which takes meson production into account and provides a good extrapolation of phase-parameters to energies above the meson production threshold.

At this time multiple-energy data searches have the following weakness. The functional form of the energy dependence of phase-parameters is not known with certainty. There is therefore the choice of employing functional forms that are uncertain[18], and may in consequence be introducing artificial features into the fit or else of employing the method of correction functions which is subject to very little theoretical control, aside from the relatively easily imposed requirements of correct limiting zero-energy forms and the final check of satisfying the causality requirements. The method of correction functions could be made to furnish fits of higher quality than those obtained so far by localizing the correction functions more strongly in energy. If such a policy were followed to an extreme the fits would become a succession of single-energy fits and would lose all the advantages of multiple-energy data searches. It is therefore necessary to combine the requirements of flexibility in the correction functions with human judgment regarding plausibility of energy dependence of the phases. This judgment enters again in the removal of improbable kinks in the plots of the phases against energy which appear at times after several correction functions are superposed. The danger of human judgment having affected the starting point for the next gradient or least squares adjustment is always present.

Another uncertainty is introduced by the possible presence of unknown sources of error in the data. Some data selection is necessary since occasionally values of observables are definitely out of line with the general trends. A way out favored by some is to obtain a consensus of opinion among experimentalists regarding the reliability of data. It is hard to be sure however that such a consensus is not influenced by subjective judgment. Some measurements may be condemned because of the omission of the application of a correction but it is hard to be sure that data admitted by the consensus do not omit the application of a correction for another effect or do not contain errors. Such scepticism appears justifiable since much of the p–p polarization data had to be revised relatively recently on account of errors found in the now old p–C polarization measurements. There was a similar change of opinion regarding the absolute values of the Harvard p–p differential cross sections which were finally recommended for use only as determinations of relative values. There is no assurance that some of the measurements free of suspicion at present will not be found to contain sources of error. The detection of hidden sources of error is naturally more difficult when large and costly equipment is involved than it was in the days of relatively unambitious instrumentation. These considerations favor removing from the analysis only data very definitely suspected because of known gross errors or because of being definitely out of line with the majority of other measurements.

It is often believed that the employment of the same mathematical forms in data analysis as occur for the energy dependence of observables in incompletely formulated theories, such as the dispersion relations formulations, has a special virtue in data fitting. This remark has less bearing on such attempts as that of Scotti and Wong[17] than on the Midpop fits of the Livermore group[18] and the more recent fits obtained through the employment[19] of the same type of terms involving the Legendre functions of the second kind as enter the OPE equations. To be sure such procedure are free of the previously described objections to the method of correction functions such as the danger of introducing too much flexibility in the energy dependence and of the necessity of exercising human judgment. But in final analysis the employment of mathematical forms suggested by an incomplete form of theory has obvious limitations. Were the degree of incompleteness of the theoretical representation known quantitatively at least to the extent of being able to put reasonable error limits on the accuracy of the theory the situation would be appreciably better. In such a case it would be possible to adjust the constants not only as they are adjusted now but also adding and subtracting the uncertainties of the theory to the data analyzed. An additional uncertainty in the parameters entering the energy dependent formulas would result and there would be a corresponding addition to the uncertainties of the phase-parameters derived from the analysis. This however is not the way the game is played. It may also be mentioned that the employment of mathematical forms suggested by incomplete theories for multiple energy analysis is not obviously free of the possibility of introducing an error of unknown magnitude in the determination of the pion–nucleon coupling constant g^2 because the omitted part may happen to contain effects overlapping those represented by the OPE parts of the scattering amplitude. The advantages of the parametrizations of energy parameters by employing mathematical forms similar to those occurring in incomplete theories of the $\mathcal{N}-\mathcal{N}$ interaction appear questionable therefore.

IV. Models

The boundary-value treatment of the $\mathcal{N}-\mathcal{N}$ interaction is somewhat more concretely formulated than the types of representations just discussed but shares some of their weaknesses. It originated[20] as an alternative to the improbable description of the $\mathcal{N}-\mathcal{N}$ interaction by means of static local potentials. The many body problem presented by the collection of mesons and $\mathcal{N}-\mathcal{N}$ pairs at small distances was sidestepped through the introduction of the logarithmic derivative of the radial wave function at a distance at which the identity of nucleons as separate particles begins to make sense. The fact that in a limited energy range of ~ 10 MeV scattering data may be satisfied either by a slow and essentially linear variation of this derivative with energy or an energy independent value was interpreted as evidence for the essentially many body character of the interaction inside the boundary value radius r_b. It also appeared reasonable to consider[21] the additional effects of a potential outside r_b. In a series of papers Feshbach, Lomon, and collaborators[22] have used the boundary-value method for the treatment of data in a wide energy range employing field theoretical potentials outside r_b and energy independent boundary conditions. They have obtained good representations of the data by assigning suitable values to the logarithmic derivatives and their generalizations in the case of coupled states. Marshak, Saylor, and Bryan[23] have made closely related calculations. The significance of the success is not clear. There appears to be no binding reason for supposing that the boundary conditions are energy independent in such a wide energy range. The field theoretical potentials used are approximate, not only because they stop with the introduction of TPE and of the ρ meson, but also because their derivation does not presuppose the existence of an inner region in which a much larger density of pions is present. Since field theoretical potentials are in the first instance results of calculations of the scattering matrix, the localization in space of parts corresponding to the OPE, TPE, etc. effects is not justified by the derivation. There is no proof of convergence of the series and no assurance that higher order exchanges do not interfere with the applicability of the terms kept. But even though some scepticism regarding the boundary-value treatment appears to be justified it should be stated that the good quality of the fits obtained by Feshbach, Lomon, and coworkers and the general reasonableness of the picture have definitely contributed to the understanding and establishment of the principal processes involved in the $\mathcal{N}-\mathcal{N}$ interaction.

Static[24] local potentials have been used for the description of the $\mathcal{N}-\mathcal{N}$ interaction from the beginning of work on the subject. The fact that the picture has limitations has been realized practically as long. Although somewhat improbable this picture proved useful. A classic example of usefulness was the establishment by Wigner of the difference between the $^3S_1$ and $^1S_0$ interactions and it has been useful in work on charge independence of nuclear forces on spin–orbit interactions between nucleons which has been under consideration in nuclear physics since the thirties and has been used in a later period by Case and Pais[5] and has assumed new importance in the work of M. G. Mayer and of Jensen, Haxel, and Suess[25]. Somewhat later data on the polarization parameter $P(\theta)$ in p–p scattering have indicated the presence of differences in phase shifts of the three ^3P phase shifts which spoke for a strong spin–orbit interaction. This inference became somewhat more firmly established through the appreciable improvement in data fits obtained by Signell and Marshak[26], Gammel and Thaler[27] and by Zinn, Signell, and Marshak[28] through the addition of a spin–orbit potential. Although improvement in data representation has been a decided one at some energies closer examination[29,30] showed cases of decided disagreement. These were removed by the phenomenological multiple energy fits and by the static-potential fits of Hamada[31], Hamada and Johnston[32], and of the Yale group[33] which were obtained partly with the aid of the Yale phenomenological phase-parameter fits. The former of these had to be modified later on account of the presence of spurious bound states[34]. There is no assurance that these hard-core potentials provide more than another parametrization of the dependence of phase parameters on incident energy.

Static local potentials have also proved useful in another way. Bryan[35] found it possible to improve agreement with experiment through the employment of a spin–orbit potential with a range of force decidedly shorter than that expected from TPE. This indicated[36] a connection with an old classification[37] of possible spin–orbit effects according to which the sign and magnitude of the V_{LS} term in $I = 1$ states would be attributable to the exchange of vector mesons. Sakurai[38] has independently postulated the presence of vector meson effects in $\mathcal{N}$–$\mathcal{N}$ interactions and the relationship of differences in mass estimates has been discussed elsewhere[39]. The ω and ρ mesons have since been found and have proved useful in providing more detailed models of $\mathcal{N}$–$\mathcal{N}$ interactions.

These models go under the name of one-boson-exchange (OBE) models. There are several types of OBE calculations. In one of them[40] (a) the effective potentials caused by the exchange of any one type of boson are added to each other and after a modification at short distances are used in a Schroedinger equation. In another[17] (b) approximate dispersion theoretical considerations are used. In a third (c) the scattering amplitude expressions obtained for the exchange of each boson separately are added to each other and after a modification consisting in the use of only the real part of some expressions are used for data fitting.

It is characteristic of these models that two-pion exchange is not explicitly considered. Calculations of its effect have been made in a completely covariant form by Gupta[41] and by Gupta, Haracz, and Kaskas[42]. The same problem has been treated by Amati, Leader, and Vitale making use of dispersion relations[43]. The latter authors have obtained encouraging results for phase parameters with $L > 0$, especially after the effects of the ω meson were brought in. Similar encouraging results have been obtained in related work by Cottingham and Mau[44]. The work in the last two references is not typically in the OBE class. In OBE models of type (a) the TPE effects are not used directly but a meson is introduced instead. This meson has been associated with the ABC phenomenon but now that this phenomenon is not supposed to indicate a resonance, this identification has lost credibility. It is not probable that in (a) models the employment of a Schroedinger equation for the composite action of the bosons has a justification beyond that of first order effects. At small internucleon separations the density of bosons is high and interactions between π, ρ, and ω mesons leading to a breakdown of the OBE model are expected. It is perhaps possible that the adjustment of the potential at short distances used in the class (a)

OBE papers compensates for effects caused by interactions of the boson fields. The OBE model in class (b) has the previously mentioned advantage of joining on satisfactorily to the region above the pion production threshold. But in its present form it also has questionable features. Among them are the unrealistic employment of the scalar σ meson of isospin 1 which has much in common with treatments in class (a); the treatment of unstable particles such as the ρ and ω mesons without an explicit consideration of how they disintegrate and how the equilibrium between the mesons is maintained; the somewhat arbitrary employment of the cutoff parameter t_c in the alternative treatment that avoids the introduction of the σ meson; the large shift of the mass of the ρ meson from ~ 750 MeV to 591 MeV. Level shifts are of course not objectionable in principle having a time-honored place in physics. But since a large level shift indicates a strong interaction with a continuum, the employment of so large a shift indicates the possible importance of effects arising from the continuum and the undesirability of omitting effects of the disintegration of the vector mesons into pions. In phenomenological multiple-energy searches the distinction between the masses of charged and neutral pions produces an appreciable difference in OPE adjustments. The corresponding distinction is not made in the work of Scotti and Wong. The quality of the data fit is good but a chi-squared of 822 for 377 data is relatively high according to phenomenological multiple-energy search standards. OBE data representations[45] of class (c) are not numerous as yet. They may have an advantage of definite mathematical characterization of the scattering amplitudes but many of the questions that arise in connection with formulations of types (a) and (b) arise here also. It does not appear likely therefore that current OBE models will lead to a solution of fundamental questions, unless the validity of the approximations implied can be ascertained much more definitely.

V. The Outlook

The cursory review raises the question of the purpose of various attempts to study $\mathcal{N}$–$\mathcal{N}$ interactions. To what extent is it important to ascertain the phase-parameters with more precision and be able to account for them by means of a sound and quantitatively accurate approach? The value of its complete quantitative understanding of $\mathcal{N}$–$\mathcal{N}$ scattering can hardly be judged without the consideration of

related fields. From a very broad viewpoint these embrace a large
fraction of modern research. A discussion of all the implications of the
knowledge of $\mathcal{N}$–$\mathcal{N}$ interactions would be beyond the scope of this
paper. But it appears practical to consider the general question briefly
from two viewpoints, the first being that of fundamental processes
involved in the $\mathcal{N}$–$\mathcal{N}$ interactions and the second that of reaching a
sufficiently good knowledge of the interactions to make reliable
applications to other fields possible.

The clarification of the fundamental processes does not necessarily
depend on the attainment of a complete mastery of the quantitative
aspects of scattering. In atomic physics there was a high degree of
certainty regarding the essential adequacy of nonrelativistic quantum
mechanics combined with the assumption of the applicability of
Coulomb's law of force in accounting for all ordinary atomic and
molecular phenomena, as expressed in Dirac's famous statement, considerably before there were accurate tests for many electron systems.
Even now accurate tests appear not to have gone beyond the two-
electron atoms. It is conceivable therefore that the laws of interaction
between nucleons, pions, and the vector mesons will be known before
meaningful and accurate calculations of $\mathcal{N}$–$\mathcal{N}$ interactions will be
carried out. It appears of interest to list some of the questions to be
answered before Dirac's statement can be paraphrased for $\mathcal{N}$–$\mathcal{N}$
interactions.

The simplest question is that of the nature of the pion–nucleon
interaction and of the value of the pion–nucleon coupling constant. It
is not certain that the coupling between nucleons and pions is purely
pseudoscalar. The pion may be an elementary particle in some sense.
The physical pion is not an elementary particle however. Virtual
nucleon–antinucleon pairs are produced in its vicinity and it thus
resembles the pion of the Fermi–Yang model[46], credence in which is
strengthened by the relative success of the Sakata model and its developments in terms of SU_3, SU_6, and other symmetry classifications of
elementary particles. An approximate reproduction of the properties
of the pion can be obtained[47] by employing vector mesons for the
binding of nucleons to antinucleons in place of the weak interactions
used by Fermi and Yang. On such a view the physical pion, being in
part a composite particle, has dimensions and does not interact with
nucleons as a point. The latter view corresponds however to the partial
presence of pseudoscalar coupling.

In first approximation it does not matter whether the coupling is pseudoscalar or pseudovector. The conversion factor between the usual coupling constants involves however the ratio $(m_\pi/M)^2$ with m_π and M representing the pion and nucleon mass, respectively. There appears to be no reason for expecting the usual f^2 of the pseudovector coupling to contain exactly this factor on the above mentioned adaptation of the Fermi–Yang model, the creation and destruction of pions depending in such a model on the action of vector mesons and on nucleons and antinucleons within the pion. If a modification of the factor is to be made, however, the treatment of OPE interactions is affected and this in turn affects conclusions regarding the phenomenological tests of long-range charge independence. It is desirable therefore to test this independence well enough to detect effects of conversion factors between f and g. The accuracy of the determinations of the effective value of g^2 is not as yet sufficient for such purposes but is not far from the desired one.

The determination of g from the adjustment of the amplitude of the OPE set of phases is limited in accuracy by the incomplete elimination of TPE and vector meson effects. It is not as yet practical to confine this set to such high L as to make the undesirable effects completely negligible, because the nominal precision of the determination of g^2 suffers if complete safety is assured by including in the OPE set only phases with very high L, the whole effect of the OPE set becoming then too small. The errors introduced are partly eliminated by arranging the grouping of phases into OPE and searched sets according to values of L, some cancellation of spurious effects taking place if this is done. It would be desirable therefore to be able to make reliable corrections for the presence of TPE, and of vector meson effects for members of the OPE set with $L \geq L_{\min}$, where $L_{\min}$ is the minimum value included. In this respect the development of the OBE models should prove useful. One may hope that since the effects to be corrected for are small the omissions of the OBE models are not of major importance for the immediate purpose and that the corrections can be made sufficiently reliably. One might hope also that the TPE effects could be corrected for, without recourse to the OBE theories.

Certainty in the practicability of such a plan is not available however. It might be argued that the OBE theories supplemented by calculations of the TPE effects should provide the dominant terms in power series expansions of the amplitudes in terms of coupling constants, and that the presence of higher order terms should not matter. A doubt regarding the legitimacy of neglecting higher-order terms arises however from the relative success of the boundary-value method with energy-independent boundary conditions. These make the radial wave functions just outside the boundary radius r_b differ from the field free functions at low E and high L even if the potential in the interval (r_b, ∞) is neglected. The model implies therefore that the essentially many-body interaction in $r < r_b$ which depends on effects of higher-order terms in the coupling constants affects the wave function in the region $r > r_b$ within which the low-order effects arise. If the effects to be corrected for should be pictured as caused by a potential their origin would be moved out toward larger r since the regular function at small r is small and the effect of the interactions in $r < r_b$ would result in the admixture of the irregular radial wavefunction. Since localization of effects by means of a potential is questionable, a safe estimate of the corrections appears premature.

Another aspect of tests of long-range charge independence and of the value of g is that of electrostatic effects and the apparent violation of short-range charge independence in $^1S_0$ states. This has been looked into in some recent work by Seamon, Friedman, and the writer[48]. For p–p scattering the usual formulas giving the contributions of OPE effects to the scattering amplitudes are slightly in error because of the distortion of field free functions by the Coulomb field. The effect on the value of g^2 is estimated to be below 1% in the Yale multiple-energy searches on p–p data in the energy range from 9 to 350 MeV, in the direction of increasing g^2. Two other effects enter in n–p data analyses if $I = 1$ phase parameters obtained in p–p scattering are used. The reason for doing so rather than determining these parameters by adjustment to n–p scattering is that the nominal precision of all n–p parameters is increased thereby, p–p data usually being the more accurate and the combined number of $I = 1$ and $I = 0$ parameters then entering the "searched" set of n–p phases being rather large. Corrections for Coulomb effects made with the Yale potential as well as some improvements in search procedure and an allowance for an apparent violation of charge independence in $^1S_0$ states give, on the basis of the YRB1(K_0), YLAN4M searches, the values $(g_0^2)_{p-p} = 15.1$ and $(g_0^2)_{n-p} = 14.8$. The former of these is very close to the value from pion-nucleon scattering. There is reason for believing that a slight programming error exaggerated the effect of Coulomb corrections reported in reference 48. It did not affect, however, the "Coulomb corrected" values as reported in that reference. The difference between the p–p and n–p values is well within the statistical uncertainties of ± 0.4 in the former and ± 0.9 in the latter case. Since the Yale potential does not provide a reliable representation of the scattering process the numbers quoted have only limited significance. They indicate however that additional work will have to be done on this phase of the subject before the comparison of n–p and p–p coupling constants can be considered to be finished.

The violation of exact charge independence of $\mathcal{N}$–$\mathcal{N}$ interactions in the $^1S_0$ state suggested by low-energy data also needs clarification. The question of the difference of effective ranges $^1r_0$ of this state in p–p and n–p scattering is inseparable from the general one. This question has been discussed by Noyes[49] whose results indicate that $(^1r_0)_{n-p}$ is about 10% or more smaller than $(^1r_0)_{p-p}$. The problem was reconsidered by Friedman, Seamon, and the writer[50] who confirmed the results of Noyes for the "most probable" values of these quantities in the sense of a statistical analysis employing current values of measured quantities with their small statistical uncertainties such as used by Noyes. An examination of possible systematic errors in the experiments made by these authors indicates however that a combination of such errors can reduce the $(^1r_0)_{p-p} - (^1r_0)_{n-p}$ difference to a much smaller amount. Among the possible sources of error are dynamic effects of molecular electrons for experiments above the epithermal energy region, effects of molecular binding and intermolecular interactions in experiments on the coherent n–p scattering cross section and possible deviations from the effective-range approximation which enters the problem partly through the $^3S_1 + {}^3D_1$ state. The clarification of this problem would probably benefit particularly through additional experimental work. One of the crucial questions is the value of the total n–p cross section at energies from about 0.5 to about 4 MeV.

The answer to the question of charge independence in the $^1S_0$ state need not depend on measurements in the relatively narrow energy range employed in the work just cited. The effective range expansion can be made, with slight modifications, about any energy value and a comparison of p–p and n–p values of the f-function of effective range theory at some conveniently chosen energy of the order of 10 MeV, combined with a comparison of average slopes of the f-functions in the two cases through a range of the order of 15 or 20 MeV, contains information similar to that sought for in values of the scattering length and of the effective range. The advantages of this alternative are the subordination of the necessity for extreme precision that is needed for the usual formulation in terms of scattering length and effective range and of the influence of atomic and molecular physics effects which enter the interpretation of the lower energy experiments. A disadvantage is the necessity of taking into account the presence of a few of the partial waves with $L > 0$. Unpublished calculations by R. E. Seamon and the writer[51] indicate that such an approach could be carried through with the aid of measurements of the polarization parameter in n–p scattering and of triple scattering parameters. This approach has the additional advantage of providing information regarding the low-energy behavior of low-L phase parameters with $L > 0$.

The possibility that g^2 is not the same for $\pi^{\pm}$ and π^0 has been considered by the Yale group[52] in an analysis of n–p data but the difference was found to lie within the uncertainty limits of the determination. A similar distinction is encountered in a recent speculation of Noyes[53] in connection with the interaction effect in n–p gamma capture who attempts to distinguish between the four couplings of $\pi^{\pm}$ and π^0 to n and to p. The former generalization is a natural one from the viewpoint of combined effect of ps and pv couplings. The latter is of interest through the work of Noyes[53] in connection with the question of charge symmetry of $\mathcal{N}$–$\mathcal{N}$ interactions and especially with the value of the n–n scattering length $^1a_{n-n}$. In the convention of positive scattering lengths for small positive K_0 at energies close to zero Wong and Noyes[54] obtained from approximate dispersion theoretical calculations $(27 \pm 1.4)F$ for $^1a_{n-n}$. Measurements gave a value of approximately $17F$ from $\pi^- + d \rightarrow n + n + \gamma$ as measured by Ryan[55], of $(22.5 \pm 1)F$ by Cerineo et al.[56] and $23.6^{+2}_{-1.6}F$ by Voitovestskii, Korsumskii, and Pazhin[57], from $D(n, p)2n$. The theory of experiments appears to be more accurate in the former case indicating a discrepancy. According to Heller, Signell, and Yoder[57a] this is due to the inadequacy of the approximation in reference[54]. Heller et al. test these approximations by means of potential models and find on that basis values between 18 and $19F$. Noyes[53] making use of a private communication from Heller concerning a manipulative error in reference[54], modifies the calculation and obtains $19.8F$. There appears to be no reason to doubt charge symmetry on this score, in agreement with general evidence from nuclear structure and particularly that of Wilkinson[58]. From n–d and n–p scattering Riddle et al. and later Measday and Palmieri[59] derived by subtraction values of the total n–n cross section σ^t_{n-n}. The former work is interpreted by the authors with the aid of Yale data fits as supporting charge symmetry. The later work of Measday and Palmieri is discussed in reference[48]. Fair agreement is obtained at the higher energies subject to uncertainties of multiple scattering corrections. Henley and Morrison[60], making use of a charge-independent boundary condition estimate the effect of mass differences of $\pi^\pm$ and π^0 and ρ^+ and ρ^0. They account in this way for approximately 60% of the measured difference between n–p and p–p scattering lengths and suggest ways of removing the remaining difference by small changes in the boundary condition or in the ratio of charged to neutral coupling constants. Although there is no evidence for a violation of charge symmetry, it is obviously desirable to have the conclusions on a firmer footing. Tests of parity and time-reversal noninvariance have been made by Thorndike[61].

$\mathcal{N}$–$\mathcal{N}$ interactions are closely related to the $d(\gamma, n)p$ reaction and the electrodisintegration of the deuteron. The apparent presence[53] of the interaction effect of Austern and of Austern and Rost is not definitely understood even though a promising step has been taken by Adler and Drell[62] in the suggestion that the π–γ–ρ interaction which is useful in accounting for the magnetic moment of the deuteron provides also a qualitative explanation of the interaction effect. The close connection of the theory of photon and electron interactions with the $\mathcal{N}$–$\mathcal{N}$ system makes it difficult to separate this subject from that of $\mathcal{N}$–$\mathcal{N}$ scattering.

Nuclear structure has an intimate connection with the $\mathcal{N}$–$\mathcal{N}$ interaction. Calculations on nuclear matter examine the consequences of $\mathcal{N}$–$\mathcal{N}$ interactions under relatively simple conditions. The advances made in the mathematical treatment of the problems involved by Brueckner and Watson, Brueckner and more realistically by Bethe[63] make it probable that close ties will be established between the nuclear matter and the two-nucleon problems. Progress is being made in the application of potentials derived from $\mathcal{N}$–$\mathcal{N}$ scattering to the energy levels of nuclei. In this connection the contributions of Kuo and Brown[64] and of Hull and Shakin[65] are among the later significant ones. In calculations on nuclear matter and on nuclear levels there are the difficulties of inferring off energy shell elements of the scattering matrix and of the lack of uniqueness of the representation of the scattering by a potential. Since the description of scattering by a static local potential amounts to the replacement of a many-body problem by a two-body problem, inconsistencies regarding off-energy matrix elements may be expected. Whether the comparison of experiment with the calculations will detect the presence of many-body forces and the inconsistencies or not, the outcome of the work may be expected to contribute not only to the understanding of nuclear matter and of nuclear structure but also to that of $\mathcal{N}-\mathcal{N}$ interactions.

Limitations of space do not permit the discussion of typically high-energy aspects of $\mathcal{N}-\mathcal{N}$ scattering which are after all so closely tied in with reactions that the omission is perhaps excusable.

Apologies are offered to the many authors of important papers whose work has not been quoted.

References

1. Wolfenstein, L., *Phys. Rev.*, **75**, 1664 (1949); *Ann. Rev. Nucl. Sci.*, **6**, 43 (1956); *Bull. Amer. Phys. Soc.*, **1**, 36 (1956).
2. Wolfenstein, L., and J. Ashkin, *Phys. Rev.*, **85**, 947 (1952).
3. Christian, R. S., and E. W. Hart, *Phys. Rev.*, **77**, 441 (1950).
4. Christian, R. S., and H. P. Noyes, *Phys. Rev.*, **79**, 85 (1950).
5. Case, K. M., and A. Pais, *Phys. Rev.*, **80**, 203 (1950).
6. Jastrow, R., *Phys. Rev.*, **79**, 389 (1950); **81**, 165 (1951).
7. Bethe, Hans A., and Frederic de Hoffmann, Mesons, Vol. II of *Mesons and Fields*, Row, Peterson and Company, Evanston, Illinois, 1956.
8. Taketani, M., S. Nakamura, and M. Sasaki, *Progr. Theoret. Phys. (Kyoto)*, **6**, 581 (1951); J. Iwadare, S. Otsuki, R. Tamagaki, and W. Watari, *Progr. Theoret. Phys. (Kyoto)*, **16**, 455 (1956); *Suppl. Progr. Theoret. Phys. (Kyoto)*, **3**, 32 (1956); S. Otsuki, *Progr. Theoret. Phys. (Kyoto)*, **20**, 171 (1958); R. Tamagaki, *Progr. Theoret. Phys. (Kyoto)*, **20**, 505 (1958).
9. Moravcsik, M. J., P. Cziffra, M. H. MacGregor, and H. P. Stapp, *Bull. Am. Phys. Soc.*, **4**, 49 (1959); P. Cziffra, M. H. MacGregor, M. J. Moravcsik, and H. P. Stapp, *Phys. Rev.*, **114**, 880 (1959).
10. Stapp, H. P., T. J. Ypsilantis, and N. Metropolis, *Phys. Rev.*, **105**, 302 (1957).
11. Pauli, W., *Meson Theory of Nuclear Forces*, 2nd ed., Interscience, New York, 1948.
12. Taketani, M., S. Machida, and S. Ohnuma, *Progr. Theoret. Phys. (Kyoto)*, **6**, 638 (1951); S. Machida, S. Ohnuma, and M. Taketani, *Progr. Theoret. Phys. (Kyoto)*, **6**, 904 (1951); M. Taketani, S. Machida, and S. Ohnuma, *Progr. Theoret. Phys. (Kyoto)*, **7**, 45 (1952).
13. The expression " phase parameter " is used to denote either a phase shift or a coupling parameter representing the coupling between two states with the same total angular momentum $J\hbar$ and different orbital angular momenta $L\hbar = (J \pm 1)\hbar$. The word "phase" is often used as an abbreviation for phase parameter.

14. Puzikov, L., R. Ryndin, and Ia Smorondinskii, *Nucl. Phys.*, **3**, 436 (1957); *J. Exptl. Theoret. Phys. (U.S.S.R.)*, **32**, 592 (1957) [Trans.: *Soviet Phys. JETP*, **5**, 489 (1957)].

15. Schumacher, Clifford R., and Hans A. Bethe, *Phys. Rev.*, **121**, 1534 (1961).

16. Breit, G., *Proc. International Conference on Nuclear Forces and the Few Nucleon Problem*, University College, London, 1959, Pergamon, New York, 1960; G. Breit, M. H. Hull, Jr., K. E. Lassila, and K. D. Pyatt, Jr., *Phys. Rev.*, **120**, 2227 (1960); G. Breit, M. H. Hull, Jr., K. E. Lassila, K. D. Pyatt, Jr., and H. M. Ruppel, *Phys. Rev.*, **128**, 826 (1962); M. H. Hull, Jr., K. E. Lassila, H. M. Ruppel, F. A. McDonald, and G. Breit, *Phys. Rev.*, **122**, 1606 (1961); **128**, 830 (1962).

17. Scotti, A., and D. Wong, *Phys. Rev. Letters*, **10**, 142 (1963); *Phys. Rev.*, **138**, B145 (1965).

18. Moravcsik, M. J., and H. P. Noyes, *Ann. Rev. Nucl. Sci.*, **11**, 95 (1961); M. J. Moravcsik, *The Two-Nucleon Interaction*, Clarendon, Oxford, 1963.

19. Arndt, R. A., and M. H. MacGregor, Univ. of Cal. Lawrence Radiation Lab. Rept. UCRL-14252.

20. Breit, G., and W. G. Bouricius, *Phys. Rev.*, **74**, 1546 (1948).

21. Saperstein, A. M., and L. Durand III, *Phys. Rev.*, **104**, 1102 (1956).

22. Feshbach, H., and E. Lomon, *Phys. Rev.*, **102**, 891 (1956); H. Feshbach, E. Lomon, and A. Tubis, *Phys. Rev. Letters*, **6**, 635 (1961), and references therein.

23. Saylor, D. P., R. A. Bryan, and R. E. Marshak, *Phys. Rev. Letters*, **5**, 266 (1960).

24. The words "static potential" are used in this paper for the specification of a potential, the parameters of which do not depend on incident energy but may nevertheless depend on parity and total spin and may also contain the specification of spin–orbit and quadratic spin–orbit interactions.

25. Mayer, M. G., *Phys. Rev.*, **74**, 235 (1948); **78**, 16 (1950); **78**, 22 (1950); J. H. D. Jensen, O. Haxel, and H. E. Suess, *Naturwiss.*, **35**, 376 (1948), **36**, 153, 155 (1949).

26. Signell, P., and R. E. Marshak, *Phys. Rev.*, **109**, 1229 (1958).

27. Gammel, J. L., and R. M. Thaler, *Phys. Rev.*, **107**, 291, 1337 (1957); *Progr. Cosmic Ray Phys.*, **5**, 99 (1960).

28. Signell, P., R. Zinn, and R. E. Marshak, *Phys. Rev. Letters*, **1**, 416 (1958).

29. Second paper in ref. 16.

30. Hull, M. H., Jr., K. D. Pyatt, Jr., C. R. Fischer, and G. Breit, *Phys. Rev. Letters*, **2**, 264 (1959).

31. Hamada, T., *Progr. Theoret. Phys. (Kyoto)*, **24**, 1033 (1960).

32. Hamada, T., and I. D. Johnston, *Nucl. Phys.*, **34**, 382 (1962).

33. Lassila, K. E., M. H. Hull, Jr., H. M. Ruppel, F. A. McDonald, and G. Breit, *Phys. Rev.*, **126**, 881 (1962).

34. Hamada, T., Y. Nakamura, and N. Tamagaki, *Progr. Theoret. Phys.*, **33**, 769 (1965).

35. Bryan, R. A., *Bull. Am. Phys. Soc.*, **5**, 35 (1960); *Nuovo Cimento*, **16**, 895 (1960).

36. Breit, G., *Phys. Rev.*, **46**, 746 (1960).

37. Breit, G., *Phys. Rev.*, **51**, 248 (1937); **53**, 153 (1938).
38. Sakurai, J. J., *Ann. Phys.* (*N. Y.*), **11**, 1 (1960); *Nuovo Cimento*, **16**, 388 (1960); *Phys. Rev.*, **119**, 1784 (1960).
39. Breit, G., *Phys. Rev.*, **20**, 287 (1960).
40. Bryan, R. A., C. R. Dismukes, and W. Ramsay, *Nucl. Phys.*, **45**, 353 (1963); R. S. McKean, *Phys. Rev.*, **125**, 1399 (1962); R. A. Bryan and B. L. Scott, *Phys. Rev.*, **135**, B434 (1964).
41. Gupta, S. N., *Phys. Rev.*, **122**, 1923 (1961).
42. Gupta, S. N., R. D. Haracz, and J. Kaskas, *Phys. Rev.*, **138**, B1500 (1965).
43. Amati, D., E. Leader, and B. Vitale, *Phys. Rev.*, **130**, 750 (1963) and references to previous work by the same authors therein. D. Amati, *Comptes Rendus du Congres Internationale de Physique Nucleaire*, Vol. I, Centre National de la Recherche Scientifique, Paris, 1964, p. 57.
44. Cottingham, W. N., and R. V. Mau, *Phys. Rev.*, **130**, 735 (1963).
45. Bryan, R. A., and R. A. Arndt, Univ. of California Radiation Laboratory Report UCRL 14297.
46. Fermi, E., and C. N. Yang, *Phys. Rev.*, **76**, 1739 (1949).
47. Breit, G., *Proc. International Conference on Nucleon Structure*, Stanford, California, Stanford Univ. Press, 1964.
48. Seamon, R. E., K. A. Friedman, and G. Breit, *Phys. Rev.*, submitted for publication.
49. Noyes, H. P., *Phys. Rev.*, **130**, 2025 (1963).
50. Breit, G., K. A. Friedman, and R. E. Seamon, *Progr. Theoret. Phys.* (*Japan*) *Supplement*, 1965.
51. Submitted as an appendix in an application to the AEC. The writer is grateful to Mr. R. E. Seamon for his permission to quote the conclusions.
52. Breit, G., M. H. Hull, Jr., F. A. McDonald, and H. M. Ruppel, *Proceedings of the 1962 International Conference on High Energy Physics at CERN*, CERN, Scientific Information Service, Geneva 23, Switzerland, 1962, p. 135.
53. Noyes, H. P., *Stanford Linear Accelerator Publication*, SLAC-PUB-59, December 1964, to be published.
54. Wong, David Y., and H. Pierre Noyes, *Phys. Rev.*, **126**, 1866 (1962).
55. Ryan, J. W., *Phys. Rev. Letters*, **12**, 564 (1964).
56. Cerineo, M., K. Ilakovac, I. Slaus, P. Tomas, and V. Valkovic, *Phys. Rev.*, **133**, B948 (1964).
57. Voitovetskii, V. K., I. L. Korsunskii, and Y. F. Pazhin, *Congres International de Physique Nucleaire*, Vol. II, Centre National de la Recherche Scientifique, Paris, 1964, paper 1 bis/C369, p. 265.
57a. Heller, L., P. Signell, and N. R. Yoder, *Phys. Rev. Letters*, **13**, 577 (1964).
58. Wilkinson, D. H., *Phys. Rev. Letters*, **13**, 571 (1964).
59. Riddle, R. A. J., A. Langsford, P. H. Bowen, and G. C. Cox, *Nucl. Phys.*, **61**, 457 (1965). D. F. Measday and J. N. Palmieri, Neutron total cross sections for neutrons, protons, and deuterons in the energy range of 90 to 150 MeV. *Nucl. Phys.* (in press). The writer is grateful to the authors for advanced information concerning their results.

60. Henley, E. M., and L. K. Morrison, The $n-n$ and $n-p$ Scattering Lengths and Charge Independence, October 1965, preprint. The writer is indebted to Professor Henley for supplying him with these results.

61. Adler, R. J., and S. D. Drell, *Phys. Rev. Letters*, **13**, 348 (1964).

62. Bethe, H. A., *Comptes Rendus du Congres International de Physique Nucleaire*, Vol. I, Centre National de la Recherche Scientifique, Paris, 1964, p. 101; *Phys. Rev.*, **138**, B804 (1965). References to older work can be traced through these papers.

63. Kuo, T. S., and G. E. Brown, *Phys. Letters*, **18**, 54 (1965).

64. Hull, M. H., Jr., and C. Shakin, *Phys. Letters*, **19**, 506 (1965).

Classical Pion Physics

J. HAMILTON

Nordisk Institut for Teoretisk Atomfysik

Hans Bethe has the art of making clear and vivid pictures of the processes which go on in strong interactions, and it was therefore a great pleasure to be asked to write an article on one aspect of strong interactions for this festschrift. Before getting down to the subject, I wish to thank him for much instruction and for many interesting and valuable discussions covering a wide range of physical phenomena.

In order to avoid confusion about the meaning of the title we shall define classical pion physics to be the study of those phenomena involving the strong interactions of pions which can be fairly well understood without introducing strange particles. The pion–pion system is of course the simplest example, but it presents considerable difficulties. Experiments show clearly the gross features, such as the ρ and f^0 mesons, or resonances, but experimental analysis of the finer details is liable to various uncertainties. On the theoretical side there are a number of detailed studies of the pion–pion system, but again there are serious difficulties. For example there is the simple and elegant idea that the ρ meson consists of a pair of pions held together by the exchange of a ρ meson—this is a simple example of the so-called bootstrap mechanism. It is easy to see that in this theory a large part of the attraction between the two pions is of very short range (say, less than 0.2×10^{-13} cm) and as yet we do not have any reliable method for treating interactions of so short a range. Thus the predictions of the mass and width of the ρ-meson are only qualitatively correct. This situation is fairly typical of direct theoretical predictions for the pion–pion system. Here we shall only discuss two-pion problems in so far as they are related to other phenomena.

On the other hand the pion–nucleon system has been the subject of intensive investigations both experimental and theoretical, and many of the main features of the π–N system at low and moderate energies are now understood. This article is therefore a brief account of the dynamical understanding of the π–N system, leading up to conjectures on what the next advances may be.

Simplifying Features of the Pion–Nucleon System

We first look at those aspects which make the π–N system comparatively simple from the theoretical viewpoint. Of course there is the obvious feature that the pion has no spin and the nucleon has spin 1/2, so only two invariant amplitudes are required to describe π–N scattering. Thus the complexity of the theoretical calculations, and of the analysis of the experimental data, is much less than in, for example, nucleon-nucleon scattering. This is an important practical point, but we shall not dwell on it; instead we shall look at some less obvious features.

Consider the partial wave dispersion relations for π–N scattering. Let $f_{l\pm}^{(T)}(s)$ be the partial-wave amplitude for the π–N state having isospin $T(T = 1/2$ or $3/2)$, orbital angular momentum l, and total angular momentum $J = l \pm 1/2$. Also, s denotes the square of the total energy in the c.m. system, and

$$f(s) = \frac{\exp(2i\delta) - 1}{2iq}, \qquad (1)$$

where q is the momentum in the c.m. system. The phase shift δ may be complex, and by unitarity Im $(\delta) \geq 0$. In Fig. 1 we show the singularities of any π–N partial-wave amplitude $f(s)$ as a function of the complex variable s. Keeping this in mind we now discuss important simplifying features.

(i) The Low Masses of the Pion and the Nucleon

The pion is by far the lightest of the strongly interacting bosons, and the nucleon is the lightest baryon. This means that the structure of the singularities of $f(s)$ is simpler than would otherwise be the case. For example, the cut $|s| = M^2 - \mu^2$ (M = nucleon mass, μ = pion mass) arises from the process $\pi + \pi \to N + \bar{N}$, and it describes the effect of pion–pion scattering on pion–nucleon scattering. If however, we consider the partial-wave amplitudes $f_\eta(s)$ for $\eta + N \to \eta + N$, then in addition to a circular cut $|s| = M^2 - \eta^2$ (η = eta-meson mass), the process $\eta + \eta \to N + \bar{N}$ will give cuts along the real axis which come out of the circle at $s = M^2 - \eta^2$. This arises from the process $\eta + \eta \to$

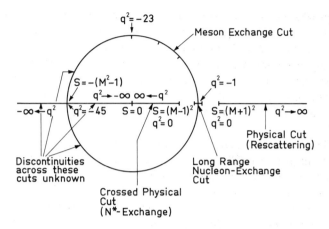

Fig. 1.   The cuts of the π–N partial wave amplitude $f_i^{(T)}(s)$ in the complex s-plane. Typical values of $q^2(s)$ on the cuts are also shown. (Units are $\mu = c = 1$.)

$\pi + \pi \to N + \bar{N}$. This will make the form of the partial-wave dispersion relation more complicated, and in addition we must know a coupling constant, or the like, to describe the process $\eta + \eta \to \pi + \pi$.

Single Channel Approximation and Inelasticity

Another important consequence of the low masses of the pion and the nucleon is that over an appreciable energy range we can treat the π–N system by the methods suitable for single channel problems. The $\pi + N$ threshold is approximately 1079 MeV and the $\eta + N$ channel opens at 1487 MeV (i.e., 558 MeV lab. pion energy), the $K + \Lambda$ channel at 765 MeV (lab.), and the $\rho + N$ channel just below 900 MeV lab. So we might hope to be able to use single channel techniques for $\pi + N$ scattering up to about 550 MeV (lab.). To investigate this point we must look at the process $\pi + N \to 2\pi + N$, and we shall see that with the exception of one amplitude † (P_{11}), $\pi + N$ scattering is close to a one channel problem over this energy range.

The $2\pi + N$ channel opens at 1219 MeV (i.e., 171 MeV lab.), but it is a good first approximation to ignore transitions to this channel

† The notation for partial waves is $L_{2T,2J}$.

except where there is a strong final state interaction. It follows that up to 800 MeV (lab.) we need only consider $\pi + N^*$, where N^* is the $T = 3/2$, $J = 3/2$ π–N resonance, and $(\pi\pi)_0 + N$ where $(\pi\pi_0)$ is a strongly attracting pair of pions in the $T = 0$, $J = 0^+$ state. We shall discuss the evidence for $(\pi\pi)_0$ below; it is sufficient to say here that a pair of pions in the $T = 0$, $J = 0^+$ state attract each other strongly when their total mass is, approximately, in the range 330 MeV to 420 MeV[1,2].

Thus we expect that the process $\pi + N \rightarrow (\pi\pi)_0 + N$ will become important just over 300 MeV lab. pion energy, with the pion pair in an S-wave relative to the nucleon†. This can only occur for the $\pi + N$ state P_{11}. Analysis of the experimental data by Auvil et al.[5] does indeed show that the $\pi + N$ amplitude P_{11} becomes appreciably inelastic just above 300 MeV (lab.), and the inelasticity increases rapidly up to about 550 MeV (lab.) (cf., Fig. 2). Also this is the only $\pi + N$ amplitude which shows large inelasticity below 500 MeV (lab.).

The state $(\pi\pi)_0 + N$, where $(\pi\pi)_0$ is in a P-wave relative to the nucleon, can be reached from the $\pi + N$ states S_{11} and D_{13}, but on account of the centrifugal barrier we would not expect inelastic processes of this type to become important until the energy exceeds around 500 MeV (lab.). It is interesting to note that the analysis of the experimental data[5] finds that S_{11} is almost elastic right up to 550 MeV (lab.).

Finally there is $\pi + N \rightarrow \pi + N^*$. The threshold is roughly 380 MeV, and if the extra pion is in an S-wave relative to N^*, this process can only occur in the $\pi + N$ states D_{13} and D_{33}. The analysis of the experimental data[5] shows that D_{13} and D_{33} do become slightly inelastic just above 400 MeV (lab.), and the inelasticity increases with energy so that by 550 MeV, in the case of D_{13}, the inelasticity is appreciable, but not large (inelasticity coefficient $\eta \gtrsim 0.7$). D_{33} shows less inelasticity. Our simple discussion of the inelastic processes is confirmed by the fact that, apart from P_{11}, D_{13}, and D_{33}, all the other $\pi + N$ partial waves are very close to elastic up to 550 MeV (lab.) and in some cases up to much higher energies (Fig. 2).

The result of all this is that, except in the case of P_{11}, $\pi + N$ scattering is essentially a single-channel problem up to 550 MeV (lab.), or in some cases to higher energies. This makes possible precise predictions of a number of partial waves up to such energies. (This is quite

† This inelastic process was discussed by Kirz et al.[3]. See also, Donnachie et al.[4].

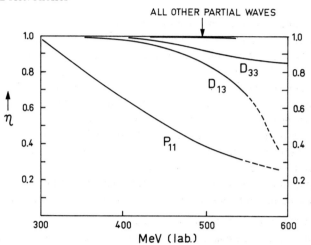

Fig. 2.   The inelasticity coefficient $\eta = \exp(-2\mathrm{Im}\,\delta)$ for the π–N partial waves up to around 550 MeV lab. energy.

apart from the fact that if we find there is a very strong attraction in the elastic channel in some amplitudes, we can predict resonances at high energies, on the assumption that inelasticity will only modify the position and width of the resonance.)

(ii) The Small Value of μ/M

The smallness of the ratio of the pion and nucleon masses ($\mu/M = 1/6.7$) is also important. It is very desirable to be able to distinguish between the long range and the short range parts of the $\pi - N$ interaction. The long range parts arise from those unphysical cuts in Fig. 1 which are nearest to the physical threshold $(M + \mu)^2$, and the short range parts from unphysical cuts which are further away, such as $-\infty \le s \le 0$. The distance from the physical threshold to the nearby cuts (which are around $s = M^2$) is approximately $(2M\mu + \mu^2)$, while the distance to the nearest part of the cut $-\infty \le s \le 0$ is $(M + \mu)^2$. For a fairly clean separation between long range and short range parts of the interaction it is necessary that the ratio of these distances, namely

$$\frac{2M\mu + \mu^2}{(M + \mu)^2}$$

should be small. For the actual masses it is 0.24, but if μ/M were 1/2, the ratio would be 0.55, and the distinction between long range and short range interactions would be much less clear. Moreover, the peripheral method[4] (see below), which makes it possible to suppress the role of the short range interactions, would be much less effective if μ/M were not small.

There is another aspect of the small mass ratio. In a static model the nucleon is at rest, and it can only emit or absorb P-wave pions. Thus in the real world, pions with higher orbital angular momentum can only be absorbed or emitted *via* nucleon recoil and various relativistic effects, and the strength of these processes depends markedly on μ/M. We can say, roughly speaking, that at low and moderate energies, so far as the N-exchange and N^*-exchange interactions are concerned, the real situation is only of order μ/M away from the static model.

(iii) Simplicity of the Crossed Channel

By the crossed channel we mean the process which is reached from the physical channel by the crossing symmetry $s \leftrightarrow u$, $t \leftrightarrow t$. In Fig. 1 this gives the cut $-\infty \le s \le (M - \mu)^2$. For $\bar{K} + N$ scattering, for example the crossed channel refers to $K + N$ scattering, and we must treat K–N and $\bar{K}$–N scattering together. For π–N scattering the crossed channel is again π–N scattering, and this fact places severe restrictions on the partial wave amplitudes $f_l(s)$; these restrictions can be used to good effect.

We shall call $0 < s \le (M - \mu)^2$ the *crossed physical cut*. We can easily determine the value of any π–N amplitude $f_l(s)$ on this cut by a simple procedure if we know the π–N scattering amplitudes on the physical cut; and this is true for the real part of $f_l(s)$ as well as the imaginary part. For values of s on the crossed physical cut which are near the end $(M - \mu)^2$, we only need to know the physical values of π–N scattering for low energies. However, to calculate $f_l(s)$ on the crossed physical cut, we need to know the physical values of $f_{l'}(s)$ for $l' \ne l$ as well as for $l' = l$. Using this procedure we can easily determine the interactions which cause S-wave π–N scattering, as we shall see next.

S-wave Pion–Nucleon Scattering and Pion–Pion Scattering

The values of the S-wave $T = 1/2$ and $T = 3/2$ π–N amplitudes $f_0^{(1/2)}(s)$ and $f_0^{(3/2)}(s)$ on the portion† $20 < s \le (M - \mu)^2 = 32.7$ of the

† We use the units $\hbar = c = \mu$ (pion mass) $= 1$. The units of length and energy are $1.4 \ 10^{-13}$ cm and 140 MeV.

crossed physical cut are readily found[6] by using the experimental data on the low energy S-wave π–N phase shifts, and the low energy P_{33} phase shift. This gives the *experimental values* of the S-wave amplitudes $f_0^{(T)}(s)$ on the right-hand part of the crossed physical cut.

If we try to continue the analytic functions $f_0^{(T)}(s)$ from the neighborhood of the physical cut towards the crossed physical cut, we come up against the circular cut $|s| = M^2 - \mu^2$. The Mandelstam representation[7] tells us that $f_0^{(T)}(s)$ has a discontinuity across this circle which is given by the absorptive part of the amplitude for $\pi + \pi \rightarrow N + \bar{N}$. This absorptive part is in turn related to pion–pion scattering $(\pi + \pi \rightarrow \pi + \pi)$, and if pions did not scatter pions there would be no discontinuity across the circle. Using the experimental values of $f_0^{(T)}(s)$ on the physical and crossed physical cuts, we can evaluate the partial wave dispersion relations for these amplitudes on these two cuts. The results show clearly that $f_0^{(T)}(s)$ are discontinuous across $|s| = M^2 - \mu^2$.

Crossing relates $\pi^+ + p \rightarrow \pi^+ + p$ to $\pi^- + p \rightarrow \pi^- + p$ and it is convenient to use new ($\pm$) charge combinations of the π–N amplitudes. These are defined by

$$(+): \tfrac{1}{2}[(\pi^- p \rightarrow \pi^- p) + (\pi^+ p \rightarrow \pi^+ p)]$$

$$(-): \tfrac{1}{2}[(\pi^- p \rightarrow \pi^- p) - (\pi^+ p \leftarrow \pi^+ p)]$$

Clearly the (+) and (−) partial waves will behave differently under crossing.

Now look at the discontinuities in $f_0^{(+)}(s)$ and $f_0^{(-)}(s)$ across $|s| = M^2 - \mu^2$. They are produced, respectively, by pion–pion scattering in the $T = 0$ and $T = 1$ isospin states, and in these states the pair of pions have, respectively, even and odd angular momentum. The discontinuity across the part of the circle near $|s| = M^2 - \mu^2$ is due to low-energy pion–pion scattering, so we need only consider, respectively, pion–pion scattering in the $T = 0$, $J = 0^+$ and $T = 1$, $J = 1^-$ states. The physical picture is that a pion cloud surrounds the nucleon. This cloud constitutes the outer part of the nucleon, and it gives rise to the charge and current distributions which are measured by scattering electrons on nucleons. In π–N scattering the discontinuity across the circle represents the scattering of the incoming pion on the pion cloud of the nucleon.

It can be shown from general theoretical arguments that the discontinuities in $f_0^{(+)}(s)$ and $f_0^{(-)}(s)$ across the circle are very different.

In the case of $T = 0$, $J = 0^+$ the discontinuity is almost purely imaginary, while for $T = 1$, $J = 1^-$ it is almost real[8]. This enables us to predict that the contribution of the circle to $\mathrm{Re}\, f_0^{(+)}(s)$ on the physical and the crossed physical cuts is of the form

$$\frac{c_+(\mathrm{Im}\, s_1)}{(s - \mathrm{Re}\, s_1)^2 + (\mathrm{Im}\, s_1)^2} \tag{2}$$

where c_+ is a real constant and s_1 is some fixed point on the circle such that $|\arg s_1|$ is no more than about 30°. Similarly, the contribution to $\mathrm{Re}\, f_0^{(-)}(s)$ is of the form

$$\frac{c_-(s - \mathrm{Re}\, s_1')}{(s - \mathrm{Re}\, s_1')^2 + (\mathrm{Im}\, s_1')^2} \tag{3}$$

where c_- is a real constant, and s_1' is defined in the same way as s_1.

Using the experimental values of $f_0^{(\pm)}(s)$ on the physical and crossed physical cuts, and evaluating the π–N partial-wave dispersion relations on these cuts, it is found that the *experimental values* of the circle's contributions to $\mathrm{Re}\, f_0^{(+)}(s)$ and $\mathrm{Re}\, f_0^{(-)}(s)$ are indeed of the form in Eqs. (2) and (3), respectively[1,6]. In this way the experimental data on low energy π–N scattering gives a check on the relation which necessarily exists between crossing symmetry ($s \leftrightarrow u$), and the description of the circle discontinuity in terms of pion–pion scattering (i.e., the t-channel). This begins to provide a physical proof of the validity of the Mandelstam representation for moderate energies and moderate momentum transfers. Moreover, a detailed analysis of the results gives much information about low-energy S-wave π–N scattering, and about low-energy π–π scattering[1,6].

The Causes of S-wave π–N Scattering

We look on the unphysical cuts in Fig. 1 as giving rise to the driving forces or interactions which cause $\pi + N$ scattering. Nucleon exchange (or N-exchange, for short) is given by the pole $G^2/(\mu - M^2)$, and is associated with the cut $(M - \mu^2/M)^2 \leq s \leq M^2 + 2\mu^2$, which we call the *short cut*, and the cut $-\infty \leq s \leq 0$. Exchange of the $(3/2, 3/2)$ resonance N^* is associated with the cut $-\infty \leq s \leq (M - \mu)^2$. The long-range part of N-exchange is given by the short cut, and it is

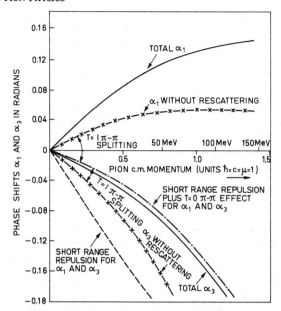

Fig. 3. Contributions from the main parts of the interaction to the S-wave, π–N phase shifts $\alpha_1(T = 1/2)$ and $\alpha_3(T = 3/2)$ in the low-energy region.

very small in S-wave scattering. The long-range part of N^*-exchange is given by the crossed physical cut $0 < s \leq (M - \mu)^2$, and it is not a large term in the S-wave case. The short-range parts of both processes are associated with the cut $-\infty \leq s \leq 0$, but so are many other more complicated exchange processes. We shall lump together all these processes, plus the effect of the left-hand part of the circle $|s| = M^2 - \mu^2$, and call the result the short-range interaction. As a rough approximation this is represented by a simple pole lying somewhere on $-\infty \leq s \leq 0$.

Then the method described above shows that the main interactions producing low-energy S-wave π–N scattering are[1,6]:

(1) A strong, short-range repulsion (range $\gtrsim 0.2 \times 10^{-13}$ cm) which is almost the same in the $T = 1/2$ and $T = 3/2$ states;

(2) A moderately-strong, long-range attraction (range approx. 10^{-13} cm) which is associated with $T = 0$, $J = 0^+$ π–π scattering. This is the same in the $T = 1/2$ and $T = 3/2$ states;

(3) A moderately strong interaction of intermediate range which is

associated with $T = 1, J = 1^-$ $\pi-\pi$ scattering. This splits the degeneracy of the $T = 1/2$ and $T = 3/2$ $\pi-N$ states, being attractive in $T = 1/2$, while it is repulsive and only half as strong in $T = 3/2$.

In addition both the $T = 1/2$ and $T = 3/2$ amplitudes are enhanced somewhat by the effect of rescattering. Figure 3 shows the contributions of the various interactions to the S-wave $\pi-N$ phases at low energies. The interactions associated with $\pi-\pi$ scattering fit in well with our knowledge of other phenomena, as we shall see, but the physical cause of the strong, short-range repulsion is not known at present.

$T = 0, J = 0$ Pion–Pion Scattering

The sign and magnitude of the effect, (2) above, yield further information if we assume that the $T = 0, J = 0$ $\pi-\pi$ scattering amplitude obeys a simple relativistic effective-range formula at low energies. Then it is seen (1) that in this state there is a strong attraction between the two pions; the scattering length a_0 is about 1.3 $\hbar/\mu c$ and the phase shift rises to a maximum of about 30° and then falls off at higher energies. The maximum of the phase occurs somewhere in the region 330–400 MeV, but the effect on $\pi-N$ scattering is not sensitive to the exact position of the maximum. On the other hand, a low-energy $T = 0$, $J = 0$ $\pi-\pi$ resonance would produce much too large an effect in $\pi-N$ scattering[9].

This strong, low-energy $\pi-\pi$ attraction shows up in other phenomena. The enhancement seen in the ABC experiment on $p + d$ scattering[10] is explained† by this $\pi-\pi$ attraction[11], and analysis[12] of that experiment gives a $T = 0, J = 0$ $\pi-\pi$ scattering length a_0 around 1.6 $\hbar/\mu c$. High-energy experiments on the production of a pair of pions[13] show an enhancement in the two-pion mass spectrum which is centered on 400 MeV; this is just what would be expected from the above analysis of S-wave $\pi-N$ scattering. Although this phenomenon and similar features in the decay $\eta \to 3\pi$ have been called the σ-resonance, there appears to be no real evidence for calling it a resonance, rather than a strong, low-energy attraction between the two pions[14].

† Because of the low energy of the proton ($T = 750$ MeV) and the geometry of the ABC experiment, only pion pairs with mass below about 370 MeV can be produced, and of course lower masses will be favored by the available phase space. The experimental enhancement is greatest at about 310 MeV.

$T = 1, J = 1$ Pion–Pion Scattering

The sign and shape of the effect (Sec. *3* above) in S-wave π–N scattering is consistent with it being due to the ρ-meson. Fitting to the S-wave π–N results, and assuming that the ratio of the tensor and vector ρ–N coupling constants obeys $g_{\rho NN}/f_{\rho NN} = -g = -1.85$, where g is the anomalous gyromagnetic ratio of the nucleons—as is required by the isovector nucleon form factors—gives

$$f_{\rho\pi\pi}f_{\rho NN}/4\pi = 2.8 \pm 0.3,$$

where $f_{\rho\pi\pi}$ is the ρ–π coupling constant. From the width of the decay $\rho \to \pi + \pi$ Sakurai[15] deduces $f_{\rho\pi\pi}^2/4\pi = 2.1$. Comparing these formula gives support to Sakurai's theory that the ρ-meson is coupled to a conserved isovector current (i.e., $f_{\rho\pi\pi} = f_{\rho NN}$).

Prediction of Pion–Nucleon Scattering and Resonances

In 1956 Chew and Low[16] explained the $N^*(T = 3/2, J = 3/2^+)\pi$–$N$ resonance as being due to the strong attraction which is produced by the nucleon-exchange (N-exchange) process in the P_{33} state. In the other three P-waves, N-exchange either gives a repulsion or a weak attraction. An important feature implicit in the calculations of Chew and Low was the suppression of the effects of short-range interactions. Since we know practically nothing about the short-range parts (range $\gtrsim 0.2 \times 10^{-13}$ cm) of the π–N interaction, in order to make progress in predicting the scattering, it is necessary to devise a technique in which the effects of the short-range interactions are small. Such a technique—which we will call a *peripheral method*—will only be valid for those energies and angular momenta for which the scattering is almost entirely due to the medium and long range parts of the inter-action (i.e., ranges from 0.3×10^{-13} cm to 10^{-13} cm). It is another great simplifying feature of the π–N system that the long and medium range parts of the π–N interaction are so strong that the region of validity of the peripheral method is large and contains numerous interesting phenomena. In boson–boson systems for example this simplification seems to be absent.

Let us look at the long and medium range parts of the π–N inter-action. First there is N-exchange (Fig. 4a); it comes from the term

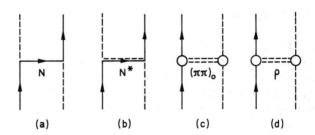

Fig. 4.   These four exchange processes give the long and medium range parts of
the π–N interaction. As the diagrams suggest, N-exchange and N^*-exchange do
indeed have a space exchange character.

$G^2/(u - M^2)^{-1}$, and in Fig. 1 it gives the cuts $(M - \mu^2/M)^2 \leq s \leq$
$M^2 + 2\mu^2$ and $-\infty \leq s \leq 0$. The former gives the long-range part
and the latter gives a short-range part. Then there is N^*-exchange
(Fig. 4b); this gives a medium-range interaction from (the right-hand
part of) the crossed physical cut $0 \leq s \leq (M - \mu)^2$, plus a short-range
part from $-\infty \leq s \leq 0$. Finally, there are the two interactions
associated with π–π scattering which we learned from the analysis of
S-wave π–N scattering above. There is $(\pi\pi)_0$-exchange (Fig. 4c), where
$(\pi\pi)_0$ is the strongly attracting low-energy pair of pions in the $T = 0$,
$J = 0$ state, and there is ρ-meson exchange (Fig. 4d). $(\pi\pi)_0$-exchange
gives a long-range interaction and ρ-exchange a medium range interaction. In addition, both processes give short-range parts coming from
$-\infty \leq s \leq 0$ and from the left-hand part of the circle $|s| = M^2 - \mu^2$.*

From the analysis of S-wave π–N scattering we know the
parameters which determine $(\pi\pi)_0$-exchange and ρ-exchange, while for
N-exchange we need the π–N coupling constant G^2, and for N^*-exchange,
the mass and width of N^*.†

The Peripheral Method[4]

Instead of the partial wave amplitude $f_l(s)$ of Eq. (1) we use the
reduced partial wave amplitude

$$F_l(s) = f_l(s)/q^{2l}(s) = \frac{\exp(2i\delta_l) - 1}{2iq^{2l+1}},\qquad(4)$$

where l is the orbital angular momentum, and as usual q is the

† For further details of the π–N interactions see ref. 4.

momentum in the c.m. system. Now $q^2(s)$ is a fairly simple function of s, and it is easy to see that the function $F_l(s)$ has the same structure of singularities as $f_l(s)$ (Fig. 1). Also, $F_l(s)$ is bounded in the neighborhood of the physical threshold $s_0 = (M + \mu)^2$, since for small q the phase δ_l behaves like q^{2l+1}.

This threshold behavior indicates that by using a dispersion relation for $F_l(s)$, instead of $f_l(s)$, we will automatically build in the effect of the centrifugal force (for $l \geq 1$). Now, the centrifugal force prevents a pion of moderate or low energy, which has orbital angular momentum $l(l \geq 1)$, from approaching close to the center of the nucleon, and so the effect of the short-range interactions is much reduced. Next, we shall trace how this shows up in the mathematical formalism.

The dispersion relation is

$$\text{Re } F_l(s) = \frac{1}{\pi} \int \frac{\text{Im } F_l(s')}{s' - s} \, ds + \frac{1}{\pi} P \int_{(M+\mu)^2}^{\infty} \frac{\text{Im } F(s')}{s' - s} \, ds. \qquad (5)$$

$$\underset{\substack{\text{(unphysical} \\ \text{cuts)}}}{} \qquad \underset{(M+\mu)^2}{}$$

On all the unphysical cuts in Fig. 1, $q^2(s)$ is real, so on all cuts

$$\text{Im } F_l(s) = (q^{2l}(s))^{-1} \text{Im } f_l(s). \qquad (6)$$

Consider the values of $q^2(s)$ on the unphysical cuts. On the short cut and the part of the circle near $s = M^2 - \mu^2$ we have $q^2 \approx -\mu^2$, and as we move around the circle (either way) $|q^2|$ increases to the value $q^2 = -M^2$ at $s = -(M^2 - \mu^2)$. On the crossed physical cut $q^2 = 0$ at $s = (M - \mu)^2$, and q^2 increases rapidly as we move along the cut towards $s = 0$ where $q^2 \to \infty$. Finally, on $-\infty \leq s \leq 0$, $|q^2| > M^2$, and $q^2 \to -\infty$ as $s \to 0$, and as $s \to -\infty$. Putting $\mu = 1$, we see that on all parts of the unphysical cuts which are associated with short-range interactions, $|q^2(s)|$ is large. It follows from Eq. (6), that the short-range parts of the interaction are strongly suppressed in the dispersion relation Eq. (5) for $l \geq 1$. It is estimated[17] that by using Eq. (5) we can make accurate predictions of the π–N interactions up to around 600 MeV for P-waves, 1 BeV for D-waves and 1.5 BeV for F-waves (lab. pion energies).

A further advantage of using Eq. (5) is that the high-energy parts of the physical integral (rescattering integral) are also suppressed, so we can make accurate predictions of the scattering at low and moderate energies without having much information about the inelasticity at high energies.

If we tried to solve Eq. (5) by the N/D method we would immediately lose the advantages we hope to gain from the peripheral method. The N/D method converges poorly, and for an accurate solution it requires detailed knowledge both of the short range interactions and of the inelasticity at high energies. Instead we use Eq. (5) directly. For partial waves where the interaction is not strong we can estimate the rescattering integral by an iterative method[17]. When the interaction is strong more general techniques must be used.†

Systematics of the π–N Interactions and the Resonances[19]

The contributions of the long- and medium-range parts of the π–N interaction (Fig. 4) are readily evaluated for P, D and F waves[4]. These give the first integral on the right of Eq. (5). For given l these interaction terms vary appreciably as we change T ($T = 1/2, 3/2$) or J ($J = l \pm 1/2$). We comment briefly on the four interactions:

(a) *N-exchange.* This has a fairly long range so it is relatively more important at low than at high energies. For given l it is much stronger in $T = 3/2, J = l + 1/2$ than in the other three states. It is attractive in P_{33} and F_{37}, but is repulsive in D_{35}; this is due to the space-exchange nature of the interaction, which can be seen in Fig. 4a.

(b) *N*-exchange.* This is of medium range and is strongest (for given l) in $T = 1/2$, $J = l - 1/2$. Due to the space-exchange characteristic it is attractive in P_{11} and F_{15}, and is repulsive in D_{13}. However, even in P_{11} it is not so strong as ρ-exchange (below) and in general it is much smaller than ρ-exchange.‡

(c) $(\pi\pi)_0$-exchange. This is of long range and is important at low energies. For given l the interaction is independent of T and almost independent of J, and it is always attractive.

(d) *ρ-exchange.* This is of medium range, and for given l is strongest, and attractive, in $T = 1/2, J = l - 1/2$. Its effects extend to high energies.

Now Eq. (5) can be written:

$$\text{Re } F_l(s) = F_l^1(s) + (\text{Rescattering Integral}), \qquad (6)$$

where $F_l^1(s)$ is the sum of the contributions from these four exchange processes for the partial wave under study. Positive $F_l^1(s)$ means an

† For a variational solution of Eq. (5) in the case of P_{33} see ref. 18.

‡ A similar account of N- and N^*-exchange has been given by Carruthers[20], but in that calculation the short-range parts are not suppressed.

attraction and negative $F_i^1(s)$ a repulsion. We get a measure of the strength of the interaction by remembering that Re $F_i(s) = \eta \sin(2\alpha)/2q^{2l+1}$, where η $(0 < \eta < 1)$ is the inelasticity parameter and α the real part of the phase shift. By unitarity $q^{2l+1} |\text{Re } F_i(s)| \leqslant 1/2$ in the physical region. Consider the function

$$Q_l(s) = q^{2l+1} F_l^1(s)$$

in the physical region. If $|Q_l|$ is much less than $1/2$ the interaction is weak, but if $|Q_l|$ is comparable with, or exceeds $1/2$, it is strong.

In particular if $Q_l(s)$ rises steadily, passes through $1/2$, and continues rising we have a strong attraction between pion and nucleon. We call the value $Q_l(s) = 1/2$ *the unitary limit*; let it occur at $s = s_u$. By Eq. (6) the rescattering integral must be negative for $s > s_u$. However the rescattering integral is positive and increasing at low energies, and this behavior indicates that the partial-wave total cross section has passed through a maximum—corresponding to a resonance—at some energy below s_u. The calculations show that only five of the P-, D-, and F-waves pass through the unitary limit: P_{11}, P_{33}, D_{13}, F_{15}, and F_{37}. In the range of validity of the peripheral method (which was given above) none of the other P-, D-, and F-waves come anywhere near the unitary limit[4,19].

Figure 5 shows $Q_l(s)$ for P_{33}, D_{13}, F_{15}, and F_{37}. Further consideration shows that we would in each case expect the resonance to be a few hundred MeV below the unitary limit. The unitary limits are at 380 MeV, 810 MeV, 1090 MeV, and (approx.) 1.5 BeV, lab. pion energy, respectively. There is thus good agreement with the experimental observations that there are resonances P_{33}, D_{13}, F_{15} and F_{37} at lab. pion energies 200 MeV, 600 MeV, 900 MeV, and 1.35 BeV, respectively. We conclude that these resonances are produced almost entirely, by the strong medium and long range attractions in the elastic π–N channel. Analysis of the experiments[5] shows that D_{13}, F_{15}, and F_{37} have a fair amount of inelasticity at their respective resonance energies; however, in all cases, $R = \sigma_{\text{tot}}/\sigma_{\text{el}}$ for the resonant partial wave, lies appreciably below 2, and this is a further indication that inelastic processes do not play a large role in producing the resonances.

The unitary limit† for P_{11} lies at a somewhat lower energy than the unitary limit for P_{33}, and this is consistent with the idea that the nucleon

---

† In calculating the unitary limit for P_{11}, the direct Born term $G^2/(s - M^2)$ is not to be included, since this pole is to be deduced *from* the interactions.

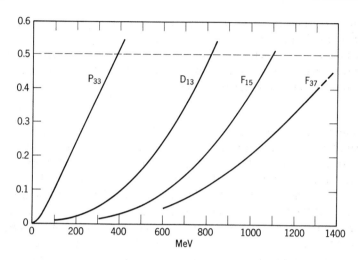

Fig. 5.   The function $Q_l(s)$ for the amplitudes P_{33}, D_{15}, F_{13}, and F_{37}.

itself is a bound state in P_{11}. This unitary limit has nothing to do with a conjectured resonance in P_{11} around 500 MeV (lab.).

The peripheral method also makes it possible to understand the classification of the resonances in the Regge plot, where there is a ρ-exchange and an N-exchange family. Details can be found in ref. 19.

The Small Phase Shifts

It is a useful check on the peripheral method, and on the values of the input parameters in the resonance calculations above, to calculate the small P-, D-, and F-waves up to around 600 MeV (lab.). Since the sum of the four exchange processes of Fig. 4 is small in these cases, it is necessary to estimate the small effects arising from the short range parts of the π–N interaction. This can be done by using a unitary sum rule[17]. The rescattering integral in Eq. (5) is very small below 600 MeV in these cases, but it can be included by using an iteration method[17], and for this purpose it is necessary to use rough experimental information about the inelasticity over the region 500–800 MeV (lab.). The resulting predictions for the seven small P-, D-, and F-waves (i.e., P_{13}, P_{31}, D_{15}, D_{33}, D_{35}, F_{17}, and F_{35}) are in good agreement with the phase shift analysis[5] up to 600 MeV, and in some cases to higher energies.

The Outlook

Analysis of the experimental data shows that around 600 MeV (lab.), and also at higher energies, S-wave π–N scattering again has interesting features. At 560 MeV, S_{11} has a noticeable threshold[5] associated with the opening of the channel $\pi + N \rightarrow \eta + N$, and this suggests that the system $\eta + N$ has either a low energy S-wave resonance, or an antibound state[21]. About 900 MeV (lab.) the π–N amplitude S_{11} appears to have a resonance which is *not* associated with strong inelasticity[22]. Also near 900 MeV (lab.), the amplitude S_{31} shows resonance behavior, but in this case the inelasticity is strong[22]. The theoretical discussion of these S-wave phenomena may be difficult because of the presence of strong unknown short range interactions.

The other striking feature shown by the π–N experimental data up to 1 BeV (lab.) is that D_{15} has a highly inelastic "resonance" about 900 MeV[22,23]. The peripheral method shows that in the elastic π–N channel D_{15} has only a weak attraction[17], so we expect that this D_{15} phenomenon must be due to some threshold effect, or else to a resonance which is primarily in some other channel. The behavior of the inelasticity coefficient η supports this idea.

Finally, there are the humps in the π–N total cross sections which have been discovered at pion lab. energies above 1.5 BeV (i.e., masses above 2 BeV). These may be highly inelastic resonances. Although in the elastic π–N channel, certain G and H waves are expected to show strong medium-range attractions at such energies, because of the possibility of strong inelasticity, one cannot at present make useful predictions concerning the nature of these humps.

It would be surprising if no other interesting phenomena were discovered in π–N scattering in the energy range above 1 BeV lab. pion energy.

References

1. Hamilton, J., P. Menotti, G. C. Oades, and L. L. J. Vick, *Phys. Rev.*, **128**, 1881 (1961).
2. Wolf, G., Physics Letters, **19**, 328 (1965).
3. Kirz, J., J. Schwartz, and R. D. Tripp, *Phys. Rev.*, **130**, 2481 (1963).
4. Donnachie, A., J. Hamilton, and A. T. Lea, *Phys. Rev.*, **135**, B515 (1964).
5. Auvil, P., C. Lovelace, A. Donnachie, and A. T. Lea, *Phys. Rev. Letters*, **12**, 76 (1964); Bareyre, P., C. Brickman, A. V. Sterling, and G. Villet, *Phys. Rev.*

Letters, **18**, 342 (1965); Donnachie, A. A. T. Lea, and C. Lovelace, *Phys. Rev. Letters*, **19**, 146 (1965); Bransden, B. H. P. J. O'Donnell, and R. G. Moorhouse, *Phys. Rev.*, **139**, B1566 (1965).

6. Hamilton, J., T. D. Spearman, and W. S. Woolcock, *Ann. Phys.*, **17**, 1 (1962).
7. Mandelstam, S., *Phys. Rev.*, **112**, 1344 (1958); **115**, 1741 and 1752 (1959).
8. Hamilton, J., P. Menotti, T. D. Spearman, and W. S. Woolcock, *Nuovo Cimento*, **20**, 519 (1961).
9. Oades, G. C., private communication, 1964.
10. Abashain, A., N. E. Booth, and K. M. Crowe, *Phys. Rev. Letters*, **5**, 528 (1960); **7**, 35 (1961).
11. Booth, N. E., and A. Abashain, *Phys. Rev.*, **132**, 2314 (1962).
12. Jacob, M., G. Mahoux, and R. Omnès, *Nuovo Cimento*, **23**, 838 (1962); also T. D. Spearman, *Phys. Rev.*, **129**, 1848 (1963).
13. Samois, N. P., et al., *Phys. Rev. Letters*, **9**, 139 (1962).
14. Brown, L. M., and P. Singer, *Phys. Rev.*, **133**, B812 (1964).
15. Sakurai, J. J., *CERN Conference on High Energy Physics*, CERN, 1962, p. 176.
16. Chew, G. F., and F. E. Low, *Phys. Rev.*, **101**, 1570 (1956).
17. Donnachie, A., and J. Hamilton, *Phys. Rev.*, **138**, B678 (1965).
18. Donnachie, A., and J. Hamilton, *Phys. Rev.*, **133**, B1053 (1964).
19. Donnachie, A., and J. Hamilton, *Ann. Phys.*, **31**, 410 (1965).
20. Carruthers, P., *Phys. Rev.*, **133**, B497 (1964).
21. Hendry, A. W., and R. G. Moorhouse, *Phys. Rev. Letters*, **18**, 171 (1965); F. Uchiyama–Campbell, *Phys. Rev. Letters*, **18**, 189 (1965).
22. Bareyre, P., C. Brickman, A. V. Stirling, and G. Villet, *Phys. Rev. Letters*, **18**, 342 (1965); Donnachie, A., A. T. Lea, and C. Lovelace, *Phys. Rev. Letters*, **19**, 146 (1965).
23. Duke, P. J., et al., *Phys. Rev. Letters*, **15**, 468 (1965).

The Higher Resonances in Pion-Nucleon Scattering

P. CARRUTHERS

Cornell University

1. Introduction

Research in elementary particle physics in the last few years has been dominated by the experimental discovery of a vast number of resonant, quasi-stable states of the strongly interacting particles[1]. Much exciting progress has been made in correlating this information by means of various internal symmetry groups[2,3]. Less spectacular but nevertheless important advances have been made in understanding the dynamical relations among the various resonances and particles. The major difficulties of dispersion theory[4] center on the same enigmas left unsolved by its progenitor, field theory. These concern the related problems of what to do about the short range forces and the very important multiparticle states. Although it is quite clear that no practical method exists for coping with the aforementioned difficulties, one cannot at present say to what extent present field theory is inadequate in principle. In the present article we shall regard dispersion relations as an especially useful formulation of field theory for strong interactions.

Although much information has been obtained about meson-baryon reactions we shall restrict our attention to the pion-nucleon interaction. It turns out that this system is fairly well decoupled from the strange meson-baryon reactions, so far as the long range forces are concerned. In any event the approximate validity of $SU(3)$ symmetry permits a straightforward extension of πN dynamics to encompass the analogous strange meson-baryon interactions. Studies of the latter extension have been made by Cutkosky[5], the author[6,7], and Golwich[8], among others. A more important factor in our choice is the relatively greater theoretical and experimental effort that has gone into the pion-nucleon problem.

159

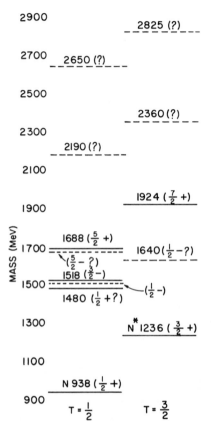

Fig. 1.   Energy levels of the nucleon and its excited states are shown. Solid lines
denote bound states (N) or resonances for which the phase shift passes through
90°. Dashed lines denote "inelastic" resonances; for these states the amplitude
varies rapidly but the the phase shift does not pass through 90°. The levels are
labeled by their total rest mass energy in MeV and spin-parity J^P. Question marks
denote inconclusive or controversial status concerning the assignment of quantum
numbers.

We shall take for granted the mass and spin of the pion and
nucleon, as well as their relative (odd) parity. We assume that isospin
is conserved and that the three pions (π^+, π^-, π^0) comprise an isospin
triplet while the proton and neutron (p, n) form an isospinor. We also
assume the existence of the $J = 1^-$, isospin one ρ meson, with mass

750 MeV, although at least the existence of such a particle is expected on the basis of bootstrap dynamics[4,9] involving the pions as input. The value of the pion-nucleon coupling constant is regarded as known. This list of input information is not unique, and might even be regarded as conservative. Given this information, we wish to describe to what extent one can understand the principal features of the pion-nucleon data.

In Fig. 1 we present a tentative energy level diagram for the excited states of the nucleon, classified according to isospin, mass in MeV, and spin-parity J^P. The energy of the excited state is really that of a bump in the pion-nucleon cross section. It has proved possible to ascribe the wiggles in cross section to rapid variation with energy of definite spin-parity states. This remark may prove to be false for the as-yet-unexplored four bumps of highest energy. Levels marked with solid lines are conventional resonances having a phase shift passing through 90° at the peak energy. Dashed line levels are given to states whose phase shift does not go through 90°. These states are quite inelastic and do not stand out so prominently in the data as the "true" resonances. Unestablished or controversial spin-parity assignments have been qualified by a question mark in parentheses. This information has been taken from refs. 1 and 10. References to previous experimental work can be traced from these sources. It will develop that a fairly adequate theory of the "true" resonances exist while the dynamical explanation of the remaining states remains as a challenge.

The most striking feature of Fig. 1 is the large number of energy levels. One is immediately reminded of the richness of atomic spectra, in particular the hydrogen atom. In the latter case the large number of bound states is due to the long range of the weakly attractive coulomb potential. In contrast, the forces in the pion-nucleon system are strong and of very short range. The first aim of any dynamical theory of the excited states of the nucleon must be to explain the systematic pattern of forces required to produce the spectrum of Fig. 1.

Generally speaking, the dominant observed reactions in the "resonance region" up to around 1.5 BeV laboratory pion kinetic energy are elastic scattering

$$\pi + N \rightarrow \pi + N \tag{1}$$

and single pion production

$$\pi + N \rightarrow 2\pi + N. \tag{2}$$

In practice the inelastic channel [Eq. (2)] is dominated by resonance production:

$$\pi + N \to \pi + N^* \to 2\pi + N \tag{3a}$$

$$\pi + N \to \rho + N \to 2\pi + N \tag{3b}$$

N^* being the 1236 MeV state of Fig. 1, the "3–3" resonance. The lab threshold energy for reaction (3a) is 490 MeV; for (3b), 890 MeV. Immediately above threshold the N^* production becomes comparable to elastic scattering; above 1 BeV, N^* production begins to give way to peripheral ρ production.

The early success of the Chew-Low theory in explaining the N^* was of great importance in establishing the value of analyticity, crossing symmetry and unitarity in strong interaction physics. However, as the so-called "higher" resonances (i.e., any resonance of energy greater than that of the N^*) appeared almost all proposed mechanisms involved coupling to the inelastic channels, as in Eq. (3). The author has given a detailed semihistorical review of these models in ref. 7. Only much later was it recognized[11] that patterns similar to those exhibited in the p-wave system of the Chew-Low theory are to be found in all orbital-momentum states. This development followed the introduction of the ideas of "Regge poles"[12] and Chew's "reciprocal bootstrap" relation[13] between the nucleon (N) and 3-3 resonance (N^*). The result of this analysis is that purely *elastic* forces would give rise to a sequence of even parity resonances [($T = 1/2$, $J = l - 1/2$), ($T = 3/2$, $J = l + 1/2$)] originating at the nucleon and N^*, respectively. The resonances are separated by $\Delta l = 2$ and give a dynamical realization of the Regge trajectories postulated in ref. 12 on the basis of analytic continuation in the orbital momentum.

An analysis of similar generality is yet to be done for the inelastic reactions of Eq. (3), and for other channels strongly coupled to the $2\pi N$ channel. The reason is simply that it is a much harder problem. Yet these reactions are of overriding importance for resonances in the non-Regge (mostly odd-parity) states, and are not negligible in their influence on the elastic channels.

2. Elastic Forces in Pion-Nucleon Scattering

The main point of this section is to elaborate the role of crossing symmetry in providing a unified dynamical framework underlying the systematics of the even-parity Regge states $P_{11}, F_{15}, \ldots; P_{33}, F_{37}, \ldots$. Our notation is spectroscopic, $L_{2T,2J}$, where T is the isospin, J the total angular momentum, and $L = J \pm 1/2$ is the orbital momentum of the large component of the asymptotic nucleon wave function. At present the only practical way of expressing the implications of crossing symmetry is by means of the "nearby-singularity" hypothesis[2] in which one "exchanges" all particles and resonances coupled to the incident particles. We shall show that there are several significant mechanisms at work, all of which collaborate in such a way as to produce simplicity in the pattern of forces. An essential result is that no single force mechanism is responsible for this pattern. As in the search for the form of the nucleon-nucleon interaction, naive attempts of oversimplification have led to defeat. In the present case the simplicity resides in the repetitive patterns exhibited in the crossing matrix.

In order to place these remarks, and the general theory to come, in perspective we give a brief sketch of the Chew-Low theory[14] and Chew's extension[13] thereof.

There are only four states in this (static nucleon) model, P_{11}, P_{13}, P_{31}, and P_{33}, labeled by $\alpha = 1, 2, 3,$ and 4. The partial-wave amplitude $h_\alpha(\omega)$ is defined by

$$h_\alpha(\omega) = e^{i\delta_\alpha} \sin \delta_\alpha / p^3 v^2(p) \tag{4}$$

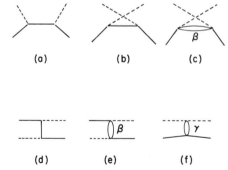

(a) (b) (c)

(d) (e) (f)

Fig. 2. Low-equation graphs associated with Eq. (5) are shown in (a), (b), and (c); (d) and (e) are relativistic analogues of (b) and (c); (f) corresponds to the exchange of zero baryon number systems in πN scattering. The dashed lines denote pions; solid lines denote nucleons.

where δ_α is the phase shift, p the momentum, and $v(p)$ the cutoff function. The amplitudes h_α satisfy the equations

$$h_\alpha(\omega) = -\delta_{\alpha,1} \frac{\gamma_{11}}{\omega} + \frac{\lambda_\alpha}{\omega} + \frac{1}{\pi} \int_1^\infty \frac{d\omega' \operatorname{Im} h_\alpha(\omega')}{\omega' - \omega - i\epsilon}$$

$$+ \frac{1}{\pi} \sum_\beta A_{\alpha\beta} \int_1^\infty \frac{\operatorname{Im} h_\beta(\omega') \, d\omega'}{\omega' + \omega} \quad (5)$$

Here ω is the total pion energy; the pion mass is taken as unity, and ϵ is a positive real infinitesimal. γ_{11} is defined as $3f^2, f^2 = 0.08$ being the renormalized unrationalized πNN coupling constant. The γ_{11} term in Eq. (5) comes from the time-ordered graph of Fig. 2a in which the nucleon absorbs, and later reemits the incident pion. As the intermediate state has $T = J = 1/2^+$, this process only affects pions in the P_{11} state. The terms λ_α/ω, which together with the term just described constitute the "renormalized Born approximation" come from the process of Fig. 2b in which the final pion is emitted by the nucleon just before the incoming pion is absorbed. The coefficients λ_α:

$$\lambda_\alpha = \frac{\gamma_{11}}{9} \begin{pmatrix} 1 \\ -2 \\ -2 \\ 4 \end{pmatrix} \quad (6)$$

are clearly related to the *crossing matrix*

$$A = \frac{1}{9} \begin{pmatrix} 1 & -4 & -4 & 16 \\ -2 & -1 & 8 & 4 \\ -2 & 8 & -1 & 4 \\ 4 & 2 & 2 & 1 \end{pmatrix}. \quad (7)$$

The meaning of the crossing matrix is easily seen. Suppose there is a sharp resonance in state β, so that $\operatorname{Im} h_\beta(\omega) \cong \pi\gamma_\beta\delta(\omega - \omega_\beta)$ (this defines γ_β). Then the contribution of the last term, which corresponds to Fig. 2c, is $A_{\alpha\beta}\gamma_\beta/(\omega + \omega_\beta)$. The strength of the force due to virtual excitation of state β is then given by the βth column of the crossing matrix. Note that with $\gamma_\beta = \gamma_{11}$ and $\omega_\beta = 0$ this expression reduces to λ_α/ω.

We shall refer to processes such as illustrated in Fig. 2b or 2c as "nucleon exchange" or "resonance β exchange" because of the relativistic counterparts of the former shown in Figs. 2d and 2e.

Equation (6) shows that the strongest force due to nucleon exchange is attractive, and occurs in the P_{33} state. One can now adjust the cutoff to obtain a resonance of the proper energy. The reduced half-width, which plays the role of $N^*N\pi$ coupling constant is defined by $\gamma_{33} = -\mathrm{Res}$ $h_{33}(\omega_r)$, the residue of h_{33} at the position of its pole. A short calculation based on the N/D method gives for the reduced width

$$\gamma_{33} = (1/2)\,\gamma_{11} \tag{8}$$

in fair agreement with experiment.

Chew points out[13] that, having obtained N^*, we ought to take account of its exchange. The last column of Eq. (7) reveals that N^* exchange gives a strong attraction in the P_{11} state. Perhaps the pole $-\gamma_{11}/\omega$ is a bound-state pole, computable in terms of γ_{33}. A similar calculation now shows that this is indeed possible, with the result

$$\gamma_{11} = 2\gamma_{33} \tag{9}$$

consistent with Eq. (8). It therefore appears that the N is no more fundamental than the N^*; it is just more fortunate in being stable. Given N we can obtain N^*; given N^* we can obtain N. (But why are we given anything?)

Notice that the P_{13} and P_{31} states have small forces due to a tendency of cancellation of forces due to N, N^* exchange. This tendency of the resonant states to help each other while suppressing small states is a remarkable and pervasive situation which holds much more generally than in the Chew-Low theory.

The extension of the preceding analysis to arbitrary angular momentum, with arbitrary (J, l) states exchanged, is exceedingly complicated, and even controversial. The technical point here concerns the analytic continuation of partial waves to crossed channels. Our procedure has been the traditional one of taking the first L terms in the partial-wave expansion, where L is large enough so that the principal resonances are represented. This method makes direct contact with field theory in that the exchanged particles are essentially treated as elementary particles. As the entire partial-wave expansion diverges in certain regions, this representation of the amplitude may be inaccurate, however. The representation of the resonant states by Regge poles offers a hopeful but as yet unfulfilled resolution of this difficulty. Since we are unable in any event to calculate amplitudes exactly in terms of given forces we shall mainly concentrate on the analysis of the structure of the general crossing matrix.

At this point it is useful to distinguish between the two different crossed channels. Forces due to the exchange between π and N of objects having unit baryon number 1 as in Fig. 2e are due to states in the "u channel", while forces due to the exchange of zero baryon number systems (Fig. 2f) arise from prominent states in the "t channel", e.g., ρ meson exchange. For a detailed explanation of these concepts, see Chew's book[2].

The crossing matrix breaks up into a simple part, the isospin crossing matrix, and a hard part, the angular momentum crossing matrix. The isospin crossing matrix for the u channel is

$$X_u = \frac{1}{3}\begin{pmatrix} -1 & 4 \\ 2 & 1 \end{pmatrix} \tag{10}$$

where the rows and columns are labeled in increasing order by $T = 1/2$, $3/2$. If a $T = 3/2$ object is exchanged the resulting amplitude is four times as big in $T = 1/2$ as in $T = 3/2$. Likewise, the exchange of a $T = 1/2$ state leads mainly to $T = 3/2$. The off-diagonal character of X_u, which is very important in our considerations, has a simple physical meaning. The physical channel and the u channel are connected with each other by turning the π's into antiparticles. Thus the π's isospin ($= 1$) points in the opposite direction when viewed from the crossed channel. This rule will also hold for the angular momentum crossing matrix, and becomes precise for large l.

Suppose we exchange a meson of isospin 0 or 1 (other values are, of course, forbidden). The resulting amplitudes[15] in $T = 1/2$, $3/2$ are given by reading down the columns of X_t:

$$X_t = \begin{pmatrix} \dfrac{\sqrt{6}}{6} & 1 \\ \dfrac{\sqrt{6}}{6} & -\dfrac{1}{2} \end{pmatrix} \tag{11}$$

The first column shows, as expected, that an isoscalar meson cannot distinguish between $T = 1/2$ and $T = 3/2$ states. However, $T = 1$ mesons (most important for our purposes because of the ρ meson) are twice as effective in $T = 1/2$ as $T = 3/2$ states, with opposite sign. As there are many more significant states in the u channel we shall mainly be concerned with it.

The simplest derivation of the "Born" amplitudes due to arbitrary (j, l) baryon exchanges has been given by Golowich[8]. His method is much shorter than that given by the author[11], although the latter method clarifies the approach to the heavy-mass limit. Here "heavy-mass limit" does not mean truly infinite mass; see ref. 11 for details. The main result of ref. 11 can be summarized in the approximate contribution to the "Born" amplitude f_{jlT}^B, where the partial-wave amplitude f is $e^{i\delta} \sin \delta/k$, k being the c.m. momentum:

$$f_{jlT}^B \cong (X_u)_{TT'} \, \Gamma_{ll'}^{jj'} \left(\frac{k}{k_r}\right)^{2l'} \frac{\Gamma_r W_r}{2k_r k^2} \, Q_{l-l'}\left(1 + \frac{s_r - u_0}{2k^2}\right) \qquad (12)$$

Here a single resonance whose width, energy, c.m. momentum, angular momentum, orbital momentum, and isospin are, respectively, Γ_r, W_r, k_r, j', l', and T'. Q is the Legendre function of the second kind, $s_r = (W_r)^2$ and $u_0 = (M^2 - \mu^2)^2/s$ where M and μ are the nucleon and pion mass. For $2k^2 \ll s_r - u_0$ the Q's behave as

$$Q_L \to \text{const } k^{2L+2} \qquad (13)$$

which guarantees that Eq. (12) has the correct threshold behavior. Equation (12) is only valid for $l' \leq l$, the most important case. The more accurate expression of Golowich should be used for numerical computations but the approximate form Eq. (12) is much more revealing of the systematics of the forces. The essential quantity is the crossing matrix $\Gamma_{ll'}^{jj'}$ shown in Table I.

We emphasize the important features of Table I. As anticipated the block matrices (i.e., given l and l') are mainly off diagonal. Further, there is an alteration in sign as l or l' are changed by one unit. The $l = l' = 1$ submatrix is of course identical to the isospin crossing matrix. In words, we can express our result as follows: *The force due to the exchange of a baryon state with $T = 1/2$ $(3/2)$ and $j' = l' \pm 1/2$ is by far the strongest in states of $T = 3/2$ $(1/2)$ and $j = l \mp 1/2$. For $l - l' = 0, 2, 4, \ldots$, this strongest force is attractive and for $l - l' = 1, 3, 5, \ldots$, it is repulsive.*

Using the previously obtained (N, N^*) states (P_{11}, P_{33}) as a foothold, let us examine Table I for possible self-consistent bootstrap patterns. Note that P_{11} exchange induces strong attractions in P_{33}, $F_{37}, H_{311}, \ldots$, and strong repulsions in $D_{35}, G_{39}, \ldots$, while P_{33} exchange gives strong attractions in $P_{11}, F_{15}, H_{19}, \ldots$, and strong repulsions in $D_{13}, G_{17}, \ldots$. Next we follow up those states in which a strong attraction is induced. We see that the pairs $(F_{15} - F_{37})$, $(H_{19} - H_{311})$, ..., tend to bootstrap each other just as did $P_{11} - P_{33}$.

It should be especially noted that a potential bootstrap relation between D_{13} and D_{35} is suppressed by repulsive forces due to P_{11} and P_{33} exchange. This pattern repeats itself through Table I; even and odd l are incompatible. The prominence of the P states at low energy determines the realization of the sequence of even-parity states. This example shows the danger of attempting to isolate a given set of partial waves from the influence of states of different orbital momenta.

Table I

	$P_{1/2}$	$P_{3/2}$	$D_{3/2}$	$D_{5/2}$	$F_{5/2}$	$F_{7/2}$	$G_{7/2}$	$G_{9/2}$	$H_{9/2}$	$H_{11/2}$
$P_{1/2}$	$-1/3$	$4/3$								
$P_{3/2}$	$2/3$	$1/3$								
$D_{3/2}$	$1/5$	$-7/5$	$-1/5$	$6/5$						
$D_{5/2}$	$-4/5$	$-2/5$	$4/5$	$1/5$						
$F_{5/2}$	$-1/7$	$10/7$	$6/35$	$-51/35$	$-1/7$	$8/7$				
$F_{7/2}$	$6/7$	$3/7$	$-36/35$	$-9/35$	$6/7$	$1/7$				
$G_{7/2}$	$1/9$	$-13/9$	$-1/7$	$11/7$	$1/7$	$-31/21$	$-1/9$	$10/9$		
$G_{9/2}$	$-8/9$	$-4/9$	$8/7$	$2/7$	$-8/7$	$-4/21$	$8/9$	$1/9$		
$H_{9/2}$	$-1/11$	$16/11$	$4/33$	$-54/33$	$-30/231$	$380/231$	$4/33$	$-49/33$	$-1/11$	$12/11$
$H_{11/2}$	$10/11$	$5/11$	$-40/33$	$-10/33$	$300/231$	$50/231$	$-40/33$	$-5/33$	$10/11$	$1/11$

The closely interdependent nature of the force pattern among the states comprising the N and N^* Regge trajectories is indicated in Fig. 3. It should be stressed that no quantitative calculation has proved that these states are self-consistent with the forces indicated in Fig. 3. Nevertheless, these forces are expected to play a significant part in a complete solution. We should mention that subsequent work by Donnachie and Hamilton[16], based on a different approximation scheme, is in qualitative agreement with our theory except that they dispute the importance of high-mass states in the bootstrap pattern [in particular their approximation leads to a lesser dependence of $(F_{15} - F_{37})$ on each other than indicated by Eq. (12)].

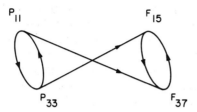

Fig. 3. Schematic representation of significant forces in the baryon bootstrap leading to Regge trajectories. The tips of the arrows point to states in which the strongest (and attractive) forces are induced by the exchange of the states at the base of the arrow.

The meson exchange forces are also of significance as has been emphasized by Hamilton and collaborators[17]. The isospin 0, s-wave π–π exchange is not negligible for quantitative purposes but is not interesting in our discussion since its contribution is nearly equal to all states of the same l. The f meson (spin 2) cannot distinguish between $T = 1/2$ and $T = 3/2$, but might become important at high energies, in the spin-orbit force. Such an analysis has not been done, to the author's knowledge. We now turn to the ρ meson exchange. This force is comparable to a typical baryon exchange term previously considered[17]. The magnitude of the effect can be reliably estimated from evidence on the electromagnetic structure of the nucleon, as discussed in ref. 7. The reader should consult that work for computational details. Recall that there are two independent couplings, vector and tensor. The Born amplitudes corresponding to these couplings are[7] ($J \neq 1/2$)

$$f_{l\pm}^V = \begin{pmatrix} 2 \\ -1 \end{pmatrix} \frac{\gamma_\rho^V}{4k^2W} [(E + M)(W - M)Q_l(y_\rho)$$
$$+ (E - M)(W + M)Q_{l\pm 1}(y_\rho)]$$

$$f_{l\pm}^T = \begin{pmatrix} 2 \\ -1 \end{pmatrix} \frac{\gamma_\rho^T}{4W} \{[(2W - E - M) + y_\rho(E + M)]Q_l(y_\rho)$$
$$- [(2W - E + M) + y_\rho(E - M)]Q_{l\pm 1}(yr)\}, \quad (14)$$

where $\gamma_\rho^V = f_{\rho NN}f_{\rho\pi\pi}/4\pi \cong 2$ and $\gamma_\rho^T/\gamma_\rho^V \cong -1.83$ measure the product of the $\rho\pi\pi$ and ρNN coupling constants. The parameter y_ρ is $1 + m^2/2k^2$, where m_ρ is 750 MeV. The upper 2 in Eq. (14) refers to $T = 1/2$, while -1 goes with $T = 3/2$.

The vector coupling term of Eq. (14) is significantly larger for $J = l - 1/2$ than for $J = l + 1/2$. Thus one obtains a sizeable attraction in $J = l - 1/2, T = 1/2$, and a weak repulsion in $J = l + 1/2, T = 3/2$. Next consider the tensor coupling, noting that γ_ρ^T is negative. For moderate energies ($\lesssim 1$ BeV) the terms containing $2W - E - M$ and $E - M$ can be neglected in comparison with the remaining terms, for a rough estimate. For the same purpose we can regard $E + M$ as about equal to $2W - E + M$. For $J = l + 1/2$ the $Q_{l \pm 1}$ term is very small, so we obtain a repulsion in $J = l + 1/2$, $T = 1/2$ and a weaker attraction in $J = l + 1/2, T = 3/2$. For $J = l - 1/2$ both Q functions give comparable contributions. In order to compare Q_{l-1} with Q_l we employ the asymptotic expression $yQ_l(y) \cong Q_{l-1}(y)$, valid when l and y are not too small. In this case we find an attraction for $T = 1/2$, $J = l - 1/2$ and a weaker repulsion for $T = 3/2, J = l - 1/2$. The $T = 1/2, J = l - 1/2$ force is largest, and is attractive. The vector and tensor terms are both largest and most attractive in $T = 1/2, J = l - 1/2$. In $T = 3/2, J = l + 1/2$ the attactive tensor force outweighs the repulsive vector force. $T = 1/2$, $J = l + 1/2$ is slightly repulsive because the repulsive tensor force is slightly larger than the attraction due to the vector coupling. In a similar fashion, the ρ-exchange contribution to $T = 3/2, J = l + 1/2$ is slightly attractive. From this calculation we learn that ρ exchange is most effective in the $J = l - 1/2, T = 1/2$ states. At a given energy the attraction in these states is substantially larger than that in the $J = l + 1/2$, $T = 3/2$ states. In the even-parity states the ρ exchange aids the previously discussed bootstrap while it mainly cancels out repulsive forces or small attractions in the odd-parity states. It should be stressed in addition that the magnitude and sign of the ρ couplings can be calculated from the N, N^* parameters and hence are not experimental parameters but rather a portion of the bootstrap[7].

As specimens of the type of calculation described in this section we plot in Fig. 4a the various contributions to the "Born phase shift" kf for F_{15} and D_{13}. In the former case all significant contributions are positive, while in the latter there is almost complete cancellation. For comparison's sake the corresponding phase shift in the P_{33} state due to nucleon exchange passes through about $12°$ at the resonance energy.

In summary, the exchange of all the observed even-parity baryon states and all low-energy meson states gives rise to forces favorable to producing the even-parity Regge trajectories originating in the nucleon

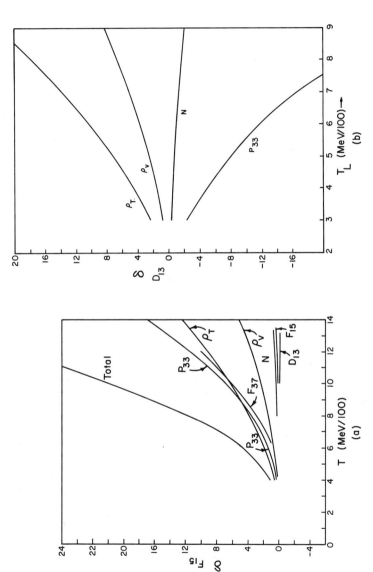

Fig. 4. (a) and (b) show the effective "Born phase shift" due to the exchange of various πN states and the ρ meson. The symbol labeling the curves represent the exchanged particle. ρ_V and ρ_T correspond to the vector and tensor coupling of the ρ to the nucleon. Note that for F_{15} all significant contributions are positive, while for D_{13} there is almost complete cancellation.

and 3–3 resonance. The odd parity states, and non-Regge even-parity states, have very small "elastic forces".

3. Inelastic Mechanisms for Resonance Formation

The elastic forces analyzed in the previous section can at best account for roughly half of the observed peaks. Although these states are most prominent in a casual look at the data, the remaining states are by no means unimportant. Their presence points up the significance of the inelastic reactions of Eq. (3). Indeed, for some time it was thought that elastic forces were quite unimportant for the higher resonances. Despite the great importance of the inelastic channels we shall be brutally brief in our discussion in view of the present confusion that prevails in this area. A detailed review will be found in ref. 7. The prominence of N^* production and the phenomenological success of the isobar model[18] led R. F. Peierls[19] to some interesting speculations on the role of N^* production in resonance formation. For example, the lowest partial wave contributing to the reaction

$$\pi + N \to N^* + s\text{-wave pion} \tag{15}$$

is $D_{3/2}$, which is appropriate to the 1516 MeV resonance. Detailed models of this reaction, employing the strong π–π interaction as an initial stage in the process, were proposed by Carruthers and Bethe[20], Carruthers[21], and Goebel and Schnitzer[22]. A more complete model along these lines has been given recently by Selleri[23]. Another promising mechanism was proposed by Peierls[24], which involves the nucleon-exchange pole in the reaction

$$\pi + N^* \to \pi + N^* \tag{16}$$

To date, it appears that these models have raised more problems than they have solved. No patterns of simplicity comparable to those of the elastic forces, or of experiment, have been extracted from the models. (It is the author's conviction that this is a matter of time and hard work, however.)

Another popular model is based on the one-pion-exchange model for ρ production. The production process itself is shown in Fig. 5a, and an associated contribution to elastic scattering in Fig. 5b. The idea that a strong π–π interaction was instrumental in the high energy πN

(a)   (b)

Fig. 5. The dashed lines denote π mesons; wiggly lines denote ρ mesons. (a) shows the long range one-pion-exchange mechanism leading to ρ production; (b) a corresponding contribution to elastic scattering.

interaction was put forward some time ago by Dyson[25] and Takeda[26]. Modern developments of the idea are due mainly to Itabashi et al.[27], Ball and Frazer[28], and Cook and Lee[29]. In these calculations the experimentally dominant πN^* part of the $\pi\pi N$ channel is neglected in favor of the (longer range) ρN part. This model has the virtue of automatically favoring isospin 1/2 over isospin 3/2 by a ratio of 4:1. It now appears[30,31] that for a state with energy below the ρN threshold, such coupling can produce an attractive force leading to a true resonance (for example, the D_{13} state at 600 MeV lab pion energy). However, for πN energies at or above threshold the elastic force will be small or repulsive and the main effect on the elastic channel will be a decrease in amplitude as the inelastic channel opens up. (The origin of such behavior can be understood in a crude way on the basis of second order perturbation theory for the energy, in Fig. 5b.) Hence we expect the ρN coupling to be of primary importance for the D_{13} resonance, but not as significant as the elastic forces for driving the phase shift through 90° for the F_{15} resonance, which is just above threshold. In fact the ρN coupling, by itself, seems incapable of producing a resonance in F_{15}. (This difference from the result of ref. 29 is due to an unfortunate approximation in the latter work.) Recently Auvil and Brehm[32] have noted that the reaction $\pi N \to Nf$ may play a significant role in the F_{15} resonance. Moreover, they suggest that $\pi N^* \to N^*f$ contributes to F_{37}. Although it seems quite plausible that this mechanism is a significant one, we do not agree with their position that the coupling to the (fN) or (fN^*) channels is the *only* significant mechanism. Our whole experience has shown that there is an almost conspiratorial interlocking of mechanisms, due largely to crossing symmetry, which is responsible for the spectrum of excited states of the nucleon. At present only a partial understanding of this pattern has been achieved. If we may venture a cautious prediction, it is this: When all the significant inelastic mechanisms are properly analyzed, they will fall into a pattern as simple and systematic as the elastic forces.

In conclusion we note that some of the "inelastic" states plotted in Fig. 1 have not been given even a speculative interpretation. The $1/2-$ state close to the $3/2-$ state at 1518 MeV is almost certainly due to the rapid rise near threshold in the reaction $\pi^- p \to \eta n$ as has been noted by many authors (e.g., ref. 33). The possible $1/2+$ state at 1480 MeV is a puzzle to the author. The 1640 $S_{31}(?)$ state may be due to the ρ-threshold effect, but then it is puzzling[30,34] why the D_{33} state shows no striking behavior. The D_{15} inelastic effect near the F_{15} resonance does not seem to be understood. There may still be some unresolved resonances lurking under the broad peak associated mainly with the F_{37} states. The four highest states are possible "merely" Regge recurrences of the lower levels and may not demand any deep thought.

It should be clear that there are many unresolved puzzles in this most fundamental problem. Recent experimental advances have sharpened up the problem to the point where real progress can be expected—and demanded.

References

1. Rosenfeld, A. H., A. Barbaro-Galtieri, W. H. Barkas, P. L. Bastian, J. Kirz, and M. Roos, *Rev. Mod. Phys.*, **37**, 633 (1965).
2. Gell-Mann, M., and Y. Ne'eman, *The Eightfold Way*, W. A. Benjamin, New York, 1964.
3. Carruthers, P., *Introduction to Unitary Symmetry*, Interscience, New York, 1966.
4. Chew, G. F., *S-Matrix Theory of Strong Interactions*, W. A. Benjamin, New York, 1960.
5. Cutkosky, R. E., *Ann. Phys.*, **23**, 415 (1963).
6. Carruthers, P., *Phys. Rev. Letters*, **12**, 269 (1964).
7. Carruthers, P., in *Lectures in Theoretical Physics*, Vol. VIIB, University of Colorado Press, 1965, p. 82.
8. Golowich, E., *Phys. Rev.*, **139**, B1297 (1965).
9. Zachariasen, F., *Lectures at the Pacific International Summer School in Physics* (1965), to be published.
10. Bareyre, P., C. Brickman, A. V. Sterling, and G. Villet, *Phys. Rev. Letters*, **18**, 342 (1965).
11. Carruthers, P., *Phys. Rev. Letters*, **10**, 538, 540 (1963); *Phys. Rev.*, **133**, B497 (1964); see refs. 6 and 7.

12. Chew, G. F., and S. C. Frautschi, *Phys. Rev. Letters*, **7**, 394 (1962); R. Blankenbecler, and M. L. Goldberger, *Phys. Rev.*, **126**, 766 (1962).
13. Chew, G. F., *Phys. Rev. Letters*, **9**, 233 (1962).
14. Chew, G. F., and F. E. Low, *Phys. Rev.*, **101**, 1570 (1956).
15. Carruthers, P., and J. P. Krisch, *Ann. Phys.*, **33**, 1 (1965).
16. Donnachie, A., and J. Hamilton, *Ann. Phys.*, **31**, 410 (1965).
17. Donnachie, A., J. Hamilton, and A. T. Lea, *Phys. Rev.*, **135**, B515 (1964).
18. Lindenbaum, S. J., and R. M. Sternheimer, *Phys. Rev.*, **109**, 1723 (1968).
19. Peierls, R. F., *Phys. Rev.*, **118**, 325 (1960).
20. Carruthers, P., and H. A. Bethe, *Phys. Rev. Letters*, **4**, 536 (1960).
21. Carruthers, P., *Ann. Phys.*, **14**, 229 (1961).
22. Goebel, C. J., and H. J. Schnitzer, *Phys. Rev.*, **123**, 1021 (1961).
23. Selleri, F., in *Lectures in Theoretical Physics*, Vol. VIIb, Univ. of Colorado Press, 1965, p. 236.
24. Peierls, R. F., *Phys. Rev. Letters*, **6**, 641 (1961).
25. Dyson, F. J., *Phys. Rev.*, **99**, 1037 (1955).
26. Takeda, G., *Phys. Rev.*, **100**, 440 (1955).
27. Itabashi, K., M. Kato, K. Nakagawa, and G. Takeda, *Prog. Theoret. Phys. (Kyoto)*, **24**, 529 (1960).
28. Ball, J. S., and W. R. Frazer, *Phys. Rev. Letters*, **7**, 204 (1961).
29. Cook, L. F., and B. W. Lee, *Phys. Rev.*, **127**, 283, 297 (1962).
30. Goldberg, H., and E. L. Lomon, *Phys. Rev.*, **134**, B659 (1964).
31. Nath, N., Ph.D. thesis, Cornell University, 1966, unpublished.
32. Auvil, P., and J. J. Brehm, *Phys. Rev.*, **140**, B135 (1965).
33. Auvil, P., C. Lovelace, A. Donnachie, and A. T. Lea, *Phys. Rev. Letters*, **12**, 76 (1964).
34. Carruthers, P., *Phys. Rev. Letters*, **6**, 567 (1961).

Electromagnetic Form Factors

J. S. LEVINGER

Rensselaer Polytechnic Institute

Introduction

Since several authors[1-7] have recently reviewed the electromagnetic form factors of nucleons, I will not attempt another review at this time. Instead, I shall give a brief survey of experimental results of the past year and a half, and then discuss two of the more controversial aspects of the form factor problem: the electric form factor of the neutron, and the isovector spectral functions.

A particle, or composite system, of spin 1/2 can interact with an external static electromagnetic field in only two ways: by its electric charge, and by its magnetic dipole moment. Similarly, in a Born approximation calculation[2] in which a single photon is exchanged in elastic electron–proton scattering as shown in Fig. 1a, we have only two interactions. These interactions are proportional to the form factors G_E and G_M corresponding to charge and magnetic moment. The electric and magnetic form factors $G_E(t)$ and $G_M(t)$ are functions of the relativistically invariant Mandelstam variable, t. (This variable corresponds to the squared momentum transfer: $t = [(E - E')^2/c^2] - (\mathbf{p} - \mathbf{p}')^2$. If we choose a Lorentz system so that the electron change of total energy $(E - E')$ is zero, then t is just the negative of $\mathbf{q}^2$, where the 3-vector $\mathbf{q}$ is the momentum transfer $\mathbf{p} - \mathbf{p}'$.)

I use G_E and G_M without any commitment concerning their interpretation as Fourier transforms of spatial distributions of charge, or magnetic moment density, respectively[8]. Instead, I *assume* analyticity and proper behavior at infinity of each form factor in the cut complex plane, and represent each form factor in terms of its *spectral function*. The spectral function, which is the imaginary part of the complex form factor at the cut, is proportional to the probability

177

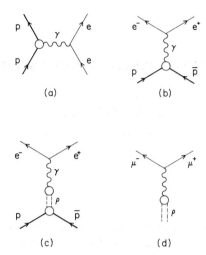

Fig. 1   Dispersion diagrams for electron–proton elastic scattering (a), and for proton–antiproton annihilation to give an electron–positron pair (b and c). Time goes upwards, the heavy lines are protons, the light lines electrons, and the wiggly lines virtual photons. In (c) we look at the photon–proton vertex with a magnifying glass, and observe (for instance) the isovector term due to the ρ (two-pion) resonance. In (d) the ρ resonance is produced by a process not shown, and decays into muon pairs.

of a timelike virtual photon being absorbed by a nucleon. If this absorption is mediated by vector mesons, the spectral function will have peaks at values of t equal to the squared masses of these mesons.

In the convention used here, spacelike momentum transfers achieved in electron-proton scattering have $t < 0$. The timelike region $0 < t < 4M^2$ is nonphysical. Form factors for large positive values, $t \geq 4M^2$ can be measured by determining the cross section for nucleon–antinucleon annihilation into lepton pairs. Figure 1b shows an electron–positron pair; annihilation could also produce a $\mu^+\mu^-$ pair. The spectral function and the corresponding cut in the t-plane, start at $t = 4m^2$. (The pion mass is m, the nucleon mass M. In Fig. 1c the intermediate state marked "ρ" could consist of two pions. Its mass must then be at least $2m$, hence $t \geq 4m^2$.) Values of t are expressed in units of m^2, $F^{-2} = 10^{26}$ cm^{-2}, or (BeV/c)^2; I choose the third set of units. Note that $4m^2 = 2F^{-2}$, $1F^{-2} = 0.0389$ (BeV/c)^2 and $4M^2 = 90F^{-2} = 3.5$ (BeV/c)^2.

I use subscript p for proton, n for neutron, V for isovector (half the difference between proton and neutron values), and S for isoscalar (the average of proton and neutron). The form factors are normalized to give observed static values: e.g., $G_{Ep}(0) = 1$; $G_{Mp}(0) = 2.793$; $G_{En}(0) = 0$; and $G_{Mn}(0) = -1.913$.

Recent Experimental Results

Experimentalists have recently made progress in four main directions: (i) Five groups (Stanford, Cornell, Orsay, CEA, and DESY) measure differential cross sections for electron–proton elastic scattering at negative t, going out to -6.8 (BeV/c)^2. (ii) Two groups at CERN and BNL are *starting* to get firm results from proton–antiproton annihilation into lepton pairs for t in the range $4M^2 < t \leq 6.8$ (BeV/c)^2. (iii) A variety of techniques are being used to study electron–neutron scattering at negative t. (iv) Several new experiments relate to the validity of quantum electrodynamics and of the Born approximation. A start has been made in determining the coupling constant for vector mesons with virtual photons.

The differential cross section σ for electron elastic scattering at laboratory angle θ by a proton is related to proton form factors through the Rosenbluth formula[1-4]

$$\sigma/\sigma_{NS} = (G_E^2 + \tau G_M^2)/(1 + \tau) + 2\tau G_M^2 \tan^2(\theta/2), \qquad (1)$$

where $\sigma_{NS} =$ Mott cross section including recoil, and $\tau = -t/4M^2$. The CEA group[9] measures σ/σ_{NS} at two or more values of angle θ at the same value of squared momentum transfer t, in the range $-3.89 \leq t < 0$. Equation (1) holds to the experimental accuracy of several percent, over a quite large range of angle. These measurements verify the form of Eq. (1) and provide separate determinations of G_E^2 and G_M^2. The magnetic form factor is determined with an accuracy varying from 2% for t near zero to 10% at the most negative values. The electric form factor is accurately measured at low momentum transfers, but is poorly determined for $t \leq -1.75$ (BeV/c)^2. At $t = -2.92$ and -3.89 (BeV/c)^2, G_E^2 is zero, within the experimental accuracy, so the sign of the (small) electric form factor is not known[10]. At $t = -4.87$ and again at -6.81 (BeV/c)^2, the CEA group measured σ/σ_{NS} at only one angle, so a clean separation into electric and magnetic form factors is impossible. Still, the magnetic form factor is determined[11] fairly well: e.g., $G_M(-6.81) = 0.038 \pm 0.007$ or only a seventy-fifth of the static value.

The annihilation of nucleon and antinucleon to form a lepton pair, with a one-photon intermediate state has frequently been used by theorists in form factor calculations: now it is measured in the laboratory, or at least an upper limit for this process is being determined. Figure 1b illustrates that the same nucleon form factors enter here as for electron scattering. The differential cross section σ_p in the CM system is[12]

$$\sigma_p/\sigma_a = G_E^2 \sin^2 \varphi - \tau G_M^2 (1 + \cos^2 \varphi)$$

$$\sigma_a = (\pi\alpha^2\hbar^2/32M^2c^2\tau^2)(-\tau)^{1/2}(1 - \tau)^{-1/2} = 1.0 \ nb/sr = 10^{-33} \ cm^2/sr$$

$$\tau = -t/4M^2 = -(E_p + M)/2M = -1.92 \tag{2}$$

In this equation, φ is the CM angle between incident antiproton and emitted positron, while E_p is the laboratory energy $(c^2p^2 + M^2)^{1/2}$ of antiproton, the proton being at rest. Numerical values are based on antiprotons of momentum $p = 2.5 \ BeV/c$, as in Zichichi's experiments[13] at CERN.

Preliminary results[13] *indicated* a total cross section of 35 nb. Recent CERN measurements[13] on electron–positron and on muon pairs give upper limits on the differential cross section at 90° of 0.1 nb/sr and 0.05 nb/sr, respectively. (Note that the theoretical cross sections are the same for either pair, if we treat the leptons in the extreme relativistic approximation, and ignore radiative corrections.) The latter more stringent limit gives

$$|G_E|^2 + 1.92|G_M|^2 \leq 0.05.$$

Since the complex form factors G_E and G_M are equal[14] at the annihilation threshold ($t = 4M^2$), we assume approximate equality at $t = 7.7 \ M^2$. This assumption gives upper limits on the modulus of each form factor as about 0.15.

Similar experiments at BNL are now in progress: Tollestrup et al.[15] study the annihilation of antiprotons of momentum 2.5 BeV/c and also 1.5 BeV/c.

The electron–neutron interaction has continued to be quite difficult to measure, because of the lack of free neutron targets. Measurements at space-like t have continued along the three lines started ten or more years ago: (*i*) the scattering[1,16] of thermal neutrons by electrons; (*ii*) inelastic electron–deuteron[1,17] scattering; (*iii*) elastic electron–deuteron[1,18] scattering.

The scattering length for thermal neutrons by closed electron shells gives[1,19] the slope of the neutron's electric form factor at $t = 0$, $dG_{En}/dt = G'_{En}(0)$. Earlier values[20]

$$G'_{En}(0) = -0.021 \pm 0.001F^2 = -(0.54 \pm 0.03)(\text{BeV}/c)^{-2} \qquad (3)$$

are confirmed by the recent careful work of Krohn and Ringo[21]

$$G'_{En}(0) = -0.018 \pm 0.001F^2 = -(0.46 \pm 0.03)(\text{BeV}/c)^{-2}. \qquad (3')$$

Inelastic electron–deuteron scattering suffers from corrections due to neutron–proton interactions in the initial and final states. The latter corrections are particularly small if the electron–neutron coincidences, and electron–proton coincidences are both measured at angles corresponding to a free neutron target and the ratio used to extract the cross section of the free neutron. Earlier measurements[22] have recently been repeated[23] by the Cornell group at $t = -5.5F^{-2} = -0.21$ (BeV/c)^2. Their earlier value[22]

$$G_{En}(-0.19) = 0.16 \pm 0.04 \qquad (4)$$

has been lowered to

$$|G_{En}(-0.21)| = 0.04 \pm 0.05. \qquad (4')$$

As I noted above this type of measurement only determines the squared electric form factor; I have used Eq. (3) to give the positive sign in Eq. (4). The sign of G_{En} in Eq. (4') is likely to be positive. Also $G_{En}(-0.39)$ is measured[23] as 0.06 ± 0.06; and G_{En}^2 is slightly negative (by only 0.6 standard errors) at $t = -0.57F^{-2}$.

The CEA group[24] measure scattered electrons in anticoincidence with recoil protons, thus inferring the neutron coincidence measured directly by the Cornell group. The CEA group, and also Hughes et al. at Stanford[25], further measure the neutron cross section by detection of the inelastically scattered electron alone. (This latter method necessitates substantial corrections, particularly at small momentum transfers.) The magnetic form factor G_{Mn} is determined by these methods in the range $-6.81 \leq t \leq -0.389$ (BeV/c)^2, an upper limit being set at the highest values. I return in the next section to the problem of the neutron's electric form factor.

Electron–deuteron elastic scattering seems an attractive method for measuring the two isoscalar form factors G_{ES} and G_{MS} directly.

Recently, Buchanan and Yearian[26] have extended earlier measurements out to $t = -0.78$ $(BeV/c)^2$. Their results for the magnetic scattering indicate a "nonadditive" contribution to magnetic scattering at large momentum transfers as calculated by Adler and Drell[27]. If nonadditive contributions are appreciable, the main interest in elastic electron–deuteron scattering lies in the determination of these contributions, rather than in determining the isoscalar form factors.

All the preceding discussion has implicitly assumed that any difference between observed electron–nucleon scattering and that calculated in Born approximation for point nucleons should be ascribed to form factors associated with the nucleons. Thus in Fig. 1 the nucleon–photon vertex is shown as a circle, associated with a form factor; while the photon–electron vertex is shown as if the electron and photon both obey quantum electrodynamics. But is quantum electrodynamics really valid[2] at these large momentum transfers?

CERN measurements[28] of the muon magnetic moment confirmed the accuracy of quantum electrodynamics for momentum transfers of order somewhat greater than the muon mass. The BNL comparison[28] of their muon–proton and Stanford electron–proton scattering extends the lack of lepton structure to the electron as well. However, Pipkin et al.[29] do find statistically significant deviations from quantum electrodynamics in their CEA experiments on the photoproduction of symmetrical electron–positron pairs from carbon at angles of order 10°, by photons from 1 to 5 BeV energy. Stanford experiments on electron–electron scattering with clashed beams are now under way, and should provide another check on quantum electrodynamics at large momentum transfer.

The Born approximation should be valid to roughly 1% accuracy, since two-photon terms involve one more power of α (the fine structure constant) than one-photon terms. (Of course, if one-photon terms happen to give an anomalously small result, e.g., due to cancellation the above argument falls on its face.) Two-photon terms can show up in three different ways[4,7]. No effects have been observed to date in the angular distribution of the scattered electrons[6], or in the polarization of the recoil protons[30]. A comparison of electron–proton and positron–proton scattering by Browman et al.[30] at Stanford at t of -0.78 $(BeV/c)^2$ showed an 8% difference, but this difference amounted only to two standard deviations.

The virtual photon could couple to a nucleon by "materializing" into a vector meson (spin one, negative parity) with the same quantum numbers as the photon, as illustrated in Fig. 1c. This vector meson, in turn, could couple to the nucleon. Three vector mesons are established at present[31]: the ρ, ω, and φ. In this model, the spectral function would have a pole at the squared meson mass; the residue at the pole would be the product of two coupling constants: the nucleon–antinucleon–meson coupling, and the meson–photon coupling. De Pagter et al.[32] have very recently obtained data on the latter coupling constant, by measurements of the rate for ρ (or ω) decay into muon pairs as shown in Fig. 1d. (They find a $2\mu/2\pi$ branching ratio of 3×10^{-5}.) The former coupling constants are being deduced from analyses of nucleon–nucleon scattering, and of the ρ contribution to pion–nucleon scattering[32]. At present I can still introduce a phenomenological nucleon–photon coupling constant, and adjust it to fit the experiments on lepton–nucleon scattering, and production of lepton pairs by annihilation. But in a couple of years, or more, this coupling constant may be determined by combining two independent experiments.

The Electric Form Factor of the Neutron

The electric form factor of the neutron, G_{En}, continues to be poorly determined experimentally just because it is so small. Experiments on what we can approximately describe as "electron–neutron scattering" shows that $G_{En}^2 < 0.03$, for all spacelike momentum transfers[23-25]. On the other hand, the nonzero electron–neutron scattering length[20,21] shows that $G'_{En}(0)$ is certainly negative: see Eqs. (3) and (3'). I conclude that G_{En} is *not* identically zero, while its absolute value is less than 0.17.

Three rather trivial points need emphasis, just because they are frequently ignored. First, if you wish to find a zero neutron form factor, you might try using the Dirac form factor[1,2,3] F_{1n} instead of G_{En}. (F_{1n} is a linear combination[3,4] of G_{En}, G_{Mn} and t.) While $F'_{1n}(0)$ is indeed zero at the static limit, F_{1n} becomes markedly negative for spacelike momentum transfers: $F_{1n} \approx -0.10$ for $-2 \leq t \leq -0.4$ $(\text{BeV}/c)^2$.

Second, group-theoretic arguments[33] that the neutron electric form factor should be identically zero are therefore in error by an appreciable amount. For instance, $|G'_{En}(0)|$ is about one sixth of the comparable quantity for the proton, $|G'_{Ep}(0)|$. This order of magnitude error in the group-theoretic result is plausible, from the following argument. If the masses of ρ, ω, and φ were indeed degenerate, and if only these three particles contributed to the spectral functions, and they contributed with appropriate coefficients, then both isovector (G_{EV}) and isoscalar (G_{ES}) form factors could have identical shapes. Since the masses *are not* degenerate, the isovector and isoscalar spectral functions have somewhat different shapes, so we should not expect exact cancellation for all momentum transfers t in the neutron form factor

$$G_{En} = G_{ES} - G_{EV}.$$

Third, since G_{En} remains close to zero, its sign is uncertain, except for small enough values of t that one can argue the sign of G_{En} from its known slope. This sign uncertainty leads to serious errors in the electric isotopic form factors based on G_{En}. Consider the case $t = -0.389$ as an arithmetic example. Stein et al.[23] give $G_{En}^2 = 0.0037 \pm 0.0141$, and $G_{Mn} = -0.825 \pm 0.064$. (The sign of the magnetic form factor is known, since the static value is negative, and G_{Mn}^2 stays well away from zero in the intervening region.) I take account of the *extra* sign uncertainty in the neutron's electric form factor by choosing $G_{En} = 0.00 \pm 0.14$. Using $G_{Ep} = 0.408$ and $G_{Mp} = 1.14$, we find a 35% error in G_{ES} and G_{EV}! However, G_{MS} suffers only a 20% error, while the error in G_{MV} is a mere 3%.

I conclude that if we cannot measure the neutron electric form factor, we should calculate it! The experimental results are too uncertain to prove us wrong! This same conclusion was in fact reached earlier by Dudelzak,[34] an experimentalist. (Wilson et al.[6,35] in their "fourth fit" treat the data in a similar manner, but less explicitly.)

The calculation proceeds in two simple steps. (i) Assume that the electric isoscalar form factor G_{ES} has a spectral function based *only* on the two known isoscalar vector meson resonances: the ω, and φ. The two unknown coupling parameters can be determined from two constraints: the static value, $G_{ES}(0) = 1/2$, and the slope $G'_{ES}(0) = (1/2)[G'_{Ep}(0) + G'_{En}(0)]$. ($ii$) Having calculated G_{ES}, we combine this with the measured G_{Ep} to calculate the neutron electric form factor G_{En}.

As a specific example, I use Dudelzak's values:

$$G'_{ES}(0) = 0.048 \pm 0.002F^2 = 1.23 \pm 0.05 \, (\text{BeV}/c)^{-2}. \tag{5}$$

[Wilson's fit[36] agrees, $G'_{ES}(0) = 1.25 \, (\text{BeV}/c)^{-2}$.] The procedure outlined above then gives

$$G_{ES} = \alpha_\omega/(1 - t/m_\omega^2) + \alpha_\phi/(1 - t/m_\phi^2)$$
$$\alpha_\omega = 1.14 \pm 0.08; \, \alpha_\phi = -0.64 \pm 0.08 \tag{6}$$

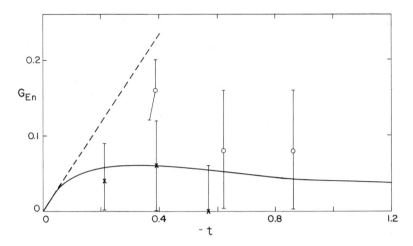

Fig. 2   The neutron electric form factor G_{En} vs. squared momentum transfer $q^2 = -t$, in $(BeV/c)^2$. The curve uses the isoscalar electric form factor, Eq. (6) taken from ref. 34, together with measurements of the proton electric form factor. The dotted line has the slope, Eq. (3). Experimental data from Cornell and CEA are plotted taking the positive square root of the measured G_{En}^2. The crosses are from ref. 23, and the circles from ref. 24.

These numerical values are within a standard error of those[37] for Wilson's "fit 4". Of course, the values for the 2 parameters in (6) have strongly correlated errors, since both parameters depend only on the value chosen for $G'_{ES}(0)$.

Equation (6) for G_{ES} combined with direct measurements of the proton electron form factor G_{Ep} gives the curve for the neutron electron form factor G_{En} shown in Fig. 2. We show as points the three recent data of Stein et al.[23] and the recent CEA data[24]. Since the curve gives positive G_{En}, we choose the positive square roots of measured G_{En}^2. We find no firm disagreements between the predicted curve and the inaccurate observation of G_{En}.

The Isovector Spectral Function

Several workers have had success in fitting the magnetic *isoscalar* form factors with spectral functions using two poles[25,35], at the *known* masses of the ω and φ. Many analogous attempts have been made to fit the *isovector* form factors but, to my way of thinking, with little success to date.

Only one vector meson of isotopic spin unity has been established[31] so far: the ρ resonance at 765 MeV, with a width of 124 MeV. While the isoscalar resonances are only 12 and 3 MeV wide, so it is a good approximation to treat them as poles, the width "shifts" this isovector resonance. We are using the resonance to give a peak in the spectral function $g(t')$ in a nonsubtracted dispersion relation[2] for the magnetic isovector form factor G_{MV}:

$$G_{MV}(t) = \frac{1}{\pi} \int_{t_0}^{\infty} g(t') \, dt'/(t' - t), \tag{7}$$

where $t_0 = 4m^2$.

For spacelike momentum transfers (negative t) the denominator in Eq. (7) shifts the peak in the spectral function to a lower energy, if we wish to replace the broad resonance by an "effective pole". This shift[38] is about half the width, giving an effective pole position of 700 MeV. (Note that if[39] we use an effective pole to calculate $G_{MV}(4M^2)$, we should shift the pole position towards *higher* energy.)

On the other hand, ever since isovector form factors have been fitted[40,1] with a single pole form, the pole position has been between near 500 and 600 MeV, appreciably below the (shifted) position of the ρ resonance: e.g., Hughes[25] finds an effective position of 548 MeV, and Chan[35] finds 540 MeV. I discard these fits as not of physical significance, since no such resonance is established.

Since a fit cannot be achieved with the (shifted) ρ pole alone, a logical step is to try a second ρ' pole. This second pole could[25,41] be identified with some known resonance which *might* be a vector meson with isotopic spin unity: the B at 1220 MeV is a popular candidate[31]. This ρ, B combination does fit[25] the data $-1.17 \leq t \leq 0$ by using a core term: but such a core term is explicitly excluded by the CEA data at large spacelike momentum transfers.

We obtain more freedom by allowing the ρ' to have an adjustable mass. Chan et al.[35] are able to make a rather good fit (called fit 4) to extensive data on cross sections taking the ρ' mass as 875 MeV, combined with a (nonshifted) ρ at 760 MeV.

Another way of getting a good fit is to choose a double pole at the position of the resonance: the form factor is proportional to $(1 - t/m_\rho^2)^{-2}$. As pointed out by Wilson[6] this "dipole" in the spectral function can be caused by two poles with opposite signs and similar magnitudes for their residues, arranged symmetrically about the position of the ρ resonance.

These last two CEA fits[6,35] are both intriguing. My only criticism is that multipion production experiments have found the ρ resonance, but have found neither a higher resonance near 875 MeV, nor a dipole splitting of the ρ resonance.

Orman[42] uses a combination of Lorentizian spectral functions with adjustable coupling, peak positions, and widths. He also constrains the spectral function to have zero slope at threshold, characteristic of a p-wave resonance. The magnetic isovector spectral function has a very broad ρ resonance (width 300 MeV) near 800 MeV, and an equally broad ρ' at 1200 MeV.

Wu and Yang[43] discuss the relation between proton–proton and electron–proton scattering at large spacelike momentum transfers. They use the former's empirical exponential dependence on $(-t)^{1/2}$ at large spacelike t to give a similar expression for the form factors G_{Mp} or G_{Ep}. Wilson et al.[35] point out that this form gives an oscillating spectral function, $t > 4m^2$. These oscillations would have shown up[13] in measurements in the annihilation region.

A different type of fit can be achieved to the form factors, and associated spectral functions, by making a conformal transformation[44] to a unit circle in the cut η plane:

$$\eta = [b - (1 - t/t_0)^{1/2}]/[b + (1 - t/t_0)^{1/2}] \qquad (8)$$

Spacelike momentum transfers lie on the real axis in this plane, and can be fitted with a power series in η. This amounts to fitting the spectral function with a Fourier series in angle ξ, where[44]

$$\cos \xi = (b^2 + 1 - t/t_0)/(b^2 - 1 + t/t_0). \qquad (9)$$

In Eqs. (8) and (9) the threshold $t_0 = 4m^2$ for the proton or isovector form factors; b is an arbitrary parameter. This arbitrariness of b was exploited by choosing $b = 2$ to fit 1963 *preliminary* values of the annihilation cross section in the far timelike region, $t = 6.8$ (BeV/c)^2. Since present values of the annihilation cross section are smaller by at least two orders of magnitude, the published fits using this particular conformal transformation should be disregarded.

I note that a very small annihilation cross section is automatically provided for by pole fits, if the poles are around 1 BeV. The imaginary part of the form factor is clearly zero. The real part at very large positive t is about the same as at equally large negative t. Thus if one fits the CEA data to obtain very small form factors ($G_{Mp} = 0.04$) at $t = -6.8$ (BeV/c)^2 one will automatically obtain similar small form factors[35] at $t = 6.8$ (BeV/c)^2, consistent with Zichichi's upper limit. On the other hand, η-plane fits tend to obtain form factors of roughly unit modulus in the annihilation region: both the imaginary and real parts tend to be appreciable. Further study is needed to ascertain whether this difficulty can be avoided.

Levinger and Peierls[44] have shown that an η-plane fit succeeds well with artificial data based on a spectral function with a single broad peak, but has only fair success in fitting a spectral function with a pole. If one has reliable *a priori* knowledge that the spectral function should be fitted with poles, and indeed we have such knowledge for isoscalar spectral functions, a fit with poles is preferable to one using a conformal transformation. But if one believes that the second isovector (ρ') pole does not represent a *bona fide* reasonably narrow resonance then it might well be worthwhile to fit the spectral function in the BeV region with a Fourier series.

My present proposal is to fit the magnetic isovector form factor G_{MV} with a spectral function which includes the ρ resonance at its known position and width, combined with η-plane fit to the rest of the spectral function. (In fact, this was the original proposal made by R. F. Peierls at the time when Kirson and Levinger[45] and Wilson[3] were trying two-pole fits, similar to the ρ–ρ' fits discussed above. Peierls argued that the assumption of a ρ' pole was artificial. However, Peierls, Levinger, and Wang[44] became so intrigued with the possibility of finding the spectral function from form factor data *alone*, that it took me 3 years to return to the original more modest proposal.)

At this time I have only *preliminary* results for a fit to G_{MV} utilizing the known ρ-resonance, combined with a Fourier series fit. I use a shifted ρ, giving a pole at 0.5 (BeV/c)^2, with an adjustable coefficient β_ρ. Thus, for $t \leq 0$,

$$G_{MV}(t) = \beta_\rho/(1 - t/0.5) + G(t). \tag{10}$$

I fit $G(t)$ using Eqs. (8) and (9) with threshold $t_0 = m_\rho^2 = 0.58$ (BeV/c)^2; and $b = 1$. (The choice of threshold is based on the belief that there is only a small additional spectral function $4m^2 < t < m_\rho^2$ not included in the ρ resonance. This belief is based on the absence of observed

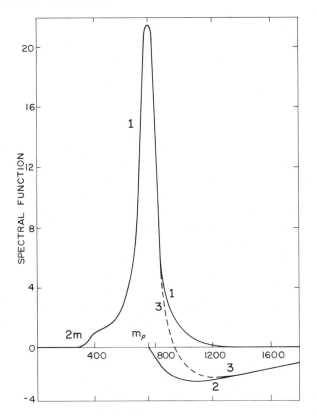

Fig. 3   The magnetic isovector spectral function vs. mass of the intermediate state in MeV. The threshold is at two pion masses, the peak of curve 1 for the ρ resonance is at $m_\rho = 762$ MeV; curve 2 shows the preliminary fit Eq. (12) to the "continuum"; curve 3, the sum of curves 1 and 2, is a preliminary fit to the total spectral function.

lower vector resonances and on the small continuum contribution in this region[2]. The choice of b is made to help keep the form factor small in the annihilation region.)

My fit in the η-plane obeys three constraints[44]

$$G(0) = 2.35 - \beta_\rho$$
$$dg/dt = 0 \text{ for } t = t_0 \tag{11}$$
$$tG(t) \text{ finite for } t \to \infty$$

I find:

$$\beta_\rho = 3.5$$

$$G = -1.15(1 + \eta)^2(1 - \tfrac{1}{2}\eta)$$

with spectral function

$$g(\xi) = -0.58(3 \sin \xi - \sin 3\xi) = -2.3 \sin^3 \xi \qquad (12)$$

I present this preliminary result here only to show an alternative to the two-pole fits. Figure 3 shows the spectral function vs. mass of the intermediate state. The ρ resonance is shown at its published[31] position and width. The spectral function g, based on Eqs. (9) and (12) starts at zero at the peak of the ρ, thus modifying the high energy side of the ρ resonance. The spectral function then goes through a broad minimum at a mass of 1080 MeV.

Does the smooth spectral function in the BeV region of Eq. (12) and Fig. 3 really have any physical significance? (For instance, does it have more physical significance than a ρ' resonance, provided that the ρ' cannot be successfully identified with the B, or some other established resonance?) It is amusing that the *magnitude* of this smooth spectral function (for $m_\rho^2 < t < 4M^2$) bears a resemblance to the old calculations[2,46,1] of isovector form factors, using only a two-pion intermediate state. I do not claim to understand the *negative* sign[47] in Eq. (12). Also, with the advent of experiments in the annihilation region the earlier theoretical arguments[46,1] concerning the behavior of the spectral function for $t > 4M^2$ are being settled by experiment. We can look forward to finding spectral functions in the nonphysical region $4m^2 < t < 4M^2$ by interpolation, using data $t < 0$, and $t > 4M^2$.

Acknowledgment

I want to thank H. A. Bethe for introducing me to these form factor questions in 1961; and for many helpful discussions about them. Several other theorists and experimentalists at Cornell have also contributed large amounts of their time toward my work in this area. I am grateful to J. Dunning, B. Dudelzak, G. Höhler, R. Hofstadter, B. A. Orman, A. V. Tollestrup, W. Woodward, and A. Zichichi for information on current work.

References

1. Hofstadter, R., Ed., *Nuclear and Nucleon Structure*, Benjamin, New York, 1963.
2. Drell, S. D., and F. Zachariasen, *Electromagnetic Structure of Nucleons*, Oxford Univ. Press, Oxford, 1963.
3. Hand, L. N., D. C. Miller, and R. Wilson, *Rev. Mod. Phys.*, **35**, 335 (1963).
4. Wilson, R. R., and J. S. Levinger, *Ann. Revs. Nuclear Sci.*, **14**, 135 (1964).
5. Schiff, L. I., and T. A. Griffy, in *High Energy Physics*, to be published.
6. Wilson, R., *Springer Tracts in Modern Physics*, **39** (1965).
7. Beckmann, P. C., Lecture Notes, CERN Easter School, 1965.
8. Sachs, R. G., *Phys. Rev.*, **126**, 2256 (1962); Foldy, L. L., *Phys. Today*, Sept. 1965, p. 26.
9. Dunning, J., A. A. Cone, N. F. Ramsey, and J. K. Walker, *Phys. Rev.*, **141**, 1267 (1966).
10. In ref. 9, Table IV, the authors write $G_{Ep}^2(-3.89) = -0.0024 \pm 0.0025$ and $G_{Ep} = 0\,(+0.012, -0)$. Since the sign of the form factor is unknown, I prefer $G_{Ep} = 0 \pm 0.012$, with an additional remark that the error quoted for G_{Ep} cannot be used in the usual error distribution.
11. See ref. 9, Table V; I ignore the possibility that the magnetic form factor is zero.
12. Barnes, K. J., *Nuovo Cimento*, **28**, 284 (1963); A. Zichichi, S. M. Berman, N. Cabibbo, and R. Gatto, *Nuovo Cimento*, **24**, 170 (1962).
13. M. Conversi, T. Massam, Th. Muller, and A. Zichichi, *Phys. Rev. Letters*, **5**, 195 (1963), and *Sienna Conf.* (1963); M. Conversi, T. Massam, Th. Muller, and A. Zichichi, *Nuovo Cimento*, **40**, 690 (1965).
14. Beriga, S., and L. Brown in *Proc. Stanford Conf. Nucleon Structure*, Stanford Univ. Press, 1964.
15. Tollestrup, A. V., Invited paper, A.P.S. meeting, Jan. 1966, New York.
16. Fermi, E., and L. Marshall, *Phys. Rev.*, **72**, 1130 (1947); M. F. Crouch, V. E. Krohn, and G. R. Ringo, *Phys. Rev.*, **102**, 1321 (1956); W. W. Havens, I. I. Rabi, and L. J. Rainwater, *Phys. Rev.*, **72**, 634 (1947); E. Melkonian, B. M. Rustad, and W. W. Havens, *Phys. Rev.*, **114**, 1571 (1959); D. J. Hughes, J. A. Harvey, M. D. Goldberg, and M. J. Stafne, *Phys. Rev.*, **90**, 497 (1953).
17. Yearian, M. R., and R. Hofstadter, *Phys. Rev.*, **110**, 552 (1958).
18. McIntyre, J. A., *Phys. Rev.*, **103**, 1464 (1956).
19. Foldy, L. L., *Phys. Rev.*, **83**, 688 (1951).
20. Foldy, L. L., *Rev. Mod. Phys.*, **30**, 471 (1958).
21. Krohn, V. E., and G. R. Ringo, *Phys. Letters*, **18**, 297 (1965).
22. Stein, P., R. W. McAllister, B. D. McDaniel, and W. M. Woodward, *Phys. Rev. Letters*, **9**, 403 (1962).
23. Stein, P., M. Binkley, R. McAllister, A. Suri, and W. M. Woodward, *Phys. Rev. Letters*, **16**, 592 (1966).
24. Chen, K. W., A. A. Cone, G. Hartwig, N. F. Ramsey, J. K. Walker, and R. Wilson, *Phys. Rev.*, 1966, to be published.

25. Hughes, E. B., T. A. Griffy, M. R. Yearian, and R. Hofstadter, *Phys. Rev.*, **139**, B458 (1965); also see T. Janssens, R. Hofstadter, E. B. Hughes, and M. R. Yearian, *Phys. Rev.*, **142**, 922 (1966).
26. Buchanan, C. D., and M. R. Yearian, *Phys. Rev. Letters*, **15**, 303 (1965); and R. Hofstadter at DESY Conf., June 1965, published by Springer, 1965.
27. Adler, R. J., and S. Drell, *Phys. Rev. Letters*, **13**, 349 (1964); R. J. Adler, *Phys. Rev.*, **141**, 1499 (1966).
28. Charpak, G., F. J. M. Farley, R. L. Garvin, T. Muller, J. C. Sens, and A. Zichichi, *Phys. Rev. Letters*, **1**, 16 (1962); A. Citron, C. Delorme, D. Fries, L. Goldzahl, J. Heintze, E. G. Michaelis, C. Richard, and H. Øverås, *Phys. Rev. Letters*, **1**, 175 (1962); R. Cool, A. Maschke, L. M. Lederman, H. J. Tinlot, and Y. Yamanouchi, *Phys. Rev. Letters*, **14**, 724 (1965).
29. Blumenthal, R. B., D. C. Ehn, W. L. Faissler, P. M. Joseph, L. J. Lanzerotti, F. M. Pipkin, and D. G. Stairs, *Phys. Rev. Letters*, **14**, 660 (1965); *Phys. Rev.*, **144**, 1199 (1966).
30. Browman, A., F. Liu, and C. Schaerf, *Phys. Rev.*, **139**, B1079 (1965); J. C. Bizot, J. M. Buon, J. Lefrancois, J. Perez-y-Jorba, and P. Roy, *Phys. Rev.*, **140**, B1387 (1965).
31. Rosenfeld, A. H., A. Barbaro–Galtieri, W. H. Barkas, P. Bastien, J. Kirz, and M. Roos, *Revs. Mod. Phys.*, **37**, 633 (1965); R. D. Tripp, *Ann. Rev. Nucl. Sci.*, **15**, 325 (1965).
32. De Pagter, J. K., J. I. Friedman, G. Glass, R. C. Chase, M. Gettner, E. von Goeler, Roy Weinstein, and A. Boyarski, *Phys. Rev. Letters*, **16**, 35 (1966); also D. J. Drickey, *Bull. Amer. Phys. Soc.*, **10**, 1179 (1965) (Invited paper). For coupling of vector mesons to nucleons, see A. Scotti and D. Y. Wong, *Phys. Rev.*, **138**, B145 (1965) and J. Hamilton, T. D. Spearman, and W. S. Woolcock, *Ann. Phys. (N.Y.)*, **17**, 1 (1962).
33. Barnes, K. J., P. Carruthers, and F. von Hippel, *Phys. Rev. Letters*, **14**, 82 (1965).
34. Dudelzak, B., Thèses, Université de Paris, May 1965. Orsay, Série A, N. D'Ordre 103.
35. Chan, L. H., K. W. Chen, J. R. Dunning, N. F. Ramsey, J. K. Walker, and R. Wilson, *Phys. Rev.*, **141**, 1298 (1966).
36. Ref. 35, Table I.
37. Ref. 35, Table II.
38. Ball, J. S., and D. T. Wong, *Phys. Rev.*, **130**, 2112 (1963); M. W. Kirson, *Phys. Rev.*, **132**, 1249 (1963).
39. Akerlof, C. W., K. Berkelman, G. Rouse, and M. Tigner, *Phys. Rev.*, **135**, B810 (1964).
40. Frazer, W. R., and J. R. Fulco, *Phys. Rev. Letters*, **2**, 365 (1959).
41. Balachandran, A. P., P. G. O. Freund, and C. P. Schumacher, *Phys. Rev. Letters*, **12**, 209 (1965).
42. Orman, B. A., *Phys. Rev.*, **138**, B1308 (1965) and to be published (1966).
43. Wu, T. T., and C. N. Wang, *Phys. Rev.*, **137**, B708 (1965).
44. Levinger, J. S., and R. F. Peierls, *Phys. Rev.*, **134**, B1341 (1964); Levinger, J. S., and C. P. Wang, *Phys. Rev.*, **136**, B733 (1964); Levinger, J. S., and C. P. Wang, *Phys. Rev.*, **138**, B1207 (1965).

45. Levinger, J. S., and M. W. Kirson, *Eastern Theor. Phys. Conf.*, Gordon and Breach, New York, 1963, p. 175.
46. Chew, G. F., R. Karplus, S. Gasiorowicz, and F. Zachariasen, *Phys. Rev.*, **110**, 265 (1958); P. Federbush, M. L. Goldberger, and S. B. Treiman, *Phys. Rev.*, **112**, 642 (1958).
47. Furuichi, S., and Watanabe, *Phys. Rev. Letters*, **14**, 724 (1965).

Scalar Mesons

LAURIE M. BROWN

Northwestern University

I. Introduction

There is some reason to believe that, while we are still far from achieving any fundamental understanding of the dynamics of processes involving the strong interactions, we are nevertheless approaching a reasonable, and perhaps correct, classification of hadron states in terms of some symmetry scheme based on $SU(3)$. We may say, metaphorically, that while we may be far from the accuracy of renormalized quantum electrodynamics in this area, we are moving from the Bohr to the Bohr–Sommerfeld model. Among the approaches whose partial successes justify some optimism in this regard we may mention $SU(3)$, $SU(6)$, etc., and quark models, current commutation relations, and bootstraps. In any of these approaches, scalar mesons appear among the simplest realizations of the hadron resonance states and their absence from nature would require explanation.

On the dynamical side, special models have been found to be valid under restricted circumstances, such as pole dominance models for two-particle and quasi-two-particle scattering. Pole approximation fits, for example, to nucleon–nucleon scattering below 1 GeV have been made successfully[1], and always require in addition to the mesons whose existence is established[2], an effective scalar meson having $I = 0$ and mass about 400 MeV. Similarly, a number of processes in which two or more pions appear in the final state display anomalies which can be ascribed to the production of scalar mesons. These include production processes[3,4], meson decays[5] (which may be weak, electromagnetic or strong), and photoproduction of pion pairs[6].

In the present context the term *scalar meson* refers to a conjectured family of even parity, spin zero mesons[7] consisting of an $SU(3)$ octet

195

and singlet, or a quark model nonet, even under charge conjugation in the octet or nonet sense, and having mass less than about 1 GeV.

Of particular interest is the conjectured sigma meson, having zero isospin and mass about 400 MeV, which would be light enough to significantly influence low-energy nuclear phenomena[8], even if it were coupled more weakly to baryons than the pseudoscalar and vector mesons. It should also be important in the long-range part of the α–α potential[9] and the lambda–nucleon potential, since one-pion exchange is forbidden by isospin invariance.

The sigma meson, since it is isoscalar, could be an $SU(3)$ singlet, or it could be a member of an octet or higher multiplet. However, another $I = 0$ scalar meson, called epsilon, has been conjectured[10,11], at a mass about equal to that of the rho meson, and an $I = 1/2$ meson, the kappa, at a mass of 725 MeV has been seen in a number of experiments. Assuming that these three mesons are real, it seems most likely that we are dealing with a nonet, like the vector meson nonet, in which the two isoscalar mesons are mixed in their $SU(3)$ character. If the mixing is small, sigma would be mostly $SU(3)$ singlet and the octet would be closely spaced in mass, the predicted (and so far unobserved) $I = 1$ member being about the mass of kappa. If the mixing is maximal, sigma will be two-thirds singlet and one-third octet, while epsilon will have the complementary mixing. In this case the predicted $I = 1$ meson would have a mass of 900 to 1000 MeV, and would presumably decay principally into eta plus pion. No such meson has yet been reported in the literature[12].

The possible existence of such a nonet structure is supported by two theoretical approaches. On the one hand, bootstrap calculations show that two pseudoscalar mesons should have a strong attraction in the singlet and octet states for zero angular momentum, the singlet state being more attractive than the octet (hence, if it resonates, lying lower in mass), and that the octet should be inverted in mass, as compared to the normal ordering of isospin states in the pseudoscalar and vector systems[13]. On the other hand, the $SU(6)$ quark model, which represents the pseudoscalar and vector mesons as quark–antiquark S-states, leads naturally to a picture of higher meson resonances as quark–antiquark states of larger orbital angular momentum. In fact, most, if not all, of the recently discovered higher meson resonances appear to fit into a classification as quark–antiquark P-states[14]— implying octets and singlets of spin–parity–charge conjugation $J^{PC} =$

1^{+-}, 0^{++}, 1^{++}, 2^{++}. If, as seems reasonable, the various multiplets are split in mass by spin–orbit coupling, because the 2^{++} mesons are several hundred MeV heavier than the 1^{++} one expects the 0^{++} mesons to be centered in mass roughly at 750 MeV.

The discussion that follows will be divided only roughly into experimental and theoretical categories, for existing theories of the fundamental particles are largely phenomenological, while experiments generally require considerable theoretical interpretation. For these reasons, also, we shall try to avoid selecting those data which support a given conjecture and ignoring others; on the other hand, bearing in mind the necessity for theoretical interpretation, we shall not attach overwhelming weight to any one class of data. We shall not attempt to prove the existence or nonexistence of scalar mesons, since at the present stage this is impossible, but rather try to indicate areas and processes in which further experimental and theoretical work may lead to more definite conclusions.

II. Experimental Evidence on the Sigma Meson

(a) Production Experiments

In a bubble chamber study of the reaction

$$\pi^- + p \to 2\pi^- + 2\pi^+ + n \tag{1}$$

at 4.7 GeV/c pion energy, Samios et al. compared the effective mass distributions of charged and neutral pairs of pions. While the charged pairs gave a pure phase-space distribution, the neutral pairs showed two new peaks above phase space, one at a mass of 395 ± 10 MeV with a width of 50 ± 20 MeV, and the other at a mass of 520 ± 20 MeV with a width of 70 ± 30 MeV. The reality of these peaks has not been confirmed, or for that matter denied, by any subsequent experiments of similar type. However, it has been suggested, without detailed demonstration, that kinematic effects might be responsible for such peaks appearing in multiparticle final states where several types of meson and baryon resonances may occur simultaneously.

In the simpler production process

$$\pi^- + p \to \pi^- + \pi^+ + n, \tag{2}$$

when studied at energies above 1 GeV, no evidence is seen of either of the above peaks[16]. However, below 1 GeV incident pion energy, and especially below 600 MeV, marked structure appears in the $I = 0$

two-pion system which does not appear in the $I = 1$ channel[17]. In this energy region the effect of the (3,3) nucleon isobar is prominent, but although the so-called isobar model accounts well for the effective mass distributions in all the other charge analogies of (2), it fails completely for reaction (2) itself[18]. On the other hand, the three effective mass plots and the cross section for reaction (2) as a function of energy can be well fitted by a resonance model[3] which is relativistic and unitarity preserving and which includes an $I = 0$ scalar dipion of mass and width close to that conjectured for the sigma meson. While it is somewhat surprising that at higher production energies no convincing evidence of this dipion appears in reaction (2), it is known that production cross sections for mesons which are peripherally produced (with the major exception of the rho meson) fall much more rapidly with energy than is predicted by the peripheral model with, or without, absorption corrections. This is especially true for vector meson exchange where the predicted cross sections are actually increasing, but it is also true in some cases where pion exchange is possible, as in K^* production[19]. Thus the production of sigma mesons at lower production energies could be reconciled with its absence at higher energies by assuming a strongly energy dependent cross section.

At the same time, it should be kept in mind that the unitarity limits on the production of scalar resonances are lower than those for higher spin resonances, and that a more favorable observational situation can be achieved when other competing background processes are suppressed, as in certain quasi-stable meson decays to be discussed below or, analogously, when one or more short-lived higher resonances are produced which have scalar mesons among their decay products, leading eventually to a many particle final state. The last remark might provide the explanation of the results of Samios et al. and the results on the kappa meson (see below) which has appeared also in multiparticle final states at higher energies.

A similar situation appears in photoproduction experiments; that is, in the reaction

$$\gamma + p \rightarrow p + \pi^+ + \pi^-. \tag{3}$$

An experimental group at Frascati has carefully studied this reaction[20], using the electron synchroton operating at 1100 MeV, and determining the momentum of the recoil proton to an accuracy of 1%. The effects of the (3,3) nucleon isobar being dominant in this experiment, comparison of the effective mass spectra was made with the Cutkosky–Zachariasen model[21], corrected to account for finite nuclear size and for relativistic effects. Marked deviations from the predictions were found in the π–π effective mass spectrum, both in shape and magnitude, and very similar deviations in shape from the normalized invariant phase space were found as well. Unsuccessful attempts were made to fit the distribution by the Chew–Mandelstam "effective range" approximation for S-wave, π–π scattering, and according to the authors this approach is "unequivocally excluded." But the data are fairly well fitted by a resonance formula involving an S-wave, π–π resonance of mass in the interval 375–414 MeV and width of the order of 200 MeV; the width includes some experimental broadening and varies with experimental conditions. Interference effects between the (3,3) nucleon isobar and the π–π resonance channels was not included and would also affect the width.

Turning to higher-energy photoproduction, the Cambridge Bubble Chamber Group has surveyed reaction (3), among other reactions, over a range of γ-ray energies[22] from 1.1 to 6.0 GeV. No statistically significant evidence is found here for sigma meson production. However, the number of events is relatively small outside of the dominant rho meson peak; for example, the f^0 meson is not seen. For reaction (3) they find that the one-pion-exchange model fails to hold for the ρ^0 or for the (3,3) isobar production.

Our conclusion from the production experiments is that for production energies above 1 BeV there is no evidence for direct production of the sigma meson and, on the other hand, no reliable way of estimating how many sigma mesons should be expected at a given energy. In particular, the one-pion exchange model with absorption appears to be useless for estimating production cross sections. Below 1 GeV, both for pions and photons incident on protons, the production of two pions in an isospin zero and (presumably) S-state exhibits distinct structure which can be explained by the conjectured sigma resonance, though other possible explanations are not necessarily excluded. There is a possibility that above 1 GeV production energy (in the experiment of Samios et al.) the sigma meson may appear in multiparticle final states as a decay product of higher resonances.

(b) Evidence from Pseudoscalar Meson Decays[5]

The pseudoscalar mesons other than the pion, namely K, η, and X^0 (960) have prominent modes of decay into three pseudoscalar mesons with Q-values of the order of 100 MeV, favoring low relative angular momenta. These decays take place, respectively, through the weak, electromagnetic, and strong interactions. Their decay spectra are strikingly similar (except possibly for the decay $K_{2^\circ} \to \pi^+\pi^-\pi^0$ about which there is conflicting evidence at very small π^0 momenta) and they are all consistent with the sigma hypothesis, other possible explanations[24] not being necessarily excluded. Additional confirmation of the sigma hypothesis, however, comes from a study of the decay branching rations, especially those of the η meson.

Since the strongest evidence for the existence of the sigma meson appears to come from the eta decay, we shall summarize the argument. The quantum numbers of the eta meson are $IJ^{PG} = 00^{-+}$ and it is observed to have the following decay modes and branching fractions[2]

$$
\begin{array}{ll}
\gamma\gamma & (38.6 \pm 2.7)\% \\
3\pi^\circ \text{ or } \pi^0 2\gamma & (30.8 \pm 2.3)\% \\
\pi^+\pi^-\pi^0 & (25.0 \pm 1.6)\% \\
\pi^+\pi^-\gamma & (5.5 \pm 1.2)\%
\end{array}
$$

According to most estimates the branching into the $\pi^0 2\gamma$ mode is supposed to be very small, and as it does not affect the discussion appreciably, we shall hereafter neglect it[25]. The three pion state cannot have $I = 0$ without violating CP invariance. Thus, as this decay mode violates either CP invariance or isospin conservation, it cannot be a strong decay and is presumably electromagnetic in nature, as are also the other decay modes, in a more obvious way. Assuming an interaction volume for all the decays to be measured roughly by the mean pseudoscalar or vector mass, the ratio ε of two-body to three-body phase space is about 500. The branching fractions should then be in approximate ratio $\gamma\gamma : 3\pi^0 : \pi^+\pi^-\pi^0 : \pi^+\pi^-\gamma = \varepsilon\alpha^2 : \alpha^2 : \alpha^2 : \alpha$, where α is the fine structure constant. Comparing with the experimental branching fractions, we see that either the $\gamma\gamma$ and $\pi^+\pi^-\gamma$ modes are *both* strongly suppressed, or the 3π modes are enhanced.

It was proposed, shortly after the discovery of the eta meson, that the latter was indeed the case[26], and that the 3π decay was effectively the two-body decay $\eta \to \sigma + \pi^0$, which would yield an enhancement of order ε as required, and would further strongly influence the π^0 momentum spectrum and the branching ratio

$$
R = \frac{\eta \to 3\pi^0}{\eta \to \pi^+\pi^-\pi^0} \tag{4}
$$

This idea, as subsequently developed[27-29], leads to the following more detailed picture:

Using the so-called vector meson dominant model[26,30], and assuming for the $\pi^0 \to 2\gamma$ decay the experimental width $\Gamma_{\pi^0} = 6.3$ eV, Faier has shown[29] that the partial widths $\Gamma\eta(\gamma\gamma) = 152$ eV, $\Gamma_\eta(\pi\pi\gamma) = 36$ eV, the ratio being in fair agreement with experiment. This result holds independently of the ω–φ mixing ratio, and implies that $\Gamma_\eta(\pi^+\pi^-\pi^0) \approx$ 125 eV. On the other hand, Behrends and Singer, using a somewhat different approach[31], have obtained for $\eta \to \pi^+\pi^-\gamma$ a width of about 400 eV, implying $\Gamma_\eta(\pi^+\pi^-\pi^0) \approx 2$ keV.

Now, assuming a structureless vertex and neglecting final state interaction in the decay $\eta \to 3\pi$, and using an effective coupling constant $\alpha G'$, one obtains

$$\Gamma_\eta(\pi^+\pi^-\pi^0) = 2G'^2 \text{ eV.} \tag{5}$$

The dimensionless constant G'^2 characterizes the strong four-pseudo-scalar-meson vertex, and is expected to be of order 0.1 to 1. Even the 25 eV estimate for $\Gamma_\eta(\pi^+\pi^-\pi^0)$ appears to require an enhancing mechanism. If, on the contrary, it is assumed that the decay is mediated by the sigma meson, assigning it a mass of about 400 MeV and a width of 100 MeV, and assigning to the sigma an unstable particle propagator, one obtains[5,26,29]

$$\Gamma_\eta(\pi^+\pi^-\pi^0) \approx 300G^2 \text{ eV,} \tag{6}$$

where G^2 again characterizes the strong four-meson vertex (since our procedure is equivalent to the use of the Watson final state interaction theorem). Here a value of G^2 in the range 0.1 to 1 can give agreement with the inferred experimental rate.

More important is the momentum correlation of the pions expected from such a model. The momentum spectrum of the π^0 meson deviates markedly from that predicted purely on the basis of phase space. A fit to 708 eta decays[5], using a sigma-meson model, gives a mass $m_\sigma = 400^{+15}_{-8}$ MeV, $\Gamma_\sigma = 95^{+12}_{-14}$ MeV with a χ^2 probability of 92%. This fit gives for the branching ratio R, Eq. (4),

$$R = 1.19 \pm 0.05,$$

to be compared with the experimental result

$$R_{\text{exp}} = 1.23 \pm 0.12,$$

based on the experimental branching fractions quoted above. By contrast, a matrix element linear in the π^0 energy, which provides a reasonable fit to a spectrum consisting of 274 events[32], gives

$$R_{\text{lin}} = 1.63 \pm 0.02.$$

A very similar situation appears to hold for the X^0 meson[33] of mass 959 MeV. Its quantum numbers are the same as those of the eta meson, and it is observed to have the decay branching ratios[2]

$$\eta\pi\pi \quad (78 \pm 4)\%$$
$$\pi\pi\gamma \quad (22 \pm 4)\%.$$

The assignment of quantum numbers is based on studies of both modes of decay, and since no known selection rules are operative to inhibit the dominant mode, it is supposed to occur via the strong interactions. Of the total width, it is known only that it is less than 4 MeV.

The vector meson dominant model can be used to estimate the $\pi^+\pi^-\gamma$ partial decay width[34]:

$$\Gamma_{X^0}(\pi^+\pi^-\gamma) = 57 \text{ keV}.$$

On this basis, and using the experimental values for the branching fractions and the upper limit for the total width, we expect $\Gamma_{X^0}(\pi^+\pi^-\eta)$ to lie in the range, say,

$$0.1 \text{ MeV} < \Gamma_{X^0}(\pi^+\pi^-\eta) < 2 \text{ MeV}.$$

However, a calculation based upon a structureless vertex with coupling constant G' gives

$$\Gamma_{X^0}(\pi^+\pi^-\eta) = 2G'^2 \text{ keV}.$$

Again, the sigma meson provides an enhancement factor, and for $m_\sigma = 400$ MeV, $\Gamma_\sigma = 95$ MeV one obtains

$$\Gamma_{X^0}(\pi^+\pi^-\eta) = 2.6G^2 \text{ MeV},$$

so that the same G^2 can agree quite well with what is presently known of both the eta and X^0 mesons. The decay spectrum of X^0 is not well enough known to permit a firm conclusion, but the existing spectrum can be fitted with a sigma mass ~ 390 MeV and a width ~ 90 MeV[35].

A rather complete discussion of the decays of K mesons into three pions has been given previously[5]. With regard to the τ' decay

$$K^\pm \rightarrow \pi^\pm + \pi^0 + \pi^0,$$

there is nothing new to report. The parameters for the sigma meson, obtained from eta decay and quoted above, were found to fit the momentum spectrum of the odd pion from one sample[36] of about $1800\tau'$ events with an absolute χ^2 probability of about 5% and from another sample of the same size[37] with a χ^2 probability better than 50%. For τ decay

$$K^{\pm} \to \pi^{\pm} + \pi^{+} + \pi^{-}, \tag{7}$$

about 3200 decays[38,39] were fitted by the sigma model, using the eta parameters, with an absolute χ^2 probability of 32%.

There has appeared recently an experimental analysis of an additional $3587\tau^+$ decays[40] which agrees completely with the previous work. All these results confirm the validity of the $I = 1/2$ rule and an $I = 1$ final state. Because the Q value available for K meson to three pion decay is about 80 MeV, as compared to 135 MeV for the eta and X^0 decays, the peak of the sigma meson mass distribution would not be visible in the final state, and the χ^2 contours plotted as a function of sigma mass and width exhibit this by being flat in the direction of the mass. However, they generally agree with a width, to which they are sensitive, in the range 80 to 120 MeV. A linear approximation to the matrix element (or even to the square of the matrix element) also gives a reasonable fit to the odd-pion momentum spectrum.

Of the decay spectrum of the process

$$K_2^0 \to \pi^{+} + \pi^{-} + \pi^{0}, \tag{8}$$

little has been known until very recently. A cloud chamber experiment involving about 300 events has now been reported[41], showing a spectrum very similar to that for τ' decay to which, according to the $\Delta I = 1/2$ rule, it should be almost identical. Corresponding to a confidence level of 63%, the experimenters obtain best fit values:

$$m_{\sigma} = 346^{+14}_{-7} \text{ MeV}, \qquad \Gamma_{\sigma} = 75^{+27}_{-16} \text{ MeV},$$

using the sigma model.

There is a systematic tendency for these K-meson spectra, when analyzed in terms of a simple sigma meson model, to give, as best fit values of the sigma mass, something closer to 350 MeV than to 400 MeV, while at the same time not excluding the larger mass. However, it is clear that even should sigma dominance prevail, there is no reason why the decay matrix elements for different types of decay interactions should not have different energy dependences. In the simple sigma model, one also ignores the possibility of other final state interactions.

Prasad[42] has dealt, in part, with this latter problem. Assuming the dominance of S-waves in the final states of the decays (6), (7), and (8), he characterizes the scattering of each of the three final pion pairs by a scattering length and an effective range, using as a starting point the Faddeev coupled integral equations[43] for a three-particle system. He further assumes only an $I = 1$ final state for the three pions, treating each of the three pairs symmetrically. Then, using the measured spectra, he minimizes χ^2, using as parameters a_I, r_I for $I = 0,2$ obtaining

$$a_0 = +1.4 \pm 0.1, \qquad a_2 = +0.7 \pm 0.1$$
$$r_0 = -2.2 \pm 0.1, \qquad r_2 = +2.0 \pm 0.1.$$

The values obtained from the rates, independently, are almost identical, and for both spectra and rates the normalized χ^2 was about 0.1. The relative signs of a_I and r_I correspond to a resonance in the $I = 0$ channel and to no resonance or bound state in $I = 2$.

Another process which is relevant to the problem of the sigma meson is the $Ke4$ decay[44]

$$K^+ \rightarrow \pi^+ + \pi^- + e^+ + \nu \tag{9}$$

and

$$K^+ \rightarrow \pi^0 + \pi^0 + e^+ + \nu. \tag{10}$$

While this is undoubtedly a very important process to study, it is very rare and has the branching ratio to all K^+ decays of $(3.6 \pm 0.8) \times 10^{-5}$. This result was obtained in an experiment[45] in which 69 events were observed, these events being further analyzed for final state correlations. The experiment is rather difficult, and the overall detection efficiency was estimated at 62%. The effective mass spectrum of the two pions was found to be consistent with no final state interaction. However, analyzing the correlation of the electron direction with the normal to the pion plane[46], the difference of S- and P-wave pion–pion phase shifts was found to be

$$(\delta_0 - \delta_1)_{av} = 35° \pm 30°,$$

where the average is taken over the spectrum of the events actually observed.

Other meson decay processes which have been suggested as possible tests of the sigma hypothesis are $\varphi \rightarrow \pi\pi\gamma$[47], the radiative τ decay[48] and, one may mention also, $A_1 \rightarrow \sigma + \pi$.

III. Evidence on the Kappa Meson

A peak in the $K\pi$ effective mass spectrum in charge states belonging to $I = 1/2$ has been reported a number of times in the literature[49-54]:

at 2.1 GeV/c, in the reaction[49]

$$\pi^- + p \rightarrow \Sigma\pi K$$
$$\rightarrow \Lambda\pi K;$$

at 2.2 GeV/c in[50]

$$K^- + p \rightarrow \Xi\pi K;$$

at various momenta from 1.90 to 2.36 GeV/c in [51]

$$\pi + p \rightarrow \Sigma\pi K;$$

at various momenta from 1.08 to 1.70 in[52]

$$K^- + p \rightarrow p\pi K;$$

at 3 GeV/c in[53]

$$K^+ + p \rightarrow Kp3\pi;$$

at 1.5 and 1.8 GeV/c in[54]

$$\pi^- + p \rightarrow K^0\Lambda^0\pi^0.$$

The observed peaks, while each at least a three standard deviation effect above background, are always small compared to the K^* (890) peak. While it is not altogether unusual for three standard deviation peaks above background to arise in effective mass plots by statistical fluctuation, the kappa peak appears to have well defined and repeatable characteristics. The reported masses are always within a few MeV of 725 MeV for the charged kappa, and perhaps 10 to 20 MeV greater for the neutral kappa[51,54] and the width is given at less than 20 MeV or, in one case[58], less than 30 MeV. Its nonappearance in states like $K^0\pi^-$, as well as its decay branching ratios suggest the assignment $I = 1/2$; Ferro-Luzzi et al. have made the experimental estimate[53]

$$\frac{K^* \rightarrow \kappa + \pi}{K^* \rightarrow K + \pi} < 0.01,$$

which together with its finite width, suggesting $J^P = 0^+$, 1^-, tends to suggest $J^P = 0^+$, since the expected ratio for 0^+ is zero, while for 1^- it has been estimated to be 0.06.

Of course, other experiments have been performed in which the kappa was not seen. This could, perhaps, be explained by production cross sections varying rapidly with the available energy. In fact, in the experiment of Wojciki et al.[52] the cross section was observed to fall in a regular manner to unobservability by $1.4\,\mathrm{GeV}/c$ incident K^- momentum. The whole situation appears reminiscent of the situation concerning the production of the sigma meson, as discussed above.

IV. Evidence on the ϵ (or s_0) Meson

The third member of the conjectural scalar nonet that we shall discuss is the ϵ (also called the s_0) meson. It is an $I = 0$ meson, decaying into two pions, and having a mass in the neighborhood of the rho meson. As already mentioned, its existence was proposed[10,11] as a possible explanation of the decay asymmetry of the neutral rho meson. As Durand and Chiu remarked[11], "The possible explanations of the forward-to-backward asymmetry ... in terms of interference between the $J = 1^-$ state and a neighboring state with $J = 0^+, 2^+, \ldots$, are severely restricted by the observation that this ratio is large at the mass of the ρ, is approximately symmetric around that mass, and decreases only slowly in the wings of the ρ peak." On these grounds they argued that the background must be essentially in phase with the ρ, i.e., that the even parity background should be resonant near the mass of the ρ and have approximately its width. With these assumptions, and the assumption $J^P = 0^+$, they obtain good agreement with all features of ρ^0 production and decay, if about 15% of the two-pion production in the ρ-mass region occurs through ϵ rather than ρ. Subsequently they announced that somewhat smaller mass and width would give a better fit to the data, suggesting $M_\epsilon = 730$ MeV, and $\Gamma_\epsilon = 90$ MeV, and a production cross section 10% of the ρ^0 cross section.

The experimental situation on direct observation of the ϵ is far from clear. Feldman et al.[55] have studied the reaction $\pi^- + p \rightarrow n + x$, where x is any neutral system, in an arrangement consisting of a hydrogen target, a neutron time-of-flight counter, and heavy spark chambers. They observe a peak in the neutron time-of-flight corresponding an x of mass 700 MeV, width 50 MeV, and also observe a peak in the spectrum of four γ-rays corresponding to the same mass. This was for π^- momentum of 1.520 GeV/c. Hagopian et al.[56] have compared the pion pairs arising from the reactions

$$\pi^- + p \to \pi^- + \pi^+ + n$$

and

$$\pi^- + p \to \pi^- + \pi^0 + p$$

at 2.75 and 3.0 GeV/c and find an indication of an $I = 0$ S-wave $\pi\pi$ resonance at 720 MeV with width $\Gamma \sim 50$ MeV. Experimental searches in other reactions have, however, so far yielded negative results[57].

V. Conclusions

We conclude that there are theoretical grounds, as well as indirect experimental indications, for the existence of scalar mesons. Some direct evidence of the accepted type, that is, peaks in effective mass spectra, comparison of decay branching ratios, etc., is also present, especially for the kappa meson, and for the sigma meson at low production energies. The indications are that the scalar nonet, if it really exists, will have low production cross sections compared to the pseudoscalar and vector mesons. The richness of resonances, both mesonic and baryonic, which appears at the present limits of observation suggests a further richness awaiting more sensitive and more directed methods of observation. The successful search for omega minus, with a cross section of a few microbarns, shows what experimental physics can achieve when a crucial theoretical question is posed.

It is with the greatest of pleasure that I take this opportunity to express my gratitude to Professor Hans A. Bethe, whose inspired, and humane teaching has been a continuous force in shaping my life and work. His achievements, and the grace with which he bears them, have not only enriched, but also ennobled, science.

References

1. Scotti, A., and D. Y. Wong, *Phys, Rev. Letters*, **10**, 142 (1963) and *Phys. Rev.*, **138**, B145 (1965); R. Bryan, C. Dismukes, and W. Ramsay, *Nucl. Phys.*, **45**, 353 (1963); J. S. Ball, A. Scotti, and D. Y. Wong, SLAC Preprint (1965).
2. Rosenfeld, A. H., A. Barbaro–Galtieri, W. H. Barkas, P. L. Bastien, J. Kirz, and M. Ross, Data on Particles and Resonance States, *Rev. Mod. Phys.*, **37**, 633 (1965), include in their table only $\kappa(725)$ among the possible scalar mesons, and list the evidence on $\sigma(390)$ and $s_0(720)$ with the notation "evidence not yet compelling."
3. Thurnauer, P. G., *Phys. Rev. Letters*, **14**, 985 (1965).

4. For a summary on the ρ^0 puzzle see G. Goldhaber, in *Symmetry Principles at High Energy*, Proceedings of the Second Coral Gables Conference, W. H. Freeman and Co., San Francisco, p. 34.

5. For a summary see L. M. Brown and H. Faier, in *Symmetry Principles at High Energy*, Proceedings of the Second Coral Gables Conference, W. H. Freeman and Co., San Francisco, p. 219.

6. Del Fabbro, R., et al., *Phys. Rev.*, **39** B701 (1965).

7. See, for example, L. M. Brown, *Phys. Rev. Letters*, **14**, 836 (1965); E. Ferrari, *Phys. Rev. Letters*, **16**, 93 (1965); D. Loebbaka and J. C. Pati, *Phys. Rev. Letters*, **14**, 929 (1965).

8. Bietti, A., and B. Touschek, *Nuovo Cimento*, **35**, 582 (1965). These authors have estimated that the σ meson forces could give the right sign and order of magnitude for the spin–orbit potential required by the nuclear shell model.

9. Preist, T. W., *Nuovo Cimento*, **37**, 166 (1965).

10. Islam, M. M., and R. Piñon, *Phys. Rev. Letters*, **12**, 310 (1964). S. H. Patil, *Phys. Rev. Letters*, **13**, 261 (1964).

11. Durand, L., III, and Y. T. Chiu, *Phys. Rev. Letters*, **14**, 329 and 680 (1965).

12. A possible candidate however, might be a $(K\bar{K})^\pm$ enhancement at 1025 MeV reported in $\bar{p}p$ annihilation at rest by R. Armenteros et al., *Phys. Rev. Letters*, **17**, 344 (1965). See also D. H. Miller et al., *Phys. Rev. Letters*, **14**, 1074 (1965), and G. H. Trilling et al., *Phys. Rev. Letters*, **19**, 427 (1965). Another possible candidate is provided by W. Kienzle et al., *Phys. Rev. Letters*, **19**, 438 (1965).

13. Chan Hong-Mo, P. C. De Celles, and J. E. Paton, *Nuovo Cimento*, **33**, 70 (1964); B. Diu and H. R. Rubinstein, *Phys. Rev. Letters*, **11**, 269 (1964); Chan Hong-Mo and C. Wilkin, *Phys. Rev. Letters*, **13**, 263 (1964), and CERN Preprint, May 1965.

14. Borchi, E., and R. Gatto, *Phys. Rev. Letters*, **14**, 352 (1965); R. Gatto, L. Maiani, and G. Preparata, *Phys. Rev.*, **140**, B1579 (1965); see also, R. H. Dalitz, this volume.

15. Samios, N. P., et al., *Phys. Rev. Letters*, **9**, 139 (1962).

16. See, for example, the discussion of results of the Penn–Saclay collaboration by Selove, following ref. 5.

17. Kirz, J., J. Schwartz, and R. Tripp, *Phys. Rev.*, **130**, 2481 (1963); T. Batusov, S. Bunyatov, V. Sidorov, and V. Jarba, *Yadern. Fiz.*, **1**, 687 (1965).

18. Olsson, M., and G. B. Yodh, *Phys. Rev. Letters*, **10**, 353 (1963).

19. For example, see M. Derrick et al., in *Resonant Particles*, Proc. of 1965 Athens Conference, Ohio University, Athens, Ohio, p. 325.

20. Del Fabbro, R., et al., *Phys. Rev.*, **39**, B701 (1965).

21. Cutkosky, R. E., and F. Zachariasen, *Phys. Rev.*, **103**, 1108 (1956).

22. Crouch, H. R., Jr., et al. (Cambridge Bubble Chamber Group), in *Resonant Particles*, Ohio University, Athens, Ohio, 1965, p. 476.

23. For example, see A. O. Barut and W. S. Au, *Phys. Rev. Letters*, **13**, 165 (1965) for an interpretation of σ as a "continuous virtual particle."

24. Chan, Lai–Him, *Phys. Rev.*, **140**, B1324 (1965), has introduced special interactions within the framework of Schwinger's field theory of matter to account for the decay of η and of X (960). See also the "pion pole model," reviewed by C. Kacser, *Phys. Rev.*, **130**, 355 (1963).

25. Cf., however, J. B. Bronzan and F. E. Law, *Phys. Rev. Letters*, **12**, 522 (1964). According to these authors, the branching fractions of η decay and other meson decays are controlled by a new multiplicative quantum number A. If η and π are assigned $A = -1$, while γ is assigned $A = +1$, then 2γ and $\pi\pi\gamma$ modes are suppressed, while 3π and $\pi2\gamma$ are allowed.

26. Brown, L. M., and P. Singer, *Phys. Rev. Letters*, **8**, 460 (1962).

27. Brown, L. M., and P. Singer, *Phys. Rev.*, **133**, B812 (1964).

28. Mitra, A. N., and Subha Ray, *Phys. Rev.*, **135**, B146 (1964).

29. Faier, H., *Meson Decays and the Sigma Hypothesis*, Northwestern University Doctoral Dissertation, June 1965.

30. Gell-Mann, M., D. H. Sharp, and W. Wagner, *Phys. Rev. Letters*, **8**, 261 (1962). See also R. F. Dashen and D. H. Sharp, *Phys. Rev.*, **133**, B1076 (1964), and Y. S. Kim, S. Oneda, and J. C. Pati, *Phys. Rev.*, **135**, B1076 (1964).

31. Behrends, F. A., and P. Singer, CERN preprint, Sept. 1965. This result is based upon the experimental value $\Gamma_\omega(\pi^0\gamma) = 1.3$ MeV.

32. Foster, M., et al., *Phys. Rev.*, **138**, B652 (1965).

33. Brown, L. M., and H. Faier, *Phys. Rev. Letters*, **13**, 73 (1964). Note that $\pi\pi\gamma$ has a much larger phase space than $\pi\pi\eta$.

34. In this case, the model is partially verified by the evident appearance of the ρ meson in the $\pi^+\pi^-\gamma$ final state. See G. R. Kalbfleisch, O. I. Dahl, and A. Rittenberg, *Phys. Rev. Letters*, **13**, 349a (1964).

35. Goldberg, M., et al., *Phys. Rev. Letters*, **13**, 249 (1965).

36. Kalmus, G. E., et al., *Phys. Rev. Letters*, **13**, 99 (1964).

37. Bisi, V., et al., *Nuovo Cimento*, **35**, 768 (1965).

38. Smith, L. T., D. J. Prowse, and D. H. Stork, *Phys. Rev. Letters*, **2**, 204 (1962).

39. Ferro-Luzzi, M., et al., *Nuovo Cimento*, **22**, 1087 (1961).

40. Huetter, T., et al., *Phys. Rev.*, **140**, B655 (1965).

41. Astbury, P., et al., *Phys. Rev. Letters*, **18**, 175 (1965).

42. Prasad, R., *Nuovo Cimento*, **35**, 682 (1965).

43. Faddeev, L. D., *Soviet Physics-JETP*, **12**, 1014 (1962).

44. There have been many theoretical treatments of this process. One of the earliest was by V. S. Mathur, *Nuovo Cimento*, **14**, 1322 (1965); among the most recent is that by C. Kacser, P. Singer, and T. N. Truong, *Phys. Rev.*, **137**, B1605 (1965). The results are highly model dependent and are complicated not only by the four-body final state, but also by the probable complex structure of the decay vertex, as evidenced by the presence of both S- and P-waves in the pion pair. Although this decay offers a nearly unique opportunity to observe a pair of pions without other strongly interacting particles, it will evidently require a large amount of detailed experimental analysis before this advantage can be fully realized.

45. Birge, R. W., et al., *Phys. Rev.*, **139**, B1600 (1965).

46. Cabibbo, N., and A. Maksymowicz, *Phys. Rev.*, **137**, B438 (1965).

47. Prentki, J., and M. Veltman, *Phys. Rev. Letters*, **17**, 77 (1965).

48. Lapidus, I. R., and M. J. Tausner, *Phys. Rev.*, **140**, B1620 (1965).

49. Alexander, G., et al., *Phys. Rev. Letters*, **8**, 447 (1962).

50. Connolly, P. L., et al., *Proc. of the Sienna Conf. on Elementary Particles*, Italian Physical Society, Bologna, p. 125, 1963.

51. Miller, D. H., et al., *Phys. Rev. Letters*, **5**, 279 (1963).
52. Wojcicki, S. G., G. R. Kalbfleisch, and M. H. Alston, *Phys. Rev. Letters*, **5**, 283 (1963).
53. Ferro–Luzzi, M., et al., *Phys. Rev. Letters*, **12**, 255 (1964).
54. Kim, Y. S., et al., *Phys. Letters*, **19**, 350 (1965).
55. Feldman, M., et al., *Phys. Rev. Letters*, **14**, 869 (1965).
56. Hagopian, V., et al., *Phys. Rev. Letters*, **14**, 1077 (1965).
57. See, for example, H. O. Cohn et al., *Phys. Rev. Letters*, **15**, 906 (1965).

The Pomeranchuk Theorem

TOICHIRO KINOSHITA

Cornell University

As is well known the Pomeranchuk theorem states, under appropriate assumptions, that the total cross sections $\sigma_+(E)$ and $\sigma_-(E)$ for the scattering of a particle and its antiparticle by the same target are equal in the limit of infinitely large energy. The original assumptions made by Pomeranchuk[1] to obtain this result are as follows:

(a) The functions $f_\pm(E)/(E^2 - \mu^2)$ satisfy dispersion relations without subtraction, where μ is the mass of the projectile, E is its total energy in the laboratory system, and $f_\pm(E)$ are the forward scattering amplitudes for the particle and the antiparticle, respectively. These functions also satisfy the crossing relation and the reality condition

$$f_-(-E) = f_+(E), \qquad f_\pm(E) = f_\pm^*(E^*). \tag{1}$$

(b) The functions $f_\pm(E)/E$ remain bounded as $E \to +\infty$.
(c) The cross sections $\sigma_\pm(E)$ tend to constant limits $\sigma_\pm$ as $E \to +\infty$.

From the beginning it has been recognized that, whereas the assumptions about the analyticity, crossing relation, and temperedness can more or less be justified on the basis of local field theory, the remaining assumptions, (b) and (c), seem to be on a much less solid ground. In view of possible physical significance of the Pomeranchuk theorem, it is therefore not surprising that many attempts have since been made to improve and generalize the theorem. Amati, Fierz, and Glaser[2] have remarked that the integral $\int^\infty [\sigma_+(E) - \sigma_-(E)] \, dE/E$ converges under the Pomeranchuk assumptions. Weinberg[3] has replaced condition (c) by a more general one that the difference $\sigma_+(E) - \sigma_-(E)$ should be of one sign for sufficiently large energies. Under

211

the assumption that $\sigma_\pm(E) \sim C_\pm(\ln E)^m$, $0 < m < 1$, he has proved the equality $C_+ = C_-$. Meiman[4] has given a very elegant proof of the theorem making use of certain general properties of analytic functions. His proof does not require dispersion relations at all. More recently Martin[5] has improved it by incorporating new results of general field theory obtained by Bros, Epstein, and Glaser[6] which enable us to apply the Pomeranchuk theorem to all elastic scattering processes of stable particles. The latest improvement of the theorem is due to Eden[7] who has shown that some of the less well-founded assumptions of the theorem can be justified by unitarity and analyticity in cos θ. There still remain some crucial assumptions of the Pomeranchuk theorem that have not been established from the axioms of quantum field theory. However the situation has been clarified to such an extent that it may not be too long before we can decide whether or not it can be called a "theorem" of quantum field theory in a rigorous sense.

The purpose of this paper is to present an up-to-date survey of these improvements and generalizations of the Pomeranchuk theorem. As the starting point, we shall first restate the assumptions (a), (b), and (c) in a somewhat more precise and convenient form:

(A) The forward scattering amplitudes $f_\pm(E)$ are analytic in the complex E plane with the two cuts $(-\infty, -\mu)$ and (μ, ∞) lying on the real axis, and satisfy the crossing relation Eq. (1).

(B) As $|E| \to \infty$, $f_\pm(E)$ increase less rapidly than any exponential, namely, for any positive ε, $f_\pm(E)$ satisfy the inequality

$$|f_\pm(E)| < e^{\varepsilon|E|}$$

for $E > E_0(\varepsilon)$.

(C) Along the cuts the function $f_\pm(E)/E$ is bounded as $E \to \pm\infty$.

(D) The difference of the cross sections $\sigma_+(E) - \sigma_-(E)$ is bounded as $E \to +\infty$.

(E) The difference $\sigma_+(E) - \sigma_-(E)$ does not oscillate indefinitely as $E \to +\infty$.

To see that these are in fact a generalization of (a), (b), and (c) we first note that $f_\pm(E)/E$ is bounded in all complex directions of the cut E plane according to (A), (B), and (C), as is easily seen making use of the Phragmén–Lindelöf theorem[8]. As a consequence $f_\pm(E)/(E^2 - \mu^2)$ are of order $1/E$ as $|E| \to \infty$ and satisfies dispersion relations without subtraction. Thus (a) follows from (A), (B), and (C). The assumption (C)

is identical with (b). The assumptions (D) and (E) express two distinct aspects of the assumption (c). Note also that in its present form (D) is a consequence of (C). They are given separately for convenience of generalization.

Before discussing refinement and generalization of these assumptions, it will be useful to write down a typical proof of the Pomeranchuk theorem, emphasizing how these assumptions are used[9]. Let us consider the function

$$g(E) = \frac{4\pi}{(E^2 - \mu^2)^{1/2}} (f_+(E) - f_-(E)), \qquad (2)$$

which is obviously analytic in the same cut plane as that of $f_\pm(E)$. From the crossing relation and the reality [Eq. (1)] we obtain

$$g(-E + i0) = g^*(E + i0), \qquad g(-E - i0) = -g(E + i0). \quad (3)$$

To take advantage of this symmetry, let us introduce the new variable

$$z = E^2.$$

Then $g(z) \equiv g(E)$ is analytic in a cut z-plane with a single cut running from $z = \mu^2$ to $z = +\infty$. The function $g(z)$ is purely real for real negative z. The discontinuity of $g(z)$ across the cut is given by

$$\text{Im } g(z + i0) = \sigma_+(z) - \sigma_-(z). \qquad (4)$$

As was noted already, it follows from the assumptions (A), (B), and (C) that $g(z)$ is bounded in all directions in the z-plane. Thus we can write for $g(z)$ a once subtracted dispersion relation

$$g(z) = g(z_0) + \frac{z - z_0}{\pi} \int_{\mu^2}^{\infty} \frac{\text{Im } g(z') \, dz'}{(z' - z)(z' - z_0)}, \qquad (5)$$

where the subtraction point z_0 is on the real axis below the threshold of the cut.

We shall now take into account the assumptions (D) and (E). Under these assumptions $\sigma_+(E) - \sigma_-(E)$ has a limit as $E \to +\infty$. Suppose this limit is a nonzero number C which we may assume to be positive without losing generality. Then, for any given ε satisfying $0 < \varepsilon < C$ we can find z_1 such that $\text{Im } g(z) > C - \varepsilon$ for $z > z_1$. We shall rewrite Eq. (5) as

$$g(z) - g(z_0) - \frac{z - z_0}{\pi} \int_{\mu^2}^{z_1} \frac{\text{Im } g(z') \, dz'}{(z' - z)(z' - z_0)}$$

$$= \frac{z - z_0}{\pi} \int_{z_1}^{\infty} \frac{\text{Im } g(z') \, dz'}{(z' - z)(z' - z_0)}, \qquad (6)$$

and examine the behavior of both sides for $z \rightarrow -\infty$. Using $\operatorname{Im} g(z) > C - \varepsilon$ for $z > z_1$, we see easily that the modulus of the right-hand side of Eq. (6) is greater than

$$\frac{C - \varepsilon}{\pi} \ln \left| \frac{z_1 - z}{z_1 - z_0} \right|, \tag{7}$$

which grows logarithmically as $z \rightarrow -\infty$. On the other hand, the left-hand side behaves as $g(z) +$ const. as $z \rightarrow -\infty$, which is bounded according to (A), (B), and (C). We have therefore a contradiction unless $C = 0$. This proves the theorem. We note that the essential feature of the proof is the contradiction between the assumption (C) and the requirement of analyticity that $\operatorname{Re} g(z)$ should be larger than $\operatorname{Im} g(z)$ by a factor of $\ln z$.

We are now ready to discuss one by one how the assumptions (A)–(E) may be generalized or refined.

Assumption A

As is obvious from the above discussion, it is actually not necessary to assume the analyticity in the entire cut plane. Namely the finite part of the domain is irrelevant to the essential feature of the Pomeranchuk theorem[4]. Thus suppose, for instance, that we have been able to prove analyticity of $f_\pm(E)$ not in the entire cut plane but only in the cut plane minus a finite region. Then we can write down a dispersion relation for $g(z)$ in the form

$$g(z) = g(z_0) + \frac{z - z_0}{2\pi i} \int_\Gamma \frac{g(z') \, dz'}{(z' - z)(z' - z_0)}$$
$$+ \frac{z - z_0}{\pi} \int_{z_2}^\infty \frac{\operatorname{Im} g(z') \, dz'}{(z' - z)(z' - z_0)} \tag{8}$$

instead of Eq. (5), where Γ is a circle of radius z_2 enclosing the non-analytic domain and z_0 is chosen outside of Γ. It is easily seen that the rest of the proof can be carried out without any trouble.

This generalization is quite useful because it enables us to apply the Pomeranchuk theorem not only to the cases where the assumption (A) has been proved from general field theory but also to all other scattering processes for which Bros, Epstein, and Glaser[6] have recently obtained analyticity in a more restricted domain. They have proved, within the framework of the Lehmann–Symanzik–Zimmermann formalism, the analyticity and crossing relation of the type just mentioned

for scattering amplitudes involving two incoming and two outgoing
stable particles with arbitrary masses. To describe their result more
precisely, let us consider the reactions[9]:

$$(I) \qquad A + B \rightarrow A + B,$$

$$(II) \qquad A + \bar{B} \rightarrow A + \bar{B},$$

$$(III) \qquad A + \bar{A} \rightarrow B + \bar{B},$$

where A and B are stable particles. In the reaction (I), $s = [(M_A^2 + k^2)^{1/2}$
$+ (M_B^2 + k^2)^{1/2}]^2$ is the square of the center-of-mass energy and
$t = -2k^2(1 - \cos \theta)$, $t < 0$, is the square of the momentum transfer.
According to Bros, Epstein, and Glaser the scattering amplitude $f(s, t)$
for reaction (I) is the boundary value $\lim_{\varepsilon \to +0} f(s + i\varepsilon, t)$ of an analytic
function which is analytic in the upper half s-plane minus a certain
finite region. In spite of this excluded region $f(s, t)$ has the following
properties: The physical region for fixed t (≤ 0), i.e.,

$$\{[M_A^2 + (|t|/4)]^{1/2} + [M_B^2 + (|t|/4)]^{1/2}\}^2 < s < +\infty$$

lies entirely on the boundary of the analyticity domain. The analytic
continuation of $f(s, t)$ to negative s is such that $\lim_{\varepsilon \to +0} f(s + i\varepsilon, t)$
coincides with the complex conjugate of the scattering amplitude for
reaction (II) with the center-of-mass energy u given by

$$u = 2M_A^2 + 2M_B^2 - t - s$$

and the same value of t. Again the region

$$\{[M_A^2 + (|t|/4)]^{1/2} + [M_B^2 + (|t|/4)]^{1/2}\}^2 < u < +\infty$$

which corresponds to

$$-\infty < s < 2M_A^2 + 2M_B^2 - t - \{(M_A^2 + (|t|/4)]^{1/2} + [M_B^2 + (|t|/4)]^{1/2}\}^2$$

lies entirely on the boundary of the analyticity domain. One can also
define an analytic function $f^*(s^*, t)$ in a domain which is the mirror
image of the above domain with respect to the real axis. In favorable
cases where dispersion relations have been proved these two functions
coincide on a finite segment of the real axis. This occurs also in some
cases where dispersion relations have not been established, for instance
the proton–proton scattering in the neighborhood of the p–p threshold[10]. In any case there is a complex path in the s, t complex space
along which one can perform analytic continuation from the upper
half plane to the lower half plane.

For fixed negative u a similar analyticity domain can be found which connects the physical region of the reaction (I) with the physical region of the reaction (III).

Although the work of Bros, Epstein, and Glaser does not produce analyticity in the entire cut plane, it establishes enough analyticity so that the crossing relation can be discussed rigorously even when dispersion relations have not been proved. In summary we may therefore state that the Pomeranchuk theorem can be applied to all scattering processes of stable particles if we replace the assumption (A) by

(A') The forward scattering amplitude $f_{\pm}(E)$ is analytic in the domain obtained by Bros, Epstein, and Glaser.

Assumption B

The assumption (B) is already much weaker than the usual assumption of polynomial boundedness (temperedness). In fact Martin[5] showed, by giving a counter example, that the assumption (B) cannot be weakened. His example is

$$f(E) = (\mu^2 - E^2)^{1/2}\psi(E), \tag{9}$$

where $\psi(E)$ is a real, entire function of E. Since there exists for any given continuous function an entire function which approaches it uniformly in the entire range $-\infty < E < +\infty$[11], it is obviously possible to find an entire function $\psi(E)$ that satisfies the assumptions (A), (C), (D), and (E) of the Pomeranchuk theorem. However there is no reason that such a $\psi(E)$ should also satisfy the equality $\psi(+\infty) = \psi(-\infty)$. Thus, if we weaken the assumption (B), we cannot have the Pomeranchuk theorem.

Assumptions C and D

On the other hand, the assumptions (C) and (D) can be replaced by less restrictive ones. As was noticed already (D) in its present form is actually contained in (C). When they are weakened, there is still a strong correlation between them. Namely, if one is weakened, the other can be correspondingly weakened without altering the conclusion of the (somewhat generalized) Pomeranchuk theorem which asserts that the ratio $\sigma_{+}(E)/\sigma_{-}(E)$ approaches one as $E \rightarrow +\infty$. For this reason these assumptions will be treated together.

To find out how these assumptions may be relaxed, it is useful to retrace the proof of the Pomeranchuk theorem given above. Let us first relax (D) and suppose instead that $\sigma_+(E) - \sigma_-(E)$ increases slowly according to the assumption[12]

(D') $|\sigma_+(E) - \sigma_-(E)| = |\text{Im } g(E + i0)| \simeq C(\ln |E|)^m$ for $E > E_1$,

where C may be assumed to be a positive number without losing generality. Under the assumption (D') the right-hand side of Eq. (6) behaves like $(C/(m + 1)\pi)(\ln |z|)^{m+1}$ as $z \to -\infty$. Thus, in order to prove the Pomeranchuk theorem (namely to obtain $C = 0$), it is sufficient to impose the condition

$$\lim_{z \to -\infty} \frac{g(z)}{(\ln |z|)^{m+1}} = 0. \tag{10}$$

For this purpose we have only to replace (C) by the weaker assumption

$$\lim_{E \to \pm\infty} \frac{g(E)}{(\ln |E|)^{m+1}} = 0, \tag{11}$$

because Eq. (10) then follows from (A), (B), and Eq. (11) with the help of Phragmén–Lindelöf theorem. Obviously the assumption in Eq. (11) is closely related to the assumption (D'). Note that even for $m = 0$, which corresponds to the assumption (C) itself, the relation Eq. (11) is weaker than the assumption (C) by one power of $\ln E$[13]. We also note that the assumption (D') and Eq. (11) together imply the behavior

(C') $\qquad \left|\dfrac{\text{Re } g(z)}{\text{Im } g(z)}\right| \dfrac{1}{\ln z} \to 0 \qquad$ as $z \to +\infty.$

In fact, we may choose this and (D') as the basic assumptions instead of Eq. (11). We shall see later that the assumption (C') is closely related to the unitarity of the scattering amplitude.

If (C') is violated, it is easy to find an example for which the Pomeranchuk theorem does not hold. One such example is[5]

$$f(E) = -AE \ln (\mu - E) + BE \ln (\mu + E), \tag{12}$$

where A and B are real and positive and $A \neq B$. In this case we have not only

$$|\sigma_+(\infty) - \sigma_-(\infty)| = 4\pi|A - B| \neq 0$$

but also

$$\lim_{E \to +\infty} \frac{\sigma_+(E)}{\sigma_-(E)} = \frac{A}{B} \neq 1.$$

Assumption E

Let us now consider the assumption (E). It is again easy to construct a counter example which violates (E)[5]:

$$f(E) = C(\mu^2 - E^2)^{1/2}\{1 + \alpha \exp [-(\mu - E)^{1/2}]\}, \qquad (13)$$

where α is to be chosen sufficiently small to fulfill the unitarity requirements on the sign of Im f. Obviously Eq. (13) has a limit for $E \rightarrow -\infty$ but has no limit for $E \rightarrow +\infty$. Thus the Pomeranchuk theorem does not hold.

However, as was shown by Meiman[4], we do not lose everything when the assumption (E) is dropped. Namely, we can still claim that there exists a certain sequence of energies $\{E_n\}$ ($E_n \rightarrow \infty$ as $n \rightarrow \infty$) such that $\sigma_+(E_n) - \sigma_-(E_n)$ tends to zero as $n \rightarrow \infty$. Meiman's argument is based on the following generalizations of the Phragmén–Lindelöf theorem[4]:

Theorem I. If $f(z)$ is regular in the upper half plane (Im $z > 0$), and is bounded on the real axis as $|f(x)| < M$, x real, then either $|f(z)| < M$ at all points in Im $z > 0$, or $f(z)$ increases faster than a certain exponential, i.e., there exists $\alpha(>0)$ such that $\max_{0 \leq \varphi \leq \pi} |f(Re^{i\varphi})| > e^{\alpha R}$ for sufficiently large R.

Theorem II. Let $f(z)$ be regular in Im $z > 0$, and let $\mathscr{E}_1$ (or $\mathscr{E}_2$) be the manifold of limit values of $f(z)$ as Re $z \rightarrow +\infty$ (or $-\infty$). $\mathscr{E}_1$ (or $\mathscr{E}_2$) consists of one point or a continuum. If $\mathscr{E}_1$ and $\mathscr{E}_2$ have no point in common, and if one of them does not surround the other, then $f(z)$ cannot be bounded in the upper half plane Im $z > 0$. (These theorems are valid even if we remove any finite part of the upper half z-plane from the analyticity domain.)

We shall now apply these theorems to $g(E)$ satisfying the assumptions (A'), (B), (C), and (D). Let $\mathscr{E}_1$ (or $\mathscr{E}_2$) be the manifold of $\lim_{E \rightarrow \pm \infty} g(E)$ along the upper edge of the right-hand (or left-hand) cut. Because of the crossing relation, (Eq. (3)), these manifolds are located symmetrically in the complex g-plane with respect to the real axis and are bounded. Let us first assume that one of these manifolds lie entirely in the upper half plane. Then the other must lie entirely in the lower half plane by symmetry, and they have no common point. Thus $g(E)$ cannot be bounded in the upper half E-plane according to Theorem II. Hence it must increase faster than some exponential $e^{\alpha|E|}$ according to Theorem I. Since this contradicts with our assumption (B), we can conclude that these manifolds must intersect with the real g-axis. Thus there has to be a *real* point c which belongs to both $\mathscr{E}_1$ and $\mathscr{E}_2$. This means that there exists a sequence of energy values $\{E_n\}$, $E_n \to +\infty$, such that $g(E_n) \to c$ and therefore

$$\lim_{n \to \infty} [\sigma_+(E_n) - \sigma_-(E_n)] = \lim_{n \to \infty} \text{Im } g(E_n) = 0. \tag{14}$$

Thus from the assumptions (A'), (B), and (C) on the boundedness of $f_\pm(E)/E$ it follows that $\sigma_+(E_n) - \sigma_-(E_n) \to 0$ along a certain sequence $\{E_n\}$. This proves Meiman's assertion. Now, if we add the assumption (E), namely assume that the limit $\sigma_+ - \sigma_-$ exists, then this limit must be equal to zero. This is Meiman's version of the proof of the Pomeranchuk theorem.

Role of Unitarity and Cos θ Analyticity

The Pomeranchuk theorem is concerned with the property of the forward scattering amplitude and as such its assumptions are all described in terms of the energy variable only. Of these assumptions, (A') and (B) are well founded in quantum field theory or at least broad enough to accommodate a wide variety of theories. On the other hand, the assumptions (C'), (D'), and (E) seem to have no field-theoretical justification insofar as we restrict ourselves to the energy variable only. It would therefore be natural to ask whether or not these assumptions are related in some way to other aspects of quantum field theory such as unitarity and analyticity in $\cos \theta$. In fact, from this point of view, we may regard the assumption (D') as a consequence of the assumption (E) and the Froissart bound[14] which follows from unitarity and analyticity of $f(s, \cos \theta)$ in an ellipse of the $\cos \theta$-plane described below. Furthermore, Eden[7] has shown that to some extent the assumption (C') can also be justified in the same manner. I shall first show how unitarity can be taken into account in our problem by a method somewhat different from that of Eden.

For simplicity let us consider the elastic scattering of spinless particles of equal mass. Suppose the scattering amplitude $f(s, \cos \theta)$ is analytic in a domain which includes an ellipse in the $\cos \theta$-plane whose foci are at $\cos \theta = \pm 1$ and whose semimajor axis is equal to $1 + (c/k^2)$, k being the center-of-mass momentum. The positive constant c must be so chosen that this domain is consistent with the Mandelstam representation. Then the forward scattering amplitude may be expanded as

$$f(s) = \frac{\sqrt{s}}{2k} \sum_{l=0}^{\infty} (2l + 1)a_l(s), \tag{15}$$

where $a_l(s)$ is the lth partial wave amplitude. The unitarity condition can be expressed by the inequalities

$$\text{Im } a_l(s) \geq [\text{Im } a_l(s)]^2 + [\text{Re } a_l(s)]^2, \qquad l = 0, 1, 2, \ldots \tag{16}$$

We shall now prove the inequality

$$\frac{|\text{Re } f(s)|}{\text{Im } f(s)} \lesssim \frac{C\sqrt{s}\ln s}{[\text{Im } f(s)]^{\frac{1}{2}}}, \tag{17}$$

which holds for sufficiently large s.

To prove this, we note that in the expansion (Eq. (15)) only the first L partial waves contribute to the scattering amplitude, where $L = C\sqrt{s}\ln s$, under our assumption of analyticity in $\cos \theta$[14]. Contributions from partial waves with $l > L$ can be shown to be smaller than s^{-n} for sufficiently large s, where n can be made arbitrarily large by choosing a large enough C[15]. Making use of the unitarity (Eq. (16)) and the Schwartz inequality, we obtain

$$\begin{aligned}
|\text{Re } f(s)| &\simeq \left| \sum_{l=0}^{L} (2l + 1) \text{ Re } a_l \right| \\
&\leq \sum_{l}^{L} (2l + 1)(\text{Im } a_l)^{\frac{1}{2}} \\
&\leq \left(\sum_{l}^{L} (2l + 1) \text{ Im } al \right)^{\frac{1}{2}} \left(\sum_{l}^{L} (2l + 1) \right)^{\frac{1}{2}} \\
&\leq L[\text{Im } f(s)]^{\frac{1}{2}}. \tag{18}
\end{aligned}$$

The inequality, Eq. (17), follows immediately from Eq. (18). Q.E.D.

It is seen from Eq. (17) that, for any process for which the total cross section becomes infinite at infinite energy, we have

$$\frac{|\text{Re } f(E)|}{\text{Im } f(E)} \frac{1}{\ln E} \to 0 \qquad \text{as} \quad E \to +\infty. \tag{19}$$

Suppose now that the imaginary parts of the forward scattering amplitudes $f_+(E)$ and $f_-(E)$ for the direct and crossed channels behave as $C_+E(\ln E)^m$ and $C_-E(\ln E)^m$, respectively, and that $C_+ \neq C_-$ and

$m > 0$. Then the assumption (C') is easily derived from Eq. (19). Thus, if $\sigma_+(E)$ and $\sigma_-(E)$ diverge as $E \to +\infty$, the assumption (C') is in fact a consequence of unitarity and $\cos \theta$ analyticity in an ellipse consistent with the Mandelstam representation.

This is equivalent to the result obtained by Eden. His own derivation is based on the observation that $f(s, \cos \theta)$ cannot vary substantially for angles between $\theta = 0$ and $\theta = C/(\sqrt{s} \ln s)$. This can be shown either by estimating the magnitude of the derivatives of $f(s, \cos \theta)$ at $\theta = 0$[16], or by applying the method of Cerulus and Martin[17]. From this we find easily the inequality

$$\sigma_{el} = \frac{8\pi}{s} \int_{-1}^{1} d(\cos \theta) |f(s, \cos \theta)|^2 \geq \frac{C'|f(s, 1)|^2}{s^2 (\ln s)^2}. \tag{20}$$

On the other hand, unitarity requires that

$$\sigma_{total} = \frac{8\pi}{k\sqrt{s}} \operatorname{Im} f(s, 1) \geq \sigma_{el}. \tag{21}$$

The inequality, Eq. (17), now follows from Eqs. (20) and (21).

Unfortunately, in the most interesting case where the total cross section is finite at $E = +\infty$, the inequality, Eq. (17), does not give us a strong enough bound for $|\operatorname{Re} f(s)|/\operatorname{Im} f(s)$[18]. It only tells us that, if $\operatorname{Im} f(E) \sim CE$, $|\operatorname{Re} f(E)|$ cannot exceed $C'E \ln E$. Thus the methods described above do not give us a complete justification of the assumption (C'). However, we can at least say that the problem of "completing" the proof of the Pomeranchuk theorem is now sharply focused on the question whether or not the possibility

$$\operatorname{Im} f(E) \sim CE,$$

$$\operatorname{Re} f(E) \sim C' E \ln E \tag{22}$$

can be ruled out within the general framework of quantum field theory [forgetting temporarily the more difficult question of justification of the assumption (E) concerning the oscillation of $f(E)$]. At present we do not have the answer to this question.

As closing remarks we shall point out some peculiar feature of the case (22) and also mention some additional assumptions which enable us to obtain Eq. (19). It is easily seen from the partial wave expansion [Eq. (15)] that Eq. (22) can be realized only if

$$\operatorname{Im} a_l \sim C(\ln s)^{-2}$$

and

$$\operatorname{Re} a_l \sim C'(\ln s)^{-1}, \qquad C' \leq \sqrt{C}, \tag{23}$$

for l of order $\sqrt{s}\ln s$. [Note that $\text{Re } a_l \leq (\text{Im } a_l)^{\frac{1}{2}}$ from unitarity [Eq. (16)] and also that a_l is a very smooth function of l for large $l^{(19)}$.] This corresponds to the case where the radius of the target increases logarithmically as the energy increases and at the same time the energy dependent part of the target becomes more and more transparent. Such a situation may arise even if the scattering is strongly inelastic insofar as σ_{el} does not tend to zero in the high-energy limit.

Conversely, if $\sigma_{\text{el}}/\sigma_{\text{total}} \to 0$ as $E \to +\infty$, we can easily prove Eq. (19) making use of the inequality

$$\frac{|\text{Re } f(s)|}{\text{Im } f(s)} \frac{1}{\ln s} \leq C\left(\frac{\sigma_{\text{el}}}{\sigma_{\text{total}}}\right)^{\frac{1}{2}}\left(\frac{1}{\sigma_{\text{total}}}\right)^{\frac{1}{2}}, \qquad (24)$$

which follows from Eqs. (20) and (21).

Another case where Eq. (19) is valid is when $\text{Re } f(s, \cos\theta)$ does not vary substantially over the range of angles between $\theta = 0$ and $\theta = C/[\sqrt{s}(\ln s)^m]$, $m < 1$. In this case $|\text{Re } f(s, 1)|$ cannot be larger than $s(\ln s)^m$ as is seen by a method similar to Eq. (20). Thus we have Eq. (19). The usual assumption of Regge type t dependence belongs to this category, where t is, of course, the square of momentum transfer.

We note finally that the amplitude, Eq. (22), has the approximate symmetry property

$$\text{Re } f_+(E) = -\text{Re } f_-(E) + 0(E/\ln E) \qquad (25)$$

for sufficiently large E, as is easily shown by the methods developed in ref. 20. This relation can be extended to the case $t < 0$ using Martin's method[21]. Taking account of the dominance of $\text{Re } f$ over $\text{Im } f$ at large E, we therefore find the amusing result

$$\frac{\sigma_{+,\text{el}}(E)}{\sigma_{-,\text{el}}(E)} \to 1 \qquad \text{as} \quad E \to +\infty, \qquad (26)$$

which looks somewhat like the Pomeranchuk theorem except that $\sigma_{\pm,\text{el}}$ are the integrated elastic cross sections. If we could show that the ratios $\sigma_{+,\text{el}}/\sigma_+$ and $\sigma_{-,\text{el}}/\sigma_-$ are equal at very large energies, we would of course have a proof of the Pomeranchuk theorem in the exceptional case (Eq. (22)). It is not clear at present, however, whether such a relation exists or not. We only want to point out that, according to Eqs. (24) and (26), in both cases where the scattering is strongly inelastic and purely elastic at high energy, we have the equality of σ_+ and σ_-.

References

1. Pomeranchuk, I., Ia., *Zh. Eksperim. i Theor. Fiz.*, **34**, 725 (1958); English trans. *Soviet Phys.–JETP*, **7**, 499 (1958).
2. Amati, D., M. Fierz, and V. Glaser, *Phys. Rev. Letters*, **4**, 89 (1960).
3. Weinberg, S., *Phys. Rev.*, **124**, 2049 (1961).
4. Meiman, N. N., *Zh. Eksperim. i Theor. Fiz.*, **43**, 2277 (1962); English trans. *Soviet Phys.–JETP*, **16**, 1609 (1963).
5. Martin, A., *Nuovo Cimento*, **39**, 704 (1965).
6. Bros, J., H. Epstein, and V. Glaser, to be published in *Communications in Mathematical Physics*.
7. Eden, R. J., *Phys. Rev. Letters*, **16**, 39 (1966).
8. See, for instance, E. C. Titchmarsh, *The Theory of Functions*, Oxford Univ. Press, New York, 1939, 2nd Ed., p. 178.
9. The following argument is based on Martin's article, ref. 5.
10. Bros, J., H. Epstein, and V. Glaser, *Nuovo Cimento*, **31**, 1265 (1964).
11. Boas, R., *Entire Functions*, Academic Press, New York, 1954, p. 248.
12. It is of course easy to generalize this assumption by replacing $(\ln |E|)^m$ with a more general smooth function of E. Since the essential feature is unchanged, we prefer to stick to the simpler assumption (D'). For a more general treatment, see ref. 4.
13. See ref. 5.
14. Froissart, M., *Phys. Rev.*, **123**, 1053 (1961); A. Martin, *Phys. Rev.*, **129**, 1432 (1963).
15. Yamamoto, K., *Phys. Rev.*, **135**, B567 (1964).
16. Kinoshita, T., *Lectures in Theoretical Physics*, Vol. VIIB, Univ. of Colorado Press, Boulder, 1965, p. 144.
17. Cerulus, F., and A. Martin, *Phys. Letters*, **8**, 80 (1964); Kinoshita, T., *Phys. Rev. Letters*, **12**, 257 (1964).
18. This is also true for the case where the total cross section vanishes in the high-energy limit. Since this case is not particularly interesting, we shall not discuss it in the following.
19. To be more precise, a_l for even l and odd l must be treated separately. This does not affect the essential feature. For details, see T. Kinoshita, J. J. Loeffel, and A. Martin, *Phys. Rev.*, **135**, B1464 (1964).
20. Khuri, N. N., and T. Kinoshita, *Phys. Rev.*, **140**, B706 (1965); N. N. Khuri and T. Kinoshita, *Phys. Rev.*, **137**, B720 (1965); Y. S. Jin and S. W. Mac-Dowell, *Phys. Rev.*, **138**, B1279 (1965).
21. Martin, A., CERN preprint, TH.630, 1965.

An Anecdotal Account of Accelerators at Cornell

ROBERT R. WILSON

Cornell University

Ever since Hans Bethe came to Cornell in 1934, particle accelerators have been built and then used in investigations of the nucleus and of nuclear particles. The relationship between the machines and Bethe has been very direct; he has inspired their construction and he has closely advised the men who have built and used them. I would like to discuss those accelerators, which range from the Livingston's one MeV cyclotron of 1934 to the 10 BeV synchrotron that is now being constructed, but because they are already described in technical articles, I have decided for this occasion to accentuate the more human aspects of the work. I will try to do this by relating, more or less at random and from a very personal point of view, stories about the machines that do not normally find their way into the literature, but yet which might illustrate that this is an activity carried out by men who are made of flesh and blood.

It's a little difficult for me to be anecdotal about the cyclotron for I was not at Cornell when it was built. I became aware of it about 1937 when I was a first year graduate student at Berkeley taking a class in electricity from Ernest Lawrence. We were studying electric fields as given by Schwarz transformations and Lawrence had assigned to us as a problem the determination by this method of the electric field between the dees of a cyclotron—remarking at the same time that it would be a useful result for the person who would eventually work out the theory of focusing in the cyclotron. Well, I couldn't make the transformation; but I did set up an electrolytic tray, measured the field, and then worked out the theory of focusing. The only relevance is that while I was doing this, Bethe and Rose completely scooped me by working out the same thing much more elegantly at Cornell. They announced their results as a limit of the energy attainable by a cyclotron and put the limit for

Fig. 1.   Professor Boyce McDaniel adjusting the ion source of the one MeV
cyclotron.

protons at about 15 MeV. Since Lawrence was already planning a
much bigger machine at the time, this did not make Bethe particularly
popular in the Radiation Laboratory, in fact, woe to him who even

mentioned him there. Bethe turned out to be right of course: Veksler and McMillan were to invent phase focusing before much higher proton energies could be attained. As a student, I also felt a bond with Cornell because I spent so much of my time pouring over those three classic volumes in the *Reviews of Modern Physics* in which Bethe, Bacher, and Livingston essentially chartered the course of nuclear physics. For me, an experimenter, their range–energy curves for protons were especially useful. I also had occasion to refer to Bethe's little known article in *The Reviews of Scientific Instruments* on the best shape of a cyclotron magnet whenever I had to build any magnet. Bethe's inspiration at Cornell was obvious in the use of the Cornell cyclotron to study the carbon-cycle reactions, and one can juxtapose his article on nuclear shadow scattering with Bacher's experimental study of this phenomenon that has been turning up in various guises in nuclear and particle physics ever since. Bethe became personally involved with experiment when he checked with his own hands whether neutrons were absorbed at specific resonance energies.

I suppose the most significant innovation on the cyclotron itself was Livingston's arc source which was immediately adopted throughout cyclotrondom. Probably of even more significance though was the development by Bacher and Baker of the time-of-flight neutron detection system. This was later moved to Los Alamos and used by Boyce McDaniel who worked in my cyclotron group there to study the all-important energy variation of the fission cross section of uranium. The Laboratory of Nuclear Studies was created in 1946 when Bethe and a group of his colleagues, most of whom had been at the Los Alamos Laboratory, returned to Cornell University. They decided to build a 300 MeV electron synchrotron but, while waiting for the new buildings and for the construction of the new machine, the old cyclotron was still the center of the research effort. As other and ever-larger accelerators were built elsewhere, we eventually came to boast of having the *smallest* machine in the world. Even after our 300 MeV synchrotron was operating, the cyclotron continued to be the object of loving attention from the one or two graduate students who were doing their thesis work with it each year. There is some question as to whether it turned out more protons or theses.

By 1954, though, we were thinking of closing down the cyclotron. Just at that time, Solly Cohen, of the University of Jerusalem, made a visit to Cornell. He was interested in building a synchrotron in Israel

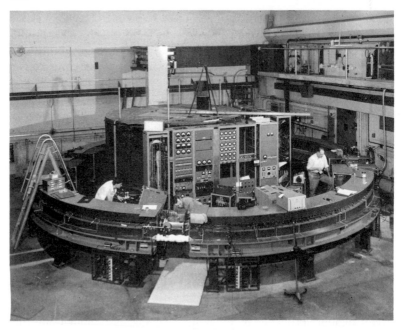

Fig. 2. The original 300 MeV synchrotron is the large cylindrical object in the center of the picture. The 1 BeV synchrotron encircles it.

but after some discussion, I put it to him, "Why don't you just take our little cyclotron back with you instead?" A look of relief came over his face for he obviously didn't want to make a large accelerator. So he did take our beloved cyclotron away, and that was about the last I heard of it except to receive, eventually, as a gift of appreciation from the Chancellor of the University of Jerusalem, a beautiful copy of the Dead Sea Scrolls. In the accompanying letter the Chancellor expressed his fear that I might have some linguistic difficulty and explained that, as one scholar to another, he was taking the liberty of enclosing a translation. When I opened the scrolls, sure enough, there was the pony . . . in modern Hebrew!

Although our first synchrotron was originally to be designed and built for us by Allis Chalmers, in fact, because of a prolonged strike at their factory, it turned out that we designed most of it ourselves and then had to construct it as well. Looking back at those times, this was not such a bad thing. We had a policy of not permitting our students to use work on the machine itself as part of their Ph.D. thesis. On the other hand, it was just their work in helping to build the machine that many of those students, some of whom by now are outstanding physicists, refer to fondly as being the most valuable part of their training. Furthermore, that early work laid a foundation of expertise that was to characterize our future work on accelerators.

A number of electron synchrotrons, all to give about 300 MeV, were being built at about that time (1947). Berkeley, Cal Tech, MIT, Michigan, and Purdue as well as Cornell were all competing. None of the machines worked upon first being turned on though. To find the difficulty at Cornell, Dale Corson spent the summer carefully measuring the magnetic field that actually obtained at injection time. It was supposed to be 8 gauss, but in fact what Dale observed was the most complicated hodge-podge imaginable. In some places, due to the effects of residual magnetism and of eddy currents, the field was even reversed in sign and as large as 10 gauss. It was no wonder that the electrons were confused in finding their way around the donut. This gave me the bright idea of reducing the excitation of the magnetic field to the point where these adverse effects were negligible. On doing this, the eagle-eyed Bob Walker almost immediately observed an accelerated beam and then it was possible to nurse the excitation up to full value without losing the beam. Bursting with pride, I immediately phoned word of our method to Ed McMillan in Berkeley. He applied the method and within a day or so also had a beam. Unfortunately for us, they were in a better position to use it, for their rf cavity was superior to ours and enabled them to reach 300 MeV at once, while we were limited by ours to 200 MeV for some months.

To go back a little, just after our machine had been put together and the wiring had been finished, we decided to excite the magnet by connecting it to the huge 1000 kVA ac generator. To be safe, though, we brought the ac voltage down to about 100 volts instead of the normal 3000 volts. On closing the switch there was a woof and a thump and then a spiral of smoke rising above the machine—all that was left of various wires. For some reason, I decided to inspect the fuses in the condenser room. To be perfectly safe, even though the voltage had been only 100 volts, I took a grounding hook along with me as I entered this terrifying room which was completely filled by large condensers and bus bars. As I touched the grounding bar to the main bus bar, a tremendous flash blinded me, my eyebrows were singed, a great bang rendered me deaf, and I nearly maimed three graduate students by the force of my sudden withdrawal from the room! The trouble had been that the third harmonic of a generator becomes important when it is connected directly across a condenser bank—and then the current, due to this third harmonic, self-excites the generator so that it climbs up to its limit of excitation. Thus, instead of 100 volts, there were many thousands of volts on the condensers and magnet before the switch tripped open—leaving all that voltage on the condensers. It was in this way that we became sophisticated about the third harmonic self-excitation of a generator. Probably there is an easier way.

To adjust the betatron flux bars in the synchrotron or to look for leaks in the donut we had to descend into a pit in the center of the magnet formed by the 24 C-shaped magnets of the synchrotron which faced inwards, leaving a cylindrical space about 5 ft in diameter and about 8 ft deep. The noise was terrific in this pit when the magnet was on, but even worse were the visual effects of the alternating magnetic field (about one kG) that were perceived there. Descending into the magnetic field region, you at first became aware that the externally received light was being modulated on and off at sixty cycles per second. Descending further though, even with your eyes closed, you were aware of beautiful optical effects not unlike fireworks, evidently due to currents induced in the optic nerve. When a calculation showed that the currents induced in the brain were comparable to or even greater than those used in shock therapy, we decided to turn off the magnet before going down into the pit.

To detect leaks in the donut we had, for a while, an ion gauge which was enclosed within a heated palladium tube—it was sensitive only to hydrogen which could permeate the hot palladium. We looked for leaks by squirting the donut with hydrogen and then looking for a response on this gauge. It worked fine—but I can remember than when the leaks were very large, as they frequently were, the amount of hydrogen sucked in by the leak could be appreciable and for some reason it would explode just as it came out of the hot vacuum pump. One could not only hear the explosion but, since the pump was right under the wooden floor of the pit, one could also detect the leak by being thrown a few inches into the air—probably the only really kinesthetic leak detector ever developed. We stopped that, too, after a while.

When we did have a leak, we had to remove the betatron flux bars each of which was about 5 ft long and which weighed somewhat more than a hundred pounds in order to get at it. Having wrestled them off the magnet, a crane would hoist them up and out of the pit, the top of which was about 8 ft above the floor. We had many leaks and seemed forever to be hoisting those flux bars up and down. One night the inevitable happened. A flux bar had been hoisted and was being swung away—but it had not been lifted quite high enough. It struck the top side of the pit and, to my horror (I was in the pit below) it came off its hook, teetered at the top and then came crashing down the pit bouncing from side to side. Whether the bar and I were obeying Pauli or Dirac statistics was difficult to ascertain, for I was doing the most fancy dodging of my life. Lucky for me, it flew just past my ear. It made a great hole in the floor instead of my head.

I suppose any of my colleagues in that machine, DeWire, Corson, Littauer, McDaniel, Silverman or Woodward, who in fact made the design and did all the work, could tell equivalent or better tales of their own experiences. From all that though, we did manage to learn something, for our safety record has been nearly perfect.

The coil of the 300 MeV synchrotron was built in a factory in Chicago and was particularly fancy. It was made of twenty turns but each turn was also made of up eighteen 1/2 in. stranded copper cables connected in parallel somehow and arranged in a vertical bank so that no total flux was included by any strand—complicated, in other words. When the coil arrived at the Laboratory we were horrified to discover that it had been constructed in the wrong way—twenty-one turns instead of twenty because the fabricator had made a classic error, namely that of dividing a line into two parts: It takes three points to define the two segments, or, so he reasoned, generalizing, $n + 1$ points to define n segments of the line. Then he applied this same reasoning to the coil, but somehow instead of getting twenty, he got twenty-one turns—which just goes to show the power of logical thinking. All I remember now is that McDaniel and our trusty shop men grimly descended into the coil. When they emerged several days later, the coil had its proper twenty turns.

The experiments we did with that machine and that were successful have found their way into *The Physical Review*. Let me describe one of my experiments that was a dismal failure. York and Panofsky had just finished their experiment with the 180 in. cyclotron at Berkeley in which they had measured the gamma-rays from a target bombarded by high-energy protons and thereby concluded that the most probable cause of these was the production of π^0 mesons. It occurred to me that it would be possible to confirm this idea by creating π^0 mesons using the x-rays from our synchrotron which at that time had reached a maximum energy of 200 MeV—we were still limited for practical reasons by the rf cavity. Jim Keck, then a student of mine, and I mounted two gamma-ray detectors made of thick NaI crystals close to a target that was placed in the x-ray beam and began to look for coincidences. We saw all sorts of things in the counters: protons galore, but no coincidences, or rather exceedingly few, maybe one or two. Most of the time, I recall, the synchrotron operated badly or was broken down. We had sent off an abstract for the Washington meeting of the Physical Society with a hope and a prayer that we would see something. Accordingly, Keck and I worked day and night to keep the machine going, but it was a losing battle. We were working at the limit of the rf cavity which failed when it got too hot. Finally, in complete desperation, we wrapped a continuous layer of rubber tubing around the section of donut that served as the cavity, then ran oil through the tubing for cooling. Well, it didn't even cool the cavity as well as the air stream from a fan would—but every so often the tubing would break and squirt oil all over us and the synchrotron. It reminded me of freshmen initiation rites at college. One day remained—everyone but Keck and myself had already left for Washington. We decided to give the problem one last, good old college try. Spending one night, we disassembled the magnet—no mean job—and replaced the rf cavity section by the old one, normally several days' work. We finally got the magnet back together, heroically got it running, and made a several-hour run in which we observed two coincidences—not enough to claim anything. Then we took off for Washington. The final twist of the screw was to have to sit there and listen to Panofsky and Steinberger describe the elegant experiment in which they had done the very thing we were trying to do—we were utterly scooped. The Berkeley synchrotron had 300 MeV: as it turned out, the π^0 cross section is still essentially zero a 200 MeV but at 300 MeV is quite robust because of the resonance at that energy. Our two miserable coincidences corresponded almost exactly to what we should have expected. No one is going to tell me that energy in a machine is not important—not without a fight. Furthermore, I even began to regret that friendly phone call to Ed McMillan about how synchrotrons work.

All was not completely lost, though. Keck investigated the copious proton background of the experiment and, with Joe Levinger's help, their origin in the photo-disintegration of quasi-deuterons in the nucleus was discovered. Once we were focused on the protons, it was then natural to measure π^0 production by looking at the recoil protons, rather than the gamma-rays from the π^0, as Silverman and Stearns did. This lead to measurements of the variation of the cross section with photon energy that, together with the results of Steinberger and Panofsky, suggested to Bruckner the existence of the 3–3 resonance level. Our π^+ production measurements also showed the same resonance but with one half the height, in confirmation of the assignment of isotopic spin, 3/2. At just that time the various proton synchrocyclotrons throughout the county started to make meson beams. By scattering mesons from protons they were able to study the same resonance. This led to the great phase-shift fiasco of the early fifties. Was there or wasn't there a resonance: this was the question. The matter was really resolved when the people at Cal Tech raised the energy of their electron synchrotron to 450 MeV, and went right up and over the resonance showing it as clean as a whistle. Again, we at Cornell had been "outgunned." We decided to raise our energy too.

The first thing that occurred to us was to revise the pole tips of our magnet in a manner to increase the magnetic field so that we might get as high as 500 MeV: in fact the ONR approved some 70 k$ for this move. However, at just this time, June 1952, I happened to attend the conference at Copenhagen for planning what eventually became CERN. There I heard a report to the effect that the Cosmotron had just worked, and indeed would work, even when the vertical aperture was reduced from six to two inches. This led me, on the MATS airplane back, while fascinated by the midnight sun, to imagine a Cosmotron-like magnet having a two inch gap but scaled down so as to fit into the Cornell accelerator room. It would be necessary to reduce the 30 ft orbit radius of the Cosmotron to 12.5 ft in order to fit it into our room. This implied a vertical aperture of a little less than an inch. Being a conservative at heart, I increased the aperature to $1\frac{1}{2}$ inches and found that our old generator and condensers were still adequate as a resonant power source even though the energy would be five times higher. The new magnet was to weigh 16 tons and was designed to reach 1.5 BeV at 13 kG, compared to 1600 tons for the Cosmotron which gave 3 BeV at 14 kG and 80 tons for our old magnet. By January 1953, the design was finished and the ONR had authorized an additional hundred thousand dollars to enable us to go ahead with the conversion. At this time, the alternate gradient principle had just been discovered at Brookhaven. Just for fun, we decided to incorporate it into our machine by designing the magnet in a manner so that either pole tips shaped to give a constant gradient field could be inserted, or alternately, we could insert pole tips shaped to give strong focusing. The tips themselves were to form part of the vacuum chamber for the weak focusing case, but for strong focusing we had a glass donut constructed, the internal aperture of which was one inch high by $2\frac{1}{2}$ inches wide. As it turned out, we never used the constant gradient pole tips.

Once started, the construction went forward very rapidly: all the shop men entered into the spirit of the thing and worked the same long hours as did we physicists. We were also lucky in having an energetic architecture student working for us just then—Bob Matyas. After getting his degree, he worked full time, spending much of it on the road. Typical of our collaboration was for him to call me from some factory— say Westinghouse. There he would have located a particular machine capable of cutting or casting, for example, bakelite in a certain length. On the basis of his findings, and while he had their shop foreman with him, we would redesign over the phone enough of the synchrotron to enable us to use that particular part of the Westinghouse factory. In this manner, the design of much of our machine was adapted in a rather sophisticated manner to industry—rather than vice versa. Also important was Charles van Amer, our shop foreman. He and the mechanics under him learned to make things very rapidly with the roughest of sketches. "Van" also knew how to use all of the regional machine shops as an extension of our own. Six months later, by June 1953, we were far enough along to be able to start injection studies in the magnet. By the end of the year, we had hundreds of turns and had thus proved out the principle of strong focusing for the first time in an accelerator. However, it took another six months before we had mastered rf and other problems connected, for example, with resonances in the alternating gradient magnets (the resonances were not known when we started, of course) so that we could get a high-energy beam.

I remember the occasion of the first high-energy beam very well. I was awakened at four in the morning by a telephone call from McDaniel and Silverman who were working that night at the Laboratory. "Come over quickly," they said excitedly. I did, and found them both peering intently at the scope that would display the beam. I looked at the scope too, but saw nothing. After five or ten minutes of this, I decided I had been the victim of a joke. They had "put me on," in modern parlance. But no, just as I was about to leave in disgust, a pulse appeared in the screen—great cheering and much congratulations. But had we really seen it? Another fifteen minutes, and sure enough, another tiny pulse of accelerated electrons. Our next year was to be spent making that pulse grow in frequency and intensity.

If we had any secret in constructing machines cheaply and rapidly that secret was our willingness, almost our eagerness, to make mistakes. I have always maintained that something that works right away is over-designed and consequently will have taken too long to build and will have cost too much. Well, if, in that case, to err is divine, we were saints indeed in building that synchrotron. We made every possible blunder. Due to a numerical error, the shape of our first pole tips was off so far that we were not even in the celebrated necktie pattern. We corrected this mistake by inserting "zero gradient" pole tips at critical spots. However, for several months, the orbits were still mysteriously erratic. We measured the lattice, i.e., the lengths and distribution of the alternating magnetic lenses, time and again. I checked it personally— just to be sure. Of course, as physicists, we just checked the last figures of the three-foot lens lengths—and they were perfect. One morning, a freshman looking at our machine for the first time innocently asked me, "Professor Wilson, why is that length of iron over there so different from the others?" I was stupefied. The lens located exactly at the position of the ladder where we clambered over the magnet, probably twenty times a day, was off in length by exactly one foot—we hadn't noticed it for several months in spite of all our checking. Even worse, though, was the occasion when I visited Brookhaven after our machine was working. I asked to see the measurements which had shown that a two-inch vertical aperture on the Cosmotron was nearly as good as six inches. I was met by absolutely blank faces. No one there had ever heard of the measurement—no record could be found.

Looking backward, I suppose that the 1.5 BeV machine was designed a little too haphazardly for comfort. Had we thought more or designed more carefully, we might have saved at least a year of time, but then, we might have spent that year thinking and still have made the same mistakes. Three of our worst difficulties come to mind as examples. The pole tips were assembled in place loosely, then rubber tubes held in grooves beneath the poletips were inflated at high pressure to lock the whole assembly in place. This worked fine at low excitation, but the vibrations induced at high excitation would cause the tubing to vibrate and then to fail because of fatigue. We must have tried everything—inner tubes within plastic tubes, polythelyne tubes, stainless steel tubes, and so on. The stainless steel tubes were typical. Under static load they would hold pressures of thousands of pounds per square inch, however, with the magnet on they would crack after a week or so even at 200 lb/in². The best tubing we found was neoprine tubing that is covered by a nylon braid and the kind that is used for hydraulic brakes in trucks. The final solution, though, was invented by the Italians in their synchrotron which also had removable pole tips, following our design. They used solid rubber in place of the tubing and then a device to compress the rubber during assembly—we followed them in this.

Another fiasco was our glass donut. After working satisfactorily for perhaps a year the donut began to collapse periodically. The donut was made up of curved lengths of glass tubing each about four feet long and having an elliptical cross section about three inches wide by $1^3/_8$ inches high—the many pieces being joined by boot gaskets. When one of the pieces would collapse, it was a disaster for the whole machine. The fragments of the collapsed piece would be impelled along the remaining donut by the inrushing air like bullets. All detectors, targets, and probes would disappear before the bombardment. At a point on the donut exactly opposite to the imploding piece, the two opposing shock waves would meet and there would be found the remnants: a pile of sand and metal bits. We would clean up the mess, insert a new piece of donut, pump down, and wait. After about a day, just as we were getting rid of all leaks, there would be a sickening whump, signalling another collapse. This went on for weeks. We never really knew whether the implosions were due to the weakening of the donut pieces by the flying fragments, or whether they were due to a graduate student who had chosen just that period to go berserk. We chose the former explanation though, because we had such a hard time not going berserk ourselves. The difficulty was eventually corrected by pretesting the individual pieces of glass by overpressuring them before they went into the machine.

To prevent this account from becoming an encyclopedia of folly let me give but one more example of how the gods of accelerators punish those mortals who challenge them. The injector for the synchrotron was a 2 MeV Van de Graaf. I had felt especially happy about it because, when I phoned High Voltage Engineering, the conversation went like this. Salesman: "We have a very nice 2 MeV machine on the floor just now." Me: "How much does it cost?" Salesman: "With accessories it comes to $52,000." Me: "Good, I'll take it"—hanging up with the deep satisfaction of an old accelerator man who never thought he would see the day anything so complicated could be bought so simply. Sure enough the Van de Graaf came and worked fine for about a year—but then it, too, got a subtle disease. Raphael Littauer had installed a device to produce a pulsed beam at injection time. He would send a pulse of light up the central tube of the Van de Graaf to a photocell on the high voltage electrode which would then actuate a circuit that would apply a pulse to the filament. All well and good, but after a year of satisfactory operation, every time the Van de Graaf would give a spark, the filament in one of the pulse tubes would burn out. It turns out that the isolation of two million volts is almost complete. We would then have to let the mixture of nitrogen and argon out of the Van de Graaf tank. Elapsed time: half an hour. Disassembly: another half hour. Change the tube: ten seconds. Peering at the circuit and wondering where in hell the transient was coming from: two hours. Putting on an electrical filter of some sort: one hour. Reassembly: one hour. Pumping down: an hour. Then refilling: one hour. Finally, bringing the voltage gently up to a possible running value: another hour. Then ping, a spark. No electrons: so the whole thing to do over again. This cycle must have been gone over perhaps thirty times, each time more frustrating than the last. Finally, we despaired of ever fixing the miserable thing, pulled everything out of the top of the Van de Graaf, jumped up and down on the chassis, then changed every wire and component—even the circuit of the modulation unit itself. After this, it worked fine—we never burned out another filament. Was it changing everything that stopped the filaments burning out? Or was it the modest little ceremony that we had also held at an old dead stump by the light of a full moon that had turned the trick?

The situation was not as completely desperate as I have indicated and in the moments between these crises we were able to discover the next two resonances of the proton and to assign correct values to their isotopic spin and angular momentum. We also measured the photoproduction of K mesons. The energy and intensity were just right to study the charge distribution in the proton by means of electron scattering—but this is not the place to boast of experiments. The crises got less frequent as time went on and when, in 1960, we replaced the Van de Graaf by a 10 MeV linac, our troubles almost completely disappeared. The beam grew to almost 10^{12} electrons per second and the energy close to 1.4 BeV. However, at this point we could see ourselves losing our position as the leader of this particular little band. The Cal Tech machine was rebuilt to give 1.5 BeV and the operation of the CEA electron synchrotron at 6 BeV was imminent, not to mention electron synchrotrons in Italy, Russia, Japan, Sweden, and Germany that were giving or were to give comparable or higher energy.

Remembering the pain as well as the fun of building the other machines—and that most of the pain was borne by my colleagues in the Laboratory—I decided we would build our next machine in high style. We would copy the CEA machine almost exactly, I proposed, and we would have a commercial outfit right in Boston make the copy. All we would do at Cornell would be to keep at our measurements with the old synchrotron, like true physicists, and leave the murky business of construction to the engineers of industry. The people at CEA could not have been kinder or more cooperative. Actually, it turned out that the space available near the laboratory was not large enough for an exact copy so we decided to install one-half the number of unit magnets around a smaller ring—but the unit magnets themselves were still to be exact copies.

The NSF liked the idea and encouraged us to submit a proposal, which we did, the study of the costs having been made by an industrial firm. It was to cost some 8M$ and was to take some five years to build. I went happily off for my sabbatic year in Italy, filled with the righteous sentiments of a director who had finally pulled himself together and had done the proper thing for his loyal cohorts. No more grubby accelerator building for them—they deserved better of life. I could hardly believe my eyes in Italy, then, to receive letters from those ingrates complaining about (a) the low energy and (b) no fun. "They weren't allowed near the design of the new machine," they said, "and it just wasn't Cornell." "Ah!" I thought, "this is just their warped idea of being kind to an old and inveterate accelerator builder. One should ignore their generosity—for their own good."

On returning from Italy in June 1962, I was happy to learn that our proposal was very near to being accepted by the NSF. In the meantime, it did appear to be a good idea to have one of the unit magnets built as a prototype. Don Edwards and I calculated the cost for this to be some $10,000, surprisingly small. This led me to think, as before, about replacing our old magnet with the largest one possible in our accelerator room, which had subsequently been enlarged by an underground addition. By doing a little more excavation on one side, it appeared possible to arrange twelve of the new magnet units around a roughly 50-foot diameter circle. Our good old power supply would still be able to excite this to about 1.8 BeV, and with modest additions we could hope to reach 2.2 BeV or even more in the magnet. All the other components, such as the injector and control circuits and stainless steel donut that we were already planning to build and install in the old synchrotron anyway. Although our old rf system would be adequate to reach 1.5 BeV, a new one would have to be constructed to reach 2.2 BeV. In fact, it appeared that by spending some $200,000, much of which we happened to have then for various other changes, we could hope to change our old synchrotron into one capable of eventually giving over 2 BeV, the initial part of the change to occur within a year or two. This was to be compared with our other proposal for spending over 8 M$ to get a 3 BeV synchrotron in five years.

With barely a pause, I picked up the phone, called the people in the NSF, and politely informed them that I was sorry but no longer wanted their money. For people who had worked so hard for several years to secure funds for our 3 BeV machine, they were magnificent. The ONR people too, were sympathetic, but out of funds just then. They suggested that the change-over be made with such money as we already had in hand. By the end of the month, the details of the design had been progressed far enough so that the ONR people approved our going ahead on that basis.

By then our blood was up. "If we can get 2 BeV out of our petty cash," we asked ourselves, "what energy can we get for about 8 M$, the approximate cost of our proposed 3 BeV machine?" The answer to this was 10 BeV or more. I called the appropriate people at the NSF to ask if they were interested. "Come down to Washington and let's talk about it," they said. I did go and during the discussion I was given to believe that if a formal proposal, comparable to our 3 BeV proposal, could be submitted within two weeks there was just an outside chance of still getting funds for the new 10 BeV machine. On returning to Cornell, the whole lab went into a paroxysm of design on the one hand

Fig. 3.   The physicists who constructed the 2 BeV synchrotron are shown inside
the ring. From left to right are: D. Edwards, A. Silverman, W. Woodward, J.
Kenemuth, M. Tigner, B. McDaniel, R. Littauer, R. Wilson, R. Anderson, B.
Borgia, P. Stein, E. Gabathuler, K. Berkelman, J. DeWire, R. Talman (not shown)

and cost estimating on the other. Within the two weeks, we did come
up with a beautifully printed and bound new proposal in which we
estimated the cost of the machine and building to be 6.7 M$ exclusive
of contingency, escalation, or overhead costs. Alas, no miracles happened in getting any immediately available money. At just this time
the Ramsey Panel was appointed, and so our proposal was referred to
them. Necessarily, it had to await their findings. Fortunately, when they
did make their recommendations a year later, one was that funds,
estimated at about 15 M$, be provided to build our synchrotron.

    With our 10 BeV proposal in the works, we turned to the actual
construction of the 2 BeV machine. Boyce McDaniel took over the
general supervision of that, while I pretty much concentrated on the
design of the 10 BeV machine. The other members of the laboratory,

who in fact do all the actual design and work, distributed themselves between the two projects. The new 2 BeV machine was to serve where possible as a prototype for the larger synchrotron. For example, the 2 BeV magnet had been designed with two long Collins-type straight sections, each 12 feet in length. For this reason, all the cost of the model work for the 2 BeV magnet was borne by a study grant of the NSF for the 10 BeV machine. After about a year spent in constructing such parts of the 2 BeV synchrotron as the magnet units and a new ceramic and stainless steel donut, the 1.5 BeV machine was finally turned off in January 1964 and the old magnet was torn out by the roots. A little more than 3 months later, in April, the new magnet had been assembled and we were ready to look for a beam. Remembering the traumatic experiences of bringing in the other machines, we all grimly assembled for the arduous task ahead. To our utter amazement, just as soon as the magnet was powered, and the time of the injection pulse was adjusted to its correct value, a fat beam appeared before our unbelieving eyes. We are getting old, I thought. We have over-designed and over-built! Even so, we all retired to the nearest bar for a celebration—not knowing quite how to behave so early in the evening.

A result of too much accuracy in the design showed up almost immediately. The beam ran into a resistively induced blow-up at a beam intensity that was roughly ten times less than in our old machine. The addition of an octupole lens corrected this at once: apparently, our old magnetic field had inadvertently contained components of all the various kinds of poles! But the new machine is a gem; it comes on at command, runs reliably day and night, and the energy can be varied with great ease. It has already turned out three significant pieces of research: a measurement of the radius of the pion (Berkelman), a test of the breakdown of quantum electrodynamics (Talman and Silverman) and a study of the scattering of positrons compared to electrons by protons (DeWire). It should have a happy and busy future.

In the meantime, the NSF had moved rapidly and funds for the 10 BeV machine were provided by April 1965. In anticipation of this, we spent most of our study money for the first stages of the injector linac, with NSF approval, and it has already been delivered. Between our first request for about 9 M$, i.e., the 6.7 M$ plus contingency, etc. and the 15 M$ recommended by the Ramsey Panel, we finally were given about 12 M$. Nearly all of the increase in funds came about because of the laboratory building and the tunnel. The tunnel was more expensive because the facility is located right on the campus below an athletic playing field. Part of the deal made with the University in locating there was that we would not dig up the field. This meant that we had to have a genuine tunnel dug deep underground, rather than using the cheaper method of cutting and filling. Most of the rest of the increase came about because, at the request of the NSF, we enlarged the experimental area over that which we had originally planned. In part, too, I must confess that I had underestimated the size and thus the cost of the necessary buildings. I suppose it has been false pride that has led us to keep the costs of the machine proper at exactly those that we had arrived at during our two-week study: so far though, we have seen no reason to change them. By great good fortune, in spite of general cost increases in the intervening years, most of the items have come in very close to our original off-the-cuff estimates.

Any anecdotes connected with this machine must await its construction which I am confident will have its harrowing moments too. During the design period, the specification and plans of our buildings and tunnel were being drawn up by Brobeck and Associates, our architect-engineer. Because they are on the West Coast, the rather frequent meetings with them were a problem. The best solution that we were able to work out was a one-day round-trip. Leaving Ithaca by the last plane, four of us arrived at Berkeley about midnight our time (nine by theirs) and we went directly to bed. We were there at their request and so we had specified that the whole meeting be held on Eastern time rather than their local time. The next morning we were called at seven (four their time) and met by our very sleepy-eyed architect, Ian MacKinley and his half-awake associates. They took us to the Brobeck factory where a great breakfast had been laid on the previous evening. Danish pastries heated in their automatically timed electric brazing ovens, printed menus—it was not clear whether we were having a banquet or a breakfast. In any case, we consumed it and then alertly faced our still sleepy architects for the day's meeting. At noon (nine their time) we insisted on lunch, and as our total number, about ten, trooped into a posh restaurant, the hostess was somewhat taken back, but did manage to rise to the occasion. It certainly solved the usual luncheon-time crush of a city, for no one else was there. Finally, we caught the two o'clock plane (their time) from San Francisco to return to Ithaca by midnight.

I don't know if it was at that meeting where we very nearly had to get a new architect. They had spent many months of hard work placing the laboratory building on the side of the gorge next to the athletic field under which the tunnel was to be dug. A lot of their time had gone into designing a very fancy wall, anchored by cables placed in holes dug into the bank, that was to hold back the dirt of the field while the building was being constructed and also to serve later as a wall of the building—but it was expensive. Although I had insisted on the particular location of the building, I now innocently suggested moving the building away from the bank by about 40′, which meant that their fine wall was no longer necessary. Now it turns out that architects are funny people and are not at all like ordinary people such as physicists, who are only pleased to think about this kind of a helpful suggestion. Instead, the architects turned absolutely green—arose in a body and stomped out of the room. After fifteen minutes had elapsed—one of them came back. He had torn the list of architects from the yellow pages of the telephone book. "Here", he said handing it to me with obvious disgust, "we'll help you get one of these."

In building a synchrotron, one tends to learn about all sorts of peripheral things. The experimental area of our new synchrotron is near the bottom of the Cascadilla Gorge on the campus. At one point in the negotiations with the trustees of the University, an old-timer remembered the 1935 flood and claimed that if the water came up as high again, then our tunnel would be flooded. Once the possibility was raised, it meant that we had to become experts on "high water" in Ithaca. John DeWire, in charge of our building operations, looked up old newspaper accounts and flood control accounts of various floods—but especially the 1935 flood—so we could calculate the possible water level at our site. It turned out that there was an outside chance of having to run our machine under water and the cure seemed to demolish a small dam in the gorge just down stream from us. The dam had been erected by soldiers, stationed at the nearby riding stable during World War II, so that their children could skate in the winter. However, when we suggested this obvious solution, the Conservation Department of the University rose up righteous indignation. The dam had made a small pond, now silted in, and cattails were growing there—and birds were living in the cattails. Well we understood soon enough that to a conservationist cattails are more important than mesons are to a physicist. Hence, at great expense, we replaced the old dam by a fine new job which has gates that can be opened in an emergency—that is, if someone can find the gate handle that must be carefully hidden from mischievous college students. Cattails indeed!

Once we had this sort of thing straightened out, our tunnel went out for bids. The bid opening turned out to be a touching ceremony—one of the last vestiges of capitalism in this country. At a particular day and hour, all the bidders assembled in the board room of the Administration Building. They then handed in their sealed bids—and of course most of them rushed in, dramatically licking the envelope at the last minute possible. Then the bids were shuffled and opened while the competing contractors glowered at one another. Don Jacobs, who had designed the tunnel, had estimated that the cost would be 1.2 M$. The first two bids that were opened were for 2.2 M$ and 2.7 M$, respectively. I felt just awful. Many machine builders at other places had bitterly criticized our low costs as being plain irresponsible and now I could see that everything they had said was true. Our NSF grant just wouldn't cover the cost—the jig was up. A nearby open window beckoned an easy end for it all. Several new bids in the neighborhood of 1.8 to 2 M$ didn't help. Then the miracle happened. The bid of Traylor and Assoc. was opened and read—it came to 1 M$. Hallelujah, we were saved. The rest of the bids were anticlimactic. After all the bids had been opened, Mr. Traylor stood up, the obvious winner. His face was wreathed in joy, but tears were literally streaming from his eyes. The next lowest bid was 1.5 M$ and he sadly explained to us that he would have to tell his associates just why he had dropped 0.5 M$ on the table.

The tunnel is now almost finished and he has done a beautiful job. In fact we were a little amazed at just how cooperative the tunnel men were in making small changes in the design and in seeing to it that everything was nearly perfect. They explained this to us one day. Nearly all their lives have been spent up till now building one sewer after another. This time they are building a synchrotron, and "By God", it's going to be done right!

Energy Limit for Accelerators

M. STANLEY LIVINGSTON

Harvard University

Hans Bethe's career in science has spanned the golden age of accelerators. Much of the progress in research in nuclear physics and particle physics in the past thirty years was based on the continuously increasing energy achieved by a series of electronuclear machines, each larger and more effective than its predecessor. Energy has increased almost exponentially over several decades, for most of this period rising ten-fold every six years. As each new energy range was attained by the successful operation of a new type of accelerator, a flood of experimental results on the nature of matter followed. And these results stimulated scientific interest in still higher energies and justified increasing support for accelerators. Today, high-energy physicists are essentially unanimous in the view that still higher-energy machines will be required for further progress.

Bethe was the first theoretical physicist to study accelerator problems and limitations. With M. E. Rose, in 1937, he published an analysis of the energy limitation of the cyclotron. This limit is associated with the relativistic increase in mass of ions at high energy, which requires a radially increasing magnetic field to maintain resonance in the cyclotron, and the contradictory requirement of a radially decreasing field for focusing. Although new concepts for acceleration, and technical improvements, have circumvented this limitation for other types of accelerators, the principle stated by Rose and Bethe still defines the maximum practical energy which can be achieved with the standard cyclotron.

In a broad sense, this introduction of the theorist's critique to the experimental and engineering field of accelerators presaged the future. The rapid progress of accelerator development which followed was based to a large extent on the increasing and close cooperation of theoretical analysts of electromagnetics and the equations of motion with the more practical minded accelerator physicists. It was the author's good fortune to have been a colleague of Bethe's at Cornell during those early years, building and doing research with a small cyclotron. It is fitting that this anniversary volume should include a paper by an experimentalist on the topic "Energy Limit for Accelerators", which was Bethe's first interest in the early years of this golden age of accelerators.

Steps in Accelerator Development

The increasing energy of accelerators was based on a sequence of new principles and technical advances. Four major steps in this sequence can be identified:

Direct Voltage Generators

Cockcroft and Walton performed their first experiments on artificial disintegration of nuclei in 1932, with a "voltage multiplier" which produced protons of 0.4-MeV energy. This type of accelerator is still in use, primarily as a pre-accelerator for higher energy machines, with energies up to about 1 MeV. The most successful and widely used direct voltage machine is the electrostatic generator initiated by Van de Graaff in 1931, especially in the pressure-insulated modification developed between 1935 and 1950 by Herb at Wisconsin, Trump at M.I.T., and others. The modern single-stage pressure-insulated "Van de Graaff Generator" achieves up to 6 MeV energy; two- or three-stage "tandem" generators can produce particle beams of two or three times this value.

Resonance Accelerators

The principle of resonance acceleration was first demonstrated by Lawrence and Livingston with the cyclotron, in 1931. In the cyclotron a uniform and steady magnetic field retains particles in circular orbits as they traverse the gap between a pair of electrodes, in resonance with an applied radiofrequency electric field. In each traversal they acquire an increment of energy and an increase in orbit radius. Development has led to standard cyclotrons which produce protons or deuterons with energies up to 22 MeV, close to the theoretical limit. A similar principle of resonance acceleration with radiofrequency fields applies to low-energy linear accelerators, in which particles traverse a sequence of radiofrequency electrodes in line.

Synchronous Accelerators

Synchronous acceleration provides a type of phase stability in resonance accelerators, in which the phase at which particles traverse the radiofrequency electric fields oscillates stably about an equilibrium phase which leads to continuous acceleration. The principle was announced independently and nearly simultaneously by Veksler in the U.S.S.R. and McMillan at the University of California in 1945. The first applications were to synchrocyclotrons and electron synthrotrons, with which particle energies of 300 to 500 MeV were obtained. These first synchronous machines opened the field of particle physics, primarily through the production and study of mesons. With further technical development, the principle was applied to the proton synchrotron, first with the 3-GeV† cosmotron at Brookhaven in 1952 and then the 6-GeV bevatron at Berkeley in 1954. These energies were sufficient to produce "strange" particles and antiparticles, and led to major advances in particle physics. The largest of the "weak focusing" synchrotrons is the ZGS at the Argonne Laboratory, with which 12.5 GeV was obtained in 1963.

A type of phase-stable synchronous acceleration also applies to the linear accelerator, responsible for the success of proton linacs up to 70 MeV energy and electron linacs up to 1 GeV. At Stanford a 20 GeV electron linac (SLAC) is under construction and scheduled for completion in 1966.

Alternating Gradient Focusing

The latest upward step in energy has come through application of alternating gradient magnetic focusing to synchronous and resonance accelerators. This is not a new principle of acceleration, but a technical advance in the use of gradient fields for the focusing and control of particle beams. The strong focusing resulting from use of alternating magnetic gradients in the guide-field magnets of a synchrotron, for example, reduces particle oscillation amplitudes in the orbit by a large factor. This reduction in amplitude has allowed magnets to be designed with considerably smaller cross sections, and provides the opportunity to plan and build synchrotrons with larger orbit sizes and for higher energies. The concept was originated at Brookhaven in 1952, by Courant, Livingston, and Snyder. The first important applications were

† The symbol "GeV" is now accepted for "billion electron volts" (10^9 volts) and has largely displaced the "BeV" symbol previously used in the United States.

the 28 GeV "PS" at CERN in Geneva and the 32 GeV "AGS" at Brookhaven, both in operation by 1961. The first of the large AG electron synchrotrons was the Cambridge Electron Accelerator, brought into operation at 6 GeV in 1962; several larger electron synchrotrons using AG focusing are under construction.

A special application of alternating gradient focusing to accelerators with fixed-field magnets (FFAG), developed primarily by the MURA design group at the University of Wisconsin, has led to several types of accelerators of modest energies but very high intensities. The isochronous cyclotron, which utilizes radial magnetic sectors for focusing, has had the widest application. Alternating gradient magnetic "quadrupoles" are also widely used for focusing of linear beams in high current linacs, and for control and handling of emergent high energy particle beams.

Planning for Still Higher Energies

Each major increase in particle energy has disclosed new phenomena and has opened new fields for research. The reason for this exceptional productivity was that each step in energy was a large one. The cyclotron was rapidly developed to produce energies 5 to 10 times greater than direct voltage machines. The first wave of synchronous accelerators attained 300 to 500 MeV, 20 times higher than the cyclotron. The bevatron produced 6 GeV protons, further increasing the available energy by more than 10 times. And with AG focusing the CERN and Brookhaven proton synchrotrons have reached the 30 GeV range, another factor of 5. The significant feature of accelerator progress is that energy has increased exponentially rather than linearly from one generation of accelerators to another.

High-energy physics is on the frontier of physics today. It has attracted many of the most capable and ambitious physicists, who are strongly urging the construction of accelerators of still higher energy. The fascination of particle physics lies in its fundamental significance as to the nature of matter. It deals with the structure and function of the elemental particles of which matter is formed. It provides insight into basic questions concerning the meaning of space, time, and causality. It offers the hope that fundamental simplicities will be disclosed in the laws of nature. The scientific justification has been documented in a compilation of studies and speculations by theoretical physicists entitled *Nature of Matter*, edited by Luke C. L. Yuan and published as a Brookhaven Laboratory report, BNL 888, January 1965.

It can be noted that the scientific justifications all envisage another large increase in energy in order to make significant progress. It is only for a major increase, of the order of a factor of 10, that the scientific hopes are valid. Furthermore, many scientists conceive that energies of 1000 GeV or higher will be needed to disclose the fundamental simplicities of particle physics. The need, and the demand, is not for a small step but a large one.

Informal discussions on the feasibility of accelerators of several hundred GeV energy started about 1960, and by 1962 had matured into several authorized design studies. The most practical proposals were based on engineering extensions of the principles and techniques of the AG proton synchrotron. The present 30 GeV machines at Brookhaven and CERN have been highly successful. The repetitive structural character of the AG synchrotron lends itself readily to extension in size, with essentially no change in the basic characteristics or operating properties. Beam aperture and magnet dimensions need not increase with larger sizes. Orbit alignment has proven to be simpler than anticipated, and techniques can be extended to much larger orbits. The intensities achieved with the present machines are more than 100 times the design values, and still higher intensities can be anticipated with larger orbits. Accelerator designers are confident that AG proton synchrotrons can be developed to larger and larger sizes, essentially without limit.

The leading design studies have been concentrated in three laboratories. Studies at the Lawrence Radiation Laboratory at the University of California have culminated in a proposal for a "200 BeV Accelerator Design Study", June 1965, which has been presented to the U.S. Atomic Energy Commission. At time of writing this proposal is being seriously considered for construction authorization. Meanwhile, a group at the CERN laboratory in Geneva have been studying feasibility and design problems in the same energy range, and have submitted preliminary design studies for 150 GeV and 300 GeV AG proton synchrotrons to the CERN Council for study and recommendation to the member states. There is hope among many European scientists that the financial problems will be solved and that the 300 GeV machine will be authorized within the next few years. At

Brookhaven, a longer range study program is aimed at the energy range of 600 to 1000 GeV; no basic technical limitations have been disclosed, but uncertainties regarding the timing of authorization and funding have postponed the issuing of any formal proposal.

The High-Energy Physics Research Program in the United States was the subject of Hearings before a Subcommittee of the Joint Committee on Atomic Energy of the U.S. Congress, March 2–5, 1965. Material presented at these Hearings covered reports on and justifications for continued support of the present research program, and projections for the future, including summaries of the design studies and proposals for high-energy accelerators within the U.S. These Hearings are published in a volume *High-Energy Physics Research*, Joint Committee on Atomic Energy print #46-982, 1965, available from the U.S. Government Printing Office, Washington, D.C.

To appreciate the magnitude of the effort and cost involved in such super-energy accelerators, the "200 BeV" proposal can be summarized briefly: The main synchrotron would consist of a ring of alternating gradient magnets of 690 meters average radius and 4336 m (2.7 miles) circumference. Protons would circulate within a vacuum chamber between pole faces with an elliptical aperture of 12 cm by 5 cm. Total weight of the magnet would be 20,000 tons, consisting of 480 bending and focusing AG magnets and 48 quadrupoles for matching the 12 long straight sections in the orbit. Protons would first be accelerated to 750 keV in a preinjector, and to 200 MeV in a linear accelerator, and then injected into an injector synchrotron of 100 m radius where they would be accelerated to 8 GeV at a repetition rate of 18 cps. (Note that the injector synchrotron is almost as large as the Brookhaven AGS.) A sequence of 7 pulses at 8 GeV from this injector would be used to fill the orbit of the main synchrotron, when the guide field in the orbit is 667 gauss. Protons would be accelerated to 200 GeV energy (15 kilogauss at the orbit) in 0.8 sec, when they would be ejected in a pulse lasting as long as 0.6 sec. The magnet would be pulse powered at 23 pulses per minute, with a design intensity of 3×10^{13} protons per pulse. Two large external beam areas and one internal beam area are planned for experimental use. A great variety of targets would be used, with both slow- and fast-extracted beams. Each external beam area would be 80,000 ft² arranged to accommodate emergent beam runs up to 2000 ft in length. The estimated cost of the accelerator and associated facilities is $288 million; with allowance for escalation and for initial research equipment, the total construction authorization request is for $348 million.

Alternate Concepts and Techniques

Before the scientific world proceeds with super-energy AG proton synchrotrons, it is wise to consider any other concepts for acceleration to very high energies which are available, and any alternate technical opportunities.

Scientists from the U.S.S.R. have suggested two new principles of acceleration. Budker has proposed a "plasma betatron" in which the self-focusing properties of a small, very high-intensity electron beam would be utilized to maintain a circular orbit during acceleration. However, plasma experiments in several countries show that such a beam develops instabilities and destroys itself. Experimental attempts to develop this concept into a practical accelerator in the U.S.S.R. and at CERN have been inconclusive. The present consensus is that this principle cannot be exploited for a high-energy accelerator within the foreseeable future. Also, Veksler has presented an even more speculative concept, that of "coherent impact acceleration", which would utilize coherent "collisions" between plasma bunches and single ions to accelerate the ions. No significant progress in understanding the problems involved has been made, and there is little expectation that it will prove practical.

On the technical side, the use of superconductivity has been proposed to reduce power requirements for magnets and for radio-frequency accelerating circuits. This is an exciting technical development in which major progress is now being made; it will doubtless have many important applications in the future. The first useful applications in high-energy physics laboratories will probably be to the large, high-field magnets used for experimental studies, and for other auxiliary laboratory apparatus.

For accelerator applications, the usefulness of superconductivity will be in reducing power requirements or in reducing the size of components. In principle, a resonant cavity or a linac waveguide would have essentially zero losses and extremely high impedance at super-conducting temperatures. Such circuits will be sharply resonant and can operate only at constant frequency. Since frequency tuning is essential for proton synchrotrons, and since the rf power requirements are minor, it seems unlikely that superconducting rf cavities will have any advantages. With linacs, the power required to accelerate the particle beams must still be provided, and the reduction in power would be by about 50%. Radiofrequency power is a major limitation on energy and a major cost item in linacs, and such a reduction could be important. It is to be hoped that further development of cryogenic radio frequency systems will reduce costs so their application to linacs will become practical.

As applied to magnets for accelerators the primary advantage of superconducting coils would be to raise the peak magnetic fields and thereby reduce the size of the orbit for a given energy. With iron-cored magnets the permeability of iron sets a practical limit of 16 to 18 kilogauss at the orbit, and determines the orbit radius. Present technology in the cryogenic field suggests that fields of 50 kilogauss (or somewhat higher) might be achieved without iron. This could reduce orbit size to about one-third of that with iron magnets. The cost of the development of superconducting coils will be high, and will probably exceed the cost of an iron magnet of three times the size. Furthermore, the large orbits of synchrotrons have real value in increasing the beam intensity which can be captured and accelerated per pulse; there is doubt that reduction of orbit size would be desirable.

The "storage ring", in which counter-rotating beams can be made to strike head-on and interact, with the center-of-mass of particle-particle interactions in the laboratory reference frame, offers the possibility of studying very much higher energy excitation processes than would be possible with beams striking fixed targets. Beam intensities must be very large and dimensions small, to achieve an acceptable rate of particle-particle interactions. Several small electron-electron and electron-positron storage rings are in operation or under construction. Prospects for larger storage rings are good and scientists are actively engaged in design and planning for experimental use. There is hope for ultimate application to proton-proton rings which could be filled from the 28 GeV CERN proton synchrotron, for example. However, the storage ring is not an accelerator, but a highly desirable special target system for a limited range of experiments. Even proton-proton storage rings at 28 GeV cannot be expected to provide the flexibility and wide scope of experimental opportunities possible with a super-energy accelerator.

We conclude that no new principle for acceleration to very high energies exists which could provide a practical or economical alternate to the AG proton synchrotron. And we find that recent technological developments offer no hope of reducing the unit costs of accelerators significantly.

Costs of Accelerators

The only real limit on accelerator energy is the cost. With sufficient financial support, and the application of intensive engineering development efforts, accelerators can be built for any desired energy. The same can be said of the experimental equipment required for research studies with the particle beams. The scientific principles and engineering technology of the present generation of 30-GeV AG proton synchrotrons are sufficiently well understood to extend accelerator energy to 200 or 300 GeV at the present time, and with more design effort to 1000 GeV. The problem, and the limitation, is that cost will increase essentially linearly with energy. In the absence of any new principle of acceleration, or major technological improvement, the present unit cost of about $1000/MeV cannot be significantly reduced and might even become larger. The preliminary construction cost estimate for the "200 BeV" accelerator is $288 million; the cost of a 1000 GeV machine would probably exceed $1 billion.

Costs increase with size of machines and with energy, as would be expected. Costs are greater for machines specifically designed for very high beam intensity. However, for high-energy particle studies the most pertinent beam property is energy, and intensity is secondary, at least for the first machines of a new type or for much higher energy. Accelerator costs within a given type are not always proportional to energy. For the solid-core magnets of low-energy cyclotrons the magnet weight (and cost) increase nominally with the 3/2-power of energy; with synchrocyclotrons the increasing unit cost has set a practical limit on energy. For other accelerators, such as ring-magnet synchrotrons and linear accelerators, cost varies more nearly with the energy.

It is possible to estimate an average cost per unit of beam energy for comparison between the several types of accelerators. Unit costs have actually decreased with the increasing energy of accelerators, primarily due to the sequence of new concepts described above which have reduced beam aperture and magnet size. Rough estimates are listed below of the cost in dollars per MeV for basic accelerator types, listed in order of energy:

Voltage-multiplier (0.2 to 0.5 MeV)	$250,000
Electrostatic generator (2 to 6 MeV)	50,000
Standard cyclotron (5 to 15 MeV)	10,000
Proton linac (50 MeV Brookhaven injector)	20,000
Synchrocyclotron (400 to 700 MeV)	10,000
Proton synchrotron (3 to 12 GeV)	4000
AG electron synchrotron (6 GeV, Cambridge)	2000
Electron linac (20 GeV, Stanford)	6000
AG proton synchrotron (30 GeV, Brookhaven AGS)	1000

The estimates above are for total costs, including buildings, facilities, shielding, and experimental laboratories; they do not include costs of research apparatus or of rebuilding for higher energies. With the development of large-orbit, multi-GeV synchrotrons and very long multi-GeV linacs, the fraction of cost applied to the buildings, laboratories, and auxiliary facilities has become larger. With such a costly installation the urge is to utilize the machine to the maximum. So an increasing fraction of total cost goes into large experimental laboratories, power installations, multiple beam use, heavy shielding and research facilities. Cost estimates for the next generation of accelerators show that over half the cost is allocated to such buildings and facilities.

The initial installation of a new type of accelerator is usually the cheapest in unit cost. This is due to the urge to demonstrate operability before investing in auxiliary facilities. In the past such economy in initial construction has frequently led to the need to rebuild and expand the laboratory later. A second machine of the same type, even if designed for higher energy, can be planned with more confidence and more attention can be paid to the auxiliary features needed to exploit the machine to the maximum. It is reasonable to expect that unit costs for a second machine of a given type will be as much as 50% higher than for the pioneering accelerator.

Annual costs for operation and research equipment have also increased with accelerator energy, although with wide variations. A rule-of-thumb which has gained general acceptance for estimating budgets is that such operations costs per year are about the same as the average annual rate of expenditure during construction. So the operations cost for a machine which takes four years to build might reach 25% of the construction cost after a few years of development to reach maximum capacity. This proportionality may be associated with the size of staff; the staff required for full-scale operations is seldom smaller than the construction staff used for assembly of the accelerator. Budgets are usually proportional to the size of the working staff.

Conclusion

Scientists need higher energy accelerators to continue their research on the fundamental particles of matter. Accelerator experts agree that the only practical method of achieving higher energies is through extension of the principles and techniques of the present successful AG proton synchrotrons to larger orbits. A large factor of increase in energy is essential. The next practical step is the "200 BeV" proposal, which provides a factor of 7. Design studies are proceeding for energies up to 1000 GeV, another factor of 5. Costs will be large as compared with past accelerators, or as compared with the support desired for many other fields of research science. It is clear that only the Federal Government can support research installations of this size and cost. Each new accelerator installation will become a major item in the national budget, and will require the support services of a new national laboratory with a continuing large annual operations cost.

The present program in High-Energy Physics Research, supported primarily by the U.S. Atomic Energy Commission, has an annual cost (1965) of about $165 million, including new construction, operations and equipment. Projections in the AEC Hearings in March 1965 (*loc. cit.*) suggest that this would rise to $327 million annually by 1970 if the "200 BeV" were under construction, and to $490 million per year by 1978 if an "800 GeV" accelerator is added to the program. These figures seem quite reasonable to dedicated supporters of high-energy physics, but are frightening to many others, particularly those who believe that this magnitude of support for one field of science would decrease the support for other fields. Yet it is not clear that support for other fields would decrease. And arguments have been made by many responsible scientists that this magnitude of investment in such an exceptionally important field of basic research as particle physics is reasonable and proper. One argument notes that the present level of support is only some 0.02% of the gross national income, and that this is an investment which our society can well afford.

The question, then, is: should our society invest such sums to provide the opportunities for nuclear scientists to continue their studies on the fundamental properties of matter? No practical applications are visualized beyond the expected "spin off" of new technological developments and the incidental stimulation of the economy. The results will be basic new knowledge about nature; the challenge is to the human mind. Should our society support such intellectual monuments? Are super-energy accelerators to be the "cathedrals" of our scientific and technological age?

The whole hearted support of high-energy physicists, and the interest shown by Atomic Energy Commission officials and by some influential members of the U.S. Congress, justify some confidence that the "200 BeV" proposal will be authorized in the near future. Much greater uncertainty applies to the next step, now visualized as 800 GeV. The scientific requirement that each such step be a large one, coupled with the essentially linear increase in cost, suggest that serious questions will arise. The rate of increase in energy during the past decade is already below that achieved in earlier decades. The exponent of energy increase with time is decreasing. Limitations on financial support may ultimately cause this rising curve to flatten off. It is in this sense that the past thirty-five years can be described as the golden age of accelerators. What the ultimate energy limit for accelerators will be, depends on the value that our society places on this scientific challenge.

Many will agree that a great society is ultimately known for the monuments or the intellectual achievements it leaves for later generations. We can forsee only dimly the pattern and significance of the new knowledge which continued studies in high-energy physics will bring. But we can be certain that it will be an inspiration for new scientific advances and will be an intellectual monument for our age.

Conservation of Phase Space in Hamiltonian Systems and Particle Beams

E. D. COURANT

Brookhaven National Laboratory

In a dynamical system with a finite number N of degrees of freedom, where the forces are derivable from a Hamiltonian, Liouville's theorem states that the $2N$-dimensional volume of canonical phase space occupied by an ensemble of points is an invariant of the motion.

One may ask conversely whether a given region of phase space can be transformed into any other given region having the same volume by a suitably chosen Hamiltonian acting for some time. This problem may arise in practice, for example, in the case of a beam of particles having a given distribution in longitudinal and transverse position and momentum; one may wish to design a set of electromagnetic fields whose effect would be to reduce the spread in one coordinate and its conjugate momentum at the expense of increasing the spread in the other coordinates and momenta.

Since the transformation effected by a Hamiltonian† acting for any length of time is a canonical transformation, our problem is equivalent to asking whether a canonical transformation exists which accomplishes the desired reshaping of phase space. We shall see that the answer is in the negative for *linear* canonical transformations unless the initial and final regions of phase space are "similar" in a sense to be specified.

If the variables are written in the order $q_1, p_1, q_2, p_2, \ldots, q_N, p_N$, then a linear transformation is canonical if and only if its matrix T is *symplectic*[1], i.e., if it satisfies

$$\tilde{T}ST = S \tag{1}$$

or, equivalently

$$T^{-1} = -S\tilde{T}S \tag{2}$$

† It does not matter whether the Hamiltonian depends explicitly on time or not.

257

with

$$\mathbf{S} = \begin{bmatrix} 0 & 1 \\ -1 & 0 \end{bmatrix} \oplus \begin{bmatrix} 0 & 1 \\ -1 & 0 \end{bmatrix} \oplus \cdots \oplus \begin{bmatrix} 0 & 1 \\ -1 & 0 \end{bmatrix}. \tag{3}$$

A symplectic matrix always has unit determinant[2], and therefore overall phase space is conserved. But not every unimodular matrix is symplectic; therefore, it should not be surprising to find that the transformation of regions of phase space into each other is subject to more stringent conditions than the conservation of volume. [For $N = 1$, i.e., 2×2 matrices, unimodularity and symplecticity are equivalent, but in general unimodularity imposes a single constraint on the matrix elements, while symplecticity imposes $N(2N - 1)$ constraints[2].]

Now suppose we wish to transform an ellipsoid in phase space into another ellipsoid having the same volume. We take both ellipsoids in normal form, i.e., in the form

$$\sum_i \left(\frac{q_i^2}{a_i^2} + \frac{p_i^2}{b_i^2} \right) = 1 \tag{4}$$

$$\sum_i \left(\frac{Q_i^2}{A_i^2} + \frac{P_i^2}{B_i^2} \right) = 1, \tag{5}$$

where a_i and b_i are the lengths of the principal semiaxes of Eq. (4); the area of the projection of the ellipsoid on the (q_i, p_i) plane is $\pi a_i b_i$, and its volume is

$$V = \frac{\pi^N}{N!} \prod_i a_i b_i. \tag{6}$$

We now ask whether there is a symplectic matrix $\mathbf{T}$ such that when

$$\boldsymbol{Q} = \mathbf{T}\boldsymbol{q}$$

(where $\mathbf{Q}$ stands for the vector with components Q_i, P_i) the quadratic form Eq. (4) is transformed into Eq. (5). Denoting the (diagonal) coefficient matrices of Eqs. (4) and (5) by $\mathbf{C}$ and $\mathbf{D}$, respectively, we have

$$\mathbf{C} = \tilde{\mathbf{T}}\mathbf{D}\mathbf{T}. \tag{7}$$

Multiplying on the left by $\mathbf{S}$ and using Eq. (2) we have

$$\mathbf{SC} = \mathbf{T}^{-1}(\mathbf{SD})\mathbf{T}, \tag{8}$$

i.e., the matrices $\mathbf{SC}$ and $\mathbf{SD}$ are related by a similarity transformation.

Therefore, **SC** and **SD** must have the same set of eigenvalues. The eigenvalues of **SC** are

$$\pm a_1 b_1, \quad \pm a_2 b_2, \quad \ldots, \quad \pm a_N b_N$$

and similarly for **SD**. Therefore, if the numbering of the coordinates in **D** is suitably reordered, we must have

$$a_i b_i = A_i B_i, \qquad i = 1, \ldots, N \tag{9}$$

and **T** is of the form

$$\mathbf{T} = \begin{bmatrix} \mathbf{T}_{11} & 0 & 0 & \cdots & 0 \\ 0 & \mathbf{T}_{22} & 0 & \cdots & 0 \\ \vdots & \vdots & \vdots & & \vdots \\ 0 & 0 & 0 & \cdots & \mathbf{T}_{NN} \end{bmatrix}, \tag{10}$$

where each $\mathbf{T}_{ii}$ stands for a unimodular 2×2 matrix. [If two or more of the products $a_i b_i$ are equal, **T** need not be in the form of Eq. (10) but can be reduced to it by a rotation of those of the dimensions of the phase space corresponding to the degenerate eigenvalue pairs.]

We thus conclude: An ellipsoid in phase space whose principal axes are the canonical coordinate and momentum axes can be transformed by a linear canonical transformation into another such "normally oriented" ellipsoid only if the areas of the projections of the first ellipsoid on each of the (q_i, p_i) planes are separately equal, one by one, to the corresponding projections of the second ellipsoid. The transformation is then the direct sum of N separate area-preserving, two-dimensional transformations.

We may construct the rectangular parallelepipeds tangent to and surrounding the ellipsoids

$$|q_i| \le a_i, \quad |p_i| \le b_i, \qquad i = 1, \ldots, N; \tag{11}$$

evidently the same theorem applies to these.

A beam of particles passing through any externally applied electromagnetic field, static or time-dependent, is governed by Hamiltonian equations of motion, and therefore the above restriction applies to it. However, in the "resonant beam extraction" method currently in use at CERN[3] and planned for the Brookhaven alternating-gradient synchrotron, the radial phase-space area of the extracted beam is much less than that of the beam in the synchrotron before extraction. How is this possible?

Here a beam circulates in a torus surrounding a large circle of radius R; the beam has a certain extent in (r, p_r, z, p_z) phase space and has an angular momentum spread ΔW and an angular extent 2π. The whole beam is gradually moved, outward from the circle. At one azimuth a septum is inserted and the fields are arranged so that a particle which passes this azimuth on the outside of the septum is extracted into an external beam channel, while if it passes on the inside it continues to circulate for another revolution. The field in the external beam channel can be designed so that the ensembles of particles extracted on successive turns occupy identical regions of radial phase space; evidently if the beam is extracted in K turns this region need only have $1/K$ times the area occupied by the beam in the torus. At the same time the longitudinal extent of the beam is multiplied by K.

This scheme appears to violate the theorem just proved. This is possible because the conditions assumed are not met: the septum represents a nonlinearity in the equations of motion, and our considerations were based on linear equations only. Here the linear theory applies separately to each of the K regions of phase space corresponding to the particles extracted on the first, second, ..., Kth turn. These regions are separated by narrow bands, corresponding to particles which hit the septum (because it has finite thickness), and the effective (linearized) equations of motion are different on the two sides of each of these bands.

In conclusion, we have seen that linear canonical transformations cannot transform one arbitrary region of phase space into another, even though it has the same volume, since volume conservation is a necessary but not a sufficient condition for a transformation to be canonical. However, suitable nonlinear canonical transformations may accomplish this end, as was shown by an example.

References

1. See, for example, E. D. Courant and H. S. Snyder, *Ann. Phys.*, **3**, 1 (1958).
2. Weyl, H., *The Classical Groups*, 2nd Ed., Princeton University Press, Princeton, 1946, Chap. 6.
3. Hereward, H. G., "The CPS Resonant Extraction System", *Proc. of the International Conference on High-Energy Accelerators*, Dubna, 1963 (Atomizdat, Moscow, 1964), p. 690.

Experiments on Quantum Electrodynamic Level Shifts

WILLIS E. LAMB, JR.

Yale University

On the occasion of his sixtieth birthday, it is a pleasure for me to pay tribute to H. A. Bethe for the essential contributions which he made both to the experimental determination and the theoretical understanding of quantum electrodynamic level shifts in hydrogenic atoms.

I began thinking about ways and means to measure the $n = 2$ hydrogen fine structure in the summer of 1945. Having an office at Columbia University close to the molecular beam laboratory, it was natural for me to consider using an atomic beam, but the short lifetimes of the excited states of hydrogen seemed to stand in the way. On numerous occasions I have found stimulation for research in reading papers by Bethe, and especially his wonderful review articles[1,2] such as those in the *Handbuch der Physik*. In 1933, Bethe had cleared up the question of the metastability[3] of the $2^2S_{1/2}$ state of hydrogen, and great encouragement to proceed with the experiment came from his assurance that hydrogen atoms could have a metastable state if they were carefully handled. Bethe's articles have been invaluable in many other ways for the analysis of the fine structure experiments. I mention especially his treatment of collisional excitation[4], Zeeman effect[5], hyperfine structure[6], and radiative matrix elements[7].

The first experimental results on the level shift in hydrogen were obtained by Retherford[8] and the author at the beginning of May 1947. This work was presented at the Conference on the Foundations of Quantum Mechanics held at Shelter Island on June 1–3, 1947. Among the participants with special interests in quantum electrodynamics were Bethe, Oppenheimer, Weisskopf, Breit, Kramers, Schwinger, Nordsieck, Wheeler, and Feynman. The discussion at the conference did not leave more than a hope that an explanation for the level shift could be found by taking quantum electrodynamic effects into account, with some kind of subtractive procedure. When classical electromagnetic theory was applied to a point charge an infinite self-energy was obtained. The idea of a remedy via mass renormalization is a very old one and goes back to J. J. Thomson[9] and H. A. Lorentz[10], but nobody knew in the first days of June 1947 how to carry it out in quantum electrodynamics. The 1930 paper of J. R. Oppenheimer[11] came close, but was doomed to failure because the notion of filling negative energy states of the electron was not available at that time. H. A. Kramers[12] attempted to formulate a structure independent form of quantum electrodynamics. An effort by Serpe[13] to apply the method to a harmonic oscillator did not cast any light on the problem of the hydrogen fine structure. Since these calculations were non-relativistic, the divergence of the electron's radiative self-energy was too strong. Even after the calculation of Weisskopf[14] and Furry in 1934 based on positron theory, the self-energy still diverged logarithmically. From this time on, as we now know, the possibility existed to engage in a bold subtraction of two infinite expressions in order to get a finite value for the splitting of two otherwise equal atomic energy levels. No one did this until June 1947. Among the reasons were: failure to take spectroscopic measurements seriously, distractions due to the war, and the apparent need to carry out complicated calculations involving relativistic wave functions and divergent integrals.

A few days after the conference, I received a preprint of a short article by Bethe[15] which made it clear that mass renormalization was indeed the key to an understanding of the $2^2S_{1/2} - 2^2P_{1/2}$ level shift. In a characteristic manner Bethe had bypassed all of the complication of a relativistic treatment by making a nonrelativistic calculation for those virtual light quanta for which such an approximation was valid, and by ignoring the higher frequency ones for which it was not. The result obtained for the level shift was 1040 Mc/sec and was in amazingly good agreement with the early observed value 1000 Mc/sec, and still more with later values[16] ~1058 Mc/sec. When the corresponding relativistic calculation[17] was made, the result obtained was 1052 Mc/sec, closely confirming Bethe's cutoff procedure.

The subsequent developments in calculation required the covariant formulation[18] of quantum electrodynamics. Even here, Bethe[19] in association with Baranger and Feynman, made a computation of the largest contribution 7.13 Mc/sec due to terms of order $\alpha(\alpha Z)^5 mc^2$. Recent theoretical calculations on hydrogenic level shifts have been summarized by Erickson[20]. No detailed comparison between experiment and calculation will be attempted here since measurements in progress are likely to put such a discussion out of date in short order.

A brief account of relevant experiments will be given below, confining attention mostly to resonance measurements made in the last dozen years. Among the states which have been studied are $n = 2$ and $n = 3$ of hydrogen and deuterium, $n = 2$, $n = 3$ and $n = 4$ of singly-ionized helium and $n = 2$ of doubly-ionized lithium. In addition, mention should be made of other important studies which provide information about the value of the fine structure constant although they do not involve hydrogenic fine structure directly. These include the magnetic moment of the free electron[21], the $1^1S_0 - 1^3S_1$ positronium hyperfine structure[22], the hyperfine structure of the ground state of atomic hydrogen[23], the hyperfine structure of the $2^2S_{1/2}$ states of hydrogen[24] and singly ionized helium[25], the hyperfine structure of the ground state of muonium[26], and the triplet fine structure of the helium atom[27].

In 1954, Lipworth and Novick[28] reported a value of 14,040.2 $\pm$ 4.5 Mc/sec for the $2^2S_{1/2} - 2^2P_{1/2}$ separation in He$^+$. This was obtained by an extension of earlier work by Skinner and Lamb[29] in which helium gas was bombarded by electrons, and the resulting Lyman-α = 303 Å radiation observed from the $n = 2$ states of the ion. A magnetic field is present so the fine-structure levels experience a Zeeman splitting. When microwave radiation of the right frequency is applied to the bombardment region some of the metastable $2^2S_{1/2}$ ions are caused to decay, giving additional Lyman-α radiation. The resulting resonance curves can be analyzed to give the zero-field level shift.

A very similar method was applied to the $n = 3$ states of hydrogen by Sanders[30], Wilcox[31] and the author at Stanford University. In this case molecular hydrogen was bombarded by electrons. A small fraction of the excited molecules dissociate into two hydrogen atoms one of which is in the $3^2S_{1/2}$ state. Under ordinary circumstances this can decay in 1.6×10^{-7} sec only to 2^2P with emission of 6563 Å Balmer-α radiation. If, however, the $3^2S_{1/2}$ atoms are subjected to radio-frequency radiation, they may make a transition to $3^2P_{1/2}$ before decaying. The $3^2P_{1/2}$ state lifetime is 5.4×10^{-9} sec and it mostly decays directly to $1^2S_{1/2}$ with emission of 1025 Å Lyman-β radiation.

The radiofrequency radiation thereby causes a reduction in the amount of Balmer-α reaching a detector which is sensitive to the red radiation but not to the ultraviolet Lyman radiation. Because of the smaller cross sections for the higher n states and the low quantum efficiency of red-sensitive photomultipliers, it was necessary to collect as much as possible of the Balmer-α light. This was achieved by use of an elliptical cylinder mirror with the bombardment region at one focus and the photodetector (which has to be located out of the magnetic field) at the other focus. The value obtained for the $3^2S_{1/2} - 3^2P_{1/2}$ level shift of deuterium was 315.30 $\pm$ 0.80 Mc/sec. The doublet separation $3^2P^3/_2 - 3^2P_{3/2}$ was also measured but with lower precision.

Leventhal[32], Lea[33], and the author have recently been working at Yale University on a generalization of the methods for $n = 2$ of He$^+$ and $n = 3$ of H mentioned in the last two paragraphs. In order to study the $n = 2$ fine structure of hydrogen, molecular hydrogen is bombarded by electrons to excite the $2S$ and $2P$ atomic states. A large fraction of the Lyman-α radiation is collected by ellipsoidal mirrors and brought to a photodetector for 1216 Å. Ordinarily a $2S$ atom will move to a nearby metal surface and decay without emission of radiation, but if resonant radiofrequency radiation is present, some additional Lyman-radiation is produced which reaches the detector. Because of more favorable geometrical factors, many times more metastable atoms per second can be produced than in the original beam experiments. The signal-to-noise ratios have been very large, making it possible to take recorder tracings of panoramic resonance curves in a few minutes which previously required an afternoon to procure. Extensive use will be made of a computer to assist in analysis of the data and correction for the numerous instrumental and theoretical complications. This apparatus can also be used for several other transitions. Thus, some $n = 3$ and $n = 4$ resonances in singly ionized helium have recently been seen[34,35] with very good signal-to-noise ratio.

A different method of studying the $n = 3$ fine structure of hydrogen was used by Kleinpoppen[36] at Tübingen. He formed a beam of atomic hydrogen in the ground state and illuminated it with Lyman-β radiation from a discharge lamp. This raised atoms from the $1S$ to the $3P$ states. Some of these decayed to the metastable $2S$ state. He could also apply radiofrequency radiation to the atoms in the region of ultraviolet illumination. If transitions to $3S$ occurred, the yield of hydrogen metastables was reduced and the decrease could be detected as in the earlier experiments of Retherford and Lamb. Kleinpoppen's result for the level shift in hydrogen was 313.6 ± 5.7 Mc/sec.

In 1962 at Chicago, Lichten[37] and Robiscoe[38] devised a very ingenious modification of the original $n = 2$ experiment. The beam of metastable atoms in the earlier work had several hyperfine components, m_I, and the resulting resonance curves were composite with a width as much as twice the ideal radiative width for a single hyperfine component. Lichten and Robiscoe formed their metastable atoms in a magnetic field of 575 gauss transverse to the beam where the $2^2S_{1/2}$, $m_S = +1/2$ state is metastable, but the $m_S = -1/2$ state is close to the nonmetastable $2^2_{1/2}P$, $m_J = +1/2$ state. Because of motional electric fields a strong quenching of $2^2S_{1/2}$, $m_S = -1/2$ occurs and hence the beam of metastables has only atoms in the $m_S = +1/2$ sublevel. These $m_S = +1/2$ atoms then pass into a region with zero magnetic field and subsequently into a longitudinal field of about 575 gauss. Due to nonadiabatic transitions in the passage of the metastable beam through the low field region, 1/3 of the original $m_S = +1/2$ atoms are now in $m_S = -1/2$, $m_I = -1/2$, while none are in $m_S = -1/2$, $m_I = +1/2$. Since only one of the hyperfine components of $m_S = -1/2$ is occupied, the resonances involving that state are no longer composite. Robiscoe and Lichten studied the transitions to $2^2P_{1/2}$, $m_J = +1/2$ at 605 gauss induced by a small transverse electric field, and thereby avoided the need to have a radiofrequency oscillator. From the "resonant" magnetic field, they could obtain a level shift of 1058.05 Mc/sec for hydrogen which is about 0.3 Mc/sec higher than the result of Triebwasser[16], Dayhoff, and Lamb. The new method is a good one and further measurements will be awaited with interest.

In 1959 it was shown by Madansky and Owen[39] at Johns Hopkins that very large yields of metastable hydrogen atoms could be obtained by passing fast protons through a neutralizing gas from which electron pickup leads to the $2^2S_{1/2}$ state. Recently, Donnally[40] at Lake Forest College has shown that when the neutralizing gas is cesium vapor, the charge exchange cross section is greatly increased and holds up well for low proton energies. Metastable yields as high as 10^{14} per second have been obtained. To date, only rough fine structure measurements for hydrogen have been made by this method, but the very great yield opens up new possibilities for increased accuracy of level shift determination. In fact, this method has already been used by Fan, Garcia–Munoz, and Sellin[41] at the University of Chicago for a determination of the level shift in doubly ionized lithium. A beam of Li^+ ions was formed and by charge transfer some of the ions came into the metastable $2^2S_{1/2}$ state of Li^{++}. They then made a measurement of the lifetime of this state as the beam passed through a longitudinal electric field. Their value for the level shift is 62,300 Mc/sec. The theoretically expected value[20] is $62,751.5 \pm 55.1$ Mc/sec. Further improvements are being made in the method. Although this is not a resonance technique, and the accuracy is therefore not potentially high, it is very valuable to have data on level shifts for higher atomic numbers. If this work could be extended to still higher values of Z a significant test of the theory would be possible even if the results were of low percentage accuracy.

From the foregoing, it should be apparent that prospects are very good for a considerable improvement of our experimental knowledge of the fine structure of the light atoms. It will prove a real challenge to the theory to match the experimental accuracy which is very likely to become available in the near future.

References

1. Bethe, H. A., Quantenmechanik der Ein- und Zwei-Elektronen-probleme, in *Handbuch der Physik* (Geiger–Scheel), 2nd ed., Vol. 24/1, Julius Springer, Berlin, 1933.
2. Bethe, H. A., and E. E. Salpeter, Quantum mechanics of one- and two-electron atoms, in *Handbuch der Physik* (Flügge), Vol. 35, Springer–Verlag, Berlin (1957).
3. Ref. 1, Sec. 43.
4. Ref. 1, Chapt. IV.
5. Ref. 1, Chapt. II, Part A.
6. Ref. 1, Sec. 25.
7. Ref. 1, Sec. 38–42.
8. Lamb, W. E., Jr., and R. C. Retherford, *Phys. Rev.*, **72**, 241 (1947).
9. Thomson, J. J., *Phil. Mag.*, **11**, 229 (1881).
10. Lorentz, H. A., *Theory of Electrons*, Sec. 26–37, Columbia Univ. Press (1909), reprinted by Dover, N.Y., N.Y., 1952.
11. Oppenheimer, J. R., *Phys. Rev.*, **35**, 461 (1930).
12. Kramers, H. A., *Nuovo Cimento*, **15**, 108 (1938); *Ned. T. Natuurk.*, **11**, 134 (1944); *Solvay Congress 1948*, 241–265. Brussels, 1950.
13. Serpe, J., *Physica*, **7**, 133 (1940).
14. Weisskopf, V. F., *Zeit. für Physik*, **89**, 27 (1934); **90**, 817 (1934).
15. Bethe, H. A., The Electromagnetic Shift of Energy Levels, *Phys. Rev.*, **72**, 339 (1947).

16. Triebwasser, S., E. S. Dayhoff, and W. E. Lamb, Jr., *Phys. Rev.*, **89**, 98 (1953).
17. Kroll, N. M., and W. E. Lamb, Jr., *Phys. Rev.*, **75**, 388 (1949).
18. Tomonaga, S., J. S. Schwinger, and R. P. Feynman, lectures in *Les Prix Nobel en 1965*, P. A. Norstedt and Söhner, Stockholm, 1966.
19. Baranger, M., H. A. Bethe, and R. P. Feynman, *Phys. Rev.*, **92**, 482 (1953).
20. Erickson, G. W., *Phys. Rev. Letters*, **15**, 338 (1965).
21. Wilkinson, D. T., and H. R. Crane, *Phys. Rev.*, **130**, 852 (1963).
22. Weinstein, R., M. Deutsch, and S. Brown, *Phys. Rev.*, **98**, 223 (1955).
23. Crampton, S., D. Kleppner, and N. Ramsey, *Phys. Rev. Letters*, **11**, 338 (1963).
24. Heberle, J. W., H. A. Reich, and P. Kusch, *Phys. Rev.*, **101**, 612 (1956); **104**, 1585 (1956).
25. Novick, R., and E. D. Commins, *Phys. Rev.*, **111**, 822 (1958).
26. Cleland, W., J. Bailey, M. Eckhouse, V. W. Hughes et al., *Phys. Rev. Letters*, **13**, 202 (1964).
27. Lamb, W. E., Jr., and T. H. Maiman, *Phys. Rev.*, **105**, 573 (1957); I. Wieder and W. E. Lamb, Jr., *Phys. Rev.*, **107**, 125 (1957); F. M. Pichanick, R. D. Swift, and V. W. Hughes, *Bull. Amer. Phys. Soc.*, **9**, 90 (1964); J. Lifsitz and R. H. Sands, *Bull. Amer. Phys. Soc.*, **10**, 1214 (1965).
28. Lipworth, E., and R. Novick, *Phys. Rev.*, **108**, 1434 (1957).
29. Lamb, W. E., Jr., and M. Skinner, *Phys. Rev.*, **78**, 539 (1950).
30. Lamb, W. E., Jr., and T. M. Sanders, Jr., *Phys. Rev.*, **119**, 1901 (1960).
31. Wilcox, L. R., and W. E. Lamb, Jr., *Phys. Rev.*, **119**, 1915 (1960).
32. Leventhal, M., W. E. Lamb, Jr., K. R. Lea, S. L. Kaufman, and D. L. Mader. *Bull. Amer. Phys. Soc.*, **10**, 458 (1965).
33. Lea, K. R., W. E. Lamb, Jr., M. Leventhal, and S. L. Kaufman, *Bull. Amer. Phys. Soc.*, **10**, 458 (1965).
34. Leventhal, M., K. R. Lea, and W. E. Lamb, Jr., *Phys. Rev. Letters*, **16**, 163 (1966).
35. Lea, K. R., M. Leventhal, and W. E. Lamb, Jr., *Phys. Rev. Letters*, **15**, 1013 (1965).
36. Kleinpoppen, H., *Zeit. für Physik*, **164**, 174 (1961).
37. Lichten, W. L., and R. T. Robiscoe, *Bull. Amer. Phys. Soc.*, **8**, 429 (1963).
38. Robiscoe, R. T., *Phys. Rev.*, **138**, A22 (1965).
39. Madansky, L., and G. E. Owen, *Phys. Rev. Letters*, **2**, 209 (1959).
40. Donnally, B. L., T. Clapp, W. Sawyer, and M. Schultz, *Phys. Rev. Letters*, **12**, 502 (1964).
41. Fan, C. Y., M. Garcia–Munoz, and I. A. Sellin, *Phys. Rev. Letters*, **15**, 15 (1965).

Limits of Quantum Electrodynamics

F. LOW

Massachusetts Institute of Technology

I. Introduction

The laws of electrodynamics, as formulated by Maxwell a hundred years ago, have since been successfully extrapolated over a frequency range of $\times 10^{20}$ and through the two revolutions of special relativity and quantum mechanics.

The most economical way of expressing these laws makes use of the language of quantum field theory. In this language, the equations which give the dependence of the field on its sources are

$$\frac{\partial}{\partial x_\mu} f_{\mu\nu} = -j_\nu \tag{1.1}$$

$$\frac{\partial}{\partial x_\mu} \varepsilon_{\mu\nu\,\lambda\eta} f_{\lambda\eta} = 0. \tag{1.2}$$

In Eqs. (1.1) and (1.2) the $f_{\mu\nu}$ stand for the electromagnetic field strengths and the j_ν for the four-vector current density. The transition from classical to quantum theory is made, following Dirac, by considering the fields and currents to be operator functions of space and time instead of c-numbers.

Equations (1.1) and (1.2) do not provide a complete theory, since the equations for j_ν are missing. Only the continuity equation

$$\frac{\partial j_\nu}{\partial x_\nu} = 0 \tag{1.3}$$

and the conservation of charge

$$\dot{Q} = 0 \tag{1.4}$$

(where $Q = (1/i) \int j_4(x)\, dx$) are implied by Eq. (1.1).

In the nineteenth century, to be sure, the dynamics that determined the behavior of j_μ was not known, but a phenomenology was developed that was sufficient for the solution of most practical problems. Thus the current density was replaced by suitable averages, broken up into "free" and "bound" currents, etc. A similar present-day phenomenology applied to particle interactions would include contributions to j_μ from all charged and nonself-conjugate neutral particles as well as from the field strengths $f_{\mu\nu}$ themselves (as in the scattering of light by light, π_0 decay, etc.). Since we are at present unable to perform accurate calculations of processes involving the strongly interacting particles, we are usually forced to employ such a phenomenological description in describing typical e.m. interactions with hadrons (electron–proton scattering, photo–meson production, etc.).

An exception to this necessity has been the physics of electrons (and more recently of muons) and photons, or quantum electrodynamics (q.e.d.). In this theory, one considers only leptons, photons, and "external" static fields approximating those of an atomic nucleus. The photons are described by Eq. (1.1), and the leptons by the Dirac equation,

$$\gamma_\lambda\left(\frac{\partial}{\partial x_\lambda} - ieA_\lambda - ieA_\lambda^{(e)}\right)\psi + m\psi = 0, \tag{1.5}$$

where A_λ is the radiation-field vector potential, and $A_\lambda^{(e)}$ is the "external" field. The current is given by

$$j_\lambda = ie\bar\psi\gamma_\lambda\psi. \tag{1.6}$$

Equations (1.1)–(1.6), together with the commutation relations, provide a formal framework for a renormalized theory, which can be used to calculate to arbitrary order in the coupling constant $e^2/4\pi\hbar c \cong 1/137$. It is, of course, the renormalized power series, rather than the original equations, which in effect constitute what we call quantum electrodynamics, and with which we must for the present compare experiment.

II. Comparison with Experiment

It appears likely that a failure of q.e.d. will be associated in some way with a characteristic mass M_0, or equivalently with a momentum M_0c, an energy M_0c^2, or a length $r_0 \sim \hbar/M_0c$. Thus one may look for a failure by performing high-precision measurements at low energies or moderate-precision measurements at high energies.

The most spectacular success of q.e.d. has been the accurate prediction of the μ and e magnetic moments and of the energy levels of hydrogen-like atoms.

1. At present both magnetic moments are in agreement with q.e.d. calculations. A convenient mnemonic for recalling the sensitivity of an experiment to modifications of the theory at high energies is the following: replace the photon (or electron) propagator $1/k^2$ by $(1/k^2)$ $\pm (1/k^2 + M_0^2)$ and determine a lower limit for M_0 from a particular experiment. This mnemonic works only for experiments that are in agreement with theory, and it is important to remember that it is a mnemonic and not a theory. It seems extremely unlikely that if q.e.d. were to fail, it would fail according to Feynman's rules, with only a modified propagator or vertex function to tell the difference. In any case, the magnetic-moment results place $M_0 > 100$ MeV (from the electron experiment) and $M_0 > 1$ BeV (from the muon experiment).

2. The spectrum of hydrogen is very accurately accounted for by the theory. The most sensitive experimental test here is the Lamb shift, i.e., the $2P_{1/2} - 2S_{1/2}$ energy difference, which is calculated to be 1057.64 $\pm$ 0.15 Mc, in good agreement with the value of Lamb and coworkers, but in slight disagreement with a new measurement of Robiscoe, which gives 1058.07 $\pm$ 0.10 Mc. Although it is probably too soon to worry, one should note that this is quite a large discrepancy; it is three times the contribution of the "proton structure" effect that one would estimate from electron scattering measurements. It can therefore not be described by the mnemonic given in the preceding paragraph, since the same combination of propagation function and true proton-structure occurs in both the small angle electron scattering and the Lamb shift. This illustrates (*a*) the relative insensitivity of the Lamb shift to high energy modifications of q.e.d. and conversely (*b*) the difficulty of explaining a deviation from theory of the former by the latter. It is important to try to remove the purely *experimental* discrepancy (three standard deviations) as well as to make absolutely sure that all conventional effects have been included in the calculation.

3. There is a long-standing discrepancy of 35 parts per million (two standard deviations) in the h.f.s. (hyperfine structure) of the 1*s* state of hydrogen. However, this depends on the value of α^2 as measured in the 2*P* state fine structure of hydrogen, and the experimental Lamb-shift discrepancy referred to above has introduced a doubt as to the correct value of this interval. The situation seems to be the following: if we assume no change in the original measurement of the $2S_{1/2} - 2P_{3/2}$ interval, then the Robiscoe measurement of $2S_{1/2} - 2P_{1/2}$ determines a new value of α^2 which removes the h.f.s. discrepancy. In that case, however, we still have a discrepancy in the Lamb shift. Here again, further experimental and theoretical work is needed before any firm conclusion can be drawn.

4. The h.f.s. of positronium is in agreement with experiment. The accuracy here is not comparable to the previously discussed work, but the theory involves several interesting points, including a very subtle application of the general principles of renormalization. The agreement here can not be translated into a value of M_0, but it has served to increase our confidence in the over-all correctness of q.e.d. in a variety of different applications.

5. The h.f.s. of muonium ($\mu^+ + e^-$) is also in agreement provided we use the accepted value of α. In summary, the precision experiments are in excellent general agreement. There may be discrepancies, but if so they are at the limit of accuracy, and may therefore not persist.

We come now to the high-energy experiments. These are: e–e, e–p, and μ–p scattering, and $\mu^+\mu^-$ and e^+e^- production by γ's on C.

6. The e–e scattering results come from the Stanford 300 MeV storage rings. They agree with the predictions of q.e.d., and set $M_0 > 500$ MeV.

7. The e–p scattering alone is only a partial test of q.e.d. since the structure of the proton is involved. However, the ratio of e–p to μ–p scattering (neglecting the small μ mass) should be one, and it is, to accuracy $M_0 > 3$ BeV!

8. The $\mu^+\mu^-$ and e^+e^- photoproduction experiments are done at angles such that the μ mass is not always negligible, and the two cross sections might be expected to be somewhat different. However they appear to be very different. The μ-pair experiments agree with the Bethe–Heitler formula, whereas the e pairs do not, by a factor of order of magnitude 100% for a virtual e mass of 400 MeV.

Since the μ-pair experiments would have shown a discrepancy due to specifically nuclear effects, we can probably safely assume that the e-pair experiments are either wrong, or a significant breakdown of q.e.d.

III. Failure of Q.E.D.

1. In the first place, we know now that quantum electrodynamics must fail in three essentially obvious ways.

(a) Strongly interacting particles contribute to the current operator j_μ on the right-hand side of Eq. (1.1) and thus cannot be completely neglected in discussing the physics of e's, μ's, and γ's. In terms of Feynman diagrams, this means that D_{Fc} the complete photon propagator will depend on vacuum polarization of hadrons. In fact, the weight function of the spectral representation is proportional to the total $e^+ + e^-$ lowest order annihilation cross section (including annihilation into e^+e^-, but exclusive of the elastic Coulomb cross section). That is:

$$(D_{Fc})_{\mu\nu}(k) = \delta_{\mu\nu} D_{Fc}(k^2) + k_\mu k_\nu G, \tag{3.1}$$

where only the first term is of interest. The function D_{Fc} has the spectral representation

$$D_{Fc}(k^2) = \frac{1}{k^2} + \frac{137}{4\pi^2} \int \frac{\sigma_a(M^2)\, dM^2}{M^2 + k^2}, \tag{3.2}$$

where σ_a is the $e^+ + e^-$ absorption cross section at mass M previously refered to. In perturbation theory, charged spin $1/2$ particles contribute

$$\sigma_a \underset{M \to \infty}{\longrightarrow} \frac{4\pi}{3} \left(\frac{1}{137}\right)^2 \cdot \frac{1}{M^2} \tag{3.3}$$

and charged spin-zero particles

$$\sigma_a \underset{M \to \infty}{\longrightarrow} \frac{\pi}{3} \left(\frac{1}{137}\right)^2 \cdot \frac{1}{M^2}. \tag{3.4}$$

Thus every noninteracting charged spin $1/2$ particle contributes

$$\delta D \to \frac{1}{3\pi} \cdot \frac{1}{137} \log \left(\frac{k^2}{m^2}\right) \tag{3.5}$$

and every noninteracting charged spin-zero particle contributes

$$\delta D \to \frac{1}{12\pi} \cdot \frac{1}{137} \log \left(\frac{k^2}{m^2}\right) \tag{3.6}$$

to D_{Fc}, where m is the mass of the particle and k^2 the momentum transfer in the process being calculated (say e–e scattering).

Of course, since σ_a is primarily a strong production cross section, we cannot reliably estimate its true dependence on M^2. It comes entirely from one partial wave ($J = 1$), and hence the high-energy dependence $1/M^2$ is a natural one, at least for that part coming from two-body final states. There is, however, no real unitarity bound here, since the coefficient $(1/137)^2$ puts us way below the unitarity limit. In the event of a disastrous growth of σ_a, in contrast to the form (3.3), this limit would only be achieved by higher order e.m. processes at very high energy.

Even if the behavior of σ_a is as indicated by Eq. (3.3), the total contribution of all pairs, triplets, etc. to D_{Fc} can be considerable, since there are more than fifty particles below 2 BeV. which can be produced in various combinations. Since $\log (k^2/m^2)$ can also be somewhat larger than one, the small factor $1/137$ might be effectively canceled.

All the more so if σ_a turns out to grow more strongly with energy. If we have

$$\sigma_a \to \frac{1}{M^2} (M^2)^\alpha \tag{3.7}$$

then the representation (Eq. (3.2)) holds, although at high k^2 D_{Fc} will grow more rapidly than $\log (k^2/m^2)$. However, if $\alpha > 1$, then the representation (Eq. (3.2)) diverges, and D_{Fc} contains an arbitrary subtraction constant as well as a rapid growth rate. This last possibility appears unlikely, although at present we cannot rule it out. We will have a much better estimate of this problem when $e^+ + e^-$ cross sections have been measured.

(b) Aside from vacuum polarization of hadrons, it appears that either the e^2 power series expansion for the vacuum polarization in pure q.e.d. must diverge at sufficiently high energy

$$\frac{1}{3\pi} \left(\frac{e^2}{4\pi\hbar c}\right) \log \frac{k^2}{m^2} \sim 1$$

even for arbitrarily small coupling constant, or the theory must have a ghost, as has been forcefully emphasized by Landau and collaborators. The argument goes as follows: one can show that the power series for $[D_{\text{Fc}}(k^2)/k^2]^{-1}$ can be written in the form

$$[D_{\text{Fc}}(k^2)/k^2]^{-1} = 1 - \lambda + e^2 f_1(\lambda) + e^4 f_2(\lambda) + \cdots, \tag{3.8}$$

where

$$\lambda = \frac{1}{3\pi} \left(\frac{e^2}{4\pi\hbar c}\right) \log \left(\frac{k^2}{m^2}\right). \tag{3.9}$$

Thus, as $e^2 \to 0$ at fixed λ,

$$D_{\text{Fc}} \to \frac{1}{k^2} \frac{1}{1-\lambda}. \tag{3.10}$$

This function has a pole at $\lambda = 1$, which is forbidden by the required analyticity properties of D_{Fc}. Thus either the theory is inconsistent in this limit, or the power series from which Eq. (3.8) is derived diverges. As a matter of practical importance, for $(e_2/4\pi\hbar c) \sim 1/137$, the relevant values of k^2 can be ignored. However, as a matter of principle, the power-series solution is certainly sick at high k^2. Of course, the theory itself may still make sense, but so far nobody knows how to find out, since the only operations we are able to perform start with the power series.

There is also an argument of Dyson against the convergence of the power series at $e^2 = 0$. Suppose we make e pure imaginary (which is permissible if the theory is analytic at $e = 0$). Then, since like particles now attract, the vacuum is unstable: a cluster of N electrons and a distant one of N positrons can be made with binding energy $\sim N^2 e^2/R$ at the expense of mass energy $2mc^2N$. Clearly our considerations are easily valid for $R > N^{1/3}a_0$, where a_0 is a fixed length (say the Bohr radius). Thus instability sets in by $N \sim 10^6$ and probably less. Conclusion: we may not continue e to ie, and still obtain the appropriate functions (S matrix, etc.) since the latter do not exist. Of course, this argument does *not* prove that the function of e^2 correctly calculated for $e^2 > 0$ is not analytic at $e^2 = 0$.

The Landau breakdown would exist for finite photon mass, but the Dyson mechanism fails in that case, so that it is an infrared phenomenon.†

(c) The Leptons undergo weak interactions, such as $\bar{\nu}_e + e^- \rightarrow \bar{\nu}_\mu + \mu^-$ or $e^- + \nu_\mu \rightarrow \mu^- + \nu_e$, as well, presumably, as virtual reactions like $e^- \rightarrow \mu^- + \nu_e + \bar{\nu}_\mu \rightarrow e^-$, and these must contribute interaction terms to Eq. (1.5).

Although weak processes go weakly ($\sim 10^{-5}$ in amplitude) at moderate energies (~ 1 BeV), a purely local four-fermion weak coupling, aside from being unrenormalizable, becomes strong at higher energies, at least in the sense that the first-order interaction exceeds the unitarity limit at c.m. energies of order $\sqrt{10^5 M_N}c^2 \sim 300$ BeV. Thus $e^- + \mu^+$

† Other "infrared" phenomena are the existence of an infinite number of bound states for arbitrarily small values of e^2 which certainly invalidates a series expansion of the S-matrix in power of e^2, as well as the famous Bloch–Nordsieck result that the elastic (i.e., radiationless) scattering amplitude of charged particles must vanish. Although we are not yet fully able to solve all such problems, we can solve most of them, and we believe that they are a correct reflection in the theory of a real physical difficulty, the existence of zero-mass particles, and thus we do not consider this breakdown of the power series to be a breakdown of electrodynamics.

interactions at this energy would be strongly affected by the strong process

$$e^- + \mu^+ \to \nu_e + \bar{\nu}_\mu$$

which is not included in the usual electrodynamic description.

If the β-decay interaction is mediated by a locally coupled charged vector meson of moderate mass (the hypothetical W), then the effective four-fermion coupling is less singular, and the unitarity limit is exceeded at much higher energies ($\sim 10^5 \, M_N c^2$). On the other hand, the electrodynamics of charged vector particles is not renormalizable in the conventional way, so that although the "weak" interaction would be made weaker, the electromagnetic interaction would be much stronger, leading to all sorts of new difficulties, including possibly the kind of k^2 dependence discussed in this section under $I(a)$. Several interesting attempts to deal with nonrenormalizable theories by partial summation of the power series have been made. These are still in too rudimentary a state to be properly assessed, so that for the moment the whole question of virtual and high energy weak interactions is open.

2. It is possible that q.e.d. will fail in a way that is essentially similar to $I(a)$ and (c), that is, through as yet undiscovered but conventional interactions of leptons with other particles or fields. We have previously discussed the interactions of photons with hadrons, corresponding to the addition of new currents to Eq. (1.1).† We are now thinking specifically in terms of interactions of new particles with leptons (not including neutrinos) through extra terms in the Dirac equation (in field theory) or extra couplings and particles (in S-matrix theory). If we restrict ourselves to renormalizable couplings the possibilities are quite limited.

(*a*) We may have coupling to a boson field of the form

$$L_1 = g_1 \bar{l} \Gamma_b l \varphi_b, \tag{3.11}$$

where φ_b may stand for a scalar, neutral pseudo-scalar, or vector field and l the electron or muon field.

(*b*) We may have coupling to a neutral boson field and an excited lepton:

$$L_2 = g_2 \bar{l}' \Gamma_b' l \varphi_b + \text{h.c.} + g_1 \bar{l} \Gamma_b l \varphi_b + g_1' \bar{l}' \Gamma_b l' \varphi_b. \tag{3.12}$$

† It is also possible that the right-hand side of Eq. (1.2) not vanish, corresponding to the existence of a magnetic current density, $j_\mu^{(M)}$, although at present the difficulties of consistently formulating such a theory seems considerable. One should also remember that $j_\mu^{(M)}$ can be different from zero without the existence of magnetic poles. In this connection we should mention that e–He scattering experiments have shown no electric dipole moment of the electron.

(c) We may have associated $l' + b$ production only, thus

$$L_3 = g_2 \bar{l}' \Gamma_{b'} l \varphi_b + \text{h.c.} \qquad (3.13)$$

where in (3.13) φ_b need no longer be neutral.

In this last case there is a new quantum number Q' such that

$$Q'_{l'} + Q'_b = Q'_l. \qquad (3.14)$$

(If $e' = \mu$, for example, the conserved quantum number could reduce to leptonic number, with $N_e(b) = 1$, and $N_\mu(b) = -1$. If $e' = \bar{\mu}$, we would have $N_\mu(b) = +1$.)

In all these cases, there are the two possibilities: φ_b coupled or not coupled to hadrons.

Although it is certainly of interest to search directly for particles like e' and b, it appears very unlikely that they can provide an explanation of the electron pair production anomaly. In order to account for the large effect observed there one must either have (i) a strong coupling g_1 or g_2 and a moderate mass ($< 1/2$ BeV) for b (and or e') or (ii) an electromagnetic strength coupling due to exchange of b between the electron and nucleus. Both of these possibilities are unlikely. Consider (i) first. The strong coupling g_1 or g_2 must be much weaker for muons, since the μ pair production is not anomalous, and the μ magnetic moment is only normally anomalous, $(g - 2)/2 = \alpha/2\pi$. On the other hand, the μ–p scattering is very closely equal to the e–p scattering, and a strong g_1 or g_2 coupling of the e and not of the μ would destroy the equality.† Similarly, in case (ii), the extra coupling must be absent for the μ, whereas it would contribute normally to both e–p and μ–p scattering. Thus we again arrive at a contradiction, barring unforeseen small dimensionless numbers: for example the $\bar{N}Nb$ form factor [in case (ii) above] might decrease rapidly for large t, and the $\bar{e}eb$ form factor be small for small t ($\bar{e}eb$ does vanish at $t = 0$ for scalar or pseudo-scalar b and massless leptons).

3. We finally discuss very briefly the possibility that the approach based on local fields, locally coupled, is incorrect and must be modified in some way at small distances. A rationale for such a modification is frequently based on the divergence of unrenormalized q.e.d. However, we have no good reason to think that the theory is actually divergent. We have seen earlier in this section that the renormalized power series

---

† In addition, direct search for production of an e' in $e + p$ collisions has yielded negative results for $Me' \gtrsim 1$ BeV.

for D_{Fc} very probably diverges at large p^2/m^2. Yet it is precisely the high p^2/m^2 behavior of the *individual terms* in this power series which have led us to believe in the divergence of the charge renormalization constant $1/Z_3 = e_0/e$. In fact, $1/Z_3$ might as easily be finite as infinite. If $1/Z_3$ is finite, then we now know that vanishing bare electron mass leads to finite observed mass. Thus, as yet, we need not require a modification since $1/Z_3$ and $\delta m = m - m_0$ could both be finite, and q.e.d. could be a completely consistent, although incomplete, physical theory.

This view is strengthened by the enormous difficulty experienced by people who have tried to tamper with the theory as it stands. In particular, if one attempts to formulate the theory in terms of non-locally coupled fields, the whole delicately balanced structure collapses. The old formulation, at least formally, had the following properties: Lorentz invariance, gauge invariance, causality, unitarity, and a consistent simple quantization procedure. Unitarity and Lorentz invariance are fairly straightforward to maintain and causality one may be willing to give up, especially since the connection between microcausality and macrocausality, as well as the meaning of macrocausality, is somewhat obscure. On the other hand, the photon mass is known to be zero to great accuracy, $(h/m_\gamma c \gg 10^5 \text{ km})$ so that exact gauge invariance must be preserved. Nonlocality plus gauge invariance leads to highly non-linear equations of motion, so that the difficulty of quantizing (and solving) is compounded. These arguments, although clearly not compelling, make such theories aesthetically unattractive. Of course, we cannot rule out the possibility of nature choosing an ad hoc, aesthetically unattractive set of equations to follow, but we can hope that she has not.

If our present field theory insists on being wrong in some basic way, it seems much more likely that the change will not be to some highly involved patched up version with arbitrary nonlocal functions, but rather to a conceptually new and broader description. This has been our experience in the past in the transition from a mechanistic to a field theoretic description of interactions, and from classical to quantum kinematics, and it may well be again.

References

Early Formulation of q.e.d.

Maxwell, J. C., *Roy. Soc. Lond.*, **155**, 459 (1865).
Dirac, P. A. M., *Proc. Roy. Soc. (London)*, **A114**, 243 (1927).

Heisenberg, W., and W. Pauli, *Zeits Phys.*, **56**, 1 (1929).
Furry, W. H., and J. R. Oppenheimer, *Phys. Rev.*, **45**, 245 (1934).

Renormalization Theory

Tomonaga, S., *Prog. Theor. Phys.*, **I**, 27 (1946).
Schwinger, J., *Phys. Rev.*, **74**, 1439 (1948); **75**, 651 (1949); **76**, 790 (1949).
Feynman, R. P., *Phys. Rev.*, **76**, 749 (1949); **76**, 769 (1949).
Dyson, F. J., *Phys. Rev.*, **75**, 486 (1949); **75**, 1736 (1949).

Magnetic Moments and Atomic Spectra

theory:

Sommerfield, C. M., *Phys. Rev.*, **107**, 328 (1957) ⎤ Magnetic moment.
Peterman, A., *Helv. Phys. Acta.*, **30**, 407 (1957) ⎦
French, J. B., and V. F. Weisskopf, *Phys.*, *Rev.* **75**, 1240 (1949) ⎤ Lamb shift.
Kroll, N. M., and W. E. Lamb, *Phys. Rev.*, **75**, 388 (1949) ⎦
Fulton, T., and P. Martin, *Phys. Rev.*, **95**, 811 (1954) ⎤ h.f.s.
Zemach, A. C., *Phys. Rev.*, **104**, 1771 (1956) ⎦
Karplus, R., and A. Klein, *Phys. Rev.*, **86**, 257 (1952)] positronium.

experiment:

Foley, H. M., and P. Kusch, *Phys. Rev.*, **73**, 412 (1948)] e moment.
Charpak, G., et al., *Physics Letter*, **1**, 16 (1962)] μ moment.
Dayhoff, E. S., S. Triebwasser, and W. E. Lamb, *Phys. Rev.*, **89**, 106 (1953); **89**, 98 (1953)] Lamb shift.
Robiscoe, R. T., *Phys. Rev.*, **138**, A22 (1965).
Anderson, L. W., et al., *Phys. Rev. Letter*, **4**, 69 (1960) ⎤ h.f.s.
Cleland, W. E., et al., *Phys. Rev. Letter*, **13**, 202 (1964) ⎦
Deutsch, M., and S. Brown, *Phys. Rev.*, **85**, 1047 (1952)] positronium.
Sanders and Lipworth, *Phys. Rev. Letter*, **15**, 900 (1965)] e electric dipole moment.

High-Energy Experiments

Hand et al., *Rev. Mod Phys.*, **35**, 335 (1963)] e–p scattering.
Cool, R., et al., *Phys. Rev. Letter*, **14**, 724 (1965)] μ–p scattering.
dePagter, J. K., et al., *Phys. Rev. Letter*, **12**, 739 (1964)] μ-pair production.
Blumenfeld, R. B., et al., *Phys. Rev. Letter*, **14**, 660 (1965)] e-pair production.
Behrend et al., *Phys. Rev. Letter*, **15**, 900 (1965)] search for e'.

Miscellaneous Theory

McClure, J. A., and S. Drell, *Nuovo Cimento*, **37**, 1638 (1965)] cut-off calculations.
Yukawa, H., *Phys. Rev.*, **76**, 300 (1949)] nonlocal field theory.
Chrétien, M., and R. E. Peierls, *Nuovo Cimento*, **10**, 667 (1953)] nonlocal field theory.
Low, F. E., *Phys. Rev. Letter*, **14**, 238 (1965)] excited leptons–photons.
Yennie, Frautschi, and Suura, *Ann. Phys.*, **13**, 379 (1961)] infrared problems.
Drell, S., and F. Zachariasen, *Phys. Rev. Letter*, **19**, 463 (1960)] effect of strong interactions.

Landau, L., *Niels Bohr and the Development of Physics*, McGraw-Hill (1955)]
    D_{Fc} as log $p^2/m^2 \to \infty$.
Källen, G., *Helv. Phys. Acta*, **25**, 417 (1952)] spectral representation.

Reviews

Peterman, A., *Forts. der Phys.*, **6**, 505 (1958).
Feynman, R. P., Solvay Congress (1961).
Pipkin, F. M., *Proceedings of the 1965 Oxford Conference on Elementary Particle
    Physics.*
Drell, S., F. Zachariasen, *Electromagnetic Structure of Nucleons*, Oxford (1961).

Bethe-Salpeter Equation

R. E. CUTKOSKY

Carnegie Institute of Technology

The "two-body problem" has a special importance in the history of dynamics. The problem is to determine how two particles behave when they are influenced by their mutual interactions; since this is the simplest dynamical problem, it provides the most direct confrontation between a new theory and experiment, and it also serves as the example which students first consider when they are learning about older theories and developing their analytical skills. However, in the relativistic quantum field theory even the two-body problem is extremely complicated; in a certain sense it does not really exist. The paper in which E. E. Salpeter and H. A. Bethe[1] discussed the formulation of bound-state problems in the relativistic quantum theory penetrated many of the difficulties and has become one of the classics of modern theoretical physics.

In either relativistic or nonrelativistic, quantum or nonquantum mechanics, the one-body problem does not involve any dynamics because there is no source for any forces to act on the particle. The entire problem is one of description, that is, of finding a suitable definition of the force-free situation and a description of the free motion of particles. In the relativistic quantum theory, this is not a trivial problem, but it has been solved[2]. A step halfway toward the two-body problem is taken if we consider the motion of a single particle which is acted upon by given forces. This may be visualized as a two-body problem in which one of the bodies is infinitely heavy, and which is therefore immovable although it exerts forces upon the other. If the forces are indeed known, this dynamical problem can be solved by standard methods, although in some cases it may require complicated and lengthy calculations or possibly even raise novel qualitative points. In nonrelativistic mechanics, the general two-body problem is no harder when an expression for the potential energy is known explicitly; after the motion of the center of mass is separated out, one is left with an equivalent one-particle problem, in which the mass of the single fictitious particle is $m_1 m_2/(m_1 + m_2)$. The two-body problem cannot be reduced in this simple way in relativistic mechanics. In fact, since an instantaneously communicated force is not, by itself, Lorentz invariant, the problem of determining the forces between the particles and the problem of finding how they move under those forces are necessarily mixed up.

Salpeter and Bethe considered two-body problems in which the forces were transmitted by a field, and most of the complications arise from the field theory, rather than from the necessity for maintaining Lorentz invariance. It is possible to formulate relativistic equations with "action-at-a-distance" forces between particles; it is instructive to consider such theories, and note how much simpler they are. An action principle for a nonquantum relativistic particle mechanics can be written in the general form [cf., Wheeler and Feynman[3], Schild[4]]:

$$A = m_1 \int d\tau_1 + m_2 \int d\tau_2 + \iint U(\tau_1, \tau_2)\, d\tau_1\, d\tau_2, \qquad (1)$$

where τ_i is the proper time of the ith particle, and A is to be stationary with respect to small changes in each orbit $x_{i\mu}(\tau_i)$. The interaction function U is a scalar function of the displacement $x_\mu = x_{1\mu}(\tau_1) - x_{2\mu}(\tau_2)$ and of the velocities $x'_{i\mu}$ (the prime denotes a derivative with respect to the proper time). For particles interacting via half-advanced and half-retarded electromagnetic potentials, we have[3,4]:

$$U = e_1 e_2\, \delta(x^2) x'_{1\mu} x'_2. \qquad (2)$$

The equations of motion which are obtained from Eq. (1) have the form[5]:

$$x''_{1\mu} = \int F_\mu(x, x'_1, x'_2)\, d\tau_2. \qquad (3)$$

We observe that the most natural way to obtain covariant equations of motion is to associate with each particle its own proper time, which is not correlated in a simple way with the time of any inertial reference frame. Unfortunately, there is no simple way to solve equations of motion written in this form, because the acceleration of one particle at a given instant depends not only upon the past, but also upon the future motion of the other. However, there are procedures which can reduce the equations, although perhaps not for the most general interactions or orbits, to a form which more closely resembles nonrelativistic equations. We consider the motion of the two-particle system in a reference frame in which the space components of the total momentum vanish—a center of mass frame—and look only at the space components $\mathbf{x}$ of the relative coordinate (the fourth component is taken to be zero, i.e., the particles are looked at simultaneously, in this reference frame). We assume that if the values of $\mathbf{x}$ and $\dot{\mathbf{x}}$ are given at any instant, the entire orbit $\mathbf{x}(t)$ is uniquely determined; in particular, then, there must exist a relation of the general form

$$\ddot{\mathbf{x}} = \mathbf{f}(\mathbf{x}, \dot{\mathbf{x}}). \tag{4}$$

Moreover, we know that an energy integral exists, so it must be possible to cast Eq. (4) into a canonical form with a Hamiltonian

$$H(\mathbf{x}, \mathbf{p}) = (m_1^2 + \mathbf{p}^2)^{\frac{1}{2}} + (m_2^2 + \mathbf{p}^2)^{\frac{1}{2}} + V(\mathbf{x}, \mathbf{p}). \tag{5}$$

(We have taken the speed of light equal to unity and later shall also take $\hbar = 1$. It is very hard to go directly from Eq. (3) to Eq. (4), but as long as one is only interested in the two-body problem, one can just as well use Eq. (5) as the starting point for an action-at-a-distance theory, instead of Eq. (1).)

A Hamiltonian function of the general form of Eq. (5) has been used in constructing a relativistic quantum mechanics for particles interacting via action-at-a-distance by Coester[6] and Schroer[7]. It must be emphasized that in such a formalism one does not guarantee relativistic invariance through the explicit use of covariant concepts everywhere in the theory, but by being careful to work only in a co-ordinate system which has a special significance. The only difficulty of this Hamiltonian approach is to show how to use such an "effective Hamiltonian" consistently in problems involving several particles; this difficulty has been overcome by Coester and Schroer.

These action-at-a-distance theories possess a certain property of "macroscopic causality", which means, roughly speaking, that if a particle traverses a very dilute gas, it is possible to define in an unam-biguous way the time-order of its successive collisions and to ignore its future collisions in calculating its present whereabouts. However, during any given collision, a similar distinction can not be made; in particular, when several particles are simultaneously close together, it is not possible to unscramble the temporal order of their mutual influences, because of the fact that they are supposed to interact over a spacelike separation. In order to guarantee that a theory is one in which the principle of causality is valid over distances of arbitrarily small size, it is necessary that the interactions be retarded, and then the interaction must be considered to be transmitted by some physical agency which carries energy and momentum, in order that these quantities be conserved.

At first sight, it may appear that the use of a retarded interaction should simplify the two-body problem, because in calculating the forces on one particle it is no longer necessary to guess the future behavior of the other. Unfortunately, the simplification is illusory; in order to determine the forces, it is necessary to consider the equation of motion for the field which transmits them, which extends infinitely the number of degrees of freedom which must be taken into account. In the quantum field theory, it is quite explicit that an unlimited number of field quanta must be considered along with the original two particles, so that even to speak of a two-body problem requires optimism and a considerable idealization. If the interaction with the field is sufficiently weak that the amplitude for finding more than two particles is small, it is natural to describe the field through the use of perturbation theory; this is the approach through which the Bethe–Salpeter equation as well as earlier formulations were developed, and which we will describe later. However, if the interaction is strong, each particle acquires a very complicated structure, and if looked at closely, is seen to be in reality a multiparticle system itself. In this circumstance, it is more reasonable to think of the two-body problem as arising from a kind of idealization which is similar in spirit to the Hartree method.

Since a microcausal field theory is so much more complicated than a macrocausal particle theory, it is necessary to consider why it is worth bothering about microcausality, which, after all, cannot be checked directly. First, to compensate for the technical difficulties, microcausality provides a philosophical simplification. In a macrocausal particle theory, the form of the unknown functions in Eq. (1) or Eq. (5) must be chosen on an *ad hoc* basis and can not be understood in terms of a physical mechanism. In a microcausal theory, on the other hand, the forces are carried by particles which themselves move in accordance with the principles of the relativistic quantum theory, so it must be possible to predict the forces to a considerable degree, although just how far such calculations can be carried is not yet known. The essential point, of course, is that so many of the predictions of quantum field theory check with experiments. The success of quantum electrodynamics is well known. Even in the strong interactions, where so many numerical predictions have only a qualitative success, the dispersion relations, which are almost direct consequences of microcausality, are verified as exactly as the precision of the data allows. Moreover, particles have been discovered which can be identified as the quanta which are associated with the long range part of interparticle forces, and, as required by the theory, for nearly all of the known particles, the anti-particle has been also found and shown to have the same mass. In the case of the K_0 and the $\bar{K}_0$, the equality can be checked to 1 part in 10^{14}! In addition, the processes of emission and absorption of particles and antiparticles are found to be consistent with "crossing symmetry".

Now that we have, in the above somewhat lengthy introduction, described the branch of theoretical physics of which the Bethe–Salpeter equation forms a part, let us turn to the development of the equation. A good discussion of earlier attempts to construct a relativistic two-body equation for electrodynamical calculations can be found in the book by Bethe and Salpeter[8,9]. In order to understand the content of the fully covariant formulation, it is best to begin with the approach of Tamm[10] and Dancoff[11], so we shall describe here how that method works in the first approximation. Let $W_i = (m_i^2 + \mathbf{p}_i^2)^{1/2}$, and let $\psi(\mathbf{p}_1, \mathbf{p}_2)$ and $\psi(\mathbf{p}_1, \mathbf{p}_2, \mathbf{p}_3)$ be the amplitudes for the two and three particles, respectively, in the momentum representation. The equations for these two amplitudes are then, if we neglect the four-particle amplitude, as follows:

$$E\psi(\mathbf{p}_1, \mathbf{p}_2) - (W_1 + W_2)\psi(\mathbf{p}_1, \mathbf{p}_2)$$

$$= \int (2\pi)^{-3} d^3k [f_1(\mathbf{p}_1, \mathbf{k})^\dagger \psi(\mathbf{p}_1 - \mathbf{k}, \mathbf{p}_2, \mathbf{k}) + f_2(\mathbf{p}_2, \mathbf{k})^\dagger \psi(\mathbf{p}_1, \mathbf{p}_2 - \mathbf{k}, \mathbf{k})],$$

$$(6a)$$

$$(E - W_1 - W_2 - W_3)\psi(\mathbf{p}_1, \mathbf{p}_2, \mathbf{p}_3)$$

$$= f_1(\mathbf{p}_1 + \mathbf{p}_3, \mathbf{p}_3)\psi(\mathbf{p}_1 + \mathbf{p}_3, \mathbf{p}_2) + f_2(\mathbf{p}_2 + \mathbf{p}_3, \mathbf{p}_3)\psi(\mathbf{p}_1, \mathbf{p}_2 + \mathbf{p}_3). \quad (6b)$$

Here we denote by $f_i(\mathbf{p}, \mathbf{k})\delta(\mathbf{p} - \mathbf{k} - \mathbf{p}')$ the amplitude for the element-ary process of emission of a particle of momentum $\mathbf{k}$ by the particle of momentum $\mathbf{p}$, which subsequently has the momentum $\mathbf{p}'$. The form of this function f depends on the spins of the particles and is determined by kinematical arguments. Under the assumption that the elementary emission process occurs at a point, f is a sum of one or several independent known functions each multiplied by a dimensionless "coupling constant".

In the center-of-mass reference frame, with $\mathbf{p} = \mathbf{p}_1 = -\mathbf{p}_2$, we substitute from Eq. (6b) into Eq. (6a), and obtain the equation

$$E\psi(\mathbf{p}) = (W_1 + W_2)\psi(\mathbf{p}) = (2\pi)^{-3}\int d^3k\, V_E(\mathbf{p}, \mathbf{k})\psi(\mathbf{p} - \mathbf{k}), \qquad (7)$$

where we write

$$V^E(\mathbf{p}, \mathbf{k}) = -\frac{f_1(\mathbf{p}, \mathbf{k})^\dagger f_2(\mathbf{k} - \mathbf{p}, \mathbf{k})}{W'_1 + W_2 + W_3(\mathbf{k}) - E}$$
$$-\frac{f_2(-\mathbf{p}, -\mathbf{k})^\dagger f_1(\mathbf{p} - \mathbf{k}, -\mathbf{k})}{W_1 + W'_2 + W_3(\mathbf{k}) - E}. \qquad (8)$$

Note that we have also dropped the terms in which the third particle is emitted and subsequently reabsorbed by the same particle. It is not possible to justify this in a fully rigorous way within the Tamm–Dancoff method, but the heuristic idea is simple enough; it is that only particle exchanges provide an interparticle interaction, while the other terms affect the internal structure of the individual particles, and moreover, are already partly taken into account when we use the experimental value of the m_i in Eq. (7). The general form of the operator on the right-hand side of Eq. (7) is very similar to the Hamiltonian (Eq. (5)) (since a function of p and k' can be related to another function of p and $\partial/\partial p$), so we are justified in referring to this operator as an "effective Hamiltonian" for the two-particle system. We see, however, that as a result of using field theory there are two characteristic differences. In the first place, the effective potential depends explicitly upon the total energy E. This expresses the fact that the interaction is retarded, and we note that if $E > m_1 + m_2 + m_3$, the denominators in Eq. (8) become singular, and the effective potential develops an imaginary part (as it must, in order to allow for the fact that at such energies particles can be created in collision processes, with the result that the two-particle amplitude decreases). The second point is that the potential is a known function; the only arbitrariness is represented by the masses and coupling constants.

The expression (Eq. (8)) for the effective potential is only an approximation, and in order to go further it is necessary to be able to identify unambiguously the self-interaction effects which contribute to the observed values of the masses and coupling constants. It is necessary to use the Lorentz-transformation properties in this identification, and this can only be done in a formalism which explicitly maintains the relativistic invariance at every stage of the calculation. If one makes approximations to a theory which is only implicitly invariant, there is a danger that even the relativity will be lost by the approximation. Salpeter and Bethe were fortunate in having at hand the manifestly covariant formulation of quantum field theory and of the renormalization procedure which had recently been established through the work of Tomonaga, Schwinger, Feynman, and Dyson, and were able to apply it to the specific problem of constructing an equation for bound states; in doing so they were among the first to have recognized and exploited the power of Feynman graphs. In a sense, of course, the equation is implicit in the general theory, and important contributions to its formulation were also made by Schwinger[12] and by Gell–Mann and Low[13]. The eponymy is the reminder of a characteristic simplicity and lucidity of description, combined with a firm understanding of the physical problems requiring such an equation for their solution and a practical concern with techniques for coping with its mathematical complexities, which is to be found in reference 1.

It is easy to see (with the benefit of hindsight) that the way to obtain an explicitly covariant two-body equation is to ascribe to each particle its own time variable, as well as its own position in space, just as in Eq. (1) and Eq. (3). The square modulus of the two-particle Schrödinger wave function $\psi_{12}(x_1, x_2, t)$ is the probability of finding the first particle at x_1 and the second at x_2, at a given time t. The covariant amplitude $\Psi_{12}(x_{1\mu}, x_{2\mu})$ is a single function which, as $x_{1\mu}$ and $x_{2\mu}$ vary over all relatively spacelike values, provides for arbitrarily moving observers similar information about the location of the two particles. When the points are relatively timelike, however, the interpretation of the amplitude is more complicated, because the first observation necessarily disturbs the system in a way which can affect the result of the second observation through the propagation of a physical signal from the first point to the second. To describe the meaning of the amplitude in this case, it is necessary to be quite specific about the kind of experiment that one has in mind for the observation of the particles. The simplest way to detect the location of the particle (i) is to arrange to annihilate it if it arrives at the point $\mathbf{x}_i$ at the time $t_i = x_{i0}$; this is certainly consistent with the correspondence principle, and it leads to an amplitude which can be analytically continued from spacelike to timelike relative coordinates. Moreover, such an amplitude can be incorporated into the general formalism in an especially simple way[1,12,13]. The reader who would like to envisage a scattering experiment for measuring this amplitude may imagine fictitious particles a_i and b_i which interact extremely weakly via the reaction $a_i + (i) \rightarrow b_i$; the S-matrix for the reaction $a_1 + a_2 + \alpha \rightarrow b_1 + b_2$ gives directly the Fourier transform of the amplitude $\Psi_{12}(x_{1\mu}, x_{2\mu})$ for the state α, which may be either a bound state or a continuum state (cf., ref. 14).

The appearance in the Bethe–Salpeter amplitude of two time variables is the natural way to achieve a covariant formulation, and does not by itself complicate the interpretation of the amplitude. However, it does not have the same simple physical interpretation as the two-particle Schrödinger amplitude, because it describes not a two-particle state, but a state of a quantum field. The physical particles are not pointlike objects; nevertheless, it is necessary to define the amplitude in terms of annihilation operators which act at a point in order to be able to use the causality properties which are inherent in the theory. Since a local operator $\psi_i(x_{i\mu})$ influences the state of the field at the single point $x_{i\mu}$, it cannot be guaranteed that it will annihilate just the physical particle (i); it will also annihilate anything with the same quantum numbers (electrical charge, spin, etc.) which happens to be present, and it will also create the antiparticle of (i). The Bethe–Salpeter amplitude, which is defined as[13]

$$\Psi_{12}(x_{1\mu}, x_{2\mu}) = \langle 0|T\psi_1(x_{1\mu})\psi_2(x_{2\mu})|\alpha\rangle \tag{9}$$

can be interpreted as a two-particle probability amplitude only when the probability of finding additional particles is negligible, which is at least approximately true in electrodynamics and will always be correct in the limit $|\mathbf{x}| \rightarrow \infty$, where the two particles do not interact. The time-ordering operator T in Eq. (9) expresses the fact that the annihilation operator with the earliest time variable is applied to the state first.

In order to avoid the possibility that any reader might be misled into neglecting the original papers, we shall not review here the derivation of the equation, but merely state that the first step is the establishment of the following symbolically written integral equation for the two-particle propagator G_{12}:

$$G_{12} = G_1 G_2 + G_1 G_2 I_{12} G_{12}, \tag{10}$$

where the G_i are the one-particle propagators and I_{12} describes their interaction via exchanged particles. At a center-of-mass energy equal to the mass of a bound state, G_{12} has a pole, and the residue is proportional to Ψ_{12}, which satisfies the homogeneous equation

$$\Psi_{12} = G_1 G_2 I_{12} \Psi_{12}. \tag{11}$$

In order to see the general structure of this equation, let us make the simplest possible approximation, in which I_{12} arises from exchange of a single particle, and the free-particle propagators are used. This approximate equation has, in momentum space, the following simple form:

$$(p_1^2 - m_1^2)(p_2^2 - m_2^2)\Psi_{12}(p_1, p_2)$$
$$= i \int \frac{d^4 k F_1 F_2 \Psi(p_1 - k, p_2 + k)}{(2\pi)^4 (k^2 - m_3^2)}, \tag{12}$$

where we use, for four-vectors, the notation $p^2 = p_0^2 - \mathbf{p}^2$. The factors F_i are functions of momenta which depend on the spin of the particles, and are covariant analogues of the f_i which were used in discussing the Tamm–Dancoff method; they have, by virtue of the covariant formalism, a simpler form than the f_i. If all the particles have zero spin, we have $F_i = g_i$ (the renormalized coupling constant). The momenta in Eq. (12) satisfy $p_{1\mu} + p_{2\mu} = P_{\alpha\mu}$; it is convenient to choose the momentum of the bound state to have the form $P_{\alpha\mu} = (E, 0)$. Equation (12) is a good approximation to the general Bethe–Salpeter equation when the coupling constants are small, and it can be shown by consideration of the analytic structure of G_{12} and Ψ_{12}, that it always contains the correct leading term in the interaction when the particles are far apart in space.

Although the presence of the relative time variable x_0 in the Bethe–Salpeter equation helps to make the physical interpretation of the equation simple and natural, this extra variable greatly complicates the mathematical analysis of the equation. Moreover, the equation depends on the energy nonlinearly, so the energy can not be interpreted as an eigenvalue in the usual way. The artifice that is used to express Eq. (11) as an eigenvalue problem is to replace I_{12} by λI_{12} and treat E as a parameter and λ as the eigenvalue; E is then fixed by the requirement $\lambda(E) = 1$.

One of the simplest of a variety of methods for obtaining an equivalent "one-time" equation is to note that if the interaction were really instantaneous, the only dependence on x_0 would be that given explicitly by the G_i in Eq. (11). If a function satisfying this ansatz is substituted for Ψ_{12} in Eq. (12) (defining simultaneity in the center-of-mass frame), one obtains the lowest-order Tamm–Dancoff approximation (Eq. (8))[15,16]. The ansatz can be improved systematically by iteration, leading to a series for the effective potential which is essentially the same as that obtained by the Tamm–Dancoff method, except for the treatment of renormalization terms[16]. More recently, the techniques of dispersion relations have been applied to the problem of constructing an effective potential; we note, in particular, the work of Blankenbecler and Sugar[17], which is based on an explicit identification and a separate treatment of the inelastic channels. However, at least for bound states, it does not seem advantageous to go through the intermediate step of calculating an effective potential [except in electrodynamical calculations, where one is usually close to the nonrelativistic limit, and where one can use gauge invariance to separate out an instantaneous Coulomb potential as a good first approximation[15]].

For large values of $|\mathbf{x}|$, $\Psi(\mathbf{x}, x_0)$ decreases exponentially for bound states just as the Schrödinger amplitude, but the dependence on x_0 is more complicated. [We henceforth omit the subscript (12).] Wick[18] proved that it is possible to analytically continue Ψ to complex values of x_0, and that it also decreases exponentially as x_0 goes to infinity in the upper or lower half plane. The Bethe–Salpeter equation thus takes a more tractable form if it is considered for imaginary values of x_0, instead of real values. This is particularily clear in momentum space, where we obtain an integral equation in which there are no singularities near the contour of integration; it is also convenient to write $p_4 = -ip_0$, because in this case the familiar trick with the Minkowski metric actually has physical significance[18]. If the interaction has a finite range, the form of the exponentially decreasing tail of Ψ is given by the two-particle free propagator $K^{-1} = G_1 G_2$ [18], with a coefficient given by $g = \Phi(m_1^2, m_2^2)$, where we define (in momentum space) $\Phi(p_1^2, p_2^2) = K\Psi$. This quantity g can be interpreted as the renormalized coupling constant for the interaction between the bound state and the two constituents.

The adjoint amplitude is[13]

$$\bar{\Psi}(x_1, x_2) = \langle \alpha | T \bar{\psi}_1(x_1) \bar{\psi}_2(x_2) | 0 \rangle. \tag{13}$$

This is not just the complex conjugate of Ψ; if either of the particles (i) is a Dirac particle, for example, we must multiply by a Dirac matrix β, thus in general, we have a factor B. Moreover, in calculating $\bar{\Psi}$, we have to use the same prescription of giving masses in propagators small negative imaginary parts that applied to Ψ, and as a result $\bar{\Psi}$ is an analytic continuation of Ψ^* to the other side of the branch cuts in the relative energy variable[19,20,21]. The result is easiest to express if we use the Wick rotation; for real values of the modified relative momentum $p_\mu = (\mathbf{p}, p_4)$, we have:

$$\bar{\Psi}(\mathbf{p}, p_4) = \Psi^*(\mathbf{p}, -p_4)B. \tag{14}$$

With this definition of the adjoint, the Bethe–Salpeter equation is self-adjoint:

$$K\Psi = \lambda I\Psi; \qquad \bar{\Psi}K = \lambda\bar{\Psi}I. \tag{15}$$

It is implicit in these equations that we can use $\bar{\Psi}K\Psi$ (an appropriate integration is understood) to normalize the amplitude. This norm is obviously not positive definite when the constituents are Dirac particles (because of the factor B), but it can be negative even with scalar particles as a consequence of the relative-time dependence[20,21]. The physical normalization of the bound state can be obtained from the requirement that the total charge of the bound particle be the sum of the charges of its constituents[22,23], provided this charge is not zero; in the general case, the normalization can be obtained by calculating the residue of the pole of the two-particle Green's function[24,25,26]. The result is that the physical norm is equal to the implicit norm multiplied by $d\lambda^{-1}/dE$. All physical properties of the bound state, in particular, the renormalized coupling constant g defined above, can be calculated from the normalized amplitude.

It can be shown, for scalar particles with the lowest-order interaction (Eq. (12)), that the Bethe–Salpeter equation possesses solutions for which both the implicit and the physical norm are negative[20,21]. If $m_1 = m_2$, these solutions are odd functions of p_4. They occur only if λ is rather large, and it is not known if the complete Bethe–Salpeter equation also possesses such solutions, or what their significance would be. In general (but not when $m_1 = m_2$), states whose physical norm is negative contribute to the scattering matrix poles whose residues have the "wrong" sign. This does not contradict directly the unitarity of the S-matrix for two-particle elastic scattering, which is automatically guaranteed by the Bethe–Salpeter equation, but it is in conflict with the unitarity of the entire S-matrix, if use is also made of cluster and analyticity properties[27]. It is possible that this difficulty arises only from an approximate interaction in which virtual multiparticle states are not treated exactly. It should be noted that the indefiniteness of the implicit norm has the consequence that the eigenvalue $\lambda(E)$ might vary in unexpected ways as E changes, and even be complex below the elastic threshold[28].

The equation takes on a one-dimensional form in certain special circumstances, such as in the nonrelativistic limit, when $E = 0$ and $m_1 = m_2$, or when a simplified interaction is used[18,29], and in these cases it is not hard to solve. Otherwise, very complicated and extensive numerical calculations are necessary. This fact discouraged use of the Bethe–Salpeter equation in strong-interaction physics for a long time, and made it clear that the development of more general analytical methods for studying the S-matrix was essential. However, the Bethe–Salpeter equation has itself played an important role in the development of dispersion relations, because the ladder approximation provides a model which is, in a sense, intermediate between nonrelativistic two-body problems and the actual field theory. Two potentially useful conjectures about the exact S-matrix, the Mandelstam representation[30] and the Regge–Sommerfeld–Watson representation[31], have so far been verified for the ladder approximation, but not in general.

The development of fast computing machinery has made it possible to reconsider the utility of the Bethe–Salpeter equation for dynamical calculations. It is likely, therefore, that the future will see an increasing use of this equation in the strong interactions, especially as it is becoming clear that its most complicated features are really inherent in quantum field theory, and even in formalisms which are based more directly on dispersion relations can only be recast in another form, and can not be eliminated or ignored without careful attention to the possibility of error[32,33]. The progress made in the meantime with the study of analytic properties of arbitrary Feynman amplitudes can be applied directly to the problem of calculating the propagators of the physical particles and the interaction between them, and will also help to simplify the calculation of properties of their bound states.

The successes of dispersion relations and of symmetry schemes have shown that it is possible to think of all of the presently known strongly-interacting particles as entering into the theory on an equal footing. In the current view, all the known particles could be made out of some much heavier constituents whose properties are completely unknown. Nevertheless, the outermost structure of any physical particle is necessarily resolvable into relatively light virtual particles which interact with each other by exchanging other particles. The long range part of these forces between constituents are, as we have noted, determined by the masses and coupling constants of the exchanged particles. It is easy to see, therefore, that the properties of the known particles must necessarily exhibit a certain "bootstrap" effect. The problem of determining self-consistent values of particle masses and coupling constants can be formulated in a convenient way in terms of the Bethe–Salpeter equation; so far, however, it has been used only in rather simplified calculations[34]. The Bethe–Salpeter equation seems to have some advantages for the problem of understanding the physical origin of the systematic patterns observed among particle masses and coupling constants—the phenomenological symmetries. In fact, the symmetries can be considered to arise from covariance properties (in addition to the relativistic covariance) of the self-consistency equations; these properties can be exhibited especially easily when the Bethe–Salpeter equation is used[35].

In conclusion, it should be pointed out that the bootstrap applications are not really new, but were, along with the electrodynamical applications, actually foreseen in ref. (1). That paper contains an extensive discussion of the interaction between nucleons as mediated by the exchange of mesons, and also proposes that the equation be used to study the properties of mesons, as obtained as bound states of nucleon–antinucleon pairs[36].

References

1. Salpeter, E. E., and H. A. Bethe, *Phys. Rev.*, **84**, 1232 (1951).
2. Wigner, E. P., *Ann. of Math.*, **40**, 149 (1939).
3. Wheeler, J. A., and R. P. Feynman, *Rev. Mod. Phys.*, **17**, 157 (1945); **21**, 425 (1949).
4. Schild, A., *Phys. Rev.*, **131**, 2762 (1963).
5. Van Dam, H., and E. P. Wigner, *Phys. Rev.*, **138**, B1576 (1965).
6. Coester, F., *Helv. Phys. Acta*, **38**, 7 (1965).
7. Schroer, B., *Seminar on High Energy Physics and Elementary Particles*, Trieste, 1965, to be published.
8. Bethe, H. A., and E. E. Salpeter, *Quantum Mechanics of One- and Two-Electron Systems*, Springer, Berlin, 1957, p. 170.
9. Ibid., p. 195.
10. Tamm, I., *J. Phys. USSR.*, **9**, 449 (1945).
11. Dancoff, S. M., *Phys. Rev.*, **78**, 382 (1950).

12. Schwinger, J., *Proc. Nat. Acad. Sci. U.S.*, **37**, 452, 455 (1951).
13. Gell-Mann, M., and F. Low, *Phys. Rev.*, **84**, 350 (1951).
14. Cutkosky, R. E., *Phys. Rev.*, **125**, 745 (1962).
15. Salpeter, E. E., *Phys. Rev.*, **87**, 328 (1952).
16. Macke, W., *Phys. Rev.*, **91**, 195; **92**, 1075; *Naturforsch.*, **8a**, 599 (1963).
17. Blankenbecler, R., and R. Sugar, *International Conference on High-Energy Physics*, Dubna, 1964.
18. Wick, G. C., *Phys. Rev.*, **96**, 1124 (1954).
19. Nishijima, K., *Prog. Theoret. Phys. (Kyoto)*, **10**, 549 (1953); **12**, 279 (1954); **13**, 305 (1955).
20. Nakanishi, N., *Phys. Rev.*, **138**, B1182; **139**, B1401; **104**, B947 (1965).
21. Ciafaloni, M., and P. Menotti, *Phys. Rev.*, **140**, B929 (1965).
22. Mandelstam, S., *Proc. Roy. Soc. (London)*, **A232**, 248 (1955).
23. Klein, A., and C. Zemach, *Phys. Rev.*, **108**, 126 (1957).
24. Allcock, G. R., *Phys. Rev.*, **104**, 1799 (1956).
25. Cutkosky, R. E., and M. Leon, *Phys. Rev.*, **135**, B1445 (1964).
26. Lurie, D., A. J. Macfarlane, and T. Takahashi, *Phys. Rev.*, **140**, B1091 (1965).
27. Olive, D., *Phys. Rev.*, **135**, B745 (1964); K. Hepp, *J. Math. Phys.*, **6**, 1762 (1965).
28. I am grateful to Dr. G. H. Renninger for helpful discussions on these points.
29. Cutkosky, R. E., *Phys. Rev.*, **96**, 1135 (1954).
30. Wanders, G., *Nuovo Cimento*, **17**, 535 (1960).
31. Lee, B. W., and R. F. Sawyer, *Phys. Rev.*, **127**, 2266 (1962).
32. Sawyer, R. F., *Phys. Rev.*, to be published.
33. Cutkosky, R. E., *Brandeis Lectures on Theoretical Physics*, 1965, to be published.
34. Cutkosky, R. E., and M. Leon, *Phys. Rev.*, **138**, B667 (1965); K. Y. Lin and R. E. Cutkosky, *Phys. Rev.*, **140**, B205 (1965).
35. Belinfante, J. G., R. E. Cutkosky, and G. H. Renninger, *Seminar on High Energy Physics and Elementary Particles*, Trieste, 1965, to be published.
36. Fermi, E., and C. N. Yang, *Phys. Rev.*, **76**, 1739 (1949).

Asymptotic Quantum Field Theory

F. ROHRLICH

Syracuse University

It is a great pleasure for me to contribute this paper to the celebration volume in honor of Professor Hans A. Bethe. His tremendous insight into the specific consequences of physical theory have not been superseded in more than a generation. I join the many others from all over the world in extending my congratulations to him.

1. Approach

The name "asymptotic quantum field theory" characterizes the quantum field theory which developed during the last ten years and which differs in approach but not in contents from the better known "axiomatic quantum field theory". Both theories start with axioms which characterize local relativistic quantum fields in terms of operator (valued) distributions; both theories have the same goal of a mathematically as well as physically satisfactory formulation yielding the predictions which confirmed the Tomonaga–Schwinger and Feynman–Dyson quantum electrodynamics to such unprecedented precision since the late 1940's.

The primary difference between asymptotic and axiomatic quantum field theory lies in the relative emphasis on physics and mathematics in the present state of development of both formulations. The basic philosophy of the axiomatic approach is a careful investigation of the mathematical implications of certain axioms which are stated in sufficient detail to permit the full impact of present-day mathematics. The approach of the theory which I shall outline in the following attempts to permit a wider use of the physicist's intuition over that of the mathematician.

The missing mathematical rigor is to be supplied gradually. For example, at first a formalism is developed in which neither divergent integrals are encountered nor recourse to bare particles or fields is taken. Subsequently, it will have to be shown that the S-matrix and other physical consequences can be so derived and the axioms can be so stated (in their technical details), that no mathematically undefined quantities are encountered. This will involve the question of the definition of products of distributions and their test function space and eventually also domain questions of the resultant operators.

The first stage of this program is sketched here with the omission of all proofs; for the latter the relevant references are cited. The emphasis is on the structure of the theory as it is developed so far. It is essential to ascertain that the theoretical predictions are in agreement with experiment before one proceeds to the subsequent stages of mathematical rigorization.

This approach is typical for theoretical physics. Its fruitfulness is supported by many historical instances. To refer to just one, the reader should recall that the mathematical rigorization of quantum mechanics by von Neumann came *after* the developments by Heisenberg, Schrödinger, and Dirac. The existence of the helium spectrum was in fact mathematically unproven[1] until 1951. Whether one considers quantum mechanics to be a meaningful theory already before von Neumann or only after him is partly a matter of taste and partly a matter of semantics.

After the confirmation of quantum electrodynamics by experiments of very high accuracy the theoretical physicist of the early 1950's was faced with two problems. The successful theory was mathematically untenable and something very basic seems to be wrong as indicated by Källén's famous proof[2] of inconsistency. Secondly, the generalization of quantum field theory from electromagnetic to other types of interactions remained unsuccessful. The first problem seems to require solution before the second problem can be seriously attacked. But that first problem involves a difficulty which also exists in classical electrodynamics: the infinite self-energy of a point charge. Many people therefore, feel that the problem is very deep. Perhaps field theory should be abandoned altogether.

The classical theory of point charges has recently been developed sufficiently far to permit presentation as a mathematically consistent and physically meaningful theory[3]. This is important for two reasons:

it shows that the difficulties in question are not intrinsic to the classical theory, and it presents us with a theory which can reasonably be considered as the classical limit of a mathematically satisfactory quantum electrodynamics. While no such limiting procedure is known at present, its existence is in my opinion a necessary consequence of the logical coherence of physical theory in general[4]. In any case, this classical theory provides an important guide-line for the formulation of quantum field theory. We note specifically that the classical theory is free from self-energy problems despite the point nature of the particles; furthermore, the concept of "bare particle" is nowhere used so that no renormalization occurs.

2. Highlights of the Development

It has been known for a long time that Lagrangian or Hamiltonian (canonical) formulations as a basis for a quantum field theory must necessarily be heuristic. While these methods are widely used to "derive" the field equations and the commutation relations, the following is clear. First, a quantum field theory can never be *derived* from a classical field theory because the former is on a higher logical level; the quantization process is an inference of q-number equations from c-number equations which is adopted because no other guide seems available. Second, an extremum principle (which is a necessary concomitant of a Lagrangian formulation) cannot be carried through in a q-number theory because the calculus of variations is in general not defined for operators but only for c-number functionals. An attempt some years ago of defining functional differentiation with respect to interacting operator fields has led to inconsistencies (anticommuting c-numbers) and has not yielded fruitful results; it is likely to be unjustifiable mathematically[5].

The ideas of Lehmann, Symanzik, and Zimmermann[6] in which Lagrangian and Hamiltonian methods are replaced by such assumptions as an asymptotic condition and an S-operator were to be highly welcomed. Their papers mark the beginning of the development of asymptotic quantum field theory. The work of Nishijima and his collaborators[7] contributed greatly to the further development of these ideas. He also attempted to bring the dispersion relation methods back into the theory after they had become an off-shoot of the LSZ formalism (though the ideas are much older than that). However, the theory was not far enough advanced to permit dynamical calculations. It had not yet succeeded in reproducing the results of standard quantum electro-dynamics which it attempted to replace. Not surprisingly, therefore, people who wanted to obtain results which are useful to the experimenters turned to dispersion relations or gave up quantum field theory completely in favor of more promising schemes. The reason for this failure lay in the apparently unsurmountable arbitrariness of the scattering matrix off the mass shell, whose determination is essential for a meaningful dynamics. The decisive first step in this direction was taken by Pugh[8] on the basis of ideas that were latent in the literature[6,7] and in particular were hinted at by the Russian school[9]. His guess, educated by extensive electrodynamic calculations, was formulated as a basic postulate giving the definition of the interpolating field, and the functional dependence of the S-matrix elements on the interpolating field off the mass shell. He verified that up to and including third order calculations this postulate yielded exactly the same physical predictions as standard electrodynamics. Specifically, the theory reproduces exactly the known renormalized results without itself requiring renormalization, or cut-offs. He also showed that such thorny questions as the gauge problem can be handled in a satisfactory way[10].

Meanwhile Stoddart[11] obtained the result that the emerging theory does not lead to any great surprises in the analyticity structure which is so successfully used in dispersion relations. Only those singularities occur in the scattering matrix which are required by the generalized unitarity relations arising from the postulated off-mass shell behavior.

Recently, the off-mass shell structure of the n-point function which was postulated for each n in Pugh's thesis[8], was proven to be related to that of the two-point function by unitarity and the other assumptions[12]; it can be derived for all n from the off-mass shell structure for $n = 2$ as will be shown below. This was a great simplification of the previous formulation, but Pugh's axiom for $n = 2$ still appeared as a nonobvious and arbitrary assumption. The link of this dynamical axiom with more accepted assumptions was finally brought about through causality.

For some time two different causality assumptions have been used in quantum field theory. LSZ used the older microcausality statement of local commutativity of two observables at relatively spacelike points as generalized by axiom to apply not only to interacting Bose fields but also (in the form of *anti*commutation relations) to interacting Fermi fields. A different causality statement was proposed by Bogoliubov[13]. It is a statement about the retarded nature of the functional derivative of the current operator (see below). The relation of these two causality conditions was studied[14,15] and it was found that Bogoliubov causality is a very powerful tool[17] despite the fact that it can almost be derived from microcausality and Lorentz invariance[16] (see below).

The important link with Pugh's dynamical axiom was accomplished when it was possible to show that the usual axioms of symptotic quantum field theory, when expressed in terms of Bogoliubov causality, imply this dynamical axiom[17]. This means that the off-mass shell behavior of the S-matrix elements can in fact be found without this axiom.

In what follows I shall first briefly discuss the two main mathematical tools with which the theory presently operates and then discuss the axioms, and the S-operator and its matrix elements. This is followed by a discussion of the current equation which replaces the old field equations. In most of these discussions we shall restrict ourselves to the neutral scalar fields. The generalization to charged fields and to higher spins does not seem to present fundamental difficulties and has actually been carried out for several specific cases. The last section will be devoted not only to a summary of the present state of the theory but also to a brief discussion of some of the many questions that have yet to be answered. These involve problems of asymptotic quantum field theory as well as problems of the relation of this theory to S-matrix theory, and to the group theoretic approach to elementary particle physics.

3. The Mathematical Tools

In addition to the well-known mathematical apparatus of quantum field theory such as distributions, Hilbert space, etc., there are primarily two mathematical tools which are used extensively in present asymptotic quantum field theory. These are the ordering of operators (or operator distributions) and the operator derivative calculus.

Given a product of n operators, $A_1 A_2 \cdots A_n$ an ordering operation O can be defined which associates with each such product a unique ordered product, $O(A_1 \cdots A_n) = (A_1 \cdots A_n)_{\text{ord}}$. In general, more than one product may be associated with the same ordered product. Of particular interest are the positively and negatively time-ordered products and the normal (or Wick) ordered product. While these operations and their relations have been known for years[18], a few remarks may help to understand the equations below.

Let the above three operations be denoted by T_+, T_-, and N. The last one can obviously be applied only to free fields. First, it is clear that all three operations are idempotent,

$$T_+T_+ = T_+, \quad T_-T_- = T_-, \quad NN = N. \tag{3.1}$$

Secondly, these operations are *not* linear because of the equations which the operators satisfy (e.g., commutation relations); let α and β be c-numbers, let A and B be products of q-numbers[19], then in general

$$T_+(\alpha A + \beta B) \neq \alpha T_+ A + \beta T_+ B, \text{ etc.} \tag{3.2}$$

It follows that the operation O is *not* a linear operator.

Thirdly, $T_\pm$ and N are symmetric (antisymmetric) in the q-numbers on which they act for Bose (Fermi) fields. In particular, a q-number equation does not remain valid in general when each product is replaced by an ordered one. As an example consider the commutation relations under time ordering. The left-hand side vanishes while the right-hand side does not.

The time-ordering operation is defined in terms of the step function which is 1, 1/2, and 0 for $x° > 0$, $x° = 0$, and $x° < 0$. This function is not Lorentz invariant, but $T_\pm$ will be applied only to products of q-numbers which are microcausal, so that the resultant products, the T-products, will be Lorentz covariant. The definition of the T-products requires a decomposition of the unit operator in terms of θ-functions. Consider the following special case for $n = 3$. Using

$$\theta_{12} \equiv \theta(x_1 - x_2), \quad \theta_{123} \equiv \theta_{12}\theta_{23}, \quad A_1 \equiv A(x_1),$$

one has

$$\theta_{12} = \theta_{12}(\theta_{23} + \theta_{32}) = \theta_{123} + \theta_{12}\theta_{32}(\theta_{13} + \theta_{31}) \tag{3.3}$$

$$= \theta_{123} + \theta_{132}\theta_{12} + \theta_{312}\theta_{32}.$$

Therefore,

$$T_+(A_1A_2A_3) \equiv \theta_{123}A_1A_2A_3 + \theta_{132}\theta_{12}A_1A_3A_2$$
$$+ \theta_{312}\theta_{32}A_3A_1A_2 + (1 \rightleftharpoons 2).$$

The last symbol in this definition indicates that the whole expression is to be repeated with indices 1 and 2 interchanged. For equal times some

θ factors contribute $1/4$ and some $1/8$. This T-product is not symmetric and must be symmetrized. One then obtains

$$T_+(A_1 A_2 A_3) = \sum_{\text{perm.}} \bar{\Theta}_{123} A_1 A_2 A_3 \qquad (3.4)$$

$$\bar{\Theta}_{123} \equiv \tfrac{1}{3}\theta_{123}(1 + 2\theta_{13}).$$

It will be useful to define generalized commutators of two q-numbers or q-number products, $[P, Q]_G$, by the following two properties[20]: (a) the commutator is linear in P and in Q,

$$[P, \alpha Q_1 + \beta Q_2]_G = \alpha[P, Q_1]_G + \beta[P, Q_2]_G, \qquad (3.5)$$

and similarly for $P = \alpha' P_1 + \beta' P_2$; (b) it can be reduced according to

$$[P, Q_1 Q_2]_G = Q_1[P, Q_2]_G + [P, Q_1]_G Q_2 \qquad (3.6)$$

and similarly for $P = P_1 P_2$. In this way the generalized commutator of any two functionals of a field operator can be reduced to sums of products involving the generalized commutator of the field.

For example, if $a(x)$ is a free neutral scalar field (operator distribution) the following relation can be proven[21]

$$T(a(x)a_1 a_2 \cdots a_n) = T(a_1 \cdots a_n)a(x) + [a(x), T(a_1 \cdots a_n)]_R. \quad (3.7)$$

In the last term the T-product is to be written out in terms of sums of products involving θ-functions, and the result is to be reduced to expressions involving $[a(x), a_k]_R$ which is defined by

$$[a_k, a_l]_R = -i\Delta_R(x_k - x_l). \qquad (3.8)$$

If a functional F of the free field a can be written in terms of time-ordered products and c-numbers f_n,

$$F = \sum_{n=0}^{\infty} \int f_n(x_1 \cdots x_n)T(a_1 \cdots a_n) \, dx_1 \cdots dx_n, \qquad (3.9)$$

the expression $T(a(x)F)$ is defined as

$$T(a(x)F) \equiv \sum_{n=0}^{\infty} \int f_n(x_1 \cdots x_n)T(a(x)a_1 \cdots a_n) \, dx_1 \cdots dx_n. \qquad (3.10)$$

Time ordering of products of the interpolating field $A(x)$ is also defined, $T(A_1 \cdots A_n)$, in terms of θ-functions. If each A_k were expressed in terms of free fields and the ordering were carried out relative to these, a different quantity would result. In order to distinguish these two cases we shall always indicate the positive time-ordering with respect to free fields by a subscript $+$. Thus,

$$T(A_1 \cdots A_n) \neq (A_1 \cdots A_n)_+ \quad \text{but} \quad T(a_1 \cdots a_n) = (a_1 \cdots a_n)_+. \quad (3.11)$$

We could have used this notation in Eq. (3.7).

The generalization of Eq. (3.7) to the product of any local q-numbers, $A_1, \ldots, Z_n$ such as the $A(x)$, can be proven to be[22]

$$T(A(x)A_1 \cdots Z_n) = T(A_1 \cdots Z_n)A(x) + [A(x), T(A_1 \cdots Z_n)]_R. \quad (3.12)$$

Here $[A_k, B_l]_R \equiv \theta(x_k - x_l)[A_k, B_l]$, but the latter commutator is in general not known. Note that Lorentz invariance requires

$$[A_k, B_l] = 0 \qquad (x_k, x_l \text{ spacelike}). \quad (3.13)$$

The *primitive part* of a distribution $f_n(x_1 \cdots x_n)$ which occurs for example in (3.9) is obtained by omitting from it all additive terms of the form

$$K_i K_j \delta(x_i - x_j)g(x_1 \cdots x_i \cdots x_j \cdots x_n), \quad (p \geq 0, q \geq 0, p + q \geq 1)$$

where $K_i \equiv \Box_i - m^2$ is the Klein–Gordon operator[23]. We write $\mathcal{N}f_n = $ primitive part of f_n.

One can now define the derivative of a functional of a with respect to the free field $a(x)$ by[24]

$$i[\delta F/\delta a(x)] \equiv \mathcal{N} K_x[a(x), F]_R. \quad (3.14)$$

The operator $\mathcal{N}$ assures that this operator derivative commutes with differentiation (in particular with K) and with integration. Without it great care must be taken to ensure that the equation $Ka = 0$ is never violated.

The properties of the operator derivative are a consequence of those of the inhomogeneous commutator. One finds that this derivative is linear and satisfies the usual product rule[25]

$$\delta(FG)/\delta a(x) = [\delta F/\delta a(x)]G + F[\delta G/\delta a(x)]. \quad (3.15)$$

Repeated application of Eq. (3.14) leads to multiple derivatives. For scalar fields these are symmetric

$$\delta^2 F/\delta a_1 \, \delta a_2 = \delta^2 F/\delta a_2 \, \delta a_1. \quad (3.16)$$

As an example consider Eq. (3.7) for $n = 1$;

$$\mathcal{N} K_x(a(x)F)_+ = \mathcal{N} K_x(Fa(x) + [a(x), F]_R) = \mathcal{N} K_x[a(x), F]_R.$$

Therefore,

$$\mathcal{N} K_x[a(x)F]_+ = i[\delta F/\delta a(x)].\qquad(3.17)$$

By induction one then proves

$$i^n \frac{\delta^n F}{\delta a_1 \cdots \delta a_n} = \mathcal{N} K_1 \cdots K_n(a_1 \cdots a_n F)_+.\qquad(3.18)$$

Operator derivatives can also be defined in momentum space[26]. This has various advantages in the discussion of the scattering matrix which is of physical importance primarily in that space. But we shall not enter into this subject matter here.

Finally, the definition (3.14) implies

$$[a(x), F]_R = -i \int \Delta_R(x - \xi) \frac{\delta F}{\delta \xi} d\xi \qquad(3.19)$$

This follows by substitution of Eq. (3.14) on the right and differentiation by parts. The relation (Eq. (3.19)) will be useful in what follows. It is also valid for other commutators (with corresponding Δ-functions).

4. The Axioms

The axioms of quantum field theory have been stated repeatedly in full mathematical detail[27]. Our purpose in stating them here very briefly is primarily to emphasize their physical contents and to indicate the analogy with the classical theory. We feel that it is premature to commit ourselves to the precise technical form of these axioms.

Axiom I. One requires certain *invariance properties* to be satisfied in the theory. In particular, invariance under the inhomogeneous Lorentz group (Poincaré group) is assumed, possibly including the complex covering group [$SL(2, C)$]. Some invariance requirements such as gauge invariance depend on the fields under consideration. This axiom is obviously analogous to the classical case[3].

Axiom II. One requires a description of free fields and the corresponding free particles. This requirement lies at the heart of asymptotic quantum field theory which is built on asymptotically free fields. The analogy with the classical theory has only recently become clear. Thus, in the classical electrodynamics of point charges the asymptotic condition of free fields and free particles is an essential part of the theory[28].

Mathematically, axiom II is usually stated as a set of axioms. For example, one requires the following:

(*a*) Fields are described by operator-valued distributions with a suitably defined test function space; they are irreducible representations of the Lorentz group.

(*b*) An operator obtained by integrating the field over an element of the test function space acts on a (complex) Hilbert space $\mathscr{H}$. This space has a unique vacuum state.

(*c*) The free fields satisfy the usual spin-statistics relations. This means that Bose (Fermi) fields commute (anticommute) for spacelike distances. This assumption is variously stated as locality of the field, local commutativity, or microcausality. We need it here first of all for the free fields. But it is usually also assumed for the interpolating field. However, this assumption may not be necessary because the requirement of Lorentz invariance for the T-products of the $A(x)$ seems to imply microcausality.

Axiom III. The fields must be *complete* in the sense that every operator in the theory can be written in terms of them. This can be ensured in various ways. For example, one can require that the polynomials of the field operators acting on the vacuum state produce a dense set of states, or that the operators be irreducible. There is clearly no analogue to this axiom in the classical theory.

The completeness implies that any operator F of the theory can be expanded in terms of normal ordered products of free fields[29],

$$F = \sum_{n=0}^{\infty} \int f_n(x_1, \ldots, x_n) : a_1 \cdots a_n : dx_1 \cdots dx_n. \qquad (4.1)$$

For Bose fields $a(x)$, the coefficients f_n are symmetric in the n four-vectors $x_1, \ldots, x_n$. Furthermore, the free-field nature of the a_i restricts the Fourier transform of each argument of f_n to the mass shell. This means that the f_n need to be known only on the mass shell in order to determine F. However, if the operator derivatives of F are to be known too then the f_n must also be known off the mass shell. This is evident from

$$\frac{\delta F}{\delta a(x)} = \sum_{n=0}^{\infty} n \int f_n(x, x_1, \ldots, x_n) : a_1 \cdots a_n : dx_1 \cdots dx_n. \qquad (4.2)$$

The argument x is no longer restricted to the mass shell. Each successive derivative takes one more argument off the mass shell. Therefore, the knowledge of F and all its derivatives is equivalent to the knowledge of the $f_n(x_1 \cdots x_n)$ for all arguments on and off the mass shell. Infinite sets of equations for the f_n are then equivalent to q-number equations which are also valid upon differentiation to arbitrary order. Such q-number equations are called *strong* equations. Otherwise the equation is called "weak".

Axiom IV. One assumes that the physical system is asymptotically (for $t \to \pm\infty$) completely described by free fields (free particles). This is exactly the same physical condition which occurs in the classical theory as *asymptotic condition*. Of course, it takes a different mathematical form the details of which are irrelevant here. Suffice it to point out that the definition of the interpolating field is such that this condition is always satisfied.

The last two axioms imply that the set of in-fields $\{a_{\text{in}}(x)\}$ and of out-fields $\{a_{\text{out}}(x)\}$ span the same Hilbert space, $\mathscr{H}_{\text{in}} = \mathscr{H}_{\text{out}} = \mathscr{H}$. Consequently, there exists a unitary operator S,

$$S^* = S^{-1}, \tag{4.3}$$

relating these fields,

$$a_{\text{out}}(x) = S^* a_{\text{in}}(x) S. \tag{4.4}$$

Equation (4.3) is a weak equation (weak unitarity). It is sometimes postulated that this equation is to hold as a strong equation (strong unitarity). However, it can be shown that this is not necessary and that strong unitarity is a consequence of the assumptions of the theory[30] For simplicity we shall assume (4.3) to hold strongly.

The theory now becomes completely symmetrical with respect to in-fields and out-fields, i.e., to each equation in terms of a_{in} there corresponds a similar one for a_{out}. For definiteness we shall work exclusively with a_{in} and shall omit the subscript in most cases. The operator derivative will also be chosen with respect to the a_{in} and we shall adopt to symbolic notation

$$\delta F / \delta a_{\text{in}}(x) \equiv \delta F / \delta x. \tag{4.5}$$

A fifth axiom will be introduced in the next section.

5. Causality

In 1957 Glaser, Lehmann, and Zimmermann[6] proved that any interpolating field $A(x)$ which satisfies the axioms can be written in the form

$$A(x) = a_{\text{in}}(x) + \sum_{n=2}^{\infty} \frac{1}{n!} \int K_1 \cdots K_n r(x; x_1, \ldots, x_n) : a_1 \cdots a_n : dx_1 \cdots dx_n$$

where

$$r(x; x_1, \ldots, x_n) \equiv (-i)^n \sum_{\text{perm}} \theta(x - x_1)\theta(x_1 - x_2)\cdots\theta(x_{n-1} - x_n)$$
$$\cdot \langle [\ldots, [[A(x), A(x_1)], A(x_2)], \ldots, A(x_n)]\rangle_0 \quad (5.2)$$

and $\langle \ldots \rangle_0$ indicates the vacuum expectation value. If one now recalls that the current density $J(x)$ is related to $A(x)$ by the strong equation

$$J(x) = K_k A(x), \quad (5.3)$$

one has in the notation (4.5), and in view of $Ka = 0$,

$$\frac{\delta J(x)}{\delta y} = \mathscr{N} \sum_{n=1}^{\infty} \frac{1}{n!} \int K_x K_1 \cdots K_n r(x; y, x_1, \cdots, x_n) : a_1 \cdots a_n : dx_1 \ldots dx_n.$$
$$(5.4)$$

This expression vanishes for x, y spacelike to each other ($x \sim y$) as well as for all x and y for which $x^0 < y^0$,

$$\frac{\delta J(x)}{\delta y} = 0 \qquad \text{for} \quad x \sim y \quad \text{and} \quad x^0 < y^0. \quad (5.5)$$

The property (Eq. (5.5)) of the current density will be referred to as *Bogoliubov causality*. It is a consequence of the axioms of quantum field theory (Sec. 4) and of a particular off-mass shell behavior (associated with the coordinate y) implied in Eq. (5.4). The latter point is essential in the understanding of the relation of Eq. (5.5) to Eq. (5.2). In the step (5.4) it was silently assumed that (5.2) remains valid upon operator differentiation, i.e., that (5.2) is a *strong* equation. This assumption is necessary if we want (5.5) to be a strong equation. Thus, Bogoliubov causality involves more than the weak Eq. (5.2) which follows from axioms I to IV together with microcausality.

We shall adopt Bogoliubov causality as an additional axiom, thereby making an assumption about the off-mass shell behavior of a certain q-number.

Axiom V. Bogoliubov causality. We assume Eqs. (5.2) and (5.5) are *strong* equations[31]. The latter can also be written as

$$\mathscr{N} K_x \frac{\delta A(x)}{\delta y} = 0 \qquad \text{for} \quad x \sim y \quad \text{and} \quad x^0 < y^0. \quad (5.5)$$

This axiom is very strong. In particular, it implies the usual assumption of microcausality for the interpolating fields[32],

$$[A(x), A(y)] = 0 \qquad (x \sim y), \quad (5.6)$$

as a strong equation. But it also implies the complete off-mass shell behavior of the S-matrix as will be indicated below.

The exploitation of Bogoliubov causality in deriving the structure of the S-matrix is one of the main contributions to asymptotic quantum field theory in recent years.

It is clear that an important statement such as Eq. (5.5) must be fully understood in its physical meaning. A careful study of this point and, in particular, of the relation of this causality statement to the measuring process should be made. Superficially, Eq. (5.5) says that the current is not affected by a change of the a_{in} at a later or spacelike point.

6. The S-Matrix

The S-operator is introduced into the dynamics of the theory by the definition of the current density in terms of S,

$$J(x) \equiv iS^*(\delta S/\delta x). \tag{6.1}$$

In addition, one defines the interpolating field in terms of the current by

$$A(x) \equiv a(x) - \int \Delta_R(x - \xi)J(\xi) \, d\xi. \tag{6.2}$$

These two definitions imply Eq. (5.3). The Bogoliubov causality condition can now be stated in terms of the S-operator,

$$\frac{\delta}{\delta y}\left(S^* \frac{\delta S}{\delta x}\right) = 0 \qquad \text{for} \quad x \sim y \quad \text{and} \quad x^0 < y^0. \tag{6.3}$$

In this form, but with a different definition of the derivative, this condition was first stated by Bogoliubov[9].

It is already beginning to appear that $J(x)$ plays a more fundamental role in the theory than $A(x)$. Not only is causality stated most simply in terms of $J(x)$ (Eq. (5.5)), but the field equation for $A(x)$ which is the basis of the old formulation of quantum field theory will be replaced by an equation for $J(x)$ (Sec. 7).

It is therefore reasonable to ask how we could find the S-operator if $J(x)$ is given. Define

$$J_n(x_1, \ldots, x_n) \equiv i^n S^* \frac{\delta^n S}{\delta x_1 \cdots \delta x_n}; \tag{6.4}$$

then

$$J_0 = 1, \quad J_1(x) = J(x), \tag{6.5}$$

and

$$J_{n+1}(x_1, \ldots, x_{n+1}) = i^{n+1} S^* \frac{\delta^{n+1} S}{\delta x_1 \cdots \delta x_{n+1}}$$

$$= i^{n+1} \frac{\delta}{\delta x_{n+1}} \left(S^* \frac{\delta^n S}{\delta x_1 \cdots \delta x_n} \right)$$

$$- i^{n+1} \frac{\delta S^*}{\delta x_{n+1}} \frac{\delta^n S}{\delta x_1 \cdots \delta x_n}.$$

In the last term, SS^* can be inserted between the factors in view of unitarity. Furthermore, since we are dealing with a neutral scalar field, we demand that

$$J^*(x) = J(x). \tag{6.6}$$

This implies

$$-i(\delta S^*/\delta x)S = iS^*(\delta S/\delta x) \quad \text{or} \quad \delta(S^*S)/\delta x = 0 \tag{6.7}$$

consistent with (4.3) as a strong equation. We therefore find

$$J_{n+1}(x_1, \ldots, x_{n+1}) = [i(\delta/\delta x_{n+1}) + J(x_{n+1})]J_n(x_1, \ldots, x_n). \tag{6.8}$$

Equations (6.5) and (6.8) together determine the derivatives (Eq. (6.4)) for all n in terms of $J(x)$. But now we recall that S can be expanded as in Eq. (4.1),

$$S = 1 + \sum_{n=1}^{\infty} \frac{(-i)^n}{n!} \int \omega(x_1, \ldots, x_n) : a_1 \cdots a_n : dx_1 \cdots dx_n \tag{6.9}$$

and that therefore, using $S|0\rangle = |0\rangle$,

$$\langle J_n \rangle = \left\langle i^n S^* \frac{\delta^n S}{\delta x_1 \cdots \delta x_n} \right\rangle_0 = i^n \left\langle \frac{\delta^n S}{\delta x_1 \cdots \delta x_n} \right\rangle_0 = \omega(x_1, \ldots, x_n). \tag{6.10}$$

The expansion coefficients ω of the S-operator, i.e., the S-matrix, is completely determined (on and off the mass shell) by the current density $J(x)$ and its derivatives.

Let us now return to $A(x)$ given by Eq. (6.2). Operating on it with S yields, [using Eq. (3.19)]

$$SA(x) = Sa(x) - i \int \Delta_R(x - \xi)(\delta S/\delta \xi) \, d\xi = Sa + [a, S]_R.$$

Therefore, from Eq. (3.7)

$$A(x) = S^*[a_{\text{in}}(x)S]_+. \tag{6.11}$$

This relation of $A(x)$ and $a_{in}(x)$ satisfies the asymptotic condition. The analogous relation between $A(x)$ and $a_{out}(x)$ is[8]

$$A(x) = [Sa_{out}(x)]_+ S^*. \qquad (6.12)$$

The important relation Eq. (6.11) can be generalized by a judicious use of time-ordering and causality. One finds[22]

$$T(A_1 \cdots A_n) = S^*(a_1 \cdots a_n S)_+. \qquad (6.13)$$

This implies that any q-number $F[a]$ when expanded in terms of time-ordered products of in-fields as in (3.9) will give $F[A]$:

$$F[A] = \sum_{n=0}^{\infty} \int f_n(x_1, \ldots, x_n) T(A_1 \cdots A_n) \, dx_1 \cdots dx_n \qquad (6.14)$$
$$= S^*(F[a]S)_+.$$

We have a "pseudo-mapping" of the functionals of the free fields onto the functionals of the interpolating field which appears to be of considerable interest. As a special application of it we apply Eq. (6.13) to Eq. (3.18) and find

$$J_n(x_1, \ldots, x_n) \equiv i^n S^* \frac{\delta^n S}{\delta x_1 \cdots \delta x_n} = \mathcal{N} K_1 \cdots K_n S^*(a_1 \cdots a_n S)_+$$
$$= \mathcal{N} K_1 \cdots K_n T(A_1 \cdots A_n). \qquad (6.15)$$

We have thus obtained an explicit expression for any derivative of the S-operator in terms of the interpolating field. The S-matrix becomes

$$\omega(x_1, \ldots, x_n) = \langle J_n \rangle_0 = \mathcal{N} K_1 \cdots K_n \langle T(A_1 \cdots A_n) \rangle_0 \qquad (6.16)$$

which is valid on as well as off the mass shell. Because of the $\mathcal{N}$-operator the right-hand side of this equation can be written as

$$\mathcal{N} K_1 \cdots K_n \langle T(A_1 \cdots A_n) \rangle_0 = K_1 \cdots K_n \varphi(A_1 \cdots A_n), \qquad (6.17)$$

where the φ-product is defined as a linear combination of T-products as follows. From Wick's theorem we know the coefficients $c_{nn'}$ in the relation between T-products and normal-ordered products of free fields,

$$:a_1 \cdots a_n: = \sum_{n' \le n} c_{nn'}(a_1 \cdots a_{n'})_+ \qquad (c_{nn} = 1) \qquad (6.18)$$

using the same coefficients, the φ-product is defined by

$$\varphi(A_1 \cdots A_n) = \sum_{n' \le n} c_{nn'} T(A_1 \cdots A_n). \qquad (6.19)$$

The $c_{nn'}$ ($n' < n$) involve products of invariant causal functions[33] Δ_c and therefore vanish upon application of $\mathcal{N} K_1 \cdots K_n$. This is the reason for Eq. (6.17). That $\mathcal{N}$ can be omitted on the right-hand side of this equation will not be shown here.

Thus, one has, as was first conjectured by Pugh[8]

$$\omega(x_1, \ldots, x_n) = K_1 \cdots K_n \langle \varphi(A_1 \cdots A_n) \rangle_0 \tag{6.20}_c$$

and, in fact, also the q-number relation

$$i^n S^* \frac{\delta^n S}{\delta x_1 \cdots \delta x_n} = K_1 \cdots K_n \varphi(A_1 \cdots A_n). \tag{6.20}_q$$

This relation was first obtained by Pugh[12] for all n from the case for $n = 2$. Equation (6.20) for $n = 2$ was later shown to be a consequence of Bogoliubov causality and the other axioms[17].

The powerful theorem (Eq. (6.13)) thus provides for a very elegant proof of Eq. (6.20). However, it is instructive to show that the case $n = 2$ is the important one to prove and requires Bogoliubov causality. The validity of Eq. (6.20) for $n > 2$ is then a consequence of certain ordering equations only. This proof will now be sketched.

One substitutes the definition (Eq. (6.2)) of the interpolating field into $\theta(x_1 - x_2)[A(x_1), A(x_2)]$ and uses strong unitarity (Eq. (4.3)) and Bogoliubov causality to find[17]

$$\theta(x_1 - x_2)[A_1, A_2] = -i \Delta_R(x_1 - x_2)$$
$$+ \int \Delta_R(x_1 - \xi_1) \Delta_A(x_2 - \xi_2) i(\delta J(\xi_1)/\delta \xi_2) \, d\xi_1 \, d\xi_2.$$

Therefore

$$K_2(\theta(x_1 - x_2)[A_1, A_2]) = i\delta(x_1 - x_2) - \int \Delta_R(x_1 - \xi_1) i(\delta J(\xi_1)/\delta x_2) \, d\xi_1$$
$$= i(\delta A(x_1)/\delta x_2). \tag{6.21}$$

It is not difficult to show that this result is equivalent to Eq. (6.20) for $n = 2$.

Let us now differentiate the T-product, substitute Eq. (6.21), and make use of the ordering equation (Eq. 3.12)):

$$i \frac{\delta}{\delta x} T(A_1 \cdots A_n) = \sum_{k=1}^{n} T\left(A_1 \cdots A_{k-1} i \frac{\delta A_k}{\delta x} A_{k+1} \cdots A_n \right)$$
$$= \sum_{k=1}^{n} T(A_1 \cdots A_{k-1} K_x(\theta(x_k - x)[A_k, A(x)]) A_{k+1} \cdots A_n)$$
$$= K_x[T(A_1 \cdots A_n), A(x)]_R$$
$$= K_x\{[T(A_1 \cdots A_n)A(x)] - T(A_1 \cdots A_n)A(x)\}.$$

Therefore,

$$K_{n+1}(A_1 \cdots A_{n+1}) = \left(i \frac{\delta}{\delta x_{n+1}} + J(x_{n+1})\right) T(A_1 \cdots A_n). \quad (6.22)$$

If we now define

$$T_n(x_1, \ldots, x_n) \equiv K_1 \cdots K_n T(A_1 \cdots A_n) \quad (6.23)$$

we see that

$$T_1(x) = J(x) \quad (6.24)$$

and that $\mathcal{N} T_n$ satisfies exactly the same recursion relation (Eq. (6.8)) that is satisfied by J_n. Because of Eq. (6.24) the two quantities must therefore be equal,

$$J_n = \mathcal{N} T_n \quad (6.25)$$

which is just the equation (6.15).

This completes the proof that Eq. (6.20) for $n = 2$, or equivalently Eq. (6.21), implies (6.20) for all $n > 2$.

7. The Current Equation

As we have seen in the previous section, the problem of determining the S-operator and its derivatives (which imply the S-matrix) has been reduced to finding the current density $J(x)$ and its derivatives. This means that we must have a strong equation from which $J(x)$ can be determined.

Such an equation is provided by Eq. (6.20) for $n = 2$ or, equivalently by Eq. (6.21). Starting with the derivative of $J(x)$,

$$i[\delta J(x_1)/\delta x_2] = i[\delta(K_1 A(x_1))/\delta x_2] = \mathcal{N} K_1 i[\delta A(x_1)/\delta x_2]$$
$$= \mathcal{N} K_1 K_2 \{\theta(x_1 - x_2)[A(x_1), A(x_2)]\}.$$

The right-hand side separates into two types of terms, those in which the θ-function is not differentiated, and those in which it is. The latter can be combined in the form $b(x_1, x_2)$ which is a quasi-local quantity, involving δ-functions and their derivatives up to fourth order,

$$i(\delta J_1/\delta x_2) = \mathcal{N}\{\theta(x_1 - x_2)[J_1, J_2]\} + \mathcal{N} b(x_1, x_2). \quad (7.1)$$

Because of the $\mathcal{N}$-operator, the last term will contain at most first derivatives of δ-functions.

Following Pugh[23], one can define the integral operator

$$P_R(x_1 x_2; \xi_1 \xi_2) \equiv K_1 K_2 [\theta(x_1 - x_2) \Delta_A(x_1 - \xi_1) \Delta_R(x_2 - \xi_2)]. \quad (7.2)$$

Equation (7.1) can then also be written in the form

$$i(\delta J_1/\delta x_2) = \mathcal{N} P_R[J_1, J_2] + \mathcal{N} b'(x_1, x_2), \qquad (7.1')$$

where b' is of the same nature as b.

Equation (7.1') or (7.1) is called the *current equation*. It is obvious that this equation implies Bogoliubov causality (the right-hand side vanishes for $x_1^0 < x_2^0$ and for $x_1 \sim x_2$). If we accept only self-adjoint solutions, then, according to Eqs. (6.6) and (6.7) we shall also ensure strong unitarity. Thus the (real) solutions of the current equation, when substituted in Eq. (6.8) will give us the S-operator and all its derivatives on and off the mass shell and will, in particular, give us the S-matrix according to Eq. (6.10).

The unspecified quantity in the current equation is the quasilocal operator distribution $b'(x_1, x_2)$. Its specification poses the well-defined mathematical problem of solving Eq. (7.1') for self-adjoined $j(x)$. We remind the reader that this is a strong equation. Its solution involves knowledge of the expansion coefficients of $J(x)$ in normal ordered products of in-fields, on and off the mass shell.

The specification of $\mathcal{N} b'(x_1, x_2)$ is called the *dynamical postulate*, because it is essentially equivalent to the knowledge of an interaction Hamiltonian in the older theories.

Finally, the current equation can also be regarded as an equation for the S-operator directly. One only needs to substitute the definition of $J(x)$, Eq. (6.1). The intermediary step via J, however, seems to simplify the mathematics considerably.

8. Achievements and Problems

The basic equations of asymptotic quantum field theory are stated in the preceding sections for a self-interacting neutral scalar field. Generalizations to charged fields, spinor fields, and higher spins can be carried through. Various dynamical assumptions can be made by specifying the quasi-local operator in the current equation. In general, one obtains a system of simultaneous current equations, one for each type of in-field.

The difficult mathematical problem of solving these equations has so far been successful only in terms of a coupling-constant expansion (perturbation theory) whose convergence properties are unknown. One can show that only a small class of fields and interactions lead to equations that have solutions in every order of the coupling constant. This small class corresponds exactly to the so-called renormalizable theories of the usual Tomonaga–Schwinger–Feynman–Dyson formulation of field theory.

As a test case, quantum electrodynamics for Dirac particles was investigated in detail. Calculations off the mass shell in second and third order were carried out and it was found[8] that the results of asymptotic quantum field theory are identical with the *renormalized* results of the usual theory.

In particular, the electron anomalous magnetic moment, vacuum polarization effects and energy-level shifts are predicted in the present theory exactly as in the renormalization theory. The important point is of course that in these calculations no divergent integrals were encountered and no renormalization was necessary. The latter is due to the fact that "bare" masses and charges are never introduced. The interaction is such that it gives no contributions to the mass or charge of an electron.

This is of course a great achievement of the theory. That it carries through that way to all orders of the perturbation expansion can be shown by general argument. A detailed proof on a rigorous mathematical level must wait for a rigorization of the whole theory on the level of the axiomatic approach. But from the physicist's point of view there is little doubt that it does carry through.

There are of course many problems which must now be attacked. Their relative importance and the order in which they should be attacked depends on the judgment of the individual physicist. The following is a brief list of some of the general problems.

(*a*) The next step toward the rigorization of the theory must be taken. It must be proven that the $\omega(x_1, \ldots, x_n)$ in Eq. (6.20) are distributions relative to a suitable test-function space.

(*b*) It must be established whether the fifth axiom (Bogoliubov causality) can be dropped. If the extension off the mass shell is unique as indicated by the operator $\mathcal{N}$, this seems to be the case. Otherwise this axiom would entail stronger analyticity properties than those contained in microcausality.

(*c*) The search for nonperturbative solutions and the related question of solutions for the equations corresponding to nonrenormalizable theories is vital for both strong and weak interactions.

(*d*) The question of the description of bound states, both stable and unstable, is very urgent in view of the large amount of experimental data of this nature.

(*e*) The problem of coping with approximate symmetries and the associated classification of particles in quantum field theory is one of the most important tasks for the purpose of applications to various types of elementary systems.

This list is far from exhaustive. But it suffices to indicate that even as we have overcome the hurdle of divergences our problems have only begun. However, it is to be hoped that this new phase of fundamental theory will be a happier one mathematically than the phase we had to deal with in the thirty years following the inception of the theory of quantized fields.

References

1. Kato, T., *Trans. Amer. Math. Soc.*, **70**, 212 (1951).
2. Kallén, G., *K. Danske Vid. Selskab*, **27**, No. 12 (1953).
3. Rohrlich, F., *Classical Charged Particles*, Addison-Wesley Publ. Co., Reading, Mass., 1965, and references given there.
4. See ref. 3, Chap. 1.
5. This is to be contrasted with the operator differentiation with respect to free fields which can be given a mathematical meaning and which we shall use extensively.
6. Lehmann, H., K. Symanzik, and W. Zimmermann, *Nuovo Cimento*, **1**, 205 (1955); **6**, 319 (1957); see also V. Glaser, H. Lehmann, and W. Zimmermann, *Nuovo Cimento*, **6**, 1122 (1957).
7. Nishijima, K., *Phys. Rev.*, **119**, 485 (1960); **122**, 331 (1961) and other papers quoted here.
8. Pugh, R., *Ann. Phys. (N.Y.)*, **23**, 335 (1963).
9. Bogoliubov, N. N., and D. V. Shirkov, *Introduction to the Theory of Quantized Fields*, Interscience, New York, 1959, and references given there.
10. Pugh, R., *Ann. Phys. (N.Y.)*, **30**, 422 (1964).
11. Stoddart, J. C., *Nuovo Cimento*, **34**, 1073 (1964).
12. Pugh, R., *J. Math. Phys.*, **6**, 740 (1965).
13. Bogoliubov, N. N., *Izv. Akad. Nauk SSSR, Ser. Fiz.*, **19**, 237 (1955); see also ref. 9.
14. Kaschluhr, F., *Nuovo Cimento*, **12**, 541 (1959).
15. Fainberg, V. Ya., *Soviet Physics–JETP*, **13**, 1237 (1961).
16. Rohrlich, F., and J. C. Stoddart, *J. Math. Phys.*, **6**, 495 (1965).
17. Chen, T. W., F. Rohrlich, and M. Wilner, *J. Math. Phys.*, in press.
18. Wick, G. C., *Phys. Rev.*, **80**, 268 (1950).

19. A c-number is a number, function, or distribution that is not operator valued; a q-number is an operator or an operator-valued distribution.
20. For spinors a further generalization is necessary.
21. From here on we shall write T for T_+ since T_- will not occur.
22. Rohrlich, F., and J. Wray, *J. Math. Phys.*, in press.
23. Pugh, R. E., *J. Math. Phys.*, **7**, 376 (1966).
24. Rohrlich, F., *J. Math. Phys.*, **5**, 324 (1964). This definition can be made more general by replacing the subscript R by I, indicating any generalized commutator which is reduced to $[a_k, a_l] = i\Delta_I(x_k - x_l)$ with Δ_I a c-number satisfying $K\Delta_I(x) = -\delta(x)$. Such commutators are called "inhomogeneous commutators" referring to the inhomogeneous Klein–Gordon equation.
25. Derivatives with respect to Dirac fields are defined in analogy to Eq. (3.14), $-i\delta F/\delta\psi(x) = \mathcal{N}(\gamma \cdot \delta + m)[\psi(x), F]_\mp^I$ with the anticommutator (commutator) if F is a spinor (tensor) with n having an analogous meaning; Eq. (3.15) continues to hold (up to sign factors). These matters are explained in ref. 24.
26. Rohrlich, F., and M. Wilner, *J. Math. Phys.*, **7**, 482 (1966).
27. See, for example, R. Haag and B. Schroer, *J. Math. Phys.*, **3**, 248 (1962) or R. F. Streater and A. S. Wightman, *PCT, Spin and Statistics, and All That*, Benjamin, New York, 1964.
28. See ref. 3.
29. The coefficients f_n of this expansion differ of course from those in the expansion (3.9). We use the notation $\mathcal{N}(a_1 \cdots a_n) = \; : a_1 \cdots a_n :$.
30. Chen, T. W., *Nuovo Cimento*, in press.
31. From now on all our equations will be strong equations.
32. This observation and the derivation of (5.5) can be found in ref. 16.
33. For notation see J. M. Jauch and F. Rohrlich, *The Theory of Photons and Electrons*, Addison-Wesley, Reading, Mass., 2nd printing (with corrections), 1959.

Cosmic Ray Neutrons[*]

SERGE A. KORFF

New York University

1. Introduction

A. *Consideration of this Subject by Bethe*

During the years 1939–1940, Bethe became interested in the subject of cosmic ray neutrons. He had just completed the monumental review of what was up to that time known about nuclear physics, in a series of three review papers for the *Reviews of Modern Physics,* a set so well known that it was often referred to, in nuclear physics laboratories, as "the Bible". The neutrons produced by cosmic rays had just recently been discovered, and offered a field for the application of what was known about neutrons to an interesting natural phenomenon. It is a remarkable tribute to his farsightedness, and to his intuitive understanding of the processes of nuclear physics that a quarter of a century after the event, most of what he said in the original paper[1] on the subject, remains today not only correct, but the cornerstone of the current work. In working with him, the present author was repeatedly impressed, not only by his broad view and fundamental understanding, but by his instant perception of the meaning of many small details which came to light.

B. *The Early History and Bethe's Contribution*

Neutrons having been discovered in the early 1930's, it was natural to ask if they were in any way associated with the cosmic radiation. It had at that time already been known for about a quarter of a century that the earth was continually bombarded by a high energy radiation, already thought to originate outside the solar system, and to come to

* Supported in part by N.S.F. grant GP4289, by NASA contract NSG-167-61, and by AFOSR grant AF19(628)-378.

us from the "cosmos". This radiation was known to produce a wide variety of secondary effects, but at the time neither the nature of the primary radiation nor the bulk of the secondary processes which it generated were well understood. Mesons had only just been discovered and their role could at the time only be vaguely guessed at. On the other hand, it was at the time already believed that neutrons were radioactive and this automatically ruled them out as entities originating in the cosmos. Whether there are neutrons originating in the sun and which reach the earth is still today not known with certainty, and is a topic we shall reserve for later discussion. Suffice it to say that it was not widely discussed in the period of which we speak, the late 1930's. The presumption at the time was that neutrons were secondary particles, generated in one or more processes by the primary radiation. This presumption is today considered as a "well-established fact".

The earliest paper which has thus far come to my attention, in which neutrons as a part of cosmic ray phenomenology is seriously delineated, is one by Rumbaugh and Locher[2a], who sent up what we today call "nuclear emulsions" with the manned balloon flight in 1935. There were some earlier papers by Locher[2b], but the Stratosphere flight established the effect beyond argument. Other studies with plates were made by E. and L. Schopper[2c]. This flight attained an altitude of 72,395 feet, on November 11, 1935. It was supported by the National Geographic Society and the U.S. Army Air Corps, and was manned by (then Captains) Albert W. Stevens and Orville A. Anderson. Using today's terminology, we would say that it reached a level such that about 45 grams per square cm of matter remained above the detector. Actually, this is close to the level at which the neutron numbers are a maximum, and hence the conditions for a positive result were at their best. In the plates, when they were developed, Rumbaugh and Locher found tracks which they attributed to recoil protons produced by energetic neutrons. There is every reason to believe that this interpretation was indeed correct.

In the following years, the next important development was the devising of a detection system, which made use of the large cross section for neutron capture exhibited by the nucleus of B^{10}. A boron-lined ionization chamber was built and used by Funfer[3], who made observations at low ground levels and on top of the Zugspitze. The use of the gas BF_3 in proportional counters was independently and nearly simultaneously developed by W. F. Libby[4], and by the present author[5]. Counters using this gas were first flown in balloon experiments by the author and his colleagues[6] at the Bartol Research Foundation, and recoil counters[7] to study fast neutrons were also tried out. The Montgomerys[8] further added to knowledge by a series of experiments in the same laboratory. Radioactivity induced by cosmic ray neutrons was measured by von Halban, Kowarski, and Magat[9] in an experiment in which a solution containing iodine was activated during an airplane flight over Paris. With the possible exception of some peripheral experiments, this was the extent of the experimental background in the subject by 1939.

From these experiments it was known that neutrons existed in measurable fluxes and densities, and that the number of neutrons increased rapidly with elevation. The increase with elevation was more rapid than the total ionization produced by the radiation. This suggested at the time, association between the neutrons and the "soft" component, rather than an association with the "hard" component, which today is considered to be that in which mu-mesons predominate. The words "soft component" imply the electron-photon component, but the nucleonic component also has very nearly the same absorption coefficient in the atmosphere, and it is the latter that presently emerged as that with which the neutrons are indeed connected.

This was the situation at the time Bethe, his colleague Placzek, and the present author started to discuss the situation. The paper under discussion was entitled "On the Interpretation of Neutron Measurements in the Cosmic Radiation," by Bethe, Korff, and Placzek[1]. It will be referred to as BKP. It seemed worth while to make a comprehensive survey of the entire field, and to look at all facets of the problem. The analysis was therefore undertaken, and soon developed the point of view and form which we will now briefly review. First, it became evident that the neutrons were produced by one or more processes which resulted from the primaries impinging on the nuclei in the upper atmosphere. Second, after being produced, the neutrons were slowed down, at first by inelastic and later by elastic collisions. Finally, the neutrons disappeared by several processes. We may briefly look at each of these three stages in turn, consider what was originally thought about each, and then see what later developments have taken place in the analyses.

Considering first the production problem, it was evident that the neutrons were spending their lives in a diffusion equilibrium, and that since the processes had been going on for a very long time compared to the neutron lifetimes, the rate of disappearance by all processes together must be equal to that of their creation. Thus if by dn/dt we designate the rate at which neutrons are formed as a function of time, and by the same, preceded by a minus sign as the rate of their disappearance, then:

$$dn/dt = -dn/dt \qquad (1)$$

Further, at any time there would be a number density ρ of neutrons in this equilibrium, which would have an average lifetime against disappearance by all processes which we will designate by t. Then we have,

$$\rho = qt, \qquad (2)$$

where by q we designate the rate of production (or of disappearance). This is the well-known equilibrium law of a stable population. Since we could measure ρ, we might hope by computing t to evaluate q, the rate of production. The mean lifetime against disappearance will depend on the cross section of the process or processes which remove the neutrons from the equilibrium. We will discuss these in a moment, but first should say a few words about the production processes.

The various processes operating at energies above 10 MeV or so were little known or understood at the time. There is one important exception to such a generalization, and that is that the cascade process involving the electron pair production and bremsstrahlung photons had been worked out several years earlier, and was in good agreement with experiment. Since this process would generate a supply of high-energy photons, and since high-energy photons were known to generate photoneutrons, this source of neutrons was considered. Since there were probably other processes as well, the question of production was left open, and attention was focussed on the quantity which could be determined, the rate of production.

Once produced, the neutrons found themselves in an atmosphere, consisting of about 0.8 nitrogen, 0.2 oxygen, other constituents being too small in amount to alter the resulting equilibrium appreciably. The neutrons at energies above the lowest level in the nuclei would be expected to make inelastic collisions. Such inelastic collisions would very rapidly degrade the incident neutron energy, and after one or at the most two collisions, the neutron energy would be below that of the lowest energy level. The lowest level in the oxygen nucleus was considered to be about 6 MeV, while that in nitrogen was about 4 MeV.

Hence we may consider what happens to a group of neutrons, starting out at energies of about 4 MeV, and making collisions in the atmosphere. The collisions made by neutrons of energy below the lowest level cannot transfer energy to the internal structure of the nucleus, and so will be elastic. Simple classical billiard-ball theory provides a good description.

A sphere of mass m and velocity v colliding with one of mass M assumed stationary will move away at an angle θ to the original direction of its travel, while the target nucleus will recoil at an angle Φ. Conservation of momentum and energy may be written:

$$\tfrac{1}{2}mv^2 = \tfrac{1}{2}mv'^2 + \tfrac{1}{2}MV^2 \tag{3a}$$

$$0 = mv' \sin \theta + MV \sin \varphi \tag{3b}$$

$$mv = mv' \cos \theta + MV \cos \Phi \tag{3c}$$

where V is the velocity of the recoiling nucleus, and v' that of the neutron after the collision. Simultaneous solution of these equations yields a maximum transfer of energy, or ratio of:

$$MV^2/mv^2 = 4mM/(M + m)^2 \tag{4}$$

and an average of half this amount. If $M \gg m$, we may write the maximum as approximately $4/M$ and the average as $2/M$, taking m as unity. It is clear that there is little difference in the net result, whether the target is nitrogen, $M = 14$, or oxygen, $M = 16$. For simplicity therefore we shall consider the atmosphere to be entirely of mass 14. At energies much greater than the molecular bond of a couple of volts or so, the fact that nitrogen is molecular can be ignored, but one must remember the factor of two in computing the number of scattering nuclei per cc.

From the above it is evident that a neutron will lose on the average of about 14% of its energy per collision, and will therefore make of the order of 100 collisions in slowing down from 4 MeV to a few volts. At STP, there being some $2 \times 2.7 \times 10^{19}$ nuclei per cc, if σ, the collision cross section is taken as one barn, the mean free path will be $1/N\sigma$, and the free time $1/N\sigma v$, where v is the average speed of the neutron. The velocity of a 4 MeV neutron is 2.8×10^9 cm/sec, while at 4 eV it is 2.8×10^6 cm/sec. It is clear therefore that the neutron will go most of its slowing-down distance as a fast neutron, but spend most of its slowing-down time as a slow one. Variation of elastic-scattering cross section with velocity in this energy interval is not large, and will not significantly alter the result. A neutron spends 6.5 μsec on the average between collisions at an energy of 4 MeV, and 6.5 msec at 4 eV. The entire slowing-down procedure takes of the order of 0.1 sec. Since this number is some four orders of magnitude smaller than the radioactive lifetime of the neutron, practically no neutrons are lost by decay, while being slowed down in the atmosphere.

Below a few eV neutron energy, the simple analysis we have indicated above cannot be used, since a lot of effects enter. For example, the energy of the molecular bond then becomes comparable with the neutron energy and introduces other complications. However, few neutrons survive to enter such a low-energy domain, because of capture at the lower end of the energy spectrum. Actually there will also be capture at the higher energies. Thus the capture and scattering processes are in competition. The number of neutrons, starting at an energy Ei which survive capture and are slowed down by scattering to an energy Ef is given by:

$$\exp\,(M/2) \int_{Ef}^{Ei} (\sigma_C/\sigma_S)\,(dE/E), \tag{5}$$

where E is the energy, and σ_C and σ_S are the capture and scattering cross sections, respectively. The fraction preceding the integral is the reciprocal of the average fractional energy loss per scattering collision; it is sometimes written $(3M + 2)/6$ in the literature. For an M of 14, this number is 7.3, compared to 7 from the simpler expression above. Evaluation of this integral[10] depends on the best present values of the cross sections, and this is a point at which some changes have occurred since the original article was written. On the basis of the earlier cross sections, a larger fraction of the neutrons survived the slowing-down process than today's computations indicate.

Finally as the neutrons are slowed down to low energies, they enter an energy interval in which absorption processes operate importantly. For example, the absorption cross section for neutrons by nitrogen in the $N^{14}(n, p)C^{14}$ process is a $1/v$ cross section and hence as the neutrons slow down, more and more are captured by it. The result is a progressive depletion of the bottom end of the velocity spectrum, and there is no accumulation of neutrons at thermal energies. The other process mentioned in the original paper was $N^{14}(n, \alpha)B^{11}$, and in addition to this the $N^{14}(n, T)C^{12}$ process was later found to be measurable. Thus the neutrons disappear by building up new isotopes, a process which has become one of much utility in other disciplines. Since the products, for example C^{14}, or Tritium can be identified, the various studies using these isotopes as dating tools have yielded important results.

Finally, in the original paper (BKP) the effects at each of the two bounds of the atmosphere were considered. At the top, some neutrons diffuse out into space. Today these are called "leakage neutrons", or sometimes "albedo neutrons". At and near the ground, some neutrons diffuse into the ground, and some of these come back out, having had their velocity spectra modified by scattering in the ground. In the case of a water surface, this effect can be calculated, and has been experimentally verified. In the case of the solid earth, the difficulty is in defining the composition well enough. There are too many elements, with random or sometimes systematic concentrations and with cross sections varying in a complex way to produce any effects which can be calculated with accuracy.

2. Subsequent Developments in the Theory

Subsequent developments in the theory were quite slow to arrive. S. Flugge, in 1946, in his chapter in Heisenberg's book[11], reviewed the matter, and added an application of diffusion theory. He pointed out that the neutrons in the atmosphere were diffusing about, and that their positions were described by the general diffusion equation:

$$\frac{\partial \rho}{\partial t} = \frac{\partial}{\partial z} D \frac{\partial \rho}{\partial z}, \tag{6}$$

where ρ is the density of neutrons, z the coordinate, t the time, and D the diffusion coefficient, defined by:

$$D = \frac{1}{3} vL = \frac{1}{3} v(n) \frac{h}{p} L(n) \tag{7}$$

where L is the mean free path and n the number of elastic collisions which the neutron has made since its formation. He applied his solutions to the diffusion in the exponential atmosphere, and his general form has been used by other workers since them.

Since by 1950, more accurate cross-section measurements had been made, Davis recalculated[12] the energy distribution and the density distribution as a function of altitude. This was compared with experiment, in a series of balloon flights, and improved agreement was found. Actually, Flugge's original calculations for the altitude of the intensity maximum were not in very good agreement with observation, while Davis' analysis showed a much better fit.

Probably the most important event which stimulated the next step in the development of the theory was the discovery of the Van Allen radiation belts. One problem which immediately arose was the origin of the protons and electrons in these belts, It was clear that in a simple dipole model, particles of solar origin could not get into the belts, this being forbidden by the Stoermer equations, nor, if a particle was captured in the belt could it get out. This situation led to a suggestion, thought to have been first made by S. F. Singer, that these particles were the results of neutrons which had "splashed" or "leaked" out of the earth's atmosphere, and decayed in space. This suggestion stimulated a spate of both theoretical and experimental work.

The theoretical work was initiated by W. N. Hess and his colleagues[13], who considered the diffusion from the top of the atmosphere of a group of neutrons formed according to a production spectrum in the upper atmosphere, and slowed down by collisions there. By examining the boundary effects at the top of the atmosphere, he predicted the numbers of neutrons expected to diffuse out, as well as their energy spectrum. Later, Lingenfelter[14] making slightly different assumptions about the shape of the spectrum derived another distribution curve which seems to be a better fit to experiment. Newkirk[15] made a calculation based on a multigroup S_n method representing a solution of the transport equation. He employed a source spectrum differing slightly from that used by Lingenfelter. The theoretical curves obtained by these latter two calculations are quite similar, and are in good agreement with experiment. Indeed, the present discrepancies in the data are such that one cannot today tell which gives the better fit. We shall discuss the data below.

3. Neutron Measurements

In considering the observations of neutrons, it is perhaps appropriate once again to remind readers of the well-known fact that a slow-neutron detector, which has a detection characteristic depending on a

$1/v$ cross section essentially measures neutron density, while a fast-neutron detector, usually operating on the recoil principle, measures flux. This latter characteristic comes about owing to the fact that the recoil cross section varies very slowly with energy, and over small energy intervals can be regarded as constant. Thus the flux cannot be inferred from BF_3 counter measurements unless assumptions regarding unmeasured quantities are made, or unless another type of detector is used at the same time.

It is today known that rather large variations in the rates of production, density and flux of neutrons exist, as a result of changes in the sunspot cycle. Therefore, comparison of exact values must take the epoch of the observations into account. This effect was not understood two decades ago, and is responsible for some of the apparent discrepancies and disagreements between observers.

Over the nearly three decades since the date of the BKP paper, many flights have been made, by the NYU group and by others, with a variety of detectors, to study the problem. Davis[11] and Staker[16] flew a combination of enriched and depleted BF_3 counters, the counters differing in the ratio of B_{10}/B_{11} only. Korff and Hamermesh[17], and later, Korff, George, and Kerr[18], flew counters equipped with moving cadmium and boron shields, while Yuan[19] flew to identical ionization chambers containing BF_3, one surrounded by cadmium. Soberman[20] collected all the latitude effect measurements, and made some needed to complete the sequence. The net result of these measurements was that by the start of the IGY, a reasonably good background of data was available at various epochs, latitudes and altitudes. Figure 1 shows Soberman's curves, summarizing the data. These measurements are, in so far as it was possible to make them, made with thin, unshielded counters in the free atmosphere, with a minimum of material adjacent to the counters which might add local production and alter the free atmosphere energy distribution.

Attention next centered on measurements of fast neutrons. The word "fast" in this case usually means neutrons in an energy range of between about 1 and 10 MeV, although this interval may be in some cases stretched a little further up or down. Thus the adjective "fast" is used to mean a velocity of between 10^8 and 10^{10} cm/sec, appreciably below relativistic speeds. These measurements were mostly made by employing scintillation counter technique, the entity originating the scintillation being a recoil proton, formed within or immediately adjacent to the scintillator. Some of these scintillators were sent up in balloon flights, others were placed in rockets and satellites. Still other

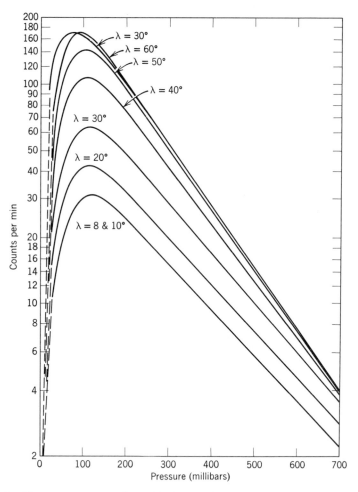

Fig. 1.   Slow neutrons at various altitudes and latitudes. Curve from R. Soberman, ref. 20.

experiments employed a BF_3 detector surrounded by a paraffin shield which moderated the fast neutrons.

Measurements of the fast neutron flux in the atmosphere, in the range between 1 and 10 MeV at various latitudes was made by Mendell, Korff, Holt, and Sandie[21], in a series of balloon flights. The curves of the counting rates as a function of latitude and altitude are shown in Fig. 2.

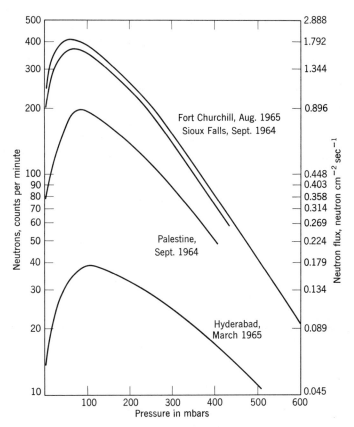

Fig. 2. Fast neutrons at various altitudes and latitudes. Curve from Korff, Mendell, and Holt, ref. 21.

A latitude-effect measurement was also made by Gauger[22], who flew two detectors to airplane altitudes (35,000 feet) between north latitudes 40 and 54. One detector was a $B^{10}F_3$ counter surrounded by

5 cm paraffin, the other a bismuth fission chamber, whose response in the interval 60 and 200 MeV had been determined using an accelerator. He reported his BF_3 data to be in good agreement with earlier measurements of others. Another set of balloon flights was made by Boella et al.[23], in which a boron-loaded plastic scintillator surrounded by paraffin was carried aloft by balloons.

Going up above the atmosphere, Reidy, Haymes, and Korff[24] placed a bundle of enriched and depleted B^{10} and $B^{11}F_3$ counters in an Aerobee, which was flown successfully to an altitude of 200 km. The neutron counting rate showed the expected leveling-off above the atmosphere. However, the absolute number of neutrons observed was somewhat higher than had been anticipated, which the authors attributed to local production in the body of the rocket. This experiment again points up the difficulty in interpreting measurements made when there is much matter near the detector, for the detector then measures (*a*) the neutrons reaching it which it is supposed to measure, (*b*) those reaching the body of the rocket and of higher energy, but moderated in the material, plus (*c*) those produced and moderated in the nearby matter. Although various workers have tried many procedures for separating or evaluating the several contributions cited above, the situation remains unsatisfactory and disagreements in the evaluations exist.

Similarly, Martin, Witten, and Katz[25] flew a detector in an Atlas up to 1000 km. This consisted of a pair of ionization chambers using enriched and depleted BF_3, and another set consisting of similar counters but wrapped in paraffin and having a cadmium shield outside to exclude slow neutrons. Bame[26] flew a BF_3 counting system with a polyethylene moderator. Williams and Bostrom[27] flew a system consisting of solid-state detectors imbedded in polyethylene, in a satellite to measure the latitude effect. The summary of the ratio of data which they observed, and observations of others, to the predicted values from the Lingenfelter[14] calculation show variations of normalizing or multiplying factors between 10 and 0.5. Only two observers found lower values than the predicted ones, and many were two to six times larger. No further comment on the impossibility of evaluating the secondary and local production seems necessary. The lowest values were obtained by Trainor and Lockwood[28] who again used BF_3 within a moderator, surrounded by a ring of anticoincidence counters to exclude ambient particles, and computed corrections for local production.

Other experiments which nearly determine the value of the "leakage" neutron flux are those made with balloons flying to high elevations. Today's top balloon altitudes, say between 140,000 and 150,000 ft, correspond to levels at which between 1.5 and 2 or 3 tenths of a per cent of the earth's atmosphere remains above the instrument. A tenth of a per cent corresponds to a thickness of 8 m of STP air. Since this is less than a free path for fast neutrons, and even for fairly slow ones, from the point of view of neutron problems this altitude may be regarded as substantially the top of the atmosphere. The neutron flux at this altitude therefore is the flux of those neutrons which, if they are going into the upward hemisphere will escape from the atmosphere. This number has been determined for fast neutrons, in the energy interval between one and ten MeV, both by the NYU group[21], and by some flights made by Haymes[29]. For slow neutrons it has been determined by a flight made by Haymes and Korff[30].

Since the experimental measurement of fast and of slow neutrons measure a different quantity, we may inquire what common quantity can be adduced. A nearly common parameter is the rate of production, q_s or q_f, for fast or slow neutrons, which is related to the flux i and to the density ρ through the two parallel equations:

$$\text{slow } \rho = q_s t(E) \tag{8}$$

$$\text{fast } i = q_f l(E) \tag{8a}$$

where t is the free time against capture, and l the free path against disappearance by all processes. To evaluate t or l, we must make some assumptions about cross sections, which vary with energy E and are not the same for fast and for slow neutrons. Indeed, putting in the best available values, one finds that q_f is greater than q_s. The meaning of q_s is slightly different than that of q_f, since q_s refers to the number which cross the upper energy threshold of the slow-neutron detector during the slowing-down process, while q_f includes not only the number which cross the upper threshold of the fast-neutron detector, but also those which are produced within the energy interval to which the detector is sensitive by various processes, such as evaporation from excited nuclei. From the fact that q_f is greater than q_s we deduce that some neutrons are captured during the slowing-down process, after they leave the bottom energy to which the fast-neutron detector is sensitive and before they reach the top energy of the slow-neutron detector. To this number of neutrons captured while being slowed down must be added those which are born with energies below the minimum of the fast-neutron detector. At one time this number was thought to be negligible, but this appears not to be the case.

Considering the actual numerical values observed, the neutron density at the level in the atmosphere where the intensity is a maximum and at about 50° north geomagnetic latitude is around 6.3×10^{-3} neutrons per cc. The determination of this quantity comes directly from the observed counting rates, and assumes knowledge of the boron cross section but not of any data for nitrogen. Similarly, for fast neutrons the actually determined fluxes at the same altitude are of the order of 1.9 neutrons per cm² sec. Dimensionally, the connecting factor is a velocity, although the interpretation of the meaning of this velocity is not simple. Numerically, it is of the order of 3×10^6 cm/sec, corresponding to a neutron of energy of a few eV.

At the top of the atmosphere the density of slow neutrons is found by observation to be about 6.3×10^{-9} neutrons per cc. If we suppose the energy of these neutrons to be of the order of 0.2 eV, then the flux leaving the earth is of the order of 0.03 neutrons per cm² sec. On the other hand, extrapolation of the flux measurements of fast neutrons gives some 0.2 neutrons per cm² sec in this energy range. This flux is roughly a tenth of that at the level of the neutron maximum. From the ratio of fast to slow neutrons, it is clear that the spectrum at the top of the atmosphere is considerably harder than that at the altitude of neutron maximum.

To derive the rates of production of neutrons we must make some assumptions about the cross sections in nitrogen. For the case of the observed density of slow neutrons, we may take the capture cross section in nitrogen to be of the $1/v$ form similar to that in boron.

The free time against capture t is related in a simple case to the cross-section σ for capture through:

$$t = 1/N\sigma v, \tag{9}$$

where N is the number of capturing nuclei per cc and v the average velocity. If we take N at the altitude of the neutron maximum as 4×10^{18} nitrogen nuclei per cc and v for slow neutrons as 2×10^5 cm/sec, a free time of 0.7 sec corresponds to a cross section of 2 barns. In this case the rate of production q_s according to Eq. (8) is 9.3×10^{-7} neutrons per cc per sec. Recalling that at the level of the neutron

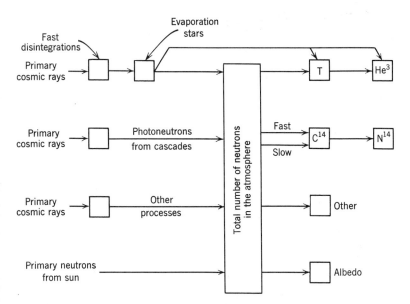

Fig. 3. Neutron balance in the atmosphere, showing various sources and disappearance processes.

maximum the air density is of the order of 10^{-4} g per cc, the rate of production is about 9.3×10^{-3} neutrons per g of air per sec.

For fast neutrons, again considering a possibly much over-simplified case, the cross section is smaller, perhaps close to the geometrical size, or about 0.25 barn. The free path, if there are 4×10^{18} centers per cc is about 10 km. In this case q_f, corresponding to an observed flux of 2 neutrons per cm^2 sec, is about 2×10^{-6} neutrons per cc per sec, or roughly double the q_s for slow neutrons.

We may therefore summarize the experimental situation by saying that the number of slow neutrons at the top of the atmosphere is known and is quite small, while the number of fast neutrons is not quite as well known, but that data exist for more latitudes. Further it is thought that the ratio of fast to slow neutrons, or in other words the energy spectrum, is latitude dependent. The extrapolated experimental value[21,29] of the flux of neutrons in the energy range between 1 and 14 MeV at the top of the atmosphere in middle latitudes and near solar minimum is of the order of 0.25 neutrons per cm^2 sec, while for slow neutrons[30] it is of the order of one-tenth of this value. The number cited is probably correct within 30%.

4. Geophysical Effects

A whole series of unanticipated but interesting geophysical effects are produced by cosmic ray neutrons. The basic reason is easy to see, for all the neutrons disappear by nuclear processes of one sort or another. That this would be the case was pointed out in the BKP paper. The earliest of the reactions to be studied was the formation of radiocarbon. By now a vast amount of literature on various aspects of this process exists[31], which we shall not attempt to review here. The process, after the thorough and excellent job which Libby did on the chemical extraction, concentration, and quantitative measurement, has become not only the cornerstone of archaeological dating methods, but also has revolutionized the time scales in Pleistocene geology.

At the time of the BKP paper, it was thought that the (n, p) process in N^{14}, leading to the formation of C^{14}, would be the principal process, and indeed this has turned out to be the case. However, other processes also have emerged, and recently several new aspects of the radiocarbon formation have come to light, which merit mention.

First we will briefly mention the matter of the radiocarbon production rate. In the early days it was thought that the BF_3 counter measurements of the rate of production of neutrons should match the amount of radiocarbon observed in present-day organic matter. However, as we have pointed out above, the actual rate of production of radiocarbon is greater than the slow-neutron measurements indicate, because of the substantial number of neutrons which are captured while they are still at energies above the upper limit of the slow-neutron counters. Also it must be recalled that other processes are in a competitive equilibrium with radiocarbon production and that not all the neutrons will end up in C^{14} nuclei. After making these two corrections, the data come into much improved agreement. Lingenfelter[32] has summarized the data about production rates and factors affecting them.

Some other factors have also entered, which complicate the interpretation. The first is that time variations in the production rate are introduced by protons and other particles which arrive at the earth from the sun. Occasional disturbances on the sun may temporarily increase the rate of production by an order of magnitude or even more. However, from the point of view of total radiocarbon accumulation, these increases tend to be smoothed out by the very long time constants operating in this case, as the radiocarbon has a half-life of around 5700 years. Nevertheless, variations in the radiocarbon accumulation have been observed as for example in the tree-ring studies made by Stuiver[33], in which he finds effects of the solar cycle. Still another factor is that radiocarbon can be produced by processes other than neutron absorption in nitrogen.

We may summarize the situation with respect to radiocarbon by citing Lingenfelter's estimates of the radiocarbon content of organic material as suggesting production rates of 1.8 to 1.9 $\pm$ 0.2 neutrons per square centimeter column in the atmosphere per second, and his estimate that the present rate of production by cosmic ray neutrons of about 2.5 $\pm$ 0.5 per second in the same units. He uses this difference to sustain his argument that detailed balancing is not present. The present author feels that while the probable errors cited are based on statistical calculations, there may still be enough systematic uncertainties which we have not yet corrected for, to make the actual errors larger than those cited, and perhaps to bracket the two values.

A summary of the "neutron budget" has been prepared by Newkirk[15], whose calculations we have already discussed. He makes the estimate that 54% of the neutrons go into radiocarbon, 2% into tritium, 31% into all other processes, and that 11% disappear by outward leakage. The average number he quotes as 2.1, with an estimated accuracy of 30%. The ratio of average to maximum in the high latitudes is 0.53, which agrees with Soberman's[20] estimate. The rate of tritium productions turns out to be in satisfactory agreement with the estimates given by Craig and Lal[34].

Another isotope produced in the atmosphere and eventually finding its way into various natural reservoirs is tritium. This substance is produced by the $N^{14}(n, T)$ process, which has a considerably smaller cross section than the (n, p) reaction discussed above. The amount of cosmic-ray tritium is measurable by today's techniques and this too provides a dating tool with quite different properties. The first serious analysis of tritium in nature was made by A. v. Grosse and his colleagues[35]. The use of this as a tool in, for example, glaciology, oceanography, and other sciences is well under way. The factor complicating the analysis is the fact that the man-made tritium at present in the atmosphere quite swamps the natural tritium and thus introduces large, uncertain corrections. Only in places where the man-made tritium is not a serious contaminant, such as for example in the glaciers and snows of the antarctic, recently analyzed by Shen, Neuburg, and Korff[36] is the procedure as straightforward as that for radiocarbon.

Some of the neutrons are involved in still other reactions. Many of these have been examined by Korff[37] and by Lingenfelter[32]. The majority of the results are disappointingly uninteresting as new geophysical tools. Either the resulting product of the reaction makes a negligible addition to an already abundant isotope, or the cross section and the production is trivial, or the substance produced is not readily identifiable.

On the other hand, not all interesting isotopes are produced by cosmic ray neutrons. The high-energy protons in the primary radiation have sufficient energy to produce spallations of the nuclei of nitrogen and oxygen, and hence one may expect to find all possible stable mass numbers below 16, plus those which are radioactive but have long enough lives to permit identification. To this list must be added the spallation fragments of argon 40, which is present in the atmosphere in an amount of about 0.93%, and which in turn will be the parent of a correspondingly smaller number of fragments of mass below 40.

Of these spallation fragments, perhaps the most exciting and potentially useful is Be^{10}. This isotope has been identified in the ocean bottom sediments by Peters[38]. Since this isotope has a half-life of the order of 2.5 million years, it constitutes a possible dating tool for longer-period phenomena such as those of geology. The present author is convinced that a very important contribution will be made by the person who works out the technique for this substance, as Libby did for radiocarbon, and shows how Be^{10} enters into the processes of mechanical mixing and geochemical reactions.

Of the other isotopes, we may cite a few which have been identified, including that of phosphorus-32 by Marquez and Costa[39], beryllium-7 by Arnold and Al-Salih[40], chlorine-38 and sulfur-38 by Perkins and his colleagues[41], which are spallative fragments of atmospheric argon. The ages of iron meteorites have been studied by measuring the neon-21 to Al-26 ratio by Lipschutz, Singer, and Anders[42]. Taken all together, the study of cosmic-ray-produced isotopes has indeed opened up new avenues in geophysics. Further research into other aspects promises to bring many interesting facets to light.

5. Time Variations

An important question bearing upon many of the geophysical and astrophysical problems and aspects of the neutron intensity is the question of time variations and of long-term stability. Several differing types of time variations are recognized. We shall briefly review several.

First we may mention the present experimental evidence. The neutrons are regularly monitored at present, by large-size monitors which in some cases count at the rate of several million neutrons per hour, thus obtaining good statistical accuracy. The world wide network of neutron monitors was established during the IGY, 1957–58, and the largest "super-monitors" were recently added. As a result, good data exist over the last few years, and slightly less good data over about a decade. Before that, there were some monitors, but only a few. This is to be contrasted with the situation in the total intensity of the ionizing component, which has been monitored for over thirty years.

These monitors have brought to light two principal types of short-term changes in neutron intensity. We shall not discuss here the diurnal variation, which is ordinarily less than a per cent in amplitude. Two large nonperiodic changes are observed to occur. We shall first mention the so-called "Forbush decreases". In these decreases, the neutron intensity is observed to fall by a few per cent, or occasionally by many per cent, dropping at first abruptly, and then slowly recovering to normal. The recovery may take a day for a small decrease to several days or more for a large one. The decreases clearly correlate with solar disturbances and are attributed to a spurt of solar plasma which, because it carries with it its own magnetic field, modulates the radiation reaching the earth from beyond the solar system. Other phenomena produced by these bursts of plasma are also well known in geomagnetism, in ionospheric physics, and in auroral intensities.

On rare occasions, increases in the neutron counting rate are observed at sea level. Less than a dozen large increases have been observed. The increases are rare but sometimes spectacular. Thus for example, in November 1960, there were two large increases, and a small one. All were clearly correlated with solar flares at a single area on the sun's surface, which gave several different bursts of activity. The counting rate resulting from this event observed at the New York University monitor at College, Alaska, is shown in Fig. 4. A glance shows that the counting rate at sea level doubled, thus indicating that a

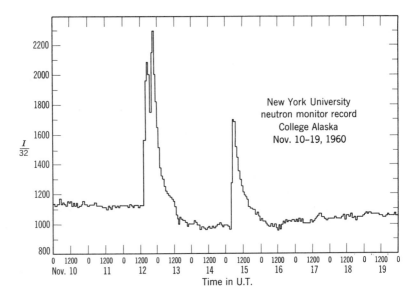

Fig. 4.   Neutron monitor record, obtained with slow neutron detector at College, Alaska, showing effects of injection of high-energy particles from sun at time of solar flare.

considerable amount of radiation, in this case clearly originating in the sun, reached the earth with sufficient energy to generate neutrons and to propagate the effect through the entire atmosphere. Geomagnetic analysis shows that the radiation generated in the sun contained protons with energies up to 4.5 GeV, and with a very steep energy spectrum.

The events of this type are produced by solar radiation called "Solar High-Energy Particles", or sometimes by the obvious misnomer "solar cosmic rays". They clearly are cases of solar injection of high-energy radiation. The largest thus far observed of these occurred on February 23, 1956, just before the IGY chain of monitors was activated, and so was studied only by a few observers. The 1960 events were seen by some three dozen different instruments widely distributed about the earth's surface. Large though the effect was at polar stations, the big increases were not observed south of about 45° geomagnetic latitude. This latitude dependence is the basis of the statement that the protons producing the increases on this occasion had energies up to 4.5 GeV.

Of the recent large solar-injection events, several have been very complex in their geophysical effects, since they produce observable changes in the ionosphere, in geomagnetism, in the aurora, and elsewhere. The event of July 1959 was the subject of an IUGG monograph presenting the work of many authors[43], as was the event of May 4, 1960[44]. The event of November 1960 was discussed in detail at the Kyoto conference[45].

Any event in which the particles have enough energy to reach sea level can easily be identified by the short travel time needed by the particles, which arrive very soon after the optical signal given by the start of the flare. On the other hand, the Forbush decrease is associated with much slower moving plasma which may require times from six to thirty-six hours to get to us from the sun, thus corresponding to velocities of the order of 10^8 cm/sec, or corresponding to proton energies of some tens of thousands of electron volts. The actual paths followed by the protons are undoubtedly much longer than the earth–sun distance, for the protons clearly follow highly twisted trajectories. The radius of gyration of the protons is small compared to the earth–sun distance, and the particles make many turns on their journey.

It should further be noted that although the November 1960 event was spectacularly large, it did not result in a large increase of the radiocarbon content of the atmosphere, because it had a period very short compared to the radiocarbon lifetime. A few hours after the event, the intensity was back to normal, and indeed a few per cent below normal, for a Forbush decrease had started in the middle of the first big injection event.

The sunspot cycle is also evident in the neutron intensity. The background counting rate clearly shows eleven-year periodicity. At times around minimum of solar activity, such as the present, the solar wind and plasma emitted are a minimum and there is a minimum of modulation produced, whereas close to solar maximum, the general background intensity may be appreciably altered and the fluctuations are larger and more frequent. The effect of this in the production data for radiocarbon is not large. Indeed several observers have not been able to find it, but as we pointed out above, others such as Stuiver[33], find it in their data. Here again, the mixing and the long period of the radiocarbon decay tend to smooth out the time averages.

Let us turn now to the longer time scales. In his careful original work on radiocarbon, in which he observed the carbon content in material with known dates, Libby[31] showed that a good fit could be found for dates going back for five or six half-lives. At ages greater than 30,000 years the surviving radiocarbon is hard to distinguish from the background. We may clearly expect that future improvement in techniques will permit the observable interval to be extended. Thus we can today say that the rate of production of neutrons has not varied by any very large amount over the past 30,000 years or so.

For the longer term questions we must turn to less well-established data. The isotope beryllium-10 has a half-life of 2.5 million years, and is perhaps our best source of information. Yet the data thus far obtained from it are very scant, and no firm conclusions can be drawn. Up to the present time, we only know that Be^{10} has been identified, and very little work on intensities implied by this isotope has been done.

The largest gap in the chronology comes next, for the data from the meteorites does indicate that these target objects were being bombarded by radiation for periods of the order of 10^8 years or so. Since we do not have a good dating method that is independent, we are in the position of having one experiment determining two variables. The amount of any isotope built up in a time interval between t_1 and t_2 is given by:

$$N = \int_{t_2}^{t_1} q(t)\, dt, \tag{10}$$

where q is the rate of formation and N the resulting amount. If $q(t)$ is constant, the result is simple, but we do not really know if this quantity may exhibit a time dependence or not. The isotope being accumulated can of course be a stable isotope, such as helium-3 which is produced by two processes, (a) the decay of tritium, and (b) direct production in nuclear reactions. While the cross sections are known from accelerator studies, and present rates of production by the cosmic radiation are known, the question about production at times in the remote past remains unsatisfactorily answered. Here again, the improved numbers which further work may hopefully bring, have much long-term significance not only in geophysics, but also in astrophysics and cosmology, for the universe may have been very different at times far past.

Further, we may ask about neutrons of solar origin. Since neutrons have a lifetime of around twelve minutes, and since the sun is eight light minutes away, neutrons of relativistic energies could clearly reach the earth from the sun. Indeed if the velocity of the neutrons was not too much below that of light, some fraction would arrive, this number being given by:

$$\exp\left(-t/T\right), \tag{11}$$

where t is the travel time and T the radioactive half-life. The special relativity time dilation will operate to increase T for high-energy neutrons. However, this effect is small at the energies of a few MeV's. The travel time will be related to the energy E, through:

$$t = r(m/2E)^{\frac{1}{2}} \tag{12}$$

for neutrons at classical energies, with mass m, r being the distance from the sum, or 1.4×10^{13} cm. For t to be in seconds and E in electron volts, we have:

$$t = 10^7(E)^{-\frac{1}{2}} \tag{12a}$$

Hence we see that neutrons of 1 MeV energy, which have speeds of 1.4×10^9 cm/sec will require 10^4 seconds, or about ten half-lives to reach the earth. The fraction given by Eq. (11) is 0.004% surviving. At 10MeV, with a travel time of three half-lives the fraction is 3.7% surviving.

The possibility that neutrons might originate in the sun has been considered for about a decade. One of the earliest suggestions was made by Bierman. The present author, about ten years ago, started a set of experiments to look for such neutrons. The idea involved was that neutrons, being uncharged, would not be affected by the earth's magnetic field, and hence if originating in the sun should show a fairly sharp geometrical shadow at sunset time. A neutron detector, floating at high elevations into the night hemisphere might be expected to show a decreased counting rate. Such day-night differences at high elevations were looked for by Haymes[46] and not found.

In considering the meaning of the experiments, we recall that any neutron detector is sensitive to neutrons in a certain energy interval only. Therefore the solar neutrons must have the right energy to be detected, at that depth in the atmosphere at which the detector finds itself. Slower neutrons might have been absorbed at higher levels, while faster ones should be looked for further down in the atmosphere. In the cases considered, we can therefore only say that the number originating in the sun and arriving at the earth on that particular day was less than about a per cent of those normally present, at high balloon altitudes and in the energy range between one and 10 or 15 MeV.

Since it is well known, as we have mentioned above, that protons are accelerated up to high energies, sometimes to energies of several

GeV in processes occurring simultaneously with solar flares, it seems likely that neutrons would be produced by these protons, through various collision processes including charge-exchange scattering. It would be surprising indeed if no neutrons whatever were produced. The difficulty in observing them is several fold. First we do not know in what energy range they will be. Second, the number reaching earth will be diminished both by the inverse-square distance factor and also by decay. Third, they may indeed be produced at energies and intensities enough to be observable only at times of solar flares or associated disturbances. Hence it would seem worth while to continue the search at such times.

Another interesting problem is that, once produced, the neutrons would have to escape from the sun. They must therefore be produced at depths in the solar atmosphere of the order of one free path or less from the outside; or if they are produced many free paths down, only a small fraction will emerge. Yet for the collisions to be frequent in which they are produced, such collisions must take place at levels where the density of the material in the corona or chromosphere is sufficient to make collisions probable. The same argument applies to the protons, which must be accelerated at levels far enough down so that the necessary fields are present, yet in regions where the rate of energy-loss through collisions is smaller than the rate of energy-gain from the fields. The combination of the two conditions leaves a fairly small interval of levels in which the processes can take place. It doubtless explains why high energy solar protons are such unusual entities, and why not more neutrons are observed.

Thus many problems, both theoretical and experimental remain to be solved in the field of solar neutrons. We have implied earlier that the neutrons could not have originated from beyond the solar system because of their radioactive half-life. It is therefore pertinent to consider the factors involved if we were to find neutrons from more distant sources.

For neutrons to arrive from great distances, the energies must be large enough to cause the relativistic time dilation to be large. For a relativistic neutron, its radioactive lifetime as seen from the earth's frame of reference would be:

$$T = \gamma T_0, \tag{13}$$

where γ is the usual special relativity factor:

$$\gamma = 1/(1 - v^2/c^2)^{1/2} \tag{14}$$

and T_0 is the rest radioactive half-life. For large values of γ, we may take the particle energy as:

$$E = \gamma m_0 c^2 \tag{15}$$

or approximately:

$$E = \gamma \text{ GeV.} \tag{16}$$

Thus for a neutron at 10^{15} electron volts energy, γ would be 10^9 and its lifetime would be 10^9 seconds. Moving at the speed of light, it could have originated thirty light years away. The average neutron can reach the earth from a distance R in the light years if it has an energy of E, in eV, given by:

$$E = 3 \times 10^{13} R \tag{17}$$

Hence we see that in order for neutrons to reach the earth from any distance comparable, for example, with the thickness of the arms of the galaxy, say a few thousand light years, the energy would have to be 10^{17} eV, while to reach the earth from a point at the center of our galactic system, about 30,000 light years, its energy would have to be 10^{18} eV. To reach us from the nearest spiral system, the necessary energy is of the order of 10^{20} eV. Hence only the very highest energy cosmic rays now known could possibly represent neutrons originating outside our own galactic system.

References

1. Bethe, H. A., S. A. Korff, and G. Placzek, On the Interpretation of Neutron Measurements in Cosmic Radiation, *Phys. Rev.*, **57**, 573–587 (1940).
2a. Rumbaugh, L. H., and G. L. Locher, *Phys. Rev.*, **44**, 855 (1936).
2b. Locher, G. L., *Phys. Rev.*, **44**, 774 (1933); **45**, 296 (1934); **50**, 394 (1936).
2c. Schopper, E., *Naturwiss.*, **25**, 557 (1937); E. and L. Schopper, *Phys. Zeits.*, **40**, 22 (1939).
3. Funfer, E., *Naturwiss.*, **25**, 235 (1937); *Zeits. f. Phys.*, **111**, 351 (1938).
4. Libby, W. F., *Phys. Rev.*, **55**, 245 (1939).
5. Korff, S. A., and W. E. Danforth, *Phys. Rev.*, **55**, 980(L) (1939).
6. Korff, S. A., *Revs. Mod. Phys.*, **11**, 211–219 (1939).
7. Korff, S. A., *Phys. Rev.*, **56**, 1241 (1939); **59**, 214 (1941).
8. Montgomery, C. G. and D. D., *Phys. Rev.*, **56**, 10 (1939).
9. Halban, H. V., L. Kowarski, and M. Magat, *Compt. Rend.*, **208**, 572 (1939).
10. For complete treatment see *Nuclear Physics*, by E. Fermi, Univ. of Chicago Press, 1950, Chap. 9.
11. Heisenberg, W., *Cosmic Radiation*, Dover Press, New York, 1946, Chap. 14, by S. Flugge, p. 144.
12. Davis, W. O., *Phys. Rev.*, **80**, 150 (1950).

13. Hess, W. N., E. H. Canfield, and R. E. Lingenfelter, *J. Geophys. Res.*, **66**, 665 (1961).
14. Lingenfelter, R. E., *J. Geophys. Res.*, **68**, 5633 (1963).
15. Newkirk, L. L., *J. Geophys. Res.*, **68**, 1825 (1963).
16. Staker, W. P., *Phys. Rev.*, **80**, 52 (1950).
17. Korff, S. A., and B. Hamermesh, *Phys. Rev.*, **71**, 842 (1947).
18. Korff, S. A., M. S. George, and J. W. Kerr, *Phys. Rev.*, **73**, 1133(L) (1948).
19. Yuan, L. C. L., *Phys. Rev.*, **74**, 504 (1948); **76**, 165 (1949).
20. Soberman, R., *Phys. Rev.*, **102**, 1399 (1956).
21. Mendell, R. B., and S. A. Korff, *J. Geophys. Res.*, **68**, 5487 (1963); Korff, S. A., R. B. Mendell, and S. Holt, *Proc. Int. Cosmic Ray Conf.*, London, 1965, paper Geo-35, W. Sandie et al., in preparation.
22. Gauger, J., *J. Geophys. Res.*, **69**, 2209 (1964).
23. Boella, G., Degli Antoni, Dilworth, Gianelli, Pani, Scarsi, and Intriligator, *J. Geophys. Res.*, **70**, 1019 (1965).
24. Reidy, W. P., R. C. Haymes, and S. A. Korff, *J. Geophys. Res.*, **67**, 459 (1962).
25. Martin, J. P., L. Witten, and L. Katz, *J. Geophys. Res.*, **68**, 2613 (1963).
26. Bame, S. J., Conner, Brumley, Hostetler, and Green, *J. Geophys. Res.*, **68**, 1221 (1963).
27. Williams, D. J., C. O. Bostrom, and G. F. Pieper, *J. Geophys. Res.*, **67**, 3610 (1962).
28. Trainor, J. H., and J. A. Lockwood, *J. Geophys. Res.*, **68**, 3115 (1964).
29. Haymes, R. C., *J. Geophys. Res.*, **69**, 841 and 853 (1964).
30. Haymes, R. C., and S. A. Korff, *Phys. Rev.*, **120**, 1460 (1960).
31. Libby, W. F., *Radiocarbon Dating*, Univ. of Chicago Press, 1955; W. F. Libby, *Science*, **140**, 278 (1963).
32. Lingenfelter, R. E., *Revs. of Geophys.*, **1**, 35 (1963).
33. Stuiver, M., *Science*, **149**, 533 (1965).
34. Craig, H., and D. Lal, *Tellus*, **13**, 85, (1961).
35. Grosse, A. V., W. M. Johnston, R. L. Wolfgand, and W. F. Libby, *Science*, **113**, 1 (1951).
36. Shen, B., S. A. Korff, and H. A. C. Neuburg, *Nature*, **199**, 60 (1963).
37. Korff, S. A., *Ann. N. Y. Acad. Sci.*, **67**, 35 (1956).
38. Peters, B., *Proc. Indian Acad Sci..*, **41**, 67 (1955).
39. Marquez, L., and N. L. Costa, *Nuovo Cimento*, series X, **2**, 1 (1955).
40. Arnold, J. R., and H. L. Al-Salih, *Science*, **121**, 451 (1955).
41. Perkins, R. W., Thomsas, Hill, and Neilsen, *Nature*, **205**, 790 (1965).
42. Lipschutz, M. E., P. Singer, and E. Anders, *J. Geophys. Res.*, **70**, 1473 (1965).
43. *IUGG Monograph* 7, Helsinki Meeting, 1960.
44. *IUGG Monograph* 12, Helsinki Meeting, 1960.
45. *Proc. Seventh Internat. Conf. on Cosmic Rad.*, IUPAP, Kyoto, Japan, Sept. 1961.
46. Haymes, R. C., *Phys. Rev.*, **116**, 1231 (1959); *J. Geophys. Res.*, **69**, 841 and 853 (1964).

Some New Channels for Astronomy

P. MORRISON

Massachusetts Institute of Technology

1. Windows on the Sky

The flowering of radio astronomy since World War II, coming as an unexpected extension of the oldest of sciences, optical astronomy, had an evident implication. Are there other channels, newly available to contemporary experimenters, which could still further generalize our astronomical viewpoint? Let us look a little into this question rationally, then confront that calm approach with the more tangled skein of events as they actually occurred.

The inborn electromagnetic detector, the eye, operates in exactly that band where the atomic level spacings of the components of the atmosphere permit rather free transmission of the solar thermal radiation. On that transparency feed a telescope and photographic plate, the true pillars of optical astronomy. The radio astronomer works up from the variable plasma frequency cutoff of the ionosphere at some few megacycles to the edge of severe oxygen absorption at a wavelength of about 0.6 cm, frequency about 50 kilomegacycles. Another octave beyond the high-frequency wing of the oxygen resonance line, and water absorption becomes dominant. Water, CO_2, and O_2 vibration and rotation levels undulate up and down across the whole submillimeter infrared, leaving occasional windows down to about 2 microns. From there to the near ultraviolet, the air is again clear, cutting off at high altitude with the famous ozone absorption at 0.3 microns. From then on upward in photon energy, the air remains opaque; more and more electrons can be sent to the continuum by photons above 5 eV. Even the Thompson scattering of the whole ten meters of water equivalent which is our atmosphere is too much to permit any reasonable input to arrive, once the photon energy has gone

343

well past the binding energy of atmospheric atomic electrons. The electron pairs formed by photons past the critical energy of 100 or 200 MeV serve to make up for the fall in Klein-Nishina cross section. The atmosphere remains black above five volts so to very high frequencies. Only when the incident energy is so great that the many electron secondaries can make a shower large enough to persist at large depths can we again say the atmosphere is clearing; rather, it is like thick ground glass past some 10^{12} eV, a region studied by the ingenious and heroic techniques of the extensive air-shower experimenters. So not many new channels remain for experimenters who must keep at least one foot on the ground.

This state of affairs is summarized in Table I. We give both the bandwidth in megacycles for the various channels, and the logarithmic width in the form of the integral $\int_{\nu_{min}}^{\nu_{max}} d\nu/\nu = L$. The bandwidth would represent the classical information capacity of a channel with negligible noise; the log interval something proportional to the instrumental limit set by the severe statistical photon noise of typical high-energy counting experiments; the true relative value of a channel is likely to lie somewhere in between, at a point fixed by the energy of the experimenter.

TABLE I.   The Atmospheric Windows

Channel	Width in Mc	Log width, L
Ionosphere-dominated radio	~ 5 Mc	2–3
Radio window	4.5×10^4 Mc	~ 10
Millimeter band, between O_2 and H_2O absorption	$\sim 10^5$ Mc	~ 1–2
Deep infrared windows	$\sim 10^7$ Mc	~ 2
Infrared uv the optical window	~ 10 Mc	~ 3

From this point of view, the infrared is clearly a region still little exploited where much information might be gained. It is encouraging that several groups like that of Leighton at California Tech. are beginning to search this channel with quite striking results already, in the recognition of very cool stars.

But since the V-2 experiments of the early postwar years and now with the most advanced of vehicles, small, even zero, atmospheric depths are well in reach. Payloads of some tens of kilograms can be carried for hundreds of seconds beyond the last milligram per cm² of atmosphere, for tenths of megadollars. Payloads of hundreds of kilograms can be sent up into the last few grams in balloons for the same sort of price, but gaining many hours of exposure. Satellites and space probes, though their cost is not commensurate with a single experiment, do accommodate a variety of instruments from kilos up to tons (for Soviet Proton probes) in orbit over weeks or even months of data gathering.

The oldest high-altitude technique is the balloon. Thus, it seemed sensible in the naive days of 1957 or '58 to suggest a study of gamma-rays beyond a few hundred kilovolts, which could well be followed below some g/cm² of atmosphere. These photons come straight as no cosmic ray particle can ever do from its source. If there exist cosmic-ray producing regions where gamma rays (say by *p-p* collisions making decaying neutral pion) too, are made, the gamma-ray flux will reveal them, it was thought. This notion, plus the speculative hope to see large scale electron-positron or proton-antiproton annihilation gammas, or to find neutrons and their hydrogen capture gammas, stimulated many courageous experiments. Even radioactivity, complete with its specific nuclear gamma cascades, was to be expected in the "fall-out" of the supernova explosions, marked by the illusion of exponential light decay. But it was not to be so. Nearly a decade of work, with counters, emulsion, spark chambers, in balloons, rockets, and space probes, has yielded a number of upper limits, both for general background at various energies, and for particular likely source directions, but at most only one positive indication of gammas of extraterrestrial origin has been obtained. The exceptional case, which from the nature of the experiment is not quite beyond question, is the excellent spectrum obtained in the energy range from 0.2 MeV up to about 2 MeV in Ranger 6 (partly also in Ranger 7), an unsuccessful lunar probe, recording gammas in a guarded scintillating pulse-height spectrometer in *cis*lunar space. Vehicle-produced gamma background was corrected for by a scheme for moving the crystal both close to and far outboard from the bulk of the probe on a long tentacle. Energy resolution was excellent; the only doubts arise from the uncheckable nature of the voyage, and the fact that certain diagnosed electronic failures did occur which vitiated the signal from the highest energy channel measured. The other bins seem correct and consistent, but the results are rather surprising, amounting to a presumed isotropic spectrum (it can be shown from a residual anisotropy of the sensitivity that the sun is not the major source) of the form $n(E)\, dE \propto dE/E^2$ with an intensity amounting to a flux integrated over all directions, at 1 MeV of 0.4 photons/sec-cm^2-MeV, extending from 0.2 or 0.3 MeV up to a little under 2 MeV, the instrumental limits. No peaks at 0.51 MeV or at 2.23 MeV are seen, to a rather good accuracy.

A comparison is useful. The optical flux from the North Star is very roughly 10^2 photons/cm^2-sec, at about 2.5 eV/photon. The total starlight from the whole sky is about 3000 times the Polaris flux; so the gamma-ray energy flux reported by Metzger and Arnold is above 10% that of starlight; large indeed for a radiation which if real is of quite unknown origin. Individual discrete sources are not known; the present sensitivity would enable rather easy detection of any source whose energy flux in the gamma-ray region was as great as that of a star of visual magnitude five or six. Present-day gamma-ray detection is about as good as the naked eye, for visible light, on an energy basis; of course, the much higher photon energy implies that the limits are set by statistical quantum noise. Palomar sensitivity, or Jodrell Banks are far away.

In another essay in this book, Professor Rossi has given an account of the discovery of cosmic x-rays, a series of enjoyable surprises. Let us here continue the rational story of how theorists ought to have come to predict x-ray sources—not how in fact they overlooked them!

We have not mentioned the opacity of interstellar space as a function of photon energy. Since the mean density in the densest region, the galactic plane, is not likely to be more than about 1 H atom/cc, the whole galaxy viewed edgewise is about a couple of grams per square centimeter thick, a few per cent of the critical length in neutral or ionized hydrogen. Intergalactic space is much less dense, so that gammas once beyond the region of strong photoeffect can traverse the distances of many Hubble constants without attenuation of importance. A new limit is then required, the Doppler shift from expansion. It is worth noting that photon-photon collisions may set a limit on high-energy gamma transmission before cosmological effects can do this; this is remarked on in the last section.

2. The Prevalence of X-rays

It is plain now that the *lowest* energy photons beyond the visible which can be of astronomical concern on the scale of the galaxy lie in the range roughly from 1 kV, or somewhat lower, on up in photon energy. The familiar gamma range, from a fraction to several MeV was first tried, and pion decay gammas, in the 100 MeV range and upwards, have also been examined. But it is at least in hindsight more to be expected that the x-ray region would first yield results. For there is a general phenomenon, early emphasized by Cocconi, that the totality of radiation tends to show a more or less monotone decline in intensity per unit frequency. It is this phenomenon which so strengthens the radio astronomers, who can deal with a fixed bandwidth. Radio flux reckoned per cycle per second amounts to some 10^{-5} eV/cm^2-sec from a typical direction in the galaxy. But starlight—barring the sun of course—amounts to a few tenths of that amount. This is the case even though we know that the nuclear energy, practically speaking, is all converted into starlight, and only mere plasma instabilities, or perhaps specialized explosions, are the source of most radio energy. Of course, the enormous frequency width of the visible spectrum implies that the total energy in the electron-volt range far outweighs the total energy of the microvolt photons of radio.

This general feature of radiation, looked at without regard to the physical process of its origin, is curious enough. If we recall the power-law decline of the energy flux of cosmic rays, computed as energy flux per unit energy of particle, the generality of the result is impressive. It may be that a general consequence of nonequilibrium processes is here foreshadowed, as the Boltzmann distribution is the consequence of the widest variety of systems which tend to equilibrium. However that may turn out, the result suggests that the *lowest* frequencies which can be transmitted through a particular region are likely to display a usable intensity. On this basis, a rational prediction might have been made that x-rays, and not gammas, would disclose the first important astronomy at high photon energy.

Most photon detection equipment, however, operates not with a fixed frequency bandwidth, like a superheterodyne radio receiver, but rather with a resolution which is some small fraction of the received energy, so that the response is integrated over the intensity with a weighting factor $K(\Delta E/E)$, where K is a number between 0.01 and unity. On this basis, then, the comparison between instruments working over a wide separation in frequency is something like $(\nu_1/\nu_2)^{n-1}$, for an intensity falloff given by dE/E^n. If now the intensity decline is not too fast—n not too large—the wide band of the high-frequency detector will still favor it, just as the optical telescope and spectroscope do win out, even though they display a prodigal lack of information economy by the use of a bandwidth at the narrowest some 10^5 Mc wide, compared to the mere kilocycles of a good 21 cm radiometer. Only with a resolution like 10^{-10} could optical equipment begin to use the information available fully. Perhaps laser-heterodyne techniques will achieve such results one day.

The upshot of these arguments is to make plausible, if not compelling, the prediction of hindsight that x-rays, ranging from the lowest energies which can penetrate the hydrogen- and helium-laden space, at 0.5 to 1 keV, up to some tens of keV, contain the next astronomy we need to understand. How brilliantly the experimenters have shown this —before the time of theorist's hindsight—Professor Rossi has already told. What remains to be described here is the still shaky nature of our understanding of what lies beyond this newly opened window.

3. Natural X-ray Source Mechanisms

(a) *Thermal Sources*

Starlight, bearing to be sure the absorption bands of resolved atomic lines, is broadly speaking, a visible thermal continuum, radiated by an optically thick near-equilibrium mix of electrons, atoms, and ions. When the strong Scorpius source of x-rays in the few kilovolt region was found, it was plausible to exploit the analogy to starlight. The Planck radiation rate increases, for a blackbody in the kilovolt region, by about 10^{12} for an emitting sphere of a given size. If the lifetime of the source was not be unacceptably short—an argument given real bite once several sources had been found—the area of the source must be very much smaller than that of a main-sequence star. A theoretical object of long standing, still without any support from observation, filled the bill. A star of normal mass, but with density like that in nuclear matter, and with the thermal content of its parent star, will radiate thermal continuum peaking in the kilovolt region, and lasting at least for thousands, perhaps millions, of years. For its surface area is down from that of the sun by some 10^{10}. The neutron star became the x-ray source. Theoretical difficulties do arise out of a new channel for losing energy, neutrino emission, which seriously threatens the length of the lifetime, and the general likelihood that an object the size of a small mountain but kilovolts hot would not meekly submit to the Planck law, but rather find nonequilibrium ways to emit light in the visible, not observed in the strong Scorpius source.

The key assumption was, of course, the small size. The Planck source had to be a point source; it was the remarkable measurement of Friedman, which disclosed that the source of x-rays in the Crab was a light year in diameter, that ended the simple form of the neutron source theory. Theorists are ingenious, though, and the neutron star, abandoned as a blackbody emitter, has become suggested seat of a magnetosphere which can emit x-rays, drawing on mechanical vibrations excited by the terrible collapse of the star to nuclear density. X-ray spectra are not yet conclusive, but they certainly do not support the Planck shape. A thick thermal source can be excluded.

Still, the thermal source is attractive, for it is efficient to make x-rays out of the characteristic motions of the electrons of the source, with $kT \sim h\nu_x$. A thin thermal source has been proposed: a cloud of hot plasma, ions and electrons in rough thermal equilibrium, emitting the typical exponential spectrum of such an object. Here the volume required is considerable, and the energy density, of course, is very much less than for a neutron star. Size is no longer a handicap, and the Crab source has been described as an expanding plasma, fed energy perhaps by radioactivity or by some other long-lasting process derivative from the initial supernova explosion. Such a plasma will lose energy less and less effectively as the density decreases. If there is any internal energy source, the plasma will heat up until after some time it reaches x-ray temperature; the total radiation rate varies with density and temperature like $\rho T^{1/2}$, so that it will eventually reach a maximum temperature, the higher the larger its internal energy source, and remain an emitter at $h\nu \sim kT$ for a substantial time even on its thermal content. This is a rather natural way to get x-ray sources, but it is not evident how such a cloud reaches low density before losing most of its energy at much lower temperatures. If indeed nuclear energy can be slowly fed in, the process is understandable. The recent alternative explanation of the near-exponential decay of the supernova light curve removes any direct support for the belief that the heavy radioactive nuclei of the r-process are formed in supernova outbursts, and somewhat weakens the plasma interpretation, at least of the Crab x-ray source. The fact that the other sources seem to be of galactic distances clustered towards the galactic center, places further demands on the energy input, for they are not weaker than the Crab, though they must be several times farther away.

(b) *Nonthermal Sources*

While thermal sources of x-rays represent efficient radiators in the region, it is known that there are nonthermal pools of energy which can yield x-rays. Here again two processes have been suggested which are very closely related. In these mechanisms, the radiating electrons are nonthermal, presumably power-law in energy spectrum, analogues to the cosmic ray particles. The radiated energy arises from interaction between the relativistic electrons and energy stored in an electromagnetic field.

If the stored energy is magnetic, the radiation is magnetic bremsstrahlung, or synchrotron radiation. If the stored energy is merely a flux of starlight photons, the radiation is said to arise from the inverse Compton effect. In either case, the power per electron is given by the formula:

$$-\frac{d}{dt}(\gamma M_0 c^2) \cong c\sigma_{\text{Thompson}} \times U_{\text{e.m.}} \cdot \gamma^2$$

where $U_{\text{e.m.}}$ is the energy density in the e.m. field, the energy of the x-ray photon emitted is expressed by the relation:

$$h\nu = \gamma^2(h\nu)_{\text{photons}},$$

if $U_{\text{e.m.}}$ is a photon flux

$$h\nu = \gamma^2(h\nu)_{\text{cyclo}}, \quad \nu_{\text{cyclo}} = eB/m_0 c,$$

if $U_{\text{e.m.}}$ is a static magnetic field, where the electron energy is γmc^2. Evidently either of these mechanisms requires highly relativistic electrons, rather than the few keV of the thermal processes. The principal attraction of these schemes is of course that we know that in the Crab, say, synchrotron light produces the polarized violet continuum so characteristic of that object. It requires an extrapolation of the spectrum by a factor of the order 10^2 to extend the emission to the x-ray region from the known optical region. The suggestion of the data is that a relatively smooth extension of the radio–optical curve would fit the data. It is less easy to overcome the short lifetime of such electrons, which last on the mean about $\tau_{\text{sec}} \cong 5 \cdot 10^8/B^2\gamma$, where B is measured in gauss. If a magnetic field of some milligauss is used, which minimizes the energy content of the Crab remnant in all forms, the lifetime for the 50–100 kilovolt region, where the extreme tail of the x-ray spectrum is observed, amounts only to days. That some process still alive in the 1000-year-old explosion debris is feeding the ultra-relativistic electron energy is not in itself a solution to the difficulties, but it cannot be excluded. Modest changes in the parameters—field, density, and so on—allow a variety of modified explanations, assuming highly nonuniform patches of field, and so on. None of these is particularly convincing, nor yet entirely excluded. There is more than a hint of time variation in the x-ray output of the Crab; if this were verified, the synchrotron mechanism would gain in appeal, rapid electron energy feed and all.

The inverse-Compton effect seems not to fit the Crab at all. The photon flux is insufficient to make this scheme prosper unless it were associated with a very strong central concentration of electrons. This is not what the source looks like. It is, of course, evident that every source which contains synchrotron emission will emit inverse-Compton secondary photons at a much higher energy. For the synchrotron electrons will strike a number of the very photons they have emitted. A small high-energy tail will thus extend beyond the eventual cutoff in the synchrotron emission which arises from the short electron life time. This is not yet observable yet in any case.

That weak fields over large volumes can contain electrons of modest energy and that such electrons could emit x-rays by inverse Compton is plain. Such sources then would be expected to be of large physical size. In the early history of this work, it was noticed that the Scorpius source, the strongest by nearly a factor of 10, lies 20° to 30° out of the galactic plane, but exactly in the longitude of the center of the galaxy. It was tempting to describe this event as a large very distant cloud of electrons, the remnant of a galactic explosion which sent out a jet long ago along the axis of the galaxy. Now only a pool of electrons remained, held by a field too weak to produce radio noise in the mega-cycle region, but able to make x-rays by collision with starlight from the great shining core of the galaxy below. This fine dramatic picture was destroyed by the ingenious work of Overbeck of MIT, who showed the absence of the ordinary bremmstrahlung gammas, with $h\nu \sim \gamma m_0 c^2$, which this picture entailed, and by M. Oda of MIT, whose moiré collimator demonstrated the source in Scorpius to be smaller than one two-hundredth of its angular distance from the galactic plane, certainly implausibly tight for such a jet remnant.

The background radiation in the kilovolt range is again of uncertain origin. It is real, and roughly isotropic. It may be merely the summed supernovae of external galaxies, or perhaps the interaction between great pools of cosmic ray electrons and the remnant blackbody millimeter radiation recently suspected. The whole subject of the background x-rays is filled with uncertainty, and we are not in possession of a highly connected model of any kind. Nor are the experiments adequate for a full conclusion. Whether the MeV radiation of the Ranger measurements is part of this same picture is one of the most tantalizing of all the many questions still open for the astronomy of these new windows.

The invisibility of the Scorpius source in optical light is an interesting point. If the source shines by thermal radiation from thin plasma, it ought to be seen in the visible unless it is extended in angular scale as to merge with the skylight noise. It can be computed that it ought to be *larger* than a minute or two of arc in that case. It is known to be *smaller* than eight minutes. This gap is pretty sure to be closed by experiment before these lines are in print. Theorists will await the result anxiously.

It is hard to resist one extension beyond the gamma-ray energy. Whatever the gas density of extragalactic space, its photon density in the visible is known. That is true also in the radio and perhaps the millimeter band. For sufficiently high gamma energies, these background photons are more attenuating than the rare gas atoms. Here we see the realization of photon-photon collisions, to yield electron-positron pairs, $\gamma + \gamma \to e^+ + e^-$. The identification of primary cosmic gamma rays at energies like 10^{16} eV or above may be a source of information on this final limit on the energy of astronomical photons. It is premature to draw conclusions yet from the air shower data.

This is a happy field of applied physics. Neutron interactions and hyperons, Klein-Nishina and pair production, atomic continuum and line spectra, stopping powers and ionization losses—all of these topics and more need to be brought to bear on the issues. Most of these subjects have for a whole generation borne the mark of the energetic hand, and clarifying mind of H. A. Bethe, without whom one feels quantum theory would mainly be a philosophical puzzle, nuclei a mass of data, and quantum electrodynamics a search for consistency. In a dozen directions to knowledge of the world, he has made the trails people use. It is an honor and a delight to greet him on his birthday.

Readings

There are many recent reviews of x-ray astronomy, in addition to the fine chapter by Rossi in the present volume. They tend to be rather specialized. The compendium of C. W. Allen, *Astrophysical Quantities* (London 1964) is almost always the best place to start for all but the latest topics.

To Section 1: For x-ray absorption, S. Strom and K. Strom, *Pub. Astro Soc. Pac.*, **73**, 43 (1961); other absorptions, see Allen. For Ranger results, see Metzger et al., *Nature*, **204**, 766 1964.

To Section 3: Hot plasmas are discussed in many papers, especially in G. Burbridge, R. Gould, and W. Tucker, *Phys. Rev. Letters*, **14**, 285 (1965). Supernovae are treated in P. Morrison and L. Sartori, *Phys. Rev. Letters*, **14**, 771 (1965). Neutron stars are handled in Chiu and Salpeter, *Phys. Rev. Letters*, **12**, 412 (1964) in the straightforward and by now excluded form. Oscillations are treated by A. G. W. Cameron in *Nature*, **205**, 787 (1965), and in later papers by Cameron and his collaborators, Tsuruta in particular. Inverse-Compton discussions are numerous; a late paper with references is J. E. Felten, *Phys. Rev. Letters*, **15**, 1003 (1965).

Experimental Gamma-Ray Astronomy

KENNETH GREISEN

Cornell University

1. Introduction

It is somewhat presumptuous to speak of gamma-ray astronomy as though it were already a developed area, rich in its yield of astronomical knowledge. Although the experiments in this field have produced a number of significant implications, these have derived chiefly from the failure to detect intensities above certain levels that were considered plausible on various astrophysical or cosmological models. The reliable positive data at hand prior to 1966 were scanty at best. Nevertheless, the field is rich in promise and hence in activity. In the United States alone, it has engaged more than a dozen different experimental research groups. The tentative results and upper limits provided by past experiments are regarded as a valuable preliminary survey, which serves to clarify the requirements for apparatus that will yield definitive measurements in the future.

It is the intent of the present article to review the state of the field at the beginning of 1966, summarizing the achievements that have been made, explaining the difficulties that must be surmounted, and attempting to forecast the character of apparatus needed in the next stage of experimentation. Section 2 defines the broad subdivisions of the field; Sec. 3 examines the contrast between gamma-ray and x-ray astronomy; Sec. 4 summarizes current knowledge of intensities from both discrete and diffuse sources, and sketches the techniques that have been used; while Sec. 5 discusses methods that may be used in the future.

Special indebtedness is acknowledged to the review paper by M. Oda on x-ray and gamma-ray astronomy, presented at the 1965 London Cosmic Ray Conference[1], and to the 1965 Woods Hole Space Science Study Panel on x-ray and gamma-ray astronomy.

2. Divisions of Gamma-Ray Energy

The envisioned field of gamma-ray astronomy spans the entire range from somewhat under 10^5 to more than 10^{19} eV, a larger logarithmic interval than that embracing all of radio, infrared, visible, ultraviolet, and x-ray astronomy. The associated variation of the probable spectral intensity is even more huge, and naturally the approaches to detection differ in widely separated parts of the spectrum. Also, different mechanisms for generation of the radiation achieve prominence in different parts of the spectrum, though some mechanisms (bremsstrahlung, synchrotron radiation, and compton scattering) may contribute continuously throughout the whole range. For the sake of discussion it is convenient to divide the spectrum into three broad parts, as follows.

0.1 to 20 MeV, the "Nuclear Transition" (NT) Region

It is in this interval that one can expect to observe line spectra indicative of neutron capture and nuclear excitation occurring in stellar atmospheres or supernovae; also the 0.5 MeV line owing to positron annihilation both in such atmospheres and in interstellar space. Gamma-rays are almost invariably detected by their production of secondary electrons; at these energies the electrons have short ranges in matter, and are completely scattered in direction within distances very short compared with the gamma-ray interaction length. Energy resolution is conveniently possible by pulse-height measurement in a counter that completely absorbs the electron; but good angular resolution is difficult and rests primarily on collimation of the incoming radiation. Since the absorption length is on the order of 10 g/cm², a collimator many absorption lengths thick is necessarily very heavy.

On account of this difficulty, there is no experimental knowledge (prior to 1966) of discrete sources in this energy range, or of the directional variation of the primary intensity. The average flux of photons exceeding energy E seems to run from 0.16 to 0.0027 per cm²-sec-sr as E goes from 0.1 to 3 MeV†.

30 MeV to 300 GeV, the "High-Energy" (HE) Region

This region achieves special significance owing to the fact that high-energy nuclear interactions produce neutral pions copiously, and

† See detailed discussion of the data in Sec. 3A. The conclusions are based on ref. 27.

these each decay into two photons of 70 MeV in the center-of-mass frame. Comparatively few of these photons have less than 30 MeV in the earth frame; and those produced by collisions of typical (10–20 GeV) cosmic-ray protons with matter are apt to have 500 MeV or more of energy. Annihilation of low-energy antiprotons usually produces several photons of about 200 MeV each, through neutral pion decay. Collisions with gas of the higher energy cosmic rays, of course, produce a continuous photon spectrum extending almost indefinitely in energy, but falling rapidly in number. Beyond 300 GeV the low flux necessitates distinctly different detection methods, which become possible at these energies by utilizing the extensive air showers which such photons generate.

Pion decay is not the only source of high-energy photons. Nonthermal radio noise and polarized light from cosmic sources require the presence there of numerous electrons of energy 10^9–10^{12} eV. By bremsstrahlung and also by inverse Compton effect on visible light (which may be primarily the synchrotron radiation in the source), such electrons are expected to generate secondary photons throughout the "high-energy" part of the spectrum.

In this spectral region the photon detectors profit from the fact that the secondary electrons are emitted at small angles with respect to the incoming radiation, and traverse significant amounts of matter before the directions are greatly altered by scattering. Therefore angular resolution is possible with reasonably light apparatus. Fine energy resolution is difficult because the secondaries are not easily absorbed, but approximate energy measurement is sufficient in this range (since line spectra are not expected) and this is possible by observation of the secondary shower development in modest thicknesses of matter.

Experimental sky surveys in this energy region have shown no discrete sources producing more than 10^{-4} photons/cm²-sec at the earth, while the average diffuse intensity is less than 10^{-3} per cm²-sec-sr†.

E > 500 GeV, the "Very High-Energy" (VHE) Region

As mentioned above, this energy region is distinguished by very low flux values and the possibility of compensating for these by use of

† See detailed discussion of the data in Sec. 3B. The conclusions are based on refs. 28–31.

air shower observation techniques. The latter include detection of the Cerenkov light emitted in the atmosphere as well as detection of the secondary charged particles. Whereas in investigating the NT and HE spectral regions, the detectors have to be taken close to the top of the atmosphere or outside it, for the VHE range the detectors may sit conveniently for long periods on the ground—though preferably on a mountain top.

The mechanisms responsible for the very high-energy gamma rays include those that generate the radiation of lower energy. However, the production by electrons diminishes in relative importance because the drain on electron energy, chiefly by the magnetic bremsstrahlung, is so severe that the electron spectrum is quite steep. Also the Compton cross section diminishes, and the energy transferable by this process increases only as the first power of the electron energy, no longer as the square (when the photons have energy exceeding mc^2 in the electron frame of reference). Thus above 500 GeV, photon production via nuclear interactions and subsequent decay of pions and kaons becomes a more dominant process. However, at extreme energies another mechanism comes into play that does not require the presence of matter. When photons above 10^{17} eV in energy encounter starlight (or synchrotron radiation) of 1 eV, the quantum energy in the center-of-mass system is enough for pion production. Near the threshold, a produced pion has almost the same velocity as the proton, hence the characteristic energy of the decay quanta in the earth system is about 10^{16} eV.

The proton flux above 10^{17} eV almost certainly pervades intergalactic space as well as the galaxies; the distances are much larger, and the thermal photon density there is estimated to be only one order of magnitude smaller than in the galaxies. The calculated photon flux above 10^{16} eV, arising from the inverse photopion process, is about 10^{-4} times the proton flux at the same energy. This should be enough to be measurable, and its measurement will provide a test of cosmology and of the content of the intergalactic regions.

Until now what is known in the very high-energy regions is that the flux above $5 \cdot 10^{12}$ eV from the most prominent discrete sources of radio noise is less than $5 \cdot 10^{-11}$ per cm²-sec[2,3]; and that the diffuse flux above 10^{15} eV appears to be about 10^{-12}–10^{-13} per cm²-sec-sr[4-6]. Tentative evidence has been presented for a point source at energies around 10^{15} eV with a flux of about 10^{-15} photons/cm²-sec[5], but it is too early to know whether this observation will stand up in time.

Positive evidence is still lacking on the actual intensity above 10^{16} eV; but it has been shown that this intensity is not higher than the value predicted (10^{-16} per cm²-sec-sr) according to the inverse photopion production mechanism outlined above[5]. This negative evidence has significance: if the cosmic ray density had been much greater billions of years ago (i.e., in the neighborhood of the most distant galaxies from which radiation is now being received), or if the interpretation of the redshift were wrong and the universe is not actually expanding, a substantially higher flux of the photons above 10^{16} eV should have been expected.

The negative results at 10^{12}–10^{13} eV from the Crab Nebula have also been significant. According to some models[7,8] of the processes in this nebula, the electrons that emit the synchrotron radiation were considered to be secondaries of a hundred-fold more energetic, non-radiating proton component. If so, the same nuclear collisions that continually regenerate the electrons would have yielded a photon flux at the earth, above 10^{13} eV, at least a hundred times greater than the observed upper limit.

From the above discussion, it is apparent that there are two rather distinct aspects of gamma-ray astronomy. One is the observation of radiation from discrete objects in space, often referred to as "point sources" (although adequate angular resolution may be able to resolve their structure). The other is the detection of a diffuse background arising from interactions in the gas, with the magnetic fields, or with the low-energy electromagnetic radiation in the interstellar regions, both within our galaxy and in intergalactic space. The experimental distinction between discrete and truly diffuse sources is apt to be difficult, and is never entirely unambiguous because, on the one hand, unresolved point sources contribute to the apparent diffuse flux and, on the other hand, distant nebulae (in contrast to interstellar space in our own galaxy) take on the character of discrete sources.

The diffuse component is not expected to be isotropic; indeed, its angular distribution should reflect the unequal distribution of gas, thermal radiation, magnetic fields and charged cosmic rays in the space around us, as governed primarily by the structure of the galaxy. When a detecting apparatus lacks angular resolution it loses evidence of such structure and reveals only an average of the intensity over all directions. In this average, it includes the signals from point sources along with the diffuse flux; but the latter tends to dominate the result unless the point sources are very strong or numerous. Thus the experiments without directional resolution are often spoken of as measuring the diffuse or so-called "isotropic" flux. Nevertheless, this usage is rather loose and can even be grossly misleading. To see this point one need only contrast the uniformity of the sky as it appears through a thick haze with the structural detail visible on a clear night. These considerations point up the necessity of directional resolution (so difficult to attain in the nuclear transition energy range) in identifying the character of the sources or mechanisms responsible for any detected radiation. Indeed, because of instrumental backgrounds caused by the charged cosmic-ray particles, observation of directional structure may also be essential just to identify the detected radiation as high-energy photons.

3. Contrast with X-ray Astronomy

The closest neighbor of the gamma-ray branch of astronomy, both in time of origin and in physical similarity, is the x-ray branch. Why have x-rays yielded such a rich harvest so quickly, while gamma-rays have been such a stubborn crop to reap?

The outstanding difference is in size of the flux. It is not the energy flux that is in contrast: In the average over all directions the number of photons has a spectral distribution approximated by 10^{-2} dE/E^2 per cm²-sec-sr-MeV, connecting smoothly from the x-ray to the gamma-ray range, and implying equal amounts of energy in equal logarithmic intervals of frequency. However, the number of x-ray photons above 1 KeV is on the order of a thousand times the number of gamma-rays above 1 MeV, and a million times the number above 1 GeV. At intermediate latitudes the primary flux of charged cosmic rays is about 0.1 per cm²-sec-sr, while that of x-rays is a hundred times greater, rendering elaborate methods of discrimination between these components unnecessary. In contrast, the number of primary gamma-rays is much less than that of the charged cosmic rays, making background rejection a major difficulty.

Secondly, the relative brightness of discrete galactic sources against the diffuse flux is in contrast. The Scorpius x-ray source was clearly detectable[9] with an instrument of acceptance angle as wide as 40°, and there are at least ten galactic sources that can stand out against the general flux in a cone of half-angle as large as 10°. It was this distinctiveness of the "point" sources that gave both radioastronomy and x-ray astronomy their great impetus in modern times, because it made rapid initial progress in these fields possible with primitive instruments. For gamma-rays, on the contrary, point sources have not yet been detected, and it appears that better angular resolution (to at least 0.01 sr) will be necessary to resolve even the strongest of them.

In the cases of both radio waves and x-rays, the large flux values were entirely unexpected. The nonthermal radio signals implied the unanticipated presence of huge concentrations of highly relativistic electrons in the sources. As for the x-rays, only one of the dozen or so discovered sources has yet been identified with an object that looks remarkable in any other way; and the nature of the emission mechanism has had to be identified (in the one case, the Scorpius source, where it has yet been possible) from empirical evidence on the shape of the spectrum. The origin of the energy is still unknown. The x-ray flux has appropriately been termed the great surprise of the space age. In the gamma-ray field, it has now been made clear that such big surprises are not in store. To the contrary, early predictions of yields from supernovae have already been shown to be too high, in all three regions of the gamma spectrum defined above. To use a colloquial phrase, laborers in this field will have to work a little harder.

Further contrasts appear upon examination of technical ease or difficulty of detection. The short range of x-rays in matter makes it possible to construct light-weight detectors having high efficiency. Typical conversion lengths are on the order of milligrams per square centimeter, whereas for gamma-rays the length is on the order of 10 g/cm^2; and in addition there is the requirement of greater area because of the smaller flux. In the thin x-ray detectors, incident charged cosmic rays produce little background of secondary nature, while in the more massive gamma-ray detectors, the production of secondary radiation is very copious. Moreover, the short range of x-rays results in little albedo from the atmosphere, and ease of shielding against it; whereas the gamma-ray albedo is many times more than the primary gamma-ray flux, and very difficult to filter out—especially since shielding materials automatically become sources of secondary radiation.

In obtaining directional resolution, x-rays offer two powerful methods that are not easily feasible for gamma-rays. One is fine angular collimation, e.g., by honeycomb cells or wire grids. The other is focussing by coherent diffraction or reflection, the latter of which even makes possible a precise imaging telescope[10]. For gamma-rays in the nuclear transition range, honeycomb collimation is not impossible, and indeed will probably be necessary; but the required weight increases as the cube of the absorption length of the radiation, making the weight of adequate gamma-ray collimators on the order of a thousand pounds (with enhanced requirements for avoiding the secondary radiation produced in the collimators themselves).

Despite these discouraging contrasts, there are compelling reasons which motivate numerous research groups to pursue the cosmic gamma-ray quest with ever increasing effort. Basically the motivation stems from numerous theoretical analyses[11-18,38] of the possible intensities and special significance of the flux in various parts of the spectrum. But it also depends on the fact that the estimated intensities are not far below the present capabilities of measurement, and on the confidence of the active experimenters that the obstacles to success are surmountable.

4. Current State of Knowledge

A. Nuclear Transition Gamma-Rays

The data available' prior to 1966 were obtained with omni-directional counters: typically a "phoswich" arrangement consisting of an alkali halide scintillation crystal to detect the gamma-rays, surrounded by a thin plastic scintillator to veto pulses due to incoming charged particles. The characteristic difference in deexcitation times of two such phosphors allows both optical signals to be distinguished by a single photomultiplier. The internal crystal is linear in response and two or three inches thick, which is long compared with the range of the secondary electrons by which the gammas are detected. A pulse-height analyzer sorts the gamma-ray events according to energy. Choice of a high atomic number for the material (e.g., CsI) emphasizes the photo-electric absorption process. Pair production followed by positron capture, and Compton scattering, give rise to low-energy secondary gammas, but use of a thick crystal of high Z causes these secondaries frequently to be absorbed in the same crystal, adding to the photopeak. The energy resolution attainable by this method is 5 to 10% near 1 MeV.

With such apparatus carried by balloons in the atmosphere, the 0.5 MeV line due to positron annihilation has been detected[19] and the gamma-ray spectrum has been studied as a function of atmospheric depth[20-21]. The counting rates were comfortably high, typically ten or more per second. However, the rates were practically entirely due to secondaries generated in the atmosphere by bremsstrahlung of the electrons, by degradation of π^0-decay gammas, and by absorption of atmospherically produced positrons. Even the extrapolated rates at the top of the atmosphere were found to be high [about 6 per cm^2-sec between 30 keV and 1 MeV, and 0.2 per cm^2-sec in the 0.5 MeV line[19]] and are probably due mainly to albedo of the atmosphere. One may infer this from the increase of the counting rate with atmospheric pressure above the transition maximum, and from the large scattering angles of electrons and photons of these low energies. Even at the much higher energies characteristic of π^0-decay gamma-rays, directional instruments have found[22-23] the upwards flux to be half the vertically downwards flux at 14 g/cm^2. This is about the same ratio as that found by Peterson between the omnidirectional flux values at zero and 14 g/cm^2.

In view of the albedo, one must also regard with suspicion the results obtained with omnidirectional instruments in rockets[24] and satellites[25] that remain near the earth. The observations of Peterson with the OSO-1 satellite[25] gave clear indication, by the presence of a latitude effect, that at least part of the counting rate was due to secondary effects of charged particles. His results were therefore stated as upper limits only. After approximate corrections for the counter efficiency and effects of local shielding, these limits for the average differential flux per unit solid angle are 0.08 per cm^2-sec-sr-MeV between 0.5 and 1.5 MeV, and 0.013 between 1.5 and 4.5 MeV, in the same units. The values obtained by Northrup and Hostetler were substantially higher.

In principle the albedo can be avoided by use of a directional detector, and the directionality would also help in identifying the sources of the extraterrestrial radiation. In fact, L. Peterson had such a counter on board the OSO satellite, in the form of a Compton coincidence telescope. With such a device, however, the valid counting rate due to gammas within the designed aperture is greatly reduced, per unit of detector area, both by the restriction of the aperture and by the efficiency, which was less than 1% in this case. As a result the instrument has an increased sensitivity to secondary effects of the charged radiation arriving in all directions, and producing showers in the nearby vehicle and instrumental material. Indeed, Peterson found by auxiliary balloon experiments that presence of the instrumental matter increased the telescope rates by a factor of 10. Thus, such devices require more elaborate precautions in background avoidance.

The most definitive measurements prior to 1966 were obtained by Arnold, Metzger, Anderson, and Van Dilla[26-27], on two flights of Ranger spacecraft between the earth and the moon. The quoted data were recorded at distances outside the radiation belts, farther than ten earth radii from the earth. The pulse-height spectrum was registered, using an omnidirectional phoswich-type scintillator housed in a thin aluminum shell at the end of an extensible six-foot boom. Data were obtained on one of the flights (Ranger 3) both with the boom in the stowed position and with the boom extended. In the second flight (Ranger 5) data were only obtained in the stowed position. Extending the boom reduced the geometrical factor for cosmic-ray-induced secondary counts by a factor of 13, and reduced the counting rate only by a factor around 2. Therefore, about half the counts in the stowed position, but only about 10% in the extended position, were due to local secondaries.

Figure 1 shows the spectrum obtained in the extended position. The flatness of the portion between 1 and 2 MeV seems to have been due to an instrumental malfunction; it did not appear in the stowed position on either flight. The remaining data agree well with the straight line drawn on the figure, which represents $0.17/E^{2.2}$ quanta/cm^2-sec-MeV, with E expressed in MeV. Since the detector was essentially isotropic (though the flux may not have been) and a correction of about 10% is needed for the local secondaries, the average differential flux per unit solid angle is inferred to be

$$dn(E) = 0.012 \, dE/E^{2.2} \text{ cm}^{-2} \text{ sec}^{-1} \text{ sr}^{-1} \qquad (1)$$

with E in MeV. With this expression one can calculate the expected flux in the intervals 0.5–1.5 and 1.5–4.5 MeV for comparison with the OSO-1 upper limits quoted above. The results are 0.017 and 0.0015 per cm^2-sec-sr-MeV, respectively, lower than those obtained from the OSO apparatus by factors of 5 and 9.

That the gamma-ray flux observed on the Ranger flights was not primarily of solar origin was inferred from the lack of observable change in counting rate upon alteration of the aspect of the apparatus.

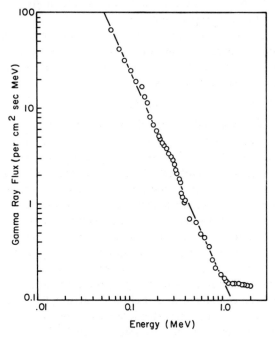

Fig. 1.   Gamma-ray spectrum obtained in *cis*lunar space with counter at end of six-foot boom on Ranger 3 spacecraft[27]. The flattening between 1 and 2 MeV is regarded as erroneous.

The detector was sufficiently anisotropic to have shown an observable effect if as much as one-fourth of the flux had been of solar origin.

The Ranger flights also provided upper limits of the primary flux in the important gamma-ray lines at 0.51 and 2.23 MeV. In the stowed position, small peaks appeared in the spectra at 0.51 MeV, but these were apparently due to positrons of local secondary origin, because no peak appeared in the extended position. Peaks at 2.23 MeV were absent in both flights even in the stowed position. From these observations, limits of 0.014 photons/cm² sec for the 0.51 MeV line, and 0.005 photons/cm² sec for the 2.23 MeV line, can be set for the sum of flux values from all discrete sources, plus the integral of the diffuse flux over all directions. The upper limits of the average flux per unit solid angle are 0.0011 quanta/cm²-sec-sr for the 0.51 MeV line, and 0.0004 quanta/cm²-sec-sr for the 2.23 MeV line. These limits are lower than those given by prior experiments.

It is of interest to extrapolate Eq. (1) into neighboring spectral regions and compare with the corresponding observed flux values. For this purpose the integral of Eq. (1), giving the flux of quanta above energy E, is convenient. This is

$$n(>E) = 10^{-2}E^{-1.2}\,\text{cm}^{-2}\,\text{sec}^{-1}\,\text{sr}^{-1} \qquad (E \text{ in MeV}). \qquad (2)$$

For instance, extrapolation into the x-ray region predicts a flux of 19 quanta/cm²-sec-sr with wavelengths between 2 and 8 angstroms, agreeing very closely with the experimental value of 10 quanta/cm²-sec-sr in this wavelength interval, estimated by M. Oda[1]. (The agreement is really too good to be other than fortuitous, since cosmic absorption of the x-rays with wavelength longer than 5 angstroms can account for the small apparent discrepancy.) Extrapolating towards high energy, Eq. (2) predicts 4×10^{-5} quanta/cm²-sec-sr at energies above 100 MeV, a factor 7 below the experimental upper limit derived by Kraushaar et al. from data recorded on the Explorer XI satellite[28].

It is of further interest to compare the gamma-ray flux with that which has been calculated by J. Felton[17], arising from the process of Compton scattering of intergalactic electrons by cosmic microwaves. The computed flux of scattered photons is $dn(E) = 5 \times 10^{-3}\,dE/E^{2.2}$ in the same units as Eq. (1). The agreement of the exponents is remarkable (as has been pointed out by Felten) since the shape of the assumed electron spectrum was not arbitrary, but determined by the observed radio spectral indices. The coefficients differ only by a factor 2.4, but this agreement is less significant since the normalization of the electron flux had a large uncertainty.

B. High-Energy Gamma-Rays

The experiments of Rossi and Hulsizer[32] and of Critchfield, Ney, and Oleksa[33], with balloon-borne ionization chambers and cloud chamber, respectively, showed that gamma-rays above 1 GeV were less than 1% of the charged primary cosmic rays in frequency. Subsequently balloon-borne emulsion experiments of Carlson, Hooper, and King[34] and of Svensson[22] demonstrated the secondary nature of most of the high-energy gamma-rays near the top of the atmosphere; and the emulsion experiment of Braccesi, Ceccarelli, and Salandin[35] set an upper limit of 10^{-2} per cm²-sec for the flux of photons above 100 MeV from Cygnus A.

In an attempt to get farther outside the atmosphere, Perlow and Kissinger[36] used the brief flight of a V2 rocket to measure the energy flux of photons in the interval 3.4–90 MeV. Their result was 0.45 MeV/cm²-sec-sr, which must be regarded as an upper limit because of some residual overlying atmosphere, imperfect rejection of charged particles, and a slight sensitivity to albedo gamma-rays. Assuming a number spectrum of the form dE/E^2, this energy flux corresponds to about 7×10^{-3} gammas/cm²-sec-sr above 20 MeV. The apparent coefficient in the spectrum, however, is an order of magnitude above that in Eqs. (1) and (2), derived from measurements in cislunar space.

More recently, T. L. Cline[23] and Duthie et al[37]. have flown detectors consisting of scintillation and Cerenkov counters (with the gamma-ray converter shielded by anticoincidence scintillators to protect against incident charged particles) to various altitudes with balloons. The apparatus was designed for π^0-decay photons in both cases, i.e., to detect gamma-rays above about 50 MeV. The attempt was to obtain the primary intensity by extrapolating the vertical flux measurements to the top of the atmosphere. The results of the two experiments were not consistent with each other, and demonstrated forcefully that the primary gamma-ray flux is too low, compared with both the charged particle flux and the secondary gammas generated in the atmosphere, to be accurately measured in this way.

This conclusion does not necessarily rule out successful detection of primary gamma-rays by balloon-borne instruments. It does mean, however, that detection of the diffuse part of the gamma-ray flux will require greater sophistication. It appears that at a pressure of about 5 g/cm², the primary gamma-ray flux is less than the vertical secondary flux by one order of magnitude, less than the horizontal secondary flux by two orders of magnitude, and less than the charged particle flux by two to three orders of magnitude, depending on the geomagnetic latitude. Overcoming the first of these inequalities can be facilitated by the attainment of higher balloon altitudes; while the other inequalities require apparatus having superior efficiency in rejection of incoming charged particles and all forms of radiation approaching from the sides or below.

A somewhat easier goal is the observation of discrete sources, since the charged primaries and their atmospheric secondaries have a broad, continuous angular distribution, against which a comparatively small flux from a pronounced direction can be distinguished by apparatus of good angular resolution. These considerations have led Frye and Smith of Case Institute of Technology[29], Ögelman et al. of Cornell[31], and Cobb et al. of Rochester[30] to carry out balloon flights with spark chambers as detectors. Prior to 1966 none of these experiments had achieved positive recognition of any point source. Table I lists 95% confidence upper limits obtained for the flux from various potential sources that were included within the scanned region of the sky.

Clearly a more favorable environment for primary gamma-ray experiments is in the space outside the atmosphere, either below or above the radiation belts. Before 1966, only the experiment of Kraushaar et al. on the Explorer XI satellite[28] had yielded data under these conditions. Future experiments may be expected greatly to surpass this exploratory one in angular resolution and minimum detectable intensity. The angular acceptance was about $\pm 20°$, defined by a combination of scintillator and Cerenkov detectors. The area solid-angle factor was small: 4.3 cm^2 sr in the forward direction, with a detection efficiency of 15%; but the operating time was seven months, in contrast to typical balloon flights of seven hours. However, much of this time was lost owing to passage through radiation belts and the limited range of the receiving station. The conclusions are therefore severely limited by poor statistics.

The angular resolution of this detector was critically essential. In the first place, it permitted the assignment of upper limits to the intensity arriving from numerous discrete sources, with the results listed in Table I (where for consistency with the reporting of other data, we have adjusted the limits given in reference 28 to conform to a 95% confidence level). Secondly, the intensity vertically upwards from the earth was observed to be an order of magnitude greater than the downwards intensity, while from the direction of the earth's horizon (at geomagnetic latitudes above 20°) the excess over the flux from space was a factor of 20. Without angular discrimination, therefore, the apparent intensity would have been almost entirely due to albedo from the earth. The authors recognized a possibility that even the residual apparent flux towards the earth could be a background effect; the statistics were not good enough to reveal such directional structure (e.g., a correlation with the galactic plane) as would have confirmed the identification of the gamma-radiation by its property of straight-line propagation. The result of this measurement was therefore given as an upper limit of the

TABLE I.   Upper Limits, of 95% Confidence Level, for the High
Energy Gamma-Ray Flux from Various Discrete Sources.

Reference	Energy	Object	Photons/m²-sec
Frye and Smith[29]	30–500 MeV	Taurus A	1.5
		Cygnus A	2.2
		3C147	1.5
		3C196	1.5
Cobb, Duthie, and Stewart[30]	> 100 MeV	Taurus A	0.7
		Orion (M42)	2.9
		Rosette	3.3
		I.C. 443	1.2
		Sun	5.3
Ögelman, Devaille, and Greisen[31]	> 1 GeV	Cygnus A	6.0
		Cygnus Loop	1.6
		3C4446	8.1
		CTA 102	2.2
		Casseiopeia A	2.9
		3C9	3.0
		Andromeda A	1.5
		3C48	1.2
		3C47	3.5
Kraushaar et al. with counter telescope[28]	> 120 MeV	Andromeda	50
		Small Mag. Cloud	30
		Large Mag. Cloud	30
		Taurus A	14
		Hydra A	5
		Virgo A	6
		Centaurus A	9
		Hercules A	8
		Cygnus A	12
		Casseiopeia A	55
		Galactic Center	11

primary flux, averaged over all directions, of gamma-rays with energy
above 100 MeV; the value being $(3.3 \pm 1.2) \times 10^{-4}$ per cm²-sec-sr.

During the Explorer XI recording period, one solar flare of class
3 and one of class 3+ occurred. In the first case the sun was observed
by the apparatus for 2¼ minutes beginning 45 minutes after the flare
maximum, and in the second the sun was observed for eight minutes

beginning one minute before the visual maximum. No gamma-rays were detected, and the upper limits set for the average high-energy gamma-ray flux from the sun during these periods were, respectively, 10^{-2} and 1.5×10^{-2} per cm²-sec.

C. Very High-Energy Gamma-Rays

The flux at extremely high energy is so small that direct detection of the individual photons above the atmosphere is impractical. The electromagnetic showers that they initiate in the air, however, make the effects of such photons detectable over a sufficiently large area to produce counting rates that are probably measurable. Two unique features of such events can be used to distinguish them from the more frequent air showers initiated by charged cosmic rays. One is the directional character: only photons can retain the unique directions of discrete sources, or the strong anisotropy of the Milky Way (neutrinos do not initiate showers with significant frequency, and neutrons with energy less than 10^{17} eV do not survive over the distances from sources more than about 1 kiloparsec away). The other feature is the composition: near the center of showers initiated by protons or heavier nuclei, several per cent of the particles are highly penetrating muons, the residue of a nuclear cascade; while the showers initiated by photons are more purely electromagnetic: the charged particles are almost entirely electrons and positrons, which have short ranges in heavy materials such as lead.

The showers can be observed by detecting the secondary particles, or by registering the radio or optical signals. When the primary energy is much less than 10^{14} eV, few particles reach sea level, and when it is much less than 10^{13} eV, few particles even reach the mountain tops. The total numbers of muons and electrons are then too few to permit measurement of the composition, or even to detect the shower particles efficiently and measure the direction of the shower axis. However, high in the atmosphere these showers produce a substantial amount of Cerenkov light, to which the air is transparent. The high-intensity part of the pool of light at sea level has a radius of about 200 meters, providing a sensitive area of about 10^5 m² per shower. With efficient parabolic mirrors of 1 m diameter, the collected light is barely detectable, against the fluctuations of the light from the night sky, for showers generated by photons of 5000 GeV. Increasing the light-gathering area decreases the minimum detectable energy in proportion to the diameter of the mirror. The angular resolution inherent in the intense part of the Cerenkov light beam is approximately $\pm 2°$. To test whether or not a given celestial object is a source of extremely high-energy photons, one may repeatedly orient a telescope so that the object will pass through the field of view, and see whether the average rate of photomultiplier pulses is enhanced during the periods of passage.

With this method, Chudakov et al.[2] examined the four strongest sources of radio noise visible in the northern hemisphere. The total mirror area was 20 m^2 and showers of as little energy as 2×10^{12} eV were detectable, but the increase of efficiency with energy made the effective threshold 5×10^{12} eV. No definitely positive source was observed, though Cygnus A gave a marginal indication. The upper limits of the intensity at the earth were about 5×10^{-11} per cm^2-sec. Fruin et al.[3] have also carried out such observations, with similar threshold energy and limiting detectable flux, but giving special attention to several of the quasi-stellar radio sources (3C147, 3C196, and 3C273). Again the results were essentially negative. A marginally positive indication was given by 3C147, but the presence of a bright star close to the field of view might have accounted for this through atmospheric scintillation effects.

The upper limits of photon intensity established in these experiments were about 10^{-2} of the charged particle-initiated showers in the same field of view, or 10^{-4} of the charged particle flux per steradian at the same energy. The method, of course, is not sensitive to an isotropic component of the primary flux.

At higher energy, 10^{15}–10^{16} eV, Firkowski et al.[6] have studied air showers with a large array of shielded and unshielded GM counters, and demonstrated the occurrence of a distinct class of showers in which the number of muons is an order of magnitude less than in normal air showers. They attribute the "mu-poor" showers to primary photons: according to their most recent report (London, 1965), the proportion of showers in this category is $(7 \pm 3) \times 10^{-3}$, which would make the flux at energies above 10^{15} eV about 10^{-12} per cm^2-sec-sr.

The BASJE project† at Mt. Chacaltaya in Bolivia[4,5] has confirmed the mu-poor shower phenomenon, using an elaborate scintillator array to analyze each shower, with 60 m^2 of lead-shielded scintillator to measure the muon density. An extra feature of this experiment is the

---

† BASJE stands for Bolivian Air Shower Joint Experiment, a cooperative project of scientists from Japan, Bolivia and the United States.

accurate timing of the counter pulses, which permits computation of the direction of each shower-initiating particle within a precision of about 4°. The primary energies of the showers investigated are mostly in the range 10^{14}–10^{16} eV.

The proportion of the showers falling in the mu-poor category in the BASJE study is only 1×10^{-3}, and consideration of the difference in development of proton-initiated and photon-initiated showers makes the proportion at equal energies lower by another factor of 2. Thus the frequency of mu-less showers above 10^{15} eV becomes 10^{-13} per cm^2-sec-sr. The Polish-French group believe the discrepancy between the two experimental results can be accounted for mainly by differences in discrimination criteria. That is, photon-initiated showers should contain some muons, and too strict a selection of mu-less events may result in underestimation of the number of primary photons.

It is still possible to challenge the interpretation of these showers as evidence of primary photons, since it is conceivable that some distinctive kind of nuclear interaction may occur at high energies, with a branching ratio of 10^{-2}–10^{-3}, such that almost all the primary energy is transferred to photons or electrons. Clear confirmation of the primary photon interpretation would be provided by finding point sources or directional asymmetry among the mu-less showers, which is not present among the others. Since a likely source of energetic photons is collisions of cosmic-ray particles with interstellar gas, the BASJE group investigated the distribution of shower coordinates with respect to galactic latitude. If an asymmetry with respect to the galaxy exists, however, it was too small to be established with the available statistical precision. More recently, it has been reported[5] that there is a significant peak in the distribution in right ascension, appearing like a point source at a right ascension between 200 and 220°. However, more data will be needed to make sure the effect is not due to a statistical fluctuation.

The BASJE group have noted that at energies above 10^{16} eV, the proportion of mu-less showers appears to be very low. Implications of this observation have already been mentioned in Sec. 2.

In the course of the BASJE experiment, no evidence was obtained of a flux from the Crab Nebula. On this basis one can set a rough upper limit of 10^{-14} per cm^2-sec at energies above 10^{15} eV. Table II combines this figure with the data obtained at x-ray and other gamma-ray energies, to give a brief summary of current knowledge of the high-energy photon flux from the Taurus A supernova. The fact that these data fit a smooth

TABLE II.   High-Energy Photon Flux from Taurus A

Energy E, eV	Photon flux at energies above E, cm^{-2} sec^{-1}	Type of measurement
10^4	1	X-ray (a measurement, not an upper limit)
10^8	$< 10^{-4}$	Spark chamber
$10^{12.5}$	$< 10^{-10}$	Cerenkov telescope
10^{15}	$< 10^{-14}$	Mu-less air showers

curve should not be taken to imply that the curve represents the actual shape of the emission spectrum. Except for the x-ray point, the data only indicate the sensitivity of the observational techniques used prior to 1966.

5. Methods of the Future

A. Nuclear Transition Energy Region

Huge apparatus seems unnecessary to obtain measurable counting rates in the MeV region; an area of 100 cm^2 can yield rates on the order of 1 per sec. Hence it appears practical to obtain fine detail in the angular and spectral distribution. Because of this feasibility and also the wealth of significance that will attach to the experimental results, the NT region of the gamma spectrum seems most promising to investigate in the immediate future.

The problems to be solved are background avoidance and the obtaining of good angular resolution. These requirements are intimately related, since angular definition is of great assistance in background reduction (witness the Explorer XI experiment), and also provides a means of confirming success in this respect. Furthermore, without angular resolution one can hardly conclude anything about the source of the radiation even in the absence of background. Apparently this capability of the apparatus has not received enough emphasis in the past, and must be regarded as an absolute essential for progress in the future. Energy resolution is another requirement, but this is obtained by well-known methods and does not need discussion.

One cannot define the angles of incident gamma-rays well by the direction of the secondary electrons, because of excessive scattering even in extremely thin converters. The Compton coincidence scheme[25] only defines a polar angle with respect to the axis of the system, and cannot define it accurately; moreover, this scheme results in low efficiency and enhanced relative sensitivity to locally produced background (especially showers from the side). Thus the only scheme that appears really promising to the writer is collimation of the gamma rays with absorbers.

This method has occasionally been tested without success in the past, but such tests were inadequate and the causes of failure are avoidable. Indeed, in the experiment of Cline on photons of somewhat higher energy[23] the use of shielding was apparently successful. Two essentials are adequate thickness and the provision of anticoincidence protection against charged particles both entering and leaving the shield: it is certainly true that small thicknesses of absorber, in the absence of such protection, add to the background instead of reducing it.

The use of thick collimators has the added advantage of reducing the sensitivity of the apparatus to secondaries generated in neighboring apparatus or the transporting vehicle.

A difficulty with collimation in the MeV range is that around 2 MeV the cross sections are low for both photoelectric effect, Compton scattering, and pair production. For instance, the absorption length in lead is about one inch. If the collimators define a small solid angle of acceptance Ω, the absorbers must attenuate the radiation in other directions by a factor on the order of $4\pi/\Omega$, which may require the thickness to be many absorption lengths. This leads inevitably to a large weight. However, balloons and satellite-launching rockets can lift apparatus weighing a thousand pounds or more.

Figure 2 shows a schematic diagram of a suggested form of gamma-ray detecting apparatus. The weight of lead is 1200 pounds. Anticoincidence scintillators both outside the shield and immediately surrounding the detecting crystal protect against charged cosmic rays entering the lead and producing secondaries there, as well as against secondary electrons from the surfaces of the collimating fins. (The inner shield should have time-extended veto pulses so as to guard against delayed production of electrons within the detector by stopping mesons.) The dimensions are small enough that the high rate of veto pulses will not jam the recording system, as long as the apparatus is not in the earth's radiation belts. The collimating fins define an aperture that is $\pm 2°$ in one dimension and about $\pm 60°$ in the other. As the

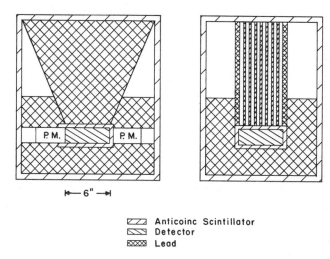

	Anticoinc Scintillator
	Detector
	Lead

Fig. 2. Schematic illustration of suggested counter for gamma-rays of energy 0.2–40 MeV, with angular resolution of $\pm 2°$ provided by collimating fins. The weight is about 1200 pounds.

apparatus rotates, this narrow band of acceptance will sweep across the sky, repeatedly sweeping over the various sources of gamma-rays. Auxiliary measurement of the aspect of the system will then permit analysis of the angular distribution of the sources with a resolution of two degrees in both coordinates. A multichannel pulse-height analyzer can provide energy resolution to at least 10% over the energy range 0.3 to 40 MeV.

It seems desirable to fly such apparatus in balloons as well as space vehicles. Gammas produced in small amounts of overlying atmosphere will interfere with measuring any isotropic part of the primary flux, but may not be so dominant as to obscure the directional structure that can be attributed to primary sources. If satellites are used, highly elliptical orbits are advisable, so as to provide measurements taken many earth-radii from the earth and outside of the magnetosphere.

With a scanning instrument such as that suggested here, attitude control is not necessary and in fact rotation is preferred. Later in the future, however, one may anticipate use of apparatus incorporating two-dimensional cellular collimators (expanded versions of present-day x-ray instruments). Such telescopes may be kept pointed at particular celestial objects for long periods of time, and be able to detect extremely low-intensity levels from very distant sources.

B. High-Energy Photons

At least five experimental groups are now planning or constructing spark chambers of area about 1 m², for use with balloons and satellites in detection of high-energy gamma-rays. One group has discussed the use of layers of nuclear emulsion together with a spark chamber, to improve the angular and energy resolution and the precision of identification of gamma-rays. The emulsion in this case would serve as the converter, and the spark chamber would provide an association between the position of an event in the emulsion and the time of its occurrence. In the more distant future, spark chambers of still larger area may be anticipated, but extremely large areas necessitate the use of independent instruments in parallel, because of the dead time of such apparatus after each recorded event.

Associated with the spark chambers, of course, are scintillation counters to provide a trigger whenever apparently neutral radiation enters the device and produces energetic charged secondary particles. In some cases it is planned to add enough dense material below the chambers for the electromagnetic showers to develop, so that the scintillators can provide a measurement of the gamma-ray energy.

Used outside of the atmosphere, such spark chambers should yield successful measurements of the diffuse flux even if it is an order of magnitude less than the limit of 3×10^{-4} per cm²-sec-sr given by the Explorer XI experiment. In balloon-borne experiments, such low isotropic flux values will be hidden by the larger secondary flux produced in the overlying air: about 10^{-2} per cm²-sec-sr in the vertical direction at 5 g/cm² pressure. However, both balloon and satellite-borne apparatus can seek to detect peaks in the angular distribution that are due to discrete primary sources or the galactic structure. It is of interest to examine the capability of the instruments to fulfill this function.

With nonvisual detecting apparatus (scintillator and Cerenkov counter combinations), a serious source of error arose from atmospheric albedo, particularly from the high intensity of secondaries in directions nearly tangential to the atmosphere. A small veto inefficiency for the abundant charged flux arriving in all directions was enough to generate the appearance of a large flux in the small ostensible angular aperture of the instrument. With visual apparatus such as spark chambers, on the contrary, each event is seen in so much detail that such background is largely eliminated. Point sources are then obscured primarily by the diffuse gamma-ray flux and unvetoed charged flux within the cone of confusion about the direction of each source.

Let θ be the angular resolution and $\Omega = \pi\theta^2$ the resolvable solid angle about a particular source direction; let D be the diffuse gamma-ray flux and C the charged flux per steradian; let I be the flux from the source, A the sensitive area of the detector, t the time during which the direction is under observation, α the efficiency for detecting gamma-rays, and β the inefficiency of the veto counter. Also, let f be the fraction of the time during which the chamber is fully recovered from previous firings and ready to accept a trigger. Then in the solid angle Ω enclosing the source, the expected number of counts from the source is $\alpha I A t f$, while the number from the combined diffuse flux is $\Omega A t f(\alpha D + \beta C)$. The signal-to-noise ratio S is the first of these quantities divided by the square root of the second. Letting S_m be the minimum required value of S, one can solve for the minimum detectable intensity:

$$I_m = S_m \frac{(\alpha D + \beta C)^{\frac{1}{2}}}{\alpha} \left(\frac{\Omega}{Atf}\right)^{\frac{1}{2}}. \tag{3}$$

In confirming the existence of a flux from one of a small number of suspected sources it may be sufficient to have $S_m \approx 3$; but in discovering a source in an unexpected direction, the fact that very many directions are examined makes the required value of S_m at least 6. For an illustrative calculation applicable to a balloon flight we take $A = 10^4$ cm^2, $t = 10^4$ sec, $\Omega = 10^{-2}$ sr, $\alpha = 0.3$, $D = 10^{-2}$ cm^{-2} sec^{-1} sr^{-1}, $\beta = 10^{-2}$, $C = 10^{-1}$ cm^{-2} sec^{-1} sr^{-1}, and $S_m = 5$. The large value of t implies a wide acceptance angle, making the total trigger rate about 64 per second. Assuming a dead time of $1/16$ sec for chamber recovery, recharging condensers and advancing the camera film, one finds $f = 0.2$. (The dead-time effect is so large in this example that a chamber of one-fourth the assumed area would be almost equally effective, and construction of even larger chambers would be a complete waste.) Under these conditions $I_m = 2.4 \times 10^{-5}$ per cm^2-sec, which is not a sufficient sensitivity, in view of the negative results displayed in Table I, to offer any hope of success in detecting point sources of the high-energy gamma-rays.

How can this sensitivity be improved? By increasing the veto efficiency and by performing the flights near the equator, the term βC can be made negligible, but it already had little importance. Higher altitudes giver lower values of D; with considerable expense a factor of 1.5 in I_m can be obtained in this way. The angular resolution was assumed to be 3°, a realistic figure for 100 MeV gamma-rays if the converter is thick enough to have the assumed efficiency. The error in angle measurements is primarily due to multiple scattering of the electrons in the converter. If the thickness is varied, the changes in Ω and in α cancel each other. A faster recording system can raise the value of f, but a large factor in I_m cannot be obtained in this way. All of these measures can hardly reduce I_m below about 1×10^{-5} per cm²-sec.

The most hopeful modification for the balloon investigations is to raise the minimum energy of the events selected for detection. Then one can decrease Ω by an order of magnitude, even while thickening the converter and thus raising the efficiency α; also the background flux D is greatly reduced, the trigger rate is much less, and the efficiency f is raised. This even makes profitable an increase in the area of the detector. By selecting photons above 1 GeV instead of 100 MeV one can gain a factor of about 50 in reduction of the detectable intensity I_m. How significant this factor would be depends on the steepness of the source spectrum: if the exponent in the integral spectrum is -1.4, for instance, the flux above 1 GeV is 25 times less than that above 100 MeV, and the net gain in detectability is only a factor of 2.

These arguments have been given in detail to clarify the limitations of the next generation of spark-chamber experiments. In order to gain big improvements in detectable source strengths the use of satellites is essential. Away from the atmosphere the diffuse flux is lower by 1.5 powers of ten and the observing time can be raised by two powers of ten, provided there is some way of getting the mountain of data back to earth (e.g., by vidicon recording and radio transmission). The reduction of the trigger rate per unit detector area also will raise the efficiency f and permit use of larger chambers. Thus the detectable intensity above 100 MeV, with spark chambers of a few square meters area, can be as low as 10^{-7} per cm²-sec. Furthermore, being outside the atmosphere makes quantitative study of the diffuse part of the flux possible.

To improve further on the sensitivity, it will be necessary to give up scanning a large area of the sky at every instant, and instead to adopt pointing instruments of large collecting area, that will focus on one direction at a time, like a radio or optical telescope. One form, that has been suggested for such an instrument by the writer, is a long gas-Cerenkov telescope with a gamma-ray converter at one end and a parabolic mirror at the other. Such an instrument has many inherent features that facilitate efficient background rejection, and its low density permits setting up a large collecting area without excessive weight. The recording of events is electronic rather than pictorial; this coupled with the limited angular aperture removes limitations associated with the rate of data recording and transmission. With such an instrument the level of detectable intensity can be brought down to 10^{-9} per cm^2-sec. The volume of course will be large (diameter and length each about 30 feet), while the weight of the large-area converter is both nontrivial and unavoidable.

In judging the significance of the levels of detectability that have been mentioned, it may be noted that one can expect with considerable confidence to find at least a few point sources yielding high-energy gammas at the earth at a flux level between 10^{-6} and 10^{-7} quanta/cm^2-sec. For instance, the relativistic electron density and optical photon density in the Crab Nebula are not in great doubt, and they certainly interact via Compton scattering. R. J. Gould[38] has calculated the yield of high-energy photons from this process and found it to be about 10^{-6} quanta/cm^2-sec at the earth. On the other hand, no point sources appear to give us as many as 10^{-5} quanta/cm^2-sec. If the field of high-energy gamma-ray astronomy is ever to develop far beyond mere detection of the existence of the few strongest sources, the instruments will have to attain sensitivities at least 100 times lower than the flux from the strongest source. In other words, levels of detectability below 10^{-8} quanta/cm^2-sec will become necessary.

C. Very High-Energy Photons

The methods already in practice in this area are promising and will probably continue to be pursued. Use of larger mirrors or more of them in parallel will be able to extend the sensitivity of the Cerenkov light detection method down to a primary energy of about 10^{11} eV. The chief difficulty in observing point sources will continue to be the comparatively large frequency of similar showers produced by cosmic-ray protons. Within the cone of angular resolution provided by the atmospheric Cerenkov light system, the number of charged-particle-initiated showers that produce as much light as the 100 GeV photons is 10^{-6} per cm²-sec. Detection of primary flux values less than 10^{-3} of this background seems infeasible; hence the limiting detectable flux will be at least 10^{-9} quanta/cm²-sec. Approaching this level of sensitivity will extend present knowledge of the primary gamma-ray spectrum quite significantly: for instance, the flux predicted by Gould[38] at 10^{11} eV, from the Compton process in the Crab Nebula, exceeds this lower limit of detectability by more than a factor of ten.

The BASJE air-shower study provides not only the angular resolution needed in identification of primary gammas and their sources, but also a way of discriminating against primary charged particles of the same energy, by vetoing showers that contain many muons. The rate of data collection has been slow, but recently the area of the counter array at Mt. Chacaltaya has been increased, and in time one may expect the data to become very high in meaning. Already, as mentioned earlier in this article, significant cosmological implications have been drawn from the data, and one point source may have been discovered. In this part of the spectrum theoretical predictions of the flux involve many unknowns, and significant surprises are probably in store.

6. Epilogue

The writing of this article provided a continual reminder of how much the present understanding of electromagnetic processes owes to the insight and theoretical calculations of Professor Hans Bethe. The writer's feeling of personal debt to him runs even deeper, for his guidance and instruction and tolerance of the writer's errors from student days onwards over twenty-eight years, but above all for his continual setting of a human example of what a scientist should be.

References and Footnotes

1. Oda, M., International Conference on Cosmic Rays, London, 1965, to be published in *Proc. Phys. Soc. London*.
2. Chudakov, A. E., V. L. Dadykin, V. I. Zatsepin, and N. M. Nesterova, *J. Phys. Soc. Japan*, **17**, Suppl. A III, 106 (1962); also, *Proceedings of the Fifth Interamerican Seminar on Cosmic Rays and Space Physics*, La Paz, Bolivia, 1962.
3. Fruin, J. H., J. V. Jelley, C. D. Long, N. A. Porter, and T. C. Weekes, *Phys. Rev. Letters*, **10**, 176 (1964).

4. Suga, K., I. Escobar, K. Murakami, V. Domingo, Y. Toyoda, G. Clark, and M. La Pointe, *Proceedings of the International Conference on Cosmic Rays*, Jaipur, India, 1963; K. Suga, I. Escobar, G. Clark, W. Hazen, A. Hendel, and K. Murakami, *J. Phys. Soc. Japan*, **17**, Suppl. A III, 128 (1962); also, *Proceedings of the Fifth Interamerican Seminar on Cosmic Rays and Space Physics*, La Paz, Bolivia, 1962.

5. Hasegawa, H., K. Murakami, S. Shibata, K. Suga, Y. Toyoda, V. Domingo, I. Escobar, K. Kamata, H. Bradt, G. Clark, and M. La Pointe, *International Conference on Cosmic Rays*, London, 1965, to be published in *Proc. Phys. Soc. London*.

6. Firkowski, R., J. Gawin, J. Hibner, J. Wdowczyk, A. Zawadski, and R. Maze, *International Conference on Cosmic Rays*, London, 1965, to be published in *Proc. Phys. Soc. London;* also *J. Phys. Soc. Japan*, **17**, Suppl. A III, 123 (1962); and *Nuovo Cimento*, **26**, 1422 (1962).

7. Oort, J. H., and Th. Walraven, *Bull. Netherlands Astron. Inst.*, **12**, 285 (1956).

8. Burbidge, G. R., *Phys. Rev.*, **103**, 264 (1956), and *Astrophys. J.*, **127**, 48 (1958); G. R. Burbidge and F. Hoyle, *Nuovo Cimento*, **4**, 558 (1956).

9. Giacconi, R., H. Gursky, F. Paolini, and B. Rossi, *Phys. Rev. Letters*, **9**, 439 (1962).

10. Giacconi, R., and B. Rossi, *J. Geophys. Res.*, **65**, 773 (1960); R. Giacconi, N. Harmon, R. F. Lacey, and Z. Szilagyi, *J. Opt. Soc. Am.*, **55**, 345 (1965); R. Giacconi, W. P. Reidy, T. Zehnpfennig, J. C. Lindsay, and W. A. Muney, *Astrophysics. J.*, **142**, 1274 (1965).

11. Morrison, P., *Nuovo Cimento*, **7**, 858 (1958).

12. Ginzburg, V. L., and S. I. Syrovatskii, *The Origin of Cosmic Rays*, Pergamon Press, Macmillan Co., New York, 1964; *Soviet Phys. Doklady*, **9**, 3 (1964).

13. Gould, R. J., and G. R. Burbidge, *Ann. Astrophys.*, **28**, 171 (1965); Handbuch der Physik, in press.

14. Pollack, J. B., and G. G. Fazio, *Phys. Rev.*, **131**, 2684 (1963).

15. Garmire, G., and W. Kraushaar, *Space Science Reviews*, **4**, 123 (1965).

16. Hayakawa, S., and M. Matsuoka, *Prog. Theor. Phys. Suppl.*, **30**, 204 (1964).

17. Felten, J. E., *Phys. Rev. Letters*, **15**, 1003 (1965).

18. Clayton, D. D., and W. L. Craddock, *Astrophys. J.*, **142**, 189 (1965).

19. Peterson, L. E., *J. Geophys. Res.*, **68**, 979 (1963).

20. Vette, J. I., *J. Geophys. Res.*, **67**, 1731 (1962).

21. Anderson, K. A., *Phys. Rev.*, **123**, 1435 (1961).

22. Svensson, G., *Arkiv Fysik*, **13**, 347 (1958).

23. Cline, T. L., *Phys. Rev. Letters*, **7**, 109 (1961).

24. Northrup, J. A., and R. L. Hostetler, *Bull. Am. Phys. Soc. II*, **6**, 52 (1961).

25. Peterson, L. E., *COSPAR International Space Science Symposium*, Buenos Aires, 1965.

26. Arnold, J. R., A. E. Metzger, E. C. Anderson, and M. A. Van Dilla, *J. Geophys. Res.*, **67**, 4878 (1962).

27. Metzger, A. E., E. C. Anderson, M. A. Van Dilla, and J. R. Arnold, *Nature*, **204**, 766 (1964).

28. Kraushaar, W., G. W. Clark, G. Garmire, H. Helmken, P. Higbie, and M. Agogino, *Astrophys, J.*, **141**, 845 (1965).

29. Frye, G. M., and L. H. Smith, *Bull. Am. Phys. Soc. II*, **10**, 705 (1965).
30. Cobb, R., J. G. Duthie, and J. Stewart, *Phys. Rev. Letters*, **15**, 507 (1965).
31. Ögelman, H. B., J. P. Devaille, and K. I. Greisen, *Phys. Rev. Letters*, **16**, 491 (1966).
32. Hulsizer, R. I., and B. Rossi, *Phys. Rev.*, **73**, 1402 (1948); **76**, 164 (1949).
33. Critchfield, C. L., E. P. Ney, and S. Oleksa, *Phys. Rev.*, **85**, 461 (1952).
34. Carlson, A. G., J. E. Hooper, and D. T. King, *Phil. Mag.*, **41**, 701 (1950).
35. Braccesi, A., M. Ceccarelli, and S. Salandin, *Nuovo Cimento*, **17**, 691 (1960).
36. Perlow, G. J., and C. W. Kissinger, *Phys. Rev.*, **81**, 552 (1951).
37. Duthie, J. G., E. M. Hafner, M. F. Kaplon, and G. G. Fazio, *Phys. Rev. Letters*, **10**, 364 (1963).
38. Gould, R. J., *Phys. Rev. Letters*, **15**, 577 (1965).

Experimental X-Ray Astronomy

BRUNO ROSSI

Massachusetts Institute of Technology

The first major surprise of astronomical observations from vehicles rising above the opaque atmospheric blanket that surrounds the earth (Fig. 1) has been the discovery of strong sources of soft x-rays external to the solar system. Today, about three years after this discovery, several localized x-ray sources are definitely known, of which only one has been identified with a visible object. The nature of the physical processes giving rise to the observed x-ray fluxes is still obscure indeed, none of the phenomena previously known to occur in our galaxy or beyond accounts for these fluxes; for this very reason x-ray astronomy holds the promise of revealing new and important features of the Universe. In addition, observation of the absorption of the x-radiation from sources at different distances will provide crucial information on the properties of the interstellar medium.

1. The Discovery of Extrasolar X-ray Sources

It shall not attempt here to trace to their origin the several lines of research that prepared the discovery of extra-solar x-rays, but I shall rather relate the early history of x-ray astronomy, as I saw it develop.

I first became interested in this field of research in 1959, during a series of discussions with Riccardo Giacconi at American Science and Engineering Inc., a company for which I was acting as a consultant.

At that time, the sun was the only known source of x-rays. The solar x-ray emission, first directly observed by Burnight in 1948[1], had been the object of many experimental and theoretical investigations. Astrophysicists at the Naval Research Laboratory (NRL), under the leadership of Herbert Friedman, had been particularly active in this

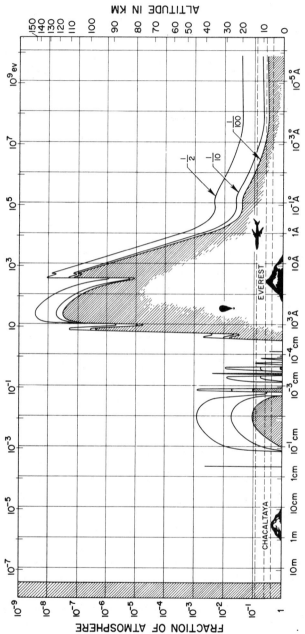

Fig. 1. Attenuation of electromagnetic radiation in the atmosphere. Solid curves indicate altitude (and corresponding pressure expressed as a fraction of one atmosphere) at which a given attenuation occurs for radiation of a given wavelength.

field, and their observations, carried out by means of rockets, had produced a wealth of new and important results. The same scientists had also attempted to detect possible extrasolar sources but this attempt had been unsuccessful[2].

The group at ASE had already been engaged in space research and was interested in expanding its activities in this field. It occurred to us that further efforts in x-ray astronomy might prove particularly fruitful, and from our discussions there emerged two research programs.

The first aimed at the development of image-forming devices, with the immediate purpose of taking pictures of the sun in the soft x-ray region of the spectrum. At the suggestion of Giacconi, it was decided to explore the feasibility of an x-ray telescope based on the phenomenon of total external reflection of x-rays under grazing incidence. We immediately realized that a single parabolic mirror would not produce an image of a source located off axis, but still could be used as a "collimator" with very fine resolution. Searching the literature, we became acquainted with the work of H. Wolter, who had shown that images could be produced by double reflection at grazing incidence over a parabolic and an hyperbolic surface[3].

Work on the development of total reflection optics for x-ray astronomy was initiated at ASE early in 1960 under NASA sponsorship. While this work was in progress, Friedman and his associates, in April 1960, succeeded for the first time in obtaining an x-ray picture of the sun by means of a pinhole camera[4]. The first x-ray picture of the sun by means of a grazing incidence telescope was taken during a rocket flight carried out jointly by the Goddard Space Flight Center and by ASE in October 1963[5]. An improved instrument (see Fig. 2) flown by the same two groups in March 1965 provided a number of pictures, one of which is reproduced on the left-hand side of Fig. 3, while the right-hand side shows a picture of the sun in CaK, taken almost simultaneously from the ground[6].

The second research program was directed at a search for extra-solar sources of soft x-rays. As a preparation for this program, ASE sponsored a study of the various possible mechanisms for the production of soft x-rays (such as bremsstrahlung and synchrotron radiation) which may be at work in certain celestial objects. The results of this analysis are contained in a technical report prepared by Giacconi, George Clark, and Rossi, which was included in a proposal presented

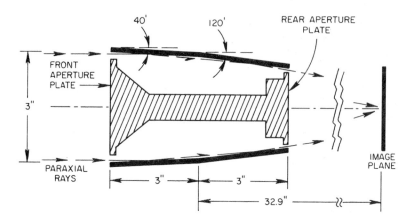

Fig. 2.   Grazing-Incidence Telescope (see ref. 6).

by ASE to the U.S. Air Force in December 1959 and in another proposal presented to NASA in February 1960. The report listed a number of celestial objects that were considered as likely x-ray emitters; prominent among them were the envelopes of supernovae, the "flare stars", and the "peculiar" A-stars with strong, rapidly varying magnetic fields. The same report stressed the fact that observations of

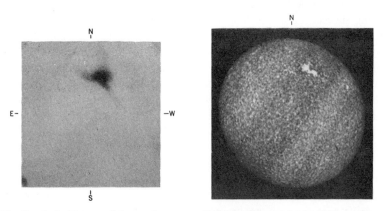

Fig. 3.   *Left:* Picture of the sun in x-rays; 49.7 sec exposure, 0.15 mil Mylar filter with 2200 Å A1 coating, Ilford Special G X-ray film. *Right:* Picture of the sun in the CaK line obtained at about the same time by the Sacramento Peak Observatory (see ref. 6).

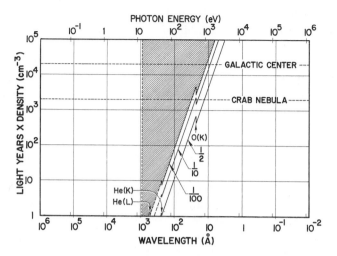

Fig. 4. Attenuation of electromagnetic radiation in interstellar space. The ordinate represents the integrated particle density in terms of light years times the number of particles per cc. The solid curves give the integrated density at which a given attenuation occurs for radiation of a given wavelength. O(K), He(K), and He(L) indicate the K-absorption edges of O and He, and the L absorption edge of He. The ordinates corresponding to the Crab Nebula and the galactic center are calculated using the known distance to these objects and an assumed particle density of 0.3 atoms per cc and 1 atom per cc, respectively.

distant x-ray sources might provide important information on the density of interstellar matter, whose absorption in the x-ray region is a rapidly varying function of wavelengths (Fig. 4).

The theoretical expectations concerning possible galactic sources of x-rays, as well as plans for the development of image-forming devices for x-ray astronomy, were discussed in some detail at a conference held at the Smithsonian Astrophysical Observatory in May 1960. This conference, called at the initiative of Albert Baez of the Smithsonian Observatory, heard reports by Baez and Robert Davis of this institution, by Paul Kirkpatrick of Stanford University, by Giacconi of ASE, and by Stanislaw Olbert of MIT.

The tentative estimates of the x-ray fluxes from the hypothetical galactic sources indicated values many orders of magnitude lower than the x-ray flux from the quiet sun. It was thus clear that much larger detectors than those used for solar x-ray astronomy were needed.

Indeed, it was felt that to jump directly from solar to galactic x-ray astronomy was perhaps too ambitious a program, and that some intermediate step was desirable. This, hopefully, would have made it possible to obtain some concrete results while instruments ultimately capable of detecting galactic sources were gradually developed. It occurred to us that a detection of a possible x-ray emission from the moon might represent a suitable intermediate step. It was thought at first that the impact on the lunar surface of high-energy electrons contained in the solar wind might produce a detectable x-ray flux. It was then realized that a more important source was probably the excitation of x-ray fluorescence by primary x-rays from the sun. An experiment aiming at the detection of this fluorescent radiation held the promise of providing some interesting information on the surface properties of the moon. Moreover, we did not discount the possibility that, contrary to the theoretical expectations, galactic sources strong enough to be detected by our instruments might exist.

Work on this experiment began early in 1960 by the ASE group (which by then included Frank Paolini, while Herbert Gursky was to join the group in 1961). This work was supported by the U.S. Air Force through the Cambridge Research Laboratory. The observations were to be carried out by means of Aerobee rockets, capable of reaching an altitude of about 200 km. The instrumentation developed for these rockets included Geiger counters with thin mica windows, of which the most sensitive had an efficiency between 10 and 20% for x-rays with wavelength in the region from 2 to 8 Å. The effective area of each counter (about 10 cm^2) was at least 10, probably close to 100 times that of any x-ray detector flown previously. Moreover, the counters were embedded in blocks of scintillating plastic, whose signals, fed to an anticoincidence arrangement, were used to suppress the cosmic-ray background. Because of this feature and because of the large effective area, our instruments had the capability of observing x-ray sources much weaker than those that would have been detectable in previous experiments.

A first flight carried out in October 1961 failed to give conclusive results, because of technical difficulties.

The second flight took place on June 12, 1962. Two out of the three Geiger counters operated properly. These counters were mounted with their axes at 55° to the rocket's axis, which remained practically vertical during the flight. No collimator was placed in front of them; consequently the counters had wide fields of view (about ±60° at half maximum, as determined primarily by the absorption in the window's material).

The rocket was launched at about midnight and reached a maximum altitude of 230 km. The counting rates of both counters began to increase rapidly as the rocket rose above 80 km (10 mg/cm² residual atmosphere) and leveled off at about 100 km (0.3 mg/cm² residual atmosphere). When plotted against the angle of rotation of the rocket, the counting rates were found to have a pronounced maximum near local south, without, however, dropping to zero at either side of the maximum (Fig. 5). These results indicated the presence of a soft radiation, coming preferentially from a limited region of the night's sky. The azimuth of the maximum, however, was about 30° from the azimuth of the moon. Therefore the radiation did not arise from this celestial object. Nor did it arise from any planet, for none was in a suitable location at the time.

Our main concern was the possibility that the counters might have detected low-energy electrons or x-rays from the upper atmosphere. I shall not repeat here the arguments by which we satisfied ourselves that effects of this kind could not explain our observations. By late summer we felt that the interpretation of our results was sufficiently well established to warrant publication. In a report presented by Giacconi at the Third International X-ray Symposium held in Stanford in August 1962, and subsequently in a letter to the Editor of Physical Review published in December 1962[7], we stated our belief that the Geiger counters had

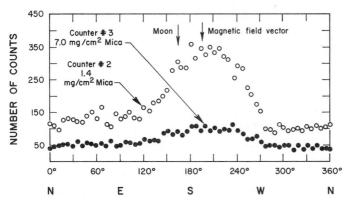

Fig. 5. Number of counts vs. azimuth angle. The numbers represent counts accumulated in 350 seconds in each 6° angular interval (ASE June 1962 flight, see ref. 7).

detected a strong extrasolar localized source of soft x-rays, which appeared to lie near to, although not exactly at, the center of the Galaxy. We estimated the intensity of this source, as recorded by our most sensitive counter, to be about 5 photons/cm²-sec.† This meant that, even if the source was as close as the nearest stars, its x-ray emission was from 10 to 100 million times greater than that of the quiet sun. In addition, there was apparently also a diffuse soft radiation, whose nature and origin were unclear.

Although the hope of detecting extrasolar sources of x-rays had been one of the motivations of the experiment, the existence of a source of the observed strength was an entirely unexpected and perplexing result. (It should be noted that, in the absence of the diffuse background radiation, whose existence was previously unknown, our instruments would have been capable of detecting celestial x-ray sources about 50 times weaker than that observed.)

Despite our confidence in the results of the June 1962 flight, we felt that, before proceeding to more elaborate experiments, we should test our conclusions with additional flights, without making any major change in the instrumentation. The next flight took place in October 1962, at a time when the presumed galactic source seen in June was under the horizon. As expected, the large peak in the azimuthal distribution of the counting rate had disappeared. The third flight took place in June 1963. Again we observed a peak practically identical to that observed one year earlier, which proved that the celestial source seen at that time was indeed a permanent feature.

The results of these two last flights were published in December 1963[8]. In addition to confirming the existence of the strong source near the galactic center, they provided some tentative evidence for two additional weaker sources, one in the general region of Cygnus, one in the general region of Taurus (which included the Crab Nebula). Comparing counting rates measured with detectors having different relative efficiencies for electrons and x-rays, it was also possible to conclude that the diffuse radiation consisted, at least for the most part, of x-rays.

In the meantime, Friedman and his collaborators at NRL (S. Bowyer, E. T. Byram, and T. A. Chubb) had joined in the search for extrasolar sources of soft x-rays. A rocket flown by this group in April 1963 carried an x-ray counter with an effective area of about 60 cm².

† This estimate was later to be revised upward.

The counter was provided with a honeycomb collimator limiting its field of view to a cone of about 10° aperture at half maximum. The rocket was despun to about 0.25 revolutions per second after traversing the dense part of the atmosphere. At this low spin rate, the rocket went into a flat spin, with its longitudinal axis precessing around a cone of large apex angle. In this manner, the detector explored during each revolution a narrow slice of the sky, which changed from one revolution to the next. The results of a preliminary analysis of the data obtained in this flight were announced at the COSPAR meeting held in Warsaw in June 1963[9]. These results confirmed the existence of the strong source observed by the ASE group. The source appeared to lie in the constellation of Scorpio, and was definitely not coincident with the galactic center, which lay a few degrees below the horizon at the time of the flight. The report by the NRL group also hinted at the likelihood that further analysis of the data might reveal some weaker sources.

With the observations described above, the existence of strong extrasolar sources of soft x-rays became definitely established. Notwithstanding the clear evidence provided by the ASE observations, the substantial agreement between the results obtained by two entirely separate groups was an important factor in dispelling whatever doubts might have been aroused by the unexpected and puzzling character of the discovery.

2. Advances in the Observational Methods

The discovery of extrasolar x-ray sources raised a number of questions requiring further and more refined observations. It was clearly important to measure the size of the x-ray sources, or to set significant upper limits to their angular diameter. It was equally important to determine with good accuracy their positions in order to identify them, if possible, with known visible objects or radio sources. It was also very desirable to obtain information on the spectral distribution of the radiation, as a guide in the search for the physical processes responsible for the x-ray emission.

In the two following years, improvements of the observational techniques and refinements in the methods of analysis provided very significant answers to the first two questions and some preliminary information concerning the third.

Both freely spinning rockets and rockets provided with an attitude control system (ACS) were employed. The ACS uses gyroscopes as sensing devices; these activate gas jets which cause any given detector mounted on the rocket to point in any prescribed direction or to scan slowly over any prescribed band of the sky.

As in the earlier flights, magnetometers and optical sensors were used to determine the rotational motion of the vehicle. However, the optical sensors and the methods for the analysis of their data were substantially improved to provide a clearer identification of the reference stars and a more accurate correlation between the angular coordinates of the stars and those of the x-ray sources.

The observations were again made primarily by means of thin-window gas counters, operated either as Geiger counters or as proportional counters. The window area, however, was considerably increased and the efficiency of the counters was improved by the use of thinner windows of low atomic number (Fig. 6). Data were also obtained by means of scintillation counters sensitive in a spectral region corresponding to higher photon energies than those covered by the gas counters (scintillation counters had already been included in the instrumentation of the early ASE flights).

The freely-spinning rockets used by the NRL group had again low spin rate and wide precession cones. Their detectors were provided with honeycomb collimators having fairly wide and nearly circular fields of view.

The ASE group (now joined by several other scientists from the Massachusetts Institute of Technology) continued to use fast spinning rockets, with precession cones of small apex angle. However, they now placed in front of their detectors cellular collimators limiting the fields of view to narrow "slits", some only 1.5° wide at half maximum (Fig. 7).

The NRL method of observation covers a large region of the sky and is therefore particularly well suited to a survey aiming at the discovery of new sources.

The ASE-MIT method provides a more limited coverage of the sky, but is capable of yielding more accurate data on the location and the angular dimensions of the sources. Because of the fast spin and the narrow field of view, it is here necessary to superpose the counts recorded in many subsequent spins in order to obtain statistically significant data from any celestial x-ray source. This requirement

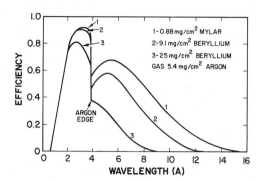

Fig. 6.   Calculated efficiency of gas counters with argon filling and different windows (from the paper quoted in ref. 11, to be referred to as the "Varenna Paper").

introduces a problem of synchronization, which is considerably complicated by the precessional motion of the rocket's axis. A detailed discussion of this problem [which appears elsewhere[10,11]] would not be appropriate to the present article. Suffice to say that it is possible to treat the data in such a way as to obtain a curve representing

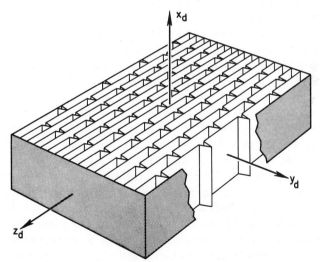

Fig. 7.   Schematic drawing of a cellular collimator (from the Varenna Paper).

essentially the azimuthal dependence of the counting rate that one would observe if the rocket's axis were fixed in space and coincident with the axis of the precession cone. The maximum of this curve, then, determines the azimuth of an x-ray source in a polar frame of reference, fixed with respect to the stars, having its axis along the axis of the precession cone ("precession frame").

The precessional motion, on the other hand, affords the possibility of obtaining information on the elevation of source in the precession frame. In fact, because of the precession, the line traced in the sky by the normal to an x-ray detector shifts gradually. The magnitude of the signal from the x-ray source changes correspondingly, being a maximum when the normal to the detector sweeps closest to the source.

Clearly, a "slit" collimator with the long dimension in the plane of the spin axis ("vertical" collimator) will explore a wider region of the sky than a "slit" collimator with the long dimension perpendicular to spin axis ("horizontal" collimator). Also the first collimator will provide more accurate information of the azimuth than on the elevation of the x-ray sources, while the second collimator will provide more accurate information on the elevation than on the azimuth.

The accuracy in the location of the sources and in the determination of their angular dimensions that may be achieved by the use of "slit" collimators is in inverse proportion to their field of view. On the other hand, the field of view cannot be decreased below a certain limit because the number of counts recorded by a detector mounted on a spinning rocket is in direct proportion to the field of view. For this reason, some of the detectors flown by the ASE–MIT group were provided with a more sophisticated type of collimator, designed by Minoru Oda of MIT (on leave of absence from the University of Tokyo), which combines high resolution with a wide field of view[12]. Known as the "modulation collimator", it consists essentially of two plane grids, placed one in front of the other at a suitable distance (Fig. 8). The diameter of the wires is nearly equal to the spacing between wires. In a parallel beam of rays, the front grid casts a sharp shadow on the rear grid. The shadow shifts as the orientation of the collimator relative to that of the incident beam changes. The transmission of the collimator changes correspondingly, being a maximum when the shadow of the front wires falls exactly on the back wires, and a minimum when it is centered half-way between adjacent wires. Figure 9 shows the

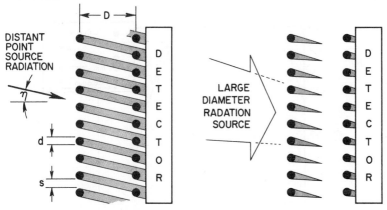

Fig. 8.   Illustrating the principle of operation of the modulation collimator. The drawing on the left indicates the shadowing that obtains with parallel radiation (from the Varenna Paper).

modulation curve obtained in the laboratory with a collimator of this type using a distant point source of x-rays. It is clear that a source with angular dimensions small compared with the separation between adjacent maxima will produce practically the same pattern of maxima and minima as a point source; whereas, if the source has angular dimensions large compared with the separation between neighboring maxima, no modulation will be observed. The resolving power turns out to be about one quarter the distance between maxima. Collimators with resolving power finer than 1′ are feasible.

A convenient way of using the modulation collimator is to mount it with the wires perpendicular to the spin axis. In this case, one relies upon the slow precessional rotation to move the source across the planes of maximum and minimum transmission. The data obtained with a modulation collimator do not determine uniquely the position of an x-ray source, but restrict this position to a discrete set of circles, these being the intersections with the celestial sphere of the planes of maximum transmission at the time when a maximum of counting rate is observed.

Another major advance in the observational techniques occurred in the summer of 1964, when George Clark succeeded in observing for the first time a celestial source of x-rays (the Crab Nebula) by means of a large scintillation counter carried aloft by a balloon[13].

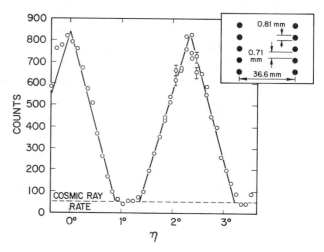

Fig. 9.   Angular response of modulation collimator measured with x-rays. The abscissa is the angle η defined in Fig. 8 (from the Varenna Paper).

3. Present Information on the Positions and Angular Sizes of the X-ray Sources

The first important development in the period following the discovery of extrasolar x-rays was the result not of new observations, but of a more careful analysis by the NRL group of the data obtained in their April 1963 flight. From this analysis, published in March 1964[14], the NRL group concluded that the source in Scorpio had an angular diameter not greater than 5° and that its center was located at about 16 h 15 min right ascension, − 15° declination. They also found evidence for the existence of another weaker source in Taurus which appeared to coincide with the Crab Nebula, within the estimated accuracy of the angular determinations (about 2°).

This latter result aroused a great deal of interest, for the Crab Nebula (a gas cloud representing the remnant of a supernova explosion which appeared in the sky the year 1054 A.D.) was known to be a very peculiar object. One of the current speculations concerned the possible existence, at the center of the cloud, of a "neutron star", resulting from the gravitational contraction of the material left behind after the explosion. Theoretical considerations assigned to the hypothetical neutron star a mass near to that of the sun, a diameter of about 10 km and an initial surface temperature of about 10 million degree Kelvin. At this temperature, the maximum of the Planck's spectrum lies in the region of soft x-rays. Thus a neutron star would be a strong x-ray emitter, while, on account of its small area, the light emission would be so small as to make this object practically invisible.

It was thus important to determine both the position of the source found near the Crab Nebula and its angular dimension with an accuracy at least an order of magnitude better than the angular diameter of the nebula (about 4 arc minutes). To achieve these aims Herbert Friedman and his group carried out an experiment designed to observe the lunar occulation of the Crab Nebula which occurred on July 7, 1964[15]. The rocket, whose launching had to be timed to within a fraction of a minute, carried two x-ray detectors which acquired the x-ray source 150 seconds after launch and observed it for 240 seconds thereafter, during which time the moon swept across the Crab Nebula in the manner shown in Fig. 10. Analysis of the data showed that the counting rates of the two detectors decreased gradually and not abruptly. This meant that the source had finite dimensions. In fact, from their observations the authors obtained a value of about 1 arc minute for the angular diameter of the x-ray source and concluded that its center was near the center of the visible nebula (which, however, has considerable large angular dimensions).

The next step was a search for additional x-ray sources and a more careful study of the location and angular size of the Scorpio source. Contributions to this program were made by the NRL group, by the ASE–MIT group (Giacconi, Gursky, John Waters, Oda, Clark, Garmire, and M. Wada), and by Philip Fisher, Willard Jordan, Arthur Meyerott, Hugh Johnson, and Loren Acton of Lockheed. (Fisher and Meyerott had previously reported the results of a rocket flight which had confirmed the existence of an x-ray flux from the night's sky, but had not given conclusive results on the location of x-ray sources because of insufficient statistical accuracy of the data.)

The NRL scientists reported the results obtained with two slowly spinning rockets, flown in June and November 1964[16]. Some of the experimental data are illustrated in Fig. 11.

The ASE–MIT scientists flew two fast-spinning rockets in August and October 1964[17,18,10]. Some of the observational data thus obtained are illustrated in Fig. 12. "Vertical" and "horizontal" slit collimators, as well as modulation collimators were used.

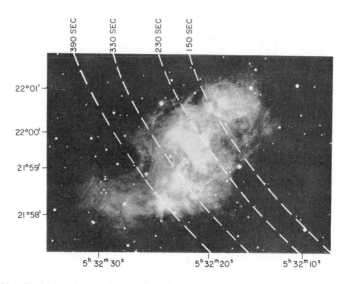

Fig. 10. Position of the edge of the Moon superimposed on a photograph of the Crab Nebula during NRL rocket flight. The maximum rate of change of the observed counting rate from the x-ray detector occurred at 230 sec; thus the centroid of the x-ray source distribution lies along the dashed line marked 230 sec (see ref. 15).

The Lockheed group reported the results of an experiment performed by means of an attitude-controlled rocket in October 1964[19]. The rocket carried three banks of proportional counters with "slit" collimators similar to those used by the ASE–MIT group. One of the "slits" was parallel to the longitudinal rocket's axis, while the other two were at 45° to the axis. During the flight, the detectors swept slowly over certain bands of the sky, as shown in Fig. 13. From the time at which a given source crossed the field of view of the first collimator, it was possible to determine the position of the source in the direction of the scan. From the time difference between the signal recorded by the other two detectors, it was possible to determine the position of the source in the direction perpendicular to the scan. The last two detectors, however, did not yield significant results during scan #1, which ran close to the galactic equator; thus only the galactic longitude of the sources detected during this scan could be measured.

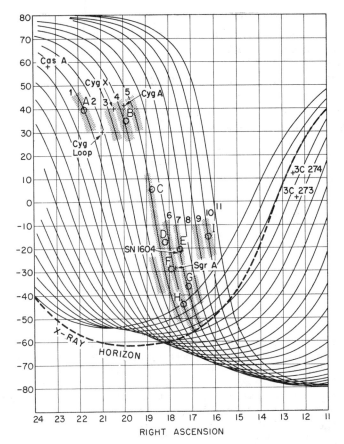

Fig. 11.   Locations of x-ray sources observed during an NRL rocket flight. Solid curves represent the path of the detector axis during the flight. Shaded regions indicate times when excess counting rates were observed and circles indicate estimates of source locations (see ref. 16).

The results of the three groups concerning locations and angular dimensions of the x-ray sources may be summarized as follows (see Fig. 14).

(a) The Scorpio Source

All three groups saw again the strong source in Scorpio (called Sco X-1 by the ASE–MIT group and Sco XR-1 by the NRL group).

Final analysis of the April 1963 flight by the NRL group placed this source within a circle of about 2° radius, as shown in Fig. 14. No further refinement on the coordinates of this source resulted from the subsequent NRL flights.

The observations by the ASE–MIT group (some made with a modulation collimator) gave for Sco X-1 two possible positions, indicated by the black squares in Fig. 14. Both of these locations fall within the circle of uncertainty of the NRL observations.

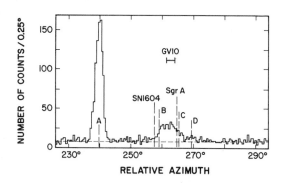

Fig. 12. Azimuthal distribution of counts observed with a "vertical" slit collimator during the October 1964 flight of the ASE-MIT group. The abscissa is essentially the azimuth of the detector axis relative to that of β-Ceti, in a frame of reference with the polar axis along the axis of the precession cone. The horizontal bar marked GV10 represents the full width at half maximum of the detector response curve. The direction of the sweep is nearly perpendicular to the galactic equator. The maximum at A is due to Sco X-1; the lower and wider maximum between B and C is due to the source complex near the galactic center. The azimuth of Sgr A (the radio center of the galaxy) and of SN 1604 (the Kepler supernova) are indicated.

The observations by the Lockheed group placed the source at the center of the cross shown in Fig. 14, a position in excellent agreement with one of the two possible locations found by the ASE–MIT group.

We thus conclude that the observations of the three groups concerning the location of Sco X-1 agree within the limits of their respective accuracy. The coordinates quoted by the Lockheed group are:

right ascension: $16^h 14^m \pm 1^m$

declination: $-15° 36' \pm 15'$

With regard to the angular dimensions of the source, the most significant results were obtained by the ASE–MIT group by means of a modulation collimator. These results place an upper limit of 7′ to the angular diameter of Sco X-1 in the direction parallel to the galactic equator[18].

(b) The Sources in Cygnus

As already mentioned, the ASE observations of 1962–1963 had produced some tentative evidence for an x-ray source in Cygnus. The ASE–MIT survey of 1964 did not cover this region of the sky.

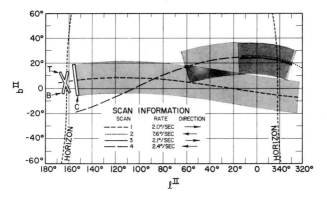

Fig. 13.   Traces of detector axes during Lockheed rocket flight. Rocket was provided with attitude control. Rectangles C, T, and B represent the fields of view of the three detectors (see ref. 18).

The signals observed in the Cygnus region during the NRL 1964 survey appeared to come from two isolated objects at the positions shown by the circles in Fig. 14 (Cyg XR-1 and Cyg XR-2). The Lockheed survey (see Fig. 13) detected a source at the galactic longitude of Cyg XR-1 without, however, providing any precise information on its galactic latitude. Cyg XR-1 and Cyg XR-2 do not coincide with any known peculiar celestial object.

(c) The Source Complex near the Galactic Center

All three groups reported the existence of several sources lying near the galactic plane, within about 20° of the galactic center (see Fig. 14).

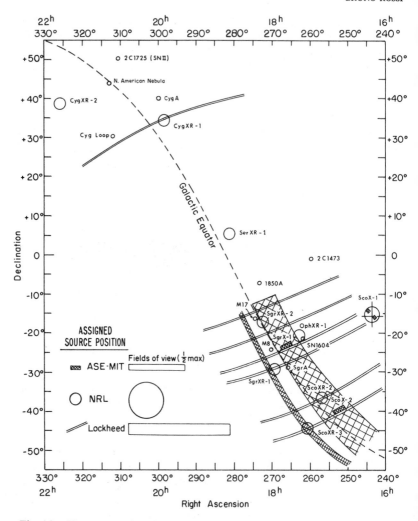

Fig. 14. X-ray source locations as determined by the ASE–MIT group, the NRL
group and the Lockheed group in 1964 (from the Varenna Paper).

The observations by the ASE–MIT group established the positions
of two such sources (Sgr X-1 and Sco X-2) with an accuracy of about
0.5° and showed that their angular dimensions are less than 1°. They
also showed that other sources must be present in the band of galactic

latitudes extending from about $-1°$ to $+5°$, and found some indication for a possible source about 5° below the galactic equator.

The Lockheed group detected six separate sources, and gave precise values for their galactic longitudes. Two of these sources have galactic longitudes that coincide, within the experimental errors, with those of the ASE–MIT sources Sgr X-1 and Sco X-2, and thus presumably are identical to them.

The observations by the NRL group in this region of the sky, and in the region immediately above it revealed "a complex of emission which could be best resolved as the sum of the contributions from six point sources" (Ser XR-1, Sgr XR-1, Sgr XR-2, Oph XR-1, Sco XR-2, Sco XR-3) in the locations shown by the circles in Fig. 14.

A small maximum of low statistical significance observed by the Lockheed group may be associated with Ser XR-1.

The NRL source Sgr XR-2 falls halfway between the galactic meridians where the Lockheed group located two separate sources, 6° apart. Thus the peak ascribed to Sgr XR-2 was probably due to the unresolved effects of these two sources. The Lockheed results tend to confirm the NRL sources Sgr XR-1 and Sco XR-2. Presumably the four sources mentioned in this paragraph are part of the complex observed by the ASE–MIT group with their "vertical" slit collimator.

However, the ASE–MIT observations are in disagreement with the existence of strong x-ray sources in the positions of Oph XR-1 and Sco XR-3, which lie in regions of the sky explored both with the "vertical" and "horizontal" slit collimators. Thus presumably the tentative positions quoted for these two sources are affected by errors of at least several degrees. Particularly significant is the fact that the Kepler supernova remnant SN 1604, which lies within the circle of uncertainty of Oph XR-1, is 5° away from the nearest ASE–MIT source (Sgr X-1). Therefore, the tentative identification of one of the NRL sources with SN 1604 does not appear to be correct.

In closing, it is worth mentioning that Sagittarius A, the radio center of the galaxy, is not an x-ray source of strength comparable to that of the sources already detected.

4. Present Information Concerning the Spectra and the Intensities of the X-ray Sources

The question concerning the absolute value of the energy flux and the question concerning the spectrum of an x-ray source are closely related because the sensitivity of the detectors used in x-ray astronomy vary rapidly with wavelength (Fig. 6). The spectral information so far available was obtained by comparing the counting rates of Geiger counters having different spectral response curves; by measuring the absorption of the radiation in the atmosphere or in filters placed in front of the counters windows; by recording the pulse height distributions of proportional counters and of scintillation counters.

The results indicate clearly that different sources have appreciably different spectra. However, they are not sufficiently precise to determine these spectra unambiguously. Often the best one can do is to make some *a priori* assumption on the form of the spectral distribution function (i.e., the function $j(E)$ such that $j(E)\, dE$ represents the energy flux due to x-rays with photon energy between E and $E + dE$) leaving a free parameter to be determined so as to obtain closest fit with the experimental observations. Although it is quite possible that a substantial fraction of the x-ray flux is concentrated in a few monochromatic lines, the analysis has been usually carried out under the assumption of a continuous spectrum. In particular, the three following spectral functions have been considered:

(1) *Power law:* $j(E) = \dfrac{\text{const}}{E^{\alpha}}$

(2) *Exponential law:* $j(E) = \text{const } e^{-E/kT}$

(3) *Planck's law:* $j(E) = \text{const } \dfrac{E^3}{e^{E/kT} - 1}$

These different laws reflect different assumptions concerning the production mechanism of x-rays. Thus synchrotron radiation and inverse Compton effect are likely to produce spectra that may be approximated by a power law over a wide range of energies. Exponential spectra are characteristic of fully ionized, optical thin, low-Z plasma clouds, containing electrons with a Maxwellian velocity distribution corresponding to a high temperature T. In this case the process responsible for x-ray emission is bremsstrahlung, while, in the presence of high-Z materials, there would be a substantial contribution from free-bound and bound-bound transitions giving rise to typical discontinuities and monochromatic lines. Finally Planck's law is characteristic of an *optically thick* object at the temperature T, such as, for example, a neutron star.

Let us now consider separately the experimental results concerning the different x-ray sources.

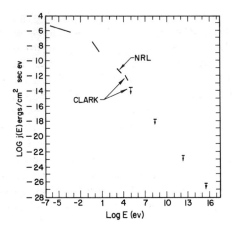

Fig. 15. Summary of experimental data on the electromagnetic spectrum of the
Crab Nebula; E is the photon energy.

(a) The Crab Nebula

The present information concerning the spectrum of this object
is summarized in Fig. 15, which contains, in addition to the results
concerning the x-ray spectrum, also the results concerning the radio
and visible spectra as well as some upper limits in the γ-ray region. The
portion of the spectrum marked "NRL" (which covers an energy range
from 1.2 to 4 keV) was obtained from a comparison between the
counting rates observed by the NRL group in their November 1964
flight with proportional counters provided with windows of different
thickness. The data marked "Clark" (giving the spectral intensity from
20 to 40 keV and an upper limit at 80 keV) were obtained by George
Clark by means of a scintillation counter flown with a balloon[13], as
mentioned previously. There are some reasons to believe that the
logarithmic slope of the spectrum in the visible region is somewhat
smaller than indicated in the graph, and that a single power law with
exponent $\alpha = 1.1$ may account for the whole spectral region from a few
eV to about 3 keV. However, beyond 10 or 20 keV the spectrum appears
to become progressively steeper.

(b) The Sco X-1 Source

Spectral information concerning the Sco X-1 source was obtained
by the ASE group[20], by the NRL group, and by the Lockheed group

in many of the flights already mentioned. In addition, spectral observations have been reported by Satio Hayakawa and his collaborators at Nagoya University[21]. A more accurate experiment was performed in June 1965 by a group at the Lawrence Radiation Laboratory (LRL) using a proportional counter carried to 170 km by a rocket[22]. A Planck-type spectrum appears to be definitely ruled out. The ASE data, in the spectral region from about 1 to about 15 keV, were found to be consistent with a power-law spectrum with ($\alpha = 1.1 \pm 0.3$) as well as with an exponential spectrum with $T = (3.8 \pm 1.8) \times 10^7$ °K. The Lockheed data had tentatively suggested a low-energy cutoff of the spectrum below about 4 keV, which, however, is not consistent with the results of the other groups. The LRL results, which apply to the energy range from 2 to 20 keV, favor an exponential spectrum corresponding to an electron temperature T of about 5.8×10^7 °K. Considering the experimental uncertainties, this value of T is consistent with that found by the ASE group.

(c) The Cyg XR-1 Source

Kenneth McCracken has recently reported the results of an experiment performed by means of a scintillation counter carried aloft by a balloon[23]. In this experiment he observed celestial x-rays, originating presumably from Cyg XR-1, and found that their spectral distribution, in the energy region from 20 to 58 keV, was similar to that of the radiation from the Crab Nebula.

(d) The Source Complex near the Galactic Center

Preliminary results by the ASE group indicate that the spectrum of the source complex near the galactic center is roughly similar to that of Sco X-1 in the energy region from 1 to 10 keV. There is some evidence, however, that above this energy the former spectrum is harder than the latter.

Using the spectral information described above, and the actual values of the observed counting rates, one can estimate the energy fluxes reaching the earth from the various x-ray sources. These estimates are still rather crude, and the data presented in Table I are given mainly for the purpose of orientation. One sees that Sco X-1 is by far the strongest source in the low-energy region (1 to 10 keV), while at high energies (>20 keV) some of the other sources, and in particular the Crab Nebula, appear to be at least as bright as Sco X-1.

5. The Diffuse Radiation

As I noted in Sec. 1, already the June 1962 flight in which the strong source in Scorpio was discovered produced evidence for the existence of a diffuse x-radiation. The later rocket experiments confirmed this result and showed that this radiation is nearly constant in time and does not exhibit strong anisotropy. Balloon experiments by R. Rothenflug et al., at Saclay detected the diffuse radiation in the 0.6–0.2 Å region[24]. The present best estimates of its intensity yield a

TABLE I.   Integrated Energy Flux for Various X-ray Sources and Two Different Ranges of Photon Energy (from the Varenna Paper)

Source	Spectral range, keV	Energy flux, ergs-cm-$^{-2}$ sec^{-1}	Remarks
Crab	1 to 10	2×10^{-8}	NRL data
	20 to 30	$(6 \pm 2) \times 10^{-9}$	G. Clark balloon data
Sco X-1	1 to 10	$(1.6 \pm 0.4) \times 10^{-7}$	ASEGeiger counter data‡
	20 to 30	$< 6 \times 10^{-9}$†	ASE scintillation counter data
Galactic equator (including Sgr X-1	1 to 10	$(0.4 \pm 0.1) \times 10^{-7}$	ASE Geiger counter data‡
Sco X-1 and probably several additional sources)	20 to 30	$(16 \pm 5) \times 10^{-9}$	ASE scintillation counter data

† Represents 2σ deviation above background; no significant excess was observed.

‡ Assuming E^{-1} power spectrum.

flux of approximately 10 photons cm^{-2} sec^{-1} sr^{-1} in the spectral range 2–8 Å. It is not yet absolutely certain that the diffuse radiation is of celestial origin, although the absence of any increase of intensity near the horizon is strong evidence against an atmospheric source. If the radiation is extraterrestrial, then its approximate isotropy suggests that it is also extragalactic. If this is so, then at sufficiently long wavelengths (greater than 10 or 20 Å) absorption by interstellar gas (see Fig. 4) should produce a minimum of intensity in the galactic plane.

It has been suggested that the diffuse radiation may simply represent the superposition of the x-ray emission for all galaxies other than our own[25]. If we assume that our galaxy is a typical x-ray emitter, and that the x-ray sources observed in a direction close to that of the galactic center are actually located near this point, we find that the contribution of external galaxies accounts for only a small fraction (from 1–10%) of the observed diffuse radiation. However, no final conclusion should be drawn from this discrepancy, because our galaxy may not be typical and because the x-radiation from sources near the galactic center, as viewed from the earth, may be considerably attenuated by absorption in interstellar matter.

6. Concluding Remarks

The theoretical implications of the observational data described in this paper, and the various hypotheses that have been presented in an attempt to explain the observed x-ray sources, from the subject of another article in this volume. Here I only wish to stress some of the experimental results that appear to be particularly significant

First and foremost among them is the truly astonishing magnitude of the observed x-ray emission, considered both in absolute value and relative to the emission in other parts of the electromagnetic spectrum.

In the case of the sun, the x-ray emission is an exceedingly minute fraction of the emission in the visible part of the spectrum. In the spectral region 1–10 Å, the energy flux at the earth from the quiet sun oscillates between 10^{-4} and 10^{-5} erg/cm²-sec. This is about one part in 10^{11} or 10^{10} of the total flux of solar radiation, most of which lies in the visible spectrum. During periods of high solar activity, especially on the occasion of solar flares, the x-ray emission of the sun increases by a very large factor, but it has never been observed to be more than one part in several million of the total energy flux.

In the case of the extrasolar x-ray sources, instead, the situation is entirely different. The only x-ray source identified with a visual object is the Crab Nebula; from the data in Table I, one finds that the x-ray flux from this object in the spectral region 1–10 Å is *about equal* to its flux in the visible region. Taking the distance of the Crab Nebula as 4000 light years, its x-ray emission turns out to be about 10^4 times the total power radiated by the sun.

Even more extreme is the situation concerning Sco X-1. As I noted above, no visible object has been identified with this x-ray source; however, the brightest star within the circle of uncertainty for the position of Sco X-1 has magnitude 9. This means that the energy flux of visible light from Sco X-1, is at most 6×10^{-9} erg/cm²-sec; from the figure quoted in Table I we thus conclude that the x-ray flux from this source is at least 25 times greater than the flux of visible light.

The second point is that, although a large portion of the sky has been scanned in the various rocket flights, all sources detected to date lie fairly close to the galactic equator. The source farthest from the galactic equator (about 25°) is Sco X-1, and its great strength suggests that it lies fairly near to the solar system. It is thus very likely that most or all of the observed localized x-sources are galactic rather than extragalactic objects.

The third point is that the only x-ray source that has been identified with a previously known celestial object turned out to be the remnant of a supernova (Crab Nebula). However, another well-known supernova remnant, SN 1604, is not an x-ray source of strength comparable to that of the Crab; the same is true of the Tycho supernova (galactic longitude $l^{\text{II}} = 120°$, galactic latitude $b^{\text{II}} = 2°$). Thus not all supernova remnants are strong x-ray emitters, Conversely the fairly large number of x-ray sources observed, and their clustering around the galactic center, appear to indicate that not all x-ray sources are supernova remnants.

Looking at the future of x-ray astronomy, one can readily identify a variety of developments in the observational techniques that cannot fail to produce new data of crucial importance. The following is a partial list:

(*a*) The use of satellites as carriers for x-ray detectors will greatly increase the time of observation over that provided by rockets, thus making it possible to discover sources of much lesser intensity than those observed thus far. To this purpose will also contribute the development of detectors with larger effective area.

(*b*) Balloons provided with accurate pointing control and carrying large detectors will probably prove competitive with space vehicles for observations in the spectral region corresponding to photon energies greater than about 15 keV.

(*c*) Further refinement in the design of mechanical collimators and improved methods of construction will provide instruments of considerably greater resolution than those already used, and free of some of the ambiguities that affect the operation of modulation collimators.

(*d*) Most important of all, perhaps, will be the application of the grazing-incidence telescope to galactic and extragalactic x-ray astronomy. The same telescope that was used to take x-ray pictures of the sun would be capable of taking a picture of Sco X-1 if it could be kept pointed to this source to an accuracy better than one arc minute for a time of about 10 minutes. Considerably larger and improved telescopes are already under construction. These instruments will be capable of resolutions on the order of 5 seconds of arc. The small size of the detector that can be used in conjunction with a telescope removes any background problem and places the telescope in a favorable competitive position with respect to large-area counters for the detection of very weak sources. The telescope will be an essential component of any dispersion spectrometer that may be developed to obtain high-resolution spectral information in the x-ray region. Similarly, any instrument designed to study the polarization of celestial x-rays will need a telescope both in order to restrict the observations to limited portions of an extended source (such as the Crab Nebula) and to concentrate an x-ray beam of sufficient intensity over a polarization detector of reasonable size.

References

1. Burnight, T. R., *Phys. Rev.*, **76**, 165 (1949).
2. Friedman, H., *Proc. IRE*, **47**, 278 (1959).
3. Wolter, H., *Ann. Phys.*, **10**, 94 (1952).
4. Friedman, H., *Rept. Progr. Phys.*, **25**, 163 (1962); R. L. Blake, T. A. Chubb, H. Friedman, and A. E. Unzicker, *Astrophys. J.*, **137**, 3 (1963).
5. Reported by J. C. Lindsay at the IAU Symposium, Liège (Belgium), August 1964.
6. Giacconi, R., W. P. Reidy, T. Zehnpfennig, J. C. Lindsay, and W. A. Muney, *Astrophys. J.*, **142**, 1274 (1965).
7. Giacconi, R., H. Gursky, F. Paolini, and B. Rossi, *Phys. Rev. Letters*, **9**, 439 (1962).
8. Gursky, H., R. Giacconi, F. Paolini, and B. Rossi, *Phys. Rev. Letters*, **11**, 503 (1963).
9. Friedman, H., *Space Research IV*, North-Holland, Amsterdam, 1964, p. 966.
10. Clark, G. A., G. Garmire, M. Oda, M. Wada, R. Giacconi, H. Gursky, and J. Waters, *Nature*, **207**, 584 (1965).
11. Giacconi, R., H. Gursky, J. R. Waters, B. Rossi, G. Clark, G. Garmire, M. Oda, and M. Wada, to be published in *Proceedings of the High-Energy Astrophysics Course of the International School of Physics "Enrico Fermi,"* held in Varenna in July 1965.
12. Oda, M., *Applied Optics*, **4**, 143 (1965).
13. Clark, G., *Phys. Rev. Letters*, **14**, 91 (1965).

14. Bowyer, S., E. T. Byram, T. A. Chubb, and H. Friedman, *Nature*, **201**, 1307 (1964).
15. Bowyer, S., E. T. Byram, T. A. Chubb, and H. Friedman, *Science*, **46**, 912 (1964).
16. Bowyer, S., E. T. Byram, T. A. Chubb, and H. Friedman, *Science*, **147**, 394 (1965).
17. Giacconi, R., H. Gursky, J. Waters, G. Clark, and B. Rossi, *Nature*, **204**, 981 (1964).
18. Oda, M., G. W. Clark, G. Garmire, M. Wada, R. Giacconi, H. Gursky, and J. Waters, *Nature*, **205**, 554 (1965).
19. Fisher, P. C., H. M. Johnson, W. C. Jordan, A. J. Meyerott, and L. W. Acton, *Astrophys. J.*, **143**, 203 (1966).
20. Giacconi, R., H. Gursky, and J. R. Waters, *Nature*, **207**, 572 (1965).
21. Hayakawa, S., M. Matsuoka, and K. Yamashita, Report at the International Conference on Cosmic Rays of the IUPAP, London, September 1965.
22. Chodil, G., R. C. Jopson, H. Mark, F. D. Seward, and C. D. Swift, *Phys. Rev. Letters*, **15**, 605 (1965).
23. McCracken, K. G., Report at the International Conference on Cosmic Rays of the IUPAP, London, September 1965.
24. Rothenflug, R., R. Rocchia, and L. Koch, Report at the International Conference on Cosmic Rays of the IUPAP, London, September 1965.
25. Gould, R. J., and G. R. Burbidge, *Astrophys. J.*, **138**, 969 (1963).

Nuclear Energy Generation in Supermassive Stars

WILLIAM A. FOWLER

California Institute of Technology

1. Introduction

Since the pioneer work of Hans Bethe[1] it has been known that the reactions of carbon and nitrogen with protons are the most important source of energy in main sequence stars with mass greater than a value approximately equal to that of the sun. Detailed analysis of the experimental reaction rates in the CN cycle and the proton-proton chain has indicated[2,3] that the cycle supplants the *pp* chain as the main source of energy in Population I stars at a central temperature near 2×10^7 °K and at a somewhat higher temperature in Population II stars. This is illustrated for Population I stars in Fig. 1. Since the central temperature in the sun[4] is 1.6×10^7 °K and since central temperature increases with mass, it follows that the crossover point occurs in stars with mass definitely in excess of the solar mass. Experimental studies of the rates of the reactions of the oxygen isotopes, O^{16} and O^{17}, with protons has shown that these isotopes react rapidly[5] at elevated temperatures with the cyclic production of N^{14}. The overall result is the CNO bi-cycle which is depicted in Table I.

At the present time there is some interest in the operation of the CNO bi-cycle in stars with mass in excess of 10^3 solar masses ($M \geq 10^3 \, M_\odot$) which have been termed *supermassive* stars. It has been suggested[6-13] that nuclear and gravitational energy release in supermassive stars is sufficient to meet the energy requirements in quasi-stellar objects or quasars and in extragalactic radio sources. This suggestion has been discussed in detail in the references just cited and will not be further elaborated upon in this paper. It will suffice in Sec. 2 to establish an average energy generation per unit mass and per unit time in supermassive

413

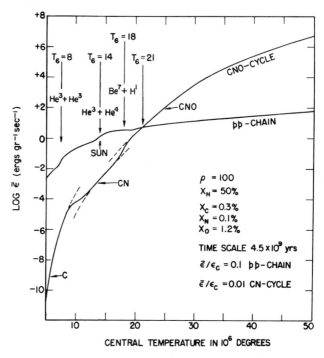

Fig. 1.   Average energy generation throughout a star in ergs per gram-second as a function of central temperature for the *p-p* chain and the CNO bi-cycle. The central density is taken as $\rho = 100$ g/cm^3, and the hydrogen concentration by weight as $x_H = 0.50$. Concentrations of C, N, and O by weight as given are those for a typical Population I star. The age of the star is taken to be 4.5×10^9 years. The points of inflection in the *p-p* chain arise from the onset of the indicated interactions. Similarly C, N, and O are successively involved in the CNO cycle. Note that the sun and the cool stars operate on the *p-p* chain; hot stars operate on the CNO cycle.

stars which is demanded by this suggestion. Nuclear energy generation in supermassive stars is of interest *per se.*

The paper then continues with an analysis in Sec. 3 of energy generation through the CNO bi-cycle using the latest nuclear reaction rate data. The central temperature at which the required energy generation is met is determined.

In Sec. 4 the general relativistic instability which arises at very low central temperatures during the early stages of contraction in super-

TABLE I. Reactions of the CNO-Bi-cycle (June, 1965)

The CNO-Bi-cycle	Energy release	S_0(keV-barns) or $\bar{\tau}$	Solar $f_0 S_0$
$\rightarrow C^{12} + H^1 \rightarrow N^{13} + \gamma$	1.94	1.53	2.2
$N^{13} \rightarrow C^{13} + \beta^+ + \nu$	1.50	$\bar{\tau} = 870$ sec	
$C^{13} + H^1 \rightarrow N^{14} + \gamma$	7.55	5.9	8.4
$\rightarrow N^{14} + H^1 \rightarrow O^{15} + \gamma$	7.29	3.0	4.5
$O^{15} \rightarrow N^{15} + \beta^+ + \nu$	1.73	$\bar{\tau} = 178$ sec	
$N^{15} + H^1 \rightarrow C^{12} + He^4$	4.96	7.5×10^4	1.1×10^5
	(6% ν-loss) 24.97 MeV		
or (1/2200)			
$N^{15} + H^1 \rightarrow O^{16} + \gamma$	12.13	32	48
$O^{16} + H^1 \rightarrow F^{17} + \gamma$	0.60	9.9	16
$F^{17} \rightarrow O^{17} + \beta^+ + \nu$	1.76	$\bar{\tau} = 95$ sec	
$O^{17} + H^1 \rightarrow N^{14} + He^4$	1.19	10	16
(1/2200)	15.68 MeV		
$4H^1 \rightarrow He^4$ Total =	26.7313 MeV ± .0005		

massive stars is introduced. The effects of uniform and differential rotation are discussed and a comparison made between the limiting temperature for dynamic stability and the required nuclear temperature. The limiting masses for operation of the CNO bi-cycle under stable conditions are found to be approximately $10^6 \ M_\odot$, $10^7 \ M_\odot$, and $10^9 \ M_\odot$ for no rotation, maximum uniform rotation, and maximum differential rotation, respectively.

2. Average Energy Generation Required in Supermassive Stars

We first seek the average energy generation required in stable supermassive stars. On the basis that such stars are largely convective polytropes of index $n = 3$ except near the surface where the flux transport is entirely radiative, and that radiative pressure is large compared to gas pressure, it is found[6] that the luminosity L is proportional to the mass M according to the relation

$$L \approx 4\pi c G M \kappa^{-1}, \tag{1}$$

where c is the velocity of light, G is the gravitational constant, and κ is the opacity. The effective surface temperature is found to be so high ($\sim 7 \times 10^4 \ {}^\circ K$) that hydrogen and helium are effectively wholly ionized at the photosphere and the opacity is primarily due to electron scattering, $\kappa = 0.19(1 + x_H)$, where x_H is the fraction by mass of hydrogen. Numerically Eq. (1) becomes

$$L \approx \frac{2.6 \times 10^{38}}{1 + x_H} \frac{M}{M_\odot} \text{ ergs sec}^{-1}, \tag{2}$$

or

$$\frac{L}{M} \approx \frac{1.3 \times 10^5}{1 + x_H} \text{ ergs g}^{-1} \text{ sec}^{-1}. \tag{3}$$

The luminosity-mass ratio given by Eq. (3) yields the average energy generation per unit mass and per unit time in a supermassive star. Since x_H is less than unity we have to order of magnitude

$$\bar{\epsilon}_{SMS} \approx 10^5 \text{ ergs g}^{-1} \text{ sec}^{-1} \tag{4}$$

The energy released in the conversion of hydrogen into helium is 6×10^{18} ergs g^{-1}. On the assumption that one-half of the mass of the star is eventually converted from hydrogen into helium, the lifetime for the main sequence stage of a supermassive star is found to be

$$\tau \approx 3 \times 10^{13} \text{ sec} \approx 10^6 \text{ yr} \tag{5}$$

independent of mass.

3. Energy Generation in the CNO Bi-cycle

A detailed analysis of the reaction rates found experimentally for the interaction of the carbon, nitrogen, and oxygen isotopes with protons has been made by Caughlan and Fowler[5]. They find that the oxygen isotopes have lifetimes considerably shorter than 10^6 yr for temperatures above 0.5×10^8 °K which is the lower limit of temperatures relevant to hydrogen burning in supermassive stars. In what follows it will be found that the relevant range falls in the interval 0.5–0.8×10^8 °K. Thus the bi-cycle, Table I, is fully operative. They also find that the $N^{14}(p, \gamma)O^{15}$ reaction is the slowest among the carbon-nitrogen isotopes and that the overall rate of the bi-cycle is essentially determined by the rate of this reaction. When all the reactions are in equilibrium, their results yield

$$\epsilon_{HCNO} =$$
$$1.23 \times 10^{26} \, \rho x_H x_{14} S_{eff} \, T_8^{-\frac{2}{3}} \exp\left(-32.81 T_8^{-\frac{1}{3}}\right) \text{ ergs g}^{-1} \text{ sec}^{-1}, \tag{6}$$

where ρ is the density, x_{14} is the concentration by mass of N_{14}, $T_8 = T/10^8$ °K is the temperature in units of 10^8 °K and S_{eff} is the effective cross section factor for the $N^{14}(p, \gamma)O^{15}$ reaction in keV-barns. The density is relatively low at hydrogen burning in supermassive stars and the usual correction for electron screening can be neglected.

It is also found at equilibrium in the temperature range previously noted that $x_{14} \approx 0.93 x_{CNO}$, where x_{CNO} is the fraction by mass of carbon, nitrogen, and oxygen. Hebbard and Bailey[14] give the empirical values $S_0 = 2.75 \pm 0.50$ keV-barns and $\langle dS/dE \rangle = 0$ from an extrapolation to zero energy of their low-energy measurements on $N^{14}(p, \gamma)$. These values yield $S_{eff} \approx 2.79$ keV-barns and thus

$$\epsilon_{HCNO} \approx 3.19 \times 10^{26} \, \rho x_H x_{CNO} T_8^{-\frac{2}{3}} \exp\left(-32.81 T_8^{-\frac{1}{3}}\right) \text{ ergs g}^{-1} \text{ sec}^{-1} \tag{7}$$

The supermassive stars will be treated as extreme Population I stars and thus reasonable values for the compositions are $x_{CNO} = 0.03$ and $x_H = 0.4$ after some exhaustion of the original hydrogen. In a massive star with polytropic index $n = 3$ the density can be expressed[15] in terms of the temperature as

$$\rho \approx 130(M_\odot/M)^{1/2} T_8^3 \text{ g cm}^{-3} \tag{8}$$

The substitution of $x_H x_{CNO} = 0.012$ and of Eq. (8) into Eq. (7) yields

$$\epsilon_{HCNO} \approx 4.98 \times 10^{26}(M_\odot/M)^{1/2} T_8^{7/3} \exp(-32.81 T_8^{-1/3}) \text{ ergs g}^{-1} \sec^{-1} \tag{9}$$

For the purposes at hand it is necessary to express the average energy generation throughout the star in terms of the central temperature. When the energy generation can be written as proportional to $\rho^{u-1} T^s$ the ratio of the average energy generation to the central energy generation in a polytrope of index $n = 3$ is given by[15]

$$\frac{\bar{\epsilon}}{\epsilon_c} = \frac{3.2}{(3u+s)^{3/2}} = 0.042 \tag{10}$$

The numerical value has been arrived at by using $u = 2$ from the ρ-dependence and $s = 12$ as the exponent in the best power-law fit to the temperature dependent factors in Eq. (7) in the range $0.5 < T_8 < 0.8$. Thus

$$\bar{\epsilon}_{HCNO} \approx 2.09 \times 10^{25}(M_\odot/M)^{1/2} T_{8c}^{7/3} \exp(-32.81 T_{8c}^{-1/3}) \text{ ergs g}^{-1} \sec^{-1} \tag{11}$$

$$\sim 2.72 \times 10^8(M_\odot/M)^{1/2} (T_{8c}/0.65)^{15} \qquad 0.5 < T_{8c} < 0.8 \tag{12}$$

The power-law exponent in Eq. (12) includes the dependence of density on temperature. T_{8c} is the *central* temperature in 10^8 °K.

The average energy generation given by Eq. (11) can now be equated to the energy required by Eq. (4), i.e.,

$$\bar{\epsilon}_{HCNO} = \bar{\epsilon}_{SMS} \tag{13}$$

This gives the result

$$(M/M_\odot)^{1/2} \approx 2.09 \times 10^{20} T_{8n}^{7/3} \exp(-32.81 T_{8n}^{-1/3}) \tag{14}$$

by which it is possible to calculate the central temperature T_{8n} at which *nuclear* energy generation through HCNO-burning yields 10^5 ergs g^{-1} sec^{-1} on the average in a supermassive star of mass M. Equation (12) can be employed to give the rough approximation

$$T_{8n} = T_n \times 10^{-8} \sim 0.38(M/M_\odot)^{1/30} \tag{15}$$

The temperature given by the more accurate Eq. (14) is plotted against mass in Figs. 2 and 3.

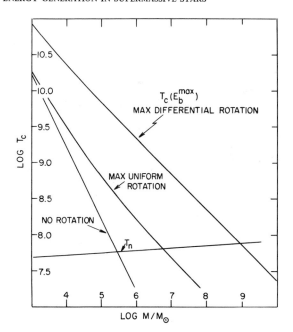

Fig. 2. The temperature $T_c(E_b^{max})$ at which the binding energy reaches its maximum value plotted as a function of stellar mass for three cases: no rotation, maximum uniform rotation, and maximum differential rotation. The temperature T_n required for the operation of the CNO bi-cycle is shown for comparison.

4. Stability of Supermassive Stars During Hydrogen Burning

The stability of supermassive stars has been discussed by several authors[8-13,16-20]. In what follows the discussion will be limited to the post-Newtonian approximation to the general relativistic treatment of the problem for rotating stars. In this approximation the binding energy E_b of a star of mass M and radius R is given by[12]

$$\frac{E_b}{Mc^2} \approx \frac{3\bar{\beta}_n}{4(5-n)} \left(\frac{2GM}{Rc^2}\right) + \frac{1}{4}(K\alpha)_n^2 \left(\frac{2GM}{Rc^2}\right) - \zeta_n \left(\frac{2GM}{Rc^2}\right)^2, \quad (16)$$

where $2GM/Rc^2$ is the characteristic expansion parameter in general relativity for spherically symmetric systems with G the gravitational constant and c the velocity of light. Distortion from spherical symmetry under rotation has been neglected. In this approximation it is not

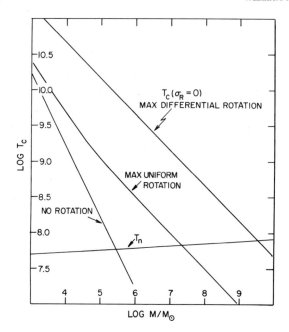

Fig. 3.   The temperature $T_c(\sigma_R = 0)$ at which dynamic instability sets in plotted as a function of stellar mass for three cases: no rotation, maximum uniform rotation, and maximum differential rotation. The temperature T_n required for the operation of the CNO bi-cycle is shown for comparison.

necessary to distinguish between the rest mass of the constituents and the inertial or gravitational mass of the contracted system measured by an external observer. Quantities which depend on the polytropic structure are designated by the use of the polytropic index n as a subscript. Numerical values will be given for $n = 3$ on the grounds that this is approximately the minimum index for convective stability. The ratio of gas pressure to total pressure, gas plus radiation, averaged throughout the star, is designated by $\bar{\beta}_n$. For the polytrope of index $n = 3$, β is a constant throughout the star, and it has been shown[15] that

$$(\mu\bar{\beta})_3 = (\mu\beta)_3 = 4.28(M_\odot/M)^{\frac{1}{2}} \qquad n = 3, \qquad (17)$$

where μ is the mean molecular weight of the stellar material. With μ of order unity, note that β is small for large M.

The coefficient of the negative post-Newtonian, general relativistic term is of order unity and is designated by ζ_n. For $n = 3$, $\zeta_3 = 1.265$. K_n is given in terms of the Newtonian rotational energy Ψ_0 and the angular velocity at the periphery ω_R by the equation

$$K_n = (2\Psi_0/MR^2\omega_R^2)^{\frac{1}{2}} \tag{18}$$

K_n can be determined when the polytropic index is given and the angular velocity $\omega = \omega(r)$ is specified as a function of radius. A model for differential rotation in a polytrope of index $n = 3$ due to Stoeckly[21] has been used in the calculations discussed here. For this model $K_3^2 = 2.47$. For uniform rotation $\omega = \omega_R$ and $K_n = k_n$, the radius of gyration in units of R. For $n = 3$, $k_3^2 = 0.075$. The quantity α_n is a measure of the amount of rotation in terms of the critical angular velocity which occurs when centrifugal forces match gravitational forces at some point in the equatorial plane. In the case of uniform rotation this first occurs at the periphery and α_n is independent of n being given by

$$\alpha_n = \alpha = \omega_R/\omega_{CR} \tag{19}$$

where

$$\omega_{CR} = (GM/R^3)^{\frac{1}{2}} \tag{20}$$

For numerical calculations on uniform rotation $\alpha = 1$ will be taken as the limiting case in the sense that angular momentum loss or transfer to the external surroundings will limit the rotation to that which corresponds to this value. In the case of differential rotation, the limit on the angular velocity occurs at the center and numerical integrations on Stoeckly's model yield the limiting value $\alpha_3^2 = 0.456$ so that $(K\alpha)_3^2 = 1.125$. This is to be compared with the limit for uniform rotation $(K\alpha)_3^2 = (k\alpha)_3^2 = 0.075$. For no rotation $\alpha_n = 0$.

In the post-Newtonian approximation the angular frequency σ_R of first-order periodic variations in the fundamental mode of radial oscillations is closely related to the binding energy and is given by

$$\sigma_R^2 \approx \frac{1}{3}\left(\frac{c^3}{2GMk_n}\right)^2\left[\frac{3\bar{\beta}_n}{2(5-n)}\left(\frac{2GM}{Rc^2}\right)^3\right.$$
$$\left. + (K\alpha)_n^2\left(\frac{2GM}{Rc^2}\right)^3 - 4\zeta_n\left(\frac{2GM}{Rc^2}\right)^4\right] \text{ sec}^{-2}. \tag{21}$$

The period of the fundamental mode is given by

$$\Pi_R = 2\pi/\sigma_R \text{ sec}$$
$$= 2\pi/86400\sigma_R \text{ day}. \tag{22}$$

For zero rotation

$$\sigma_R^2 \approx -(2/3k_n^2 MR)(dE_b/dR) \qquad \alpha_n = 0 \qquad (23)$$

When the term in $\tilde{\beta}_n$ is small enough to be neglected

$$\sigma_R^2 \approx 4E_b/3k_n^2 MR^2 \qquad \tilde{\beta}_n = 0 \qquad (24)$$

The star becomes dynamically unstable when σ_R becomes imaginary or σ_R^2 becomes negative. The role of the negative post-Newtonian term is thus apparent from Eq. (21). When the dimensionless parameter $2GM/Rc^2$ becomes large enough during contraction, σ_R^2 will become negative and small perturbations will become exponentially large rather than periodic in nature. Since $\tilde{\beta}_n$ is small for supermassive stars this instability sets in at large radii early in contraction when there is no rotation. It will be clear that rotation will postpone the onset of this instability until much smaller radii are reached and that differential rotation ($K_n^2 \alpha_n^2 = 1.125$) will be much more effective in this regard than uniform rotation ($k_n^2 \alpha_n^2 = 0.075$).

In order to determine the stability and binding energy during hydrogen burning and nuclear energy generation, it is necessary to express E_b and σ_R in terms of the central temperature. This can be done by using the Newtonian relation between radius and central temperature of a polytrope which is

$$\frac{2GM}{Rc^2} = 2(n + 1) \frac{M_n}{R_n c^2} \left(\frac{\mathcal{R}T}{\mu\beta}\right)_c \qquad (25)$$

where M_n and R_n are constants of integration corresponding to mass and radius, respectively, for the Lane-Emden second-order differential equation governing the structure of a polytrope of index n. For the polytrope of index $n = 3$, $M_3 = 2.018$, and $R_3 = 6.987$ so that Eqs. (17) and (25) yield

$$\frac{2GM}{Rc^2} = 2.60 \times 10^{-21}(\mathcal{R}T/\mu\beta)_c$$

$$\qquad\qquad\qquad\qquad\qquad\qquad\qquad\qquad n = 3 \qquad (26)$$

$$= 5.05 \times 10^{-6} (M/M_\odot)^{1/2} T_{8c}$$

In Eqs. (25) and (26), $\mathcal{R}$ is the gas constant.

When Eq. (26) is substituted into Eqs. (16) and (21) the results in terms of the central temperature, T_{8c}, in units of 10^8 °K are

$$E_b/Mc^2 \approx 1.112 \times 10^{-5} T_{8c} + 1.266 \times 10^{-6} (K\alpha)_3^2 (M/M_\odot)^{1/2} T_{8c}$$

$$- 3.236 \times 10^{-11} (M/M_\odot)T_{8c}^2 \qquad n = 3 \quad (27)$$

$$\sigma_R^2 \approx 2.614 \times 10^{-5} (M_\odot/M) T_{8c}^3 + 5.951 \times 10^{-6} (K\alpha)_3^2 (M_\odot/M)^{1/2} T_{8c}^3$$
$$- 1.521 \times 10^{-10} T_{8c}^4 \qquad n = 3 \quad (28)$$

During the contraction E_b reaches a maximum value at the temperature given by

$$T_{8c}(E_b^{max}) = T_c(E_b^{max}) \times 10^{-8}$$
$$= 1.956 \times 10^4 (K\alpha)_3^2 (M_\odot/M)^{1/2} + 1.718 \times 10^5 (M_\odot/M)$$
$$n = 3. \quad (29)$$

In general this temperature is somewhat less than that at which dynamic instability sets in. Setting $\sigma_R = 0$ in Eq. (28) the result is

$$T_{8c}(\sigma_R = 0) = T_c(\sigma_R = 0) \times 10^{-8}$$
$$= 3.913 \times 10^4 (K\alpha)_3^2 (M_\odot/M)^{1/2} + 1.718 \times 10^5 (M_\odot/M)$$
$$n = 3. \quad (30)$$

For no rotation, Eqs. (29) and (30) show that instability sets in when E_b reaches its maximum value. When rotational effects are large so that the first terms on the right-hand sides of Eqs. (27) and (28) can be neglected, instability sets in at twice the temperature at which E_b reaches its maximum value. At this temperature $E_b \approx 0$. This means that beyond $T_c(E_b^{max})$ a large amount of internal energy must be supplied if hydrostatic equilibrium is to be maintained. If this energy is to be made available from the nuclear resources of the star, it is necessary that T_n be less than $T_c(E_b^{max})$. If this is not the case, rapid adiabatic collapse occurs until T_n is reached at which point rapid nuclear burning takes place in such a way as to lead to reversal of the collapse and the setting up of large amplitude, nonlinear relaxation oscillations which have been discussed in detail by Fowler[11]. Thus in the case of no rotation, quasi-stable hydrogen burning through the CNO bi-cycle can occur at temperatures somewhat in excess of $T_c(E_b^{max}) = T_c(\sigma_R = 0)$ but when rotational effects are large T_n must not exceed a value intermediate between $T_c(E_b^{max})$ and $T_c(\sigma_R = 0) = 2T_c(E_b^{max})$.

These points are illustrated in Figs. 2 and 3 where $T_c(E_b^{max})$ and $T_c(\sigma_R = 0)$ are respectively plotted as functions of $M/M_\odot$ with T_n also plotted for comparison. Three cases are plotted:

(a) No rotation, $\qquad\qquad\qquad\qquad \alpha_3 = 0$;
(b) Maximum uniform rotation, $\quad (K\alpha)_3^2 = (k\alpha)_3^2 = 0.075$;
(c) Maximum differential rotation, $(K\alpha)_3^2 = 1.125$.

It is also of interest to know E_b/Mc^2 and Π_R as a function of stellar mass at the temperature at which hydrogen burning occurs. These quantities can be obtained by substituting T_{8n} from Eq. (14) into Eqs. (27), (28), and (22). The results are illustrated in Figs. 4 and 5.

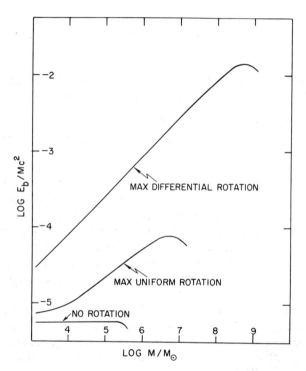

Fig. 4. The binding energy at the onset of nuclear energy generation through HCNO-burning plotted as a function of stellar mass for three cases: no rotation, maximum uniform rotation, and maximum differential rotation.

5. Conclusions

Figures 2 and 3 show that nuclear energy generation through HCNO-burning occurs under conditions of stability up to the following mass limits: for no rotation, $M \lesssim 2 \times 10^5 \, M_\odot$; for maximum uniform rotation, $M \lesssim 10^7 \, M_\odot$; for maximum differential rotation, $M \lesssim 10^9 \, M_\odot$. In the case of no rotation it has been shown[11] that relaxation oscillations under quasi-stable conditions extend the limiting mass to $M \lesssim 10^6 M_\odot$.

Figure 4 shows that the binding energy at the onset of nuclear energy generation is quite small except for $M > 10^8 M_\odot$ in the case of

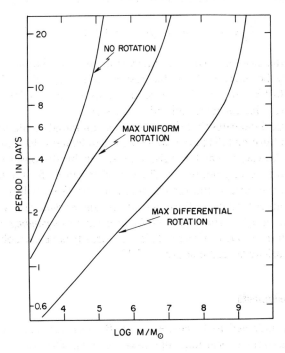

Fig. 5. The period in days of small, linear oscillations during nuclear energy generation through HCNO-burning plotted as a function of stellar mass for three cases: no rotation, maximum uniform rotation, and maximum differential rotation. The periods indicated in this plot do not hold for the large amplitude, nonlinear relaxation oscillations discussed in the text. For such oscillations the periods are a few years rather than a few days.

differential rotation. In this case the binding energy reaches slightly over 1% of the rest mass energy and is thus greater than the total nuclear energy of the star. For all masses the binding energy reaches a maximum which can be determined by the substitution of Eq. (29) into

Eq. (27). This maximum is usually reached upon further contraction after the termination of nuclear burning and is given by

$$\frac{E_b^{\max}}{Mc^2} \approx \frac{[(K\alpha)_n^2 + 3\bar{\beta}_n/(5 - n)]^2}{64\zeta_n}. \tag{31}$$

In the case of maximum differential rotation for $n = 3$ this yields

$$\frac{E_b^{\max}}{Mc^2} \approx 0.016 \qquad (K\alpha)^2 = 1.125, \qquad n = 3. \tag{32}$$

Thus in the case of maximum differential rotation the binding energy eventually becomes 1.6% of the rest mass energy. Since this energy must be lost by the star, it represents a substantial contribution to the energy available for light and radio emission.

Figure 5 indicates that the period of small radial oscillations during hydrogen burning falls in the range from 1 to 20 days. It must be borne in mind, however, that the pulsations set up by the onset of nuclear burning will be very nonlinear. The periods required for the transfer of energy to the surface and for the emission therefrom will be the order of years rather than days. *The observed light curves should show variations characteristic of a wide range of frequencies corresponding to periods from a few days to tens of years.* This may already have been observed[22] in the quasi-stellar radio source, 3C 273.

Acknowledgments

I am indebted to F. Hoyle and J. Bardeen for many discussions and suggestions concerning supermassive stars. The studies described in this paper were supported in part by the Office of Naval Research [Nonr-220(47)] and the National Science Foundation [GP-5391].

References

1. Bethe, H. A., *Phys. Rev.*, **55**, 103, 434 (1939).
2. Fowler, W. A., *Mém. Soc. R. Sci. de Liège*, Ser. 4, **13**, 88 (1954).
3. Fowler, W. A., *Mém. Soc. R. Sci. de Liège*, Ser. 5, **3**, 207 (1960).
4. Sears, R. L., *Astrophys. J.*, **140**, 477 (1964).
5. Caughlan, G. R., and W. A. Fowler, *Astrophys. J.*, **136**, 453 (1962).
6. Hoyle, F., and W. A. Fowler, *Monthly Notices Roy. Astrom. Soc.*, **125**, 169 (1963).

7. Hoyle, F., and W. A. Fowler, *Nature*, **197**, 533 (1963).
8. Fowler, W. A., *Rev. Mod. Phys.*, **36**, 545, 110E (1964).
9. Hoyle, F., and W. A. Fowler, *Quasi-Stellar Sources and Gravitational Collapse*, Univ. of Chicago Press, Chicago, 1965.
10. Hoyle, F., W. A. Fowler, G. R. Burbidge, and E. M. Burbidge, *Astrophys. J.*, **139**, 909 (1964).
11. Fowler, W. A., *Proc. Third Annual Science Conf. Belfer Grad. School of Science* Academic Press, New York, 1965.
12. Fowler, W. A., *Astrophys. J.*, **144**, 180 (1966).
13. Fowler, W. A., *Proceedings of the Summer Conference on High Energy Astro-Physics*, Varenna, Italy, 1965.
14. Hebbard, D. F., and G. M. Bailey, *Nucl. Phys.*, **49**, 666 (1963).
15. Fowler, W. A., and F. Hoyle, *Astrophys. J. Suppl.*, **91**, 201 (1964); *Nucleosynthesis in Massive Stars and Supernovae*, Univ. of Chicago Press, Chicago, 1965.
16. Iben, I., Jr., *Astrophys. J.*, **138**, 1090 (1963).
17. Chandrasekhar, S., *Phys. Rev. Letters*, **12**, 114, 437E (1964).
18. Chandrasekhar, S., *Astrophys. J.*, **140**, 417 (1964).
19. Bardeen, J. M., to be published.
20. Anand, S. P. S., to be published.
21. Stoeckly, R., *Astrophys. J.*, **142**, 208 (1965).
22. Smith, H. J., and D. Hoffleit, *Nature*, **198**, 650 (1963).

White Dwarf Stars

R. E. MARSHAK

University of Rochester

In the mid-1930's, George Gamow and Edward Teller organized a small annual theoretical conference at George Washington University (Washington, D.C.) at which topics of current interest were discussed. Hans Bethe came back from this conference at the spring of 1938, greatly challenged by the problem of the origin of stellar energy. Within several months, Bethe had examined every conceivable nuclear reaction which might produce substantial amounts of energy under stellar conditions and had reached the conclusion[1] that the carbon cycle was an important contributor at the temperatures and densities prevailing in main-sequence stars (independently, Von Weizsäcker reached a similar conclusion[2] at about the same time). Together with Charles Critchfield, Bethe had also worked out[3] the energy production due to the proton–proton reaction and realized that this sequence of reactions would be a second major source of energy for main sequence stars provided that Gamow-Teller (and not only Fermi) selection rules were applicable to nuclear beta decay. It was realized quite soon that the carbon cycle would dominate for the more massive (and luminous) stars of the main sequence—as compared to the proton–proton reaction— but that the transition point would depend on a more detailed knowledge of the temperature–density distribution within these stars which, in turn, would depend on a knowledge of the chemical composition (relative admixture of hydrogen, helium, and heavy elements). The uncertainty in the transition point was affected as well by the inaccurate knowledge of the capture widths involved in the nuclear reactions under consideration.

In 1938, digital computers were unknown, and gross approximations were made in the integration of the equations of stellar equilibrium to determine the temperature–density distribution needed to test the relevance of the various thermonuclear reactions considered by Bethe. For some years, Eddington's "standard model"[4] (wherein the product of the opacity K and the ratio of luminosity L_r to mass M_r, namely KL_r/M_r, was assumed to be constant throughout the star) had been used to obtain temperature–density distributions as a function of the chemical composition for main sequence stars (and to predict a reasonably good mass–luminosity law). Cowling's "point-convective model"[5] (wherein the luminosity was assumed to be constant—and equal to the observed luminosity—outside the central convective core where its variation with distance from the center was immaterial) was a more realistic approximation for thermonuclear sources of stellar energy. As Hans Bethe's graduate student, I was requested to calculate the temperature–density distribution for the sun on the basis of the point-convective model. The results were very encouraging and led to the conclusion that the carbon cycle was responsible for the energy production of the more massive stars of the main sequence and the proton–proton reaction for the less massive ones, with the transition point at approximately the solar mass (more accurate determinations of the nuclear constants as well as more careful numerical integration of the equations of stellar equilibrium have led in recent years to the shifting of this transition point from about one to more like two solar masses).

Hans Bethe's achievement in explaining the energy sources in main sequence stars was extraordinarily impressive and, as a graduate student looking around for a thesis topic, it seemed natural to embark on a study of the energy sources of a group of stars which differed greatly in their internal constitution from the main sequence stars, namely the white dwarf stars. Bethe was very intrigued by this problem and, as it turned out, we were led to a series of investigations whose outcome for some of them is still uncertain twenty-five years later. In pursuing this work, Bethe's vast knowledge of solid state as well as nuclear physics proved to be most helpful. As a tribute to Hans Bethe on his sixtieth birthday, I should like to summarize briefly what we tried to accomplish twenty-five years ago, what was achieved, and where we stand now with respect to a most interesting set of stellar objects, to wit, the white dwarf stars.

Twenty-five years ago, there were about seven white dwarfs known and only three (Sirius B, 40 Eridani B, and Procyon B) were members of binary systems for which the masses could be determined. (This is to be compared to at least 150 white dwarfs now known[6] although, unfortunately, the number with measured masses has not increased as yet.) Chandrasekhar's classic treatise on stellar structure[7] had just appeared and he had published several years earlier his theory of degenerate configurations, which predicted a unique relationship between the mass and radius of a very dense star at zero temperature once the hydrogen concentration was given. The theory of completely degenerate configurations led to a maximum mass corresponding to an infinite central density, above which the star could not remain in equilibrium; this famous Chandrasekhar limiting mass M_{lim} is found to be:

$$M_{\text{lim}} = \frac{5.75}{\mu_e^2} M_\odot, \tag{1}$$

where $M_\odot$ is the solar mass and μ_e is the mean molecular weight per free electron, which in turn depends on the hydrogen concentration X_H through the formula:

$$\mu_e = \frac{2}{1 + X_H}. \tag{2}$$

It follows that for a pure hydrogen star, the critical limiting mass would be 5.75 $M_\odot$ whereas for a star with no hydrogen (helium plus medium heavy elements), the limiting mass would be reduced to 1.44 $M_\odot$. This sensitive dependence on the hydrogen concentration characterizes as well the mass–radius relation below the limiting value and underlines the importance of a knowledge of the hydrogen content in the interior of a white dwarf star. Chandrasekhar was also aware of the fact that white dwarf stars should have nondegenerate envelopes of relatively small thickness surrounding the very dense degenerate cores; however, he had estimated the transition point by using the Kramers opacity law and one expected this law to break down as one proceeded through the transition region into the highly degenerate core. Since Chandrasekhar's theory of completely degenerate configurations was based on the zero temperature approximation, it was necessary to sharpen up the calculation of the temperature–density distribution inside a white dwarf star in order to estimate the effects of finite temperature on the theoretical mass-radius relation. It was also evident that a knowledge of the temperature distribution, together with the theory of the proton–proton reaction, would lead to definite statements concerning the amount of hydrogen in white dwarf stars.

The first order of business was therefore, to derive a fairly accurate expression for the radiative opacity both in the region of incipient degeneracy as well as in the region of strong degeneracy—in other words, to improve on the Kramers opacity law. This turned out to be a relatively simple task and the following expression for the radiative opacity was found to hold, to a good approximation, in both the nondegenerate and degenerate domains (and *a fortiori* in the incipient degenerate domain):

$$K_R = \frac{6.0 \times 10^{17} X_R}{\tau T^2} \log \left[\frac{1 + e^{-\psi/kT}}{1 + e^{-\psi/kT - 7}} \right], \tag{3}$$

where X_R is the concentration of heavy elements (Russell mixture) by mass, T the temperature, k the Boltzmann constant, ψ the Gibbs free energy, and τ the so-called "guillotine" factor (which approaches unity when the bound-free contribution to the radiative opacity dominates and the value 196.5 when only the free–free contribution remains). The quantity ψ is defined implicitly, in terms of the free electron density N_e, through the equation:

$$N_e = \frac{\sqrt{2}}{\pi^2} (m_e kT)^{3/2} \int_0^\infty \frac{\sqrt{q}\, dq}{e^{q + \psi/kT} + 1} \tag{4}$$

$\psi/kT = 0$ is the transition point with $\psi/kT > 0$ representing the non-degenerate side and $\psi/kT < 0$ the degenerate side. The dependence of the radiative opacity on the free-electron density required a more careful calculation of this quantity as the mass density increased and "pressure ionization" set in. Several methods were developed to take account of pressure ionization, including one based on the Thomas–Fermi method for atoms; indeed, our paper on "Application of the Generalized Thomas–Fermi Method to Stars"[8] was the starting point for some elaborate calculations of the equation of state and the radiative opacity for complicated mixtures of elements at Los Alamos during the war[9].

What turned out to be of greater interest for white dwarf stars in connection with the opacity problem, was the discovery of the surprising efficiency with which energy is transported through the degenerate electron gas inside a white dwarf star. We coined the term "conductive opacity" for this mechanism of energy transport[10]. The conductive opacity was related to the thermal conductivity of the electrons which, in turn, was calculated by a straightforward application of the electron theory of metals, treated so thoroughly in the classic "Handbuch" article by Sommerfeld and Bethe[11]. Starting from the Boltzmann stationarity condition, and assuming that for electron conduction in stars, the collision processes arise from elastic scattering of electrons by atomic nuclei, the following expression was derived for the conductive opacity for a degenerate electron gas at a finite temperature T:

$$K_c = \frac{2.8 \times 10^{41} X_R I T^2}{N_e^2} \tag{5}$$

In Eq. (5), all the quantities have been defined before except for I which is defined by:

$$2I = \log \frac{2}{(1 - \cos \theta_0)} \tag{6}$$

where θ_0 is the minimum angle which enters into the Rutherford scattering cross section and is of the order λ/a with λ the deBroglie wavelength of the electron participating in the collision and a the screening radius of the atom. Equation (5) is the leading term in the conductive opacity and must be corrected as the density decreases and/or the temperature increases, thereby reducing the "degeneracy".

Ten years later, Lee[12] and Mestel[13] rederived the conductive opacity given by Eq. (5) but found some numerical errors in the higher order corrections to this expression. Since the bulk of the mass of a star like Sirius B is in a highly degenerate state, the modification of the higher order corrections to the conductive opacity did not affect the earlier calculations of the temperature–density distribution. In any case, our calculations and those of Lee and Mestel agree that in the transition region between nondegeneracy and degeneracy the conductive opacity contributes as much to the energy transport as does the radiation, while in the degenerate core it completely dominates the energy transport. We have given in Table I the values of the radiative and conductive opacities for a pure Russell mixture of heavy elements[14] (since as we shall see hydrogen must be absent in the interior of a white dwarf star) for a realistic range of temperatures and densities in white dwarf stars; the column labelled ψ/kT gives a measure of the degree of degeneracy. It is seen that at $\rho = 3 \times 10^8$ g/cm^3 and $T = 15 \times 10^{6\,\circ}$ (the central density and temperature of Sirius B), $K_c \simeq 10^{-8} K_R$; the important implications of this result will be discussed below.

Once the radiative and conductive opacities are known as functions of the temperature and density, it is a relatively simple matter to integrate the equations of stellar equilibrium. The integration is carried from the surface of the white dwarf star and one of the striking results is the rapidity with which one passes the transition point $\psi/kT = 0$ and enters into the degenerate region for the electrons. Since the conductive opacity decreases rapidly with increasing density (in contrast to the radiative opacity (see Table I), this has the consequence that the tem-

TABLE I.   Typical Opacities under White Dwarf Conditions ($X_R = 1$)

ρ ($\times 10^{-2}$)	T ($\times 10^{-6}$)	ψ/kT	K_R	K_c
0.15	3.2	2.5	1.2×10^3	3.2×10^4
4.8	7.0	0	2.2×10^2	1.1×10^3
23	9.0	-2.7	1.5×10^2	87
86	10.0	-6.3	1.6×10^2	12
1.2×10^3	13.6	-34.6	0.9×10^2	7.4×10^{-2}
3.0×10^4	14.9	-264	0.7×10^2	1.4×10^{-4}
2.8×10^5	15.2	-1150	0.7×10^2	1.7×10^{-6}

perature decreases very slowly through the degenerate core, constituting the bulk of the star; in other words, the degenerate core of a white dwarf star is almost isothermal. The situation would be very different if the conductive opacity were absent and one had to rely on the radiative transfer mechanism; using the figures for the radiative opacity given in Table I, it is possible to make a rough estimate of the central temperature which would result and one finds central temperatures which are higher by an order of magnitude. The modifications introduced thereby into Chandrasekhar's theory of completely degenerate configurations would have been much more substantial but would not have altered the essential conclusions below. Taking proper account of the conductive opacity and anticipating that the hydrogen content would not exceed more than a fraction of a per cent [so that $\mu_e = 2$, see Eq. (2)], we found[15] $T_c \simeq 15 \times 10^6$ for Sirius B and $T_c \simeq 30 \times 10^6$ for 40 Eridani B. These values of T_c were obtained for the following choices of M, L, and R for the two stars: $M = 0.98$ $\odot$, $L = 0.26 \times 10^{-2}$ $\odot$, $R = 0.82 \times 10^{-2}$ $\odot$ for Sirius B and $M = 0.40$ $\odot$, $L = 0.54 \times 10^{-2}$ $\odot$, $R = 1.5_5 \times 10^{-2}$ $\odot$ for Eridani B; the values of M and L for each star were taken from the best observations of twenty-five years ago (see below for the new values) and the radius for each star was taken from Chandrasekhar's theory of completely degenerate configurations (see below). With the above central temperatures (characterizing the "isothermal" cores) and the associated density distributions, it was a simple task to set an upper limit on the hydrogen content of each star on the basis of the proton–proton set of reactions; we found $X_H \lesssim 2 \times 10^{-5}$ for Sirius B and $X_H \lesssim 8 \times 10^{-5}$ for 40 Eridani B—and hence justified the choice $\mu_e = 2$ for both stars. It should be noted that these results depended on assuming the validity of the Gamow–Teller selection rules which were not so well established twenty-five years ago. Fortunately, even a willingness to consider that the proton–proton reaction operated as a forbidden β process, in accordance with the Fermi selection rules, did not alter the fundamental conclusion that $\mu_e = 2$.

The choice of $\mu_e = 2$ would be necessary for white dwarf interiors, according to recent calculations[16], even if the temperature were reduced to zero. This follows from the finite energy production evolving from the proton–proton reaction due to the reduction of the potential barrier when the protons are embedded in the crystal-like structure supposed to exist at white dwarf densities. Wildhack[17] was the first to examine this effect but his numbers were smaller by a factor of 10^{-4} compared to the recent ones. The recent work predicts that the "zero-point" energy production will be a factor of 10^4 greater than the thermonuclear production at the center of Sirius B and about the same at the center of 40 Eridani B. In either case, it follows that $\mu_e = 2$ even at zero temperature.

Once the conclusion is reached that hydrogen must be absent in a white dwarf star—whether because of the "zero-point" or thermonuclear proton–proton reaction—one may compare Chandrasekhar's theoretical radii with the observational data. Bethe and I did this[15] twenty-five years ago and found satisfactory agreement for 40 Eridani B. Fifteen years later, new measurements[18] were carried out on 40 Eridani B and the agreement between theory and observation was further improved. The new mass value $M = 0.43 \pm 0.04 \odot$ was consistent with the old and the new radius (obtained from a determination of the luminosity and effective temperature) $1.6 \pm 0.2 \times 10^{-2} \odot$ was in excellent agreement with the theoretical value of $1.5 \times 10^{-2} \odot$. A further confirmation of the theory for 40 Eridani B was the agreement between the predicted red shift of 17 ± 3 km/sec and the observed value of 21 ± 4 km/sec. The situation is a happy one for 40 Eridani B which is perhaps not too surprising in view of its relatively large separation from its more luminuous companion.

In contrast, the situation for Sirius B twenty-five years ago was most disagreeable. The theoretical value of the radius of Sirius B disagreed completely with the observed radius—by a factor of more than 2. This was very disturbing and Bethe and I examined various possible modifications of the theory which could lead to an increased radius for Sirius B, including the possibility that the energy is produced in the radiative envelope and that the degenerate core does not contain any energy sources. But none of these theoretical alternatives could significantly increase the radius and, as was stated then: "the only conclusion we can draw is that the observations of the radius of Sirius B are in error . . . we are very reluctant to draw such a conclusion, in view of the approximate agreement obtained between two distinct methods of measurement of the radius—by the (L, T_{eff}) relationship and by the Einstein gravitational redshift." Indeed, the surface temperature of Sirius B was then assigned the value[19] 10,000° and the redshift was claimed to be[20] about 20 km/sec (the same as 40 Eridani B). These two measurements led to a radius in excess of 0.02 $\odot$ compared to the theoretical value 0.0082 $\odot$. While there was a general awareness twenty-five years ago that neither measurement was terribly accurate, the observational astronomers were reluctant to grant the possibility of an error of a factor of 2.5 in the redshift and an error of more than 1.5 in the effective temperature. Indeed, Henry Norris Russell, in a private conversation with the author at that time, was willing to consider the ad hoc assumption of a close, faint companion to Sirius B, which was also a white dwarf, in order to resolve the discrepancy[21].

Our investigations of the white dwarf stars had thus led us more than twenty-five years ago into a serious conflict between the claims of astrophysics and the claims of nuclear physics and, needless to say, a repetition of the measurements was called for. This was more easily said than done because of the fifty-year period of the Sirius system and the close proximity of Sirius B to the much more luminous Sirius A (a factor of 10^4). The measurements of Adams on the redshift were made in 1925 when Sirius B was near its maximum separation from Sirius A, and the measurements of Moore on the spectral type were made several years later. It was necessary to wait another thirty-five years, or at least until 1960, before it would again be feasible to repeat the measurements. About 1960, Greenstein and Oke undertook new measurements with improved techniques and Oke reported in 1963[22] that the redshift was 50–80 km/sec and the effective temperature[23] 16,800°. Since the redshift has increased by a factor of at least 2.5 and the effective temperature by a factor of 1.7, it would appear that the observations have been brought into spectacular agreement with theory. However, a careful examination of the present status of the observational data for Sirius B soon convinces one that it would be premature to celebrate the triumph of theory. My colleague, Malcolm Savedoff, has made such a careful study and has kindly permitted me to summarize his chief (unpublished) conclusions.

As regards the redshift, Savedoff points out that the error in the redshift will be seven times the error in the parallax determination of the Sirius binary system; this follows from the fact that

$$\delta(\Delta\lambda/\lambda) \sim \delta(M/R) \sim \delta\pi^7, \qquad (7a)$$

since

$$\delta M \sim \delta\pi^3, \qquad (7b)$$

and

$$\delta R/R \sim (4/3)(\delta M/M) \qquad (7c)$$

the last from Chandrasekhar's mass–radius relation in the neighborhood of the solar mass. The best value of the parallax π is 0.375 ± 0.004 where the 1% error in π is purely statistical but, as Savedoff remarks, parallax measurements are notoriously poorer than their statistical errors. The 1% statistical error in π would produce a 7% error in the redshift but this, for the reason mentioned above, may be an underestimate.

With regard to M_V, the visual absolute magnitude, and the effective temperature T_{eff} of Sirius B, Savedoff notes that the early measurements of M_V range from 7.1 to 8.5 but it is probably more sensible to take the latest value which is 8.3 ± 0.3; the error is estimated from external consistency of published material. Using the same spectroscopic observations, Eggen and Greenstein[23]—as already noted—deduce $T_{eff} = 18,000°$, implying a bolometric correction (B.C.) of -1.6 whereas Oke[22] finds $T_{eff} = 16,800°$ with B.C. $= -1.5$. Savedoff prefers the higher value and estimates an error of 10% in T_{eff}. In order to deduce the observational value of the radius of Sirius B from the formula $L = 4\pi\sigma R^2 T_{eff}^4$, it is necessary to insert an improved observational value of L. This can be done using the formula:

$$M_{Bol} = M_V + B.C. + 5 + 5 \log \pi \qquad (8)$$

Taking $M_V = 8.3$, B.C. $= -1.6$, $\pi = 0.375$, one deduces the result L (Sirius B) $= 1.1 \times 10^{-2} \odot$. Savedoff therefore concludes that the observational value of the radius using this method is $0.011 \odot$ with an uncertainty of 20%. Incidentally, the best value of the mass of Sirius B is $1.05M_\odot$, with an uncertainty of 5%; with this mass value, the theoretical prediction of the radius is 0.0074 $\odot$ with an uncertainty of 7%.

If we accept Savedoff's analysis of the situation, we conclude that while the recent measurements go a long way towards removing the discrepancy between theory and observation with regard to the radius of Sirius B, it is still necessary to improve the measurements before one can feel completely secure about the situation. Furthermore, some additional effects have recently been considered which alter to some extent the mass–radius relation of Chandrasekhar; in particular, Hamada and Salpeter[24] have studied the effect on the Chandrasekhar mass–radius relation of the lattice-like structure of the ions in the dense interior of a white dwarf star for several chemical compositions. For a white dwarf star consisting of medium heavy elements (say carbon), they predict a radius 0.0068 $\odot$ for a mass 1.05 $\odot$ instead of 0.0074 $\odot$—a result which increases the discrepancy between theory and experiment by 8%. Only improved measurements can decide whether a genuine discrepancy still remains and whether some still more novel effects (e.g., rapid rotation of the star[25]) are operative for Sirius B. It is to be hoped that preparations will be made for the most accurate possible measurements of the redshift, effective temperature, etc., at the optimum time of observation for Sirius B, which is around 1969.

But now we must return to the original question which was posed, namely what are the sources of energy in white dwarf stars and, in particular, are they thermonuclear in origin. In view of the low upper limit placed on the hydrogen concentration, the answer is negative for thermonuclear energy production in the degenerate core constituting the bulk of the white dwarf star. One might argue that there is a much higher hydrogen concentration in the surface layer of a white dwarf star, as seems to be indicated by some of the spectral observations, and that the thermonuclear energy production takes place in the surface layers themselves. Schatzman[26] argued strongly for this point of view some years back but it is now evident that a white dwarf star will be vibrationally or secularly unstable with a hydrogenous envelope and a nonhydrogenous degenerate core. One must therefore look for some other energy source.

It is now generally agreed that the chief energy source of white dwarf stars derives from the thermal energy of the ions. Since the bulk of a white dwarf star is almost isothermal, we may write down for the thermal energy of the nondegenerate ions the expression:

$$E_{th} \simeq (3/2)(\mathcal{R}TM/A), \qquad (9)$$

where $\mathcal{R}$ is the gas constant, $T \simeq T_c$, M is the total mass and A is some average atomic weight. Inserting numbers for Sirius B and choosing[27] $A = 13$ (helium plus some heavy elements), one finds:

$$E_{th} \simeq 3 \times 10^{47} \text{ ergs}$$

This is to be compared with about 3×10^{46} ergs for the thermal energy of the degenerate electrons and a comparable value for the gravitational energy[28]. A lower estimate of the lifetime of Sirius B can be obtained by dividing the total available energy by the observed luminosity and one finds a lower limit on lifetime of about 10^8 years, a result which is consistent with the density of white dwarfs in space and with the known age of the universe.

However, a closer analysis of the *past* (rather than the *future*) lifetime of Sirius B leads to some doubt as to whether all energy sources have been identified in Sirius B since the thermonuclear sources ceased to operate. Vila[29] has pointed out that the nonthermonuclear energy sources identified above would lead to 8×10^8 years as an estimate of the minimum past lifetime for Sirius B and this is too long (by at least a factor of 4) to explain why its companion in the binary system, Sirius A, has not moved off the main sequence in its evolutionary development[30]. It appears that it would be helpful to invoke another mechanism for energy loss by Sirius B so that its past lifetime could be reduced. Such a mechanism is provided by the so-called "neutrino luminosity" and, in particular, by the conversion of "plasmons" into neutrino pairs[31]. This process consists essentially of the "decay", via their virtual interaction with electron pairs, of transverse electromagnetic waves in the dense stellar plasma into neutrino pairs which easily traverse the interior of the white dwarf star. Over the period in which the central temperature decreases from $0.5 \times 10^{9\circ}$ (when the thermonuclear sources cease functioning) to its present $1.5 \times 10^{7\circ}$, Vila finds that the neutrino luminosity due to plasmons will reduce the past lifetime of Sirius B by a factor 10, sufficient to understand the evolution of Sirius A.

The contribution of neutrino emission to the luminosity of a star at sufficiently high densities and temperatures has also been invoked recently by Savedoff[32] and H. Y. Chiu[33] to explain the absence of stars in the Hertzsprung–Russell diagram between the white dwarfs and the nuclei of planetary nebulae. The neutrino luminosity appears to be sufficiently large at the temperatures and densities presumed to prevail for this range of stars that the lifetime is reduced to a value sufficiently low (less than 8×10^5 years) to explain the gap. Other uses have been made of the neutrino luminosity in order to understand certain problems of stellar evolution but it should be emphasized that the neutrino luminosity can only play the role assigned to it if the reaction $e^+ + e^- \to v_e + \bar{v}_e$ or $\gamma + e^- \to v_e + \bar{v}_e + e^-$ actually takes place. In the universal (V–A) theory of weak interactions first developed by Sudarshan and Marshak[34] [and later by Feynman and Gell-Mann[35]], these reactions are expected to take place as one of the current–current interactions of the theory but thus far there are no direct laboratory experiments which have demonstrated the existence of this term in the interaction Lagrangian. A measurement of the related neutrino–electron scattering cross section would be required and with a predicted cross section of 10^{-41} cm^2 (at a neutrino laboratory energy of 1 BeV), the experiment will not be done soon. It will be most interesting to see whether the astrophysicists can come up with more convincing evidence for the $(v_e \, e^-)$ "self-current" interaction before the particle physicists measure neutrino–electron scattering in the laboratory.

The author would like to express his gratitude to Prof. M. P. Savedoff for many helpful discussions and for a critical reading of the manuscript.

References

1. Bethe, H. A., *Phys. Rev.*, **55**, 434 (1939).
2. Von Weizsäcker, C. F., *Phys. Zs.*, **39**, 633 (1938).
3. Bethe, H. A., and C. L. Critchfield, *Phys. Rev.*, **54**, 248 (1938).
4. Eddington, A. S., *Internal Constitution of the Stars*, Cambridge Univ. Press, 1926.
5. Cowling, T. G., *Monthly Notices* (*R. A. S.*), **96**, 42 (1935).
6. Eggen, O. J., and J. L. Greenstein, *Astrophys. J.*, **141**, 83 (1965).
7. Chandrasekhar, S., *Introduction to the Study of Stellar Structure*, Univ. of Chicago Press, 1939.
8. Marshak, R. E., and H. A. Bethe, *Astrophys. J.*, **94**, 37 (1941).
9. Feynman, R., N. Metropolis, and E. Teller, *Phys. Rev.*, **75**, 1561 (1949).
10. Kothari, D. S. [*Phil. Mag.*, **13**, 361 (1932) and *Monthly Notices* (*R.A.S.*), **93**, 61 (1932)] gave the first (albeit too rough) treatment of this problem.

11. Bethe, H. A., and A. Sommerfeld, *Handbuch der Physik*, **24**(2) (1933).
12. Lee, T. D., *Astrophys. J.*, **111**, 625 (1950).
13. Mestel, L., *Proc. Cambridge Phil. Soc.*, **46**, 331 (1950).
14. The values of the radiative opacity are taken from my paper in the *Annals of the New York Academy of Sciences*, **41**, 49 (1941) while the conductive opacities are taken from Lee's paper, ref. 12.
15. Marshak, R. E., *Astrophys. J.*, **92**, 321 (1940).
16. Van Horn, H., Ph.D. Dissertation at Cornell University, 1965 under Prof. E. E. Salpeter.
17. Wildhack, W. A., *Phys. Rev.*, **57**, 81 (1940).
18. Popper, D. M., *Astrophys. J.*, **120**, 316 (1954); more recently, Oke (ref. 22) has observed a redshift of 19.5 km/sec in good agreement with Popper's result.
19. Moore, J. H., *Publ. Astron. Soc. Pacific*, **40**, 229 (1928).
20. Adams, W. S., *Publ. Aston. Soc. Pacific*, **37**, 158 (1925).
21. This possibility has received occasional support from observers [cf., W. H. van den Bos, *Observatory*, **24**, 52 (1929)] but is not generally accepted.
22. Oke, J. B., preliminary results presented at the Cleveland meeting of AAAS in Dec. 1963; the final results have not yet been published.
23. In the paper of Eggen and Greenstein (ref. 6), this temperature is given as 18,000°.
24. Hamada, T., and E. E. Salpeter, *Astrophys. J.*, **134**, 683 (1961).
25. Cf. Roxburgh, I. W., J. S. Griffith, and P. A. Sweet, *Zeits. fur Astrophys.*, **61**, 203 (1965).
26. Schatzman, E., *White Dwarfs*, North-Holland Publ. Co., 1958.
27. Deinser, W., and E. E. Salpeter [*Astrophys. J.*, **140**, 499 (1964)] have given arguments for choosing 20% C and 80% O for the present composition of Sirius B.
28. These two contributions were calculated in ref. 15 but it was argued incorrectly in that paper—in analogy with the gas pressure—that the thermal contribution of the ions would be smaller.
29. Vila, S., Ph.D. Dissertation, University of Rochester (1965) under the direction of Profs. M. Savedoff and L. Helfer.
30. Savedoff, M. P., estimates a maximum lifetime of 2×10^8 yr for Sirius A [*Proc. Conf. Stellar Evolution*, Inst. for Space Studies (1963) (in press)].
31. Adams, J. B., M. A. Ruderman, and C. H. Woo, *Phys. Rev.*, **129**, 1383 (1963).
32. Savedoff, M. P., private communication.
33. Chiu, H. Y., State University at Stony Brook, preprint (1965).
34. Sudarshan, E. C. G., and R. E. Marshak, *Proc. of Padua-Venice Conference on Mesons*, 1957; *Phys. Rev.*, **109**, 1860 (1958).
35. Feynman, R. P., and M. Gell-Mann, *Phys. Rev.*, **109**, 193 (1958).

Cosmological Theories of the Origin of
Chemical Elements

G. GAMOW

University of Colorado

In the April 1, 1948 issue of *The Physical Review*† there appeared a letter to the editors entitled "The Origin of Chemical Elements" by R. Alpher, H. Bethe, and G. Gamow. Independent of the merits or demerits of this paper, it became quite popular because of the alphabetic order (in Greek) of the authors, and its content is often referred to now as the α, β, γ theory. Many people have asked me how this alphabetic array of authors' names originated, and I feel that this article is just the proper place to give the explanation.

Ralph Alpher was for a number of years one of my best students when I was teaching at The George Washington University, and I cherished the idea of writing an article with him. When the time came for him to start research leading to a Ph.D. degree, he asked me if I would be his master and suggest a topic for his doctoral thesis. It was just the right time, since I was speculating about the possibility that various nuclear species were built up during the very early stages of the expanding universe by successive capture of neutrons which must have existed in high abundance when the temperature of space was of the order of several billion degrees. The sequence must have started with $H + n \rightarrow D + \gamma$, $D + n \rightarrow T + \gamma$, etc., reactions intermitted by β-decay processes (as $T \rightarrow He^3 + e$) when the neutron-proton ratio in a nucleus in question was becoming too large. Each step of this building-up process was governed by the equation:

$$\frac{dN_A}{dt} = F(S, T)[\sigma_{A-1}N_{A-1} - \sigma_A N_A], \tag{1}$$

where N_A is the number of nuclei with atomic weight A, and σ_A the capture cross section of neutrons by atomic weight A for the proper

† *Phys. Rev.*, **73**, No. 7, pp. 803–804 (1948).

values of kinetic temperature. The function $F(S, T)$ representing the frequency of collisions for a given density and temperature is well known from the kinetic theory of gases. The variations of S and T with time t (counted from the singularity in the beginning of expansion) could be obtained from the relativistic theory of the expanding universe, and were found to be given by:

$$T = \frac{5 \cdot 10^{10}}{t^{\frac{1}{2}}} \,^\circ K; \qquad S = \frac{\text{const.}}{t^{\frac{3}{2}}} \frac{\text{gm}}{\text{cm}^3}, \tag{2}$$

where t is measured in seconds and the value of the constant can be adjusted in an arbitrary way.

The capture cross sections σ_A for neutrons at $T \sim 10^9 \,^\circ K$ ($\sim 10^6$ eV) were measured in the Los Alamos Scientific Laboratory and were just being declassified when the work was started. The general dependence of σ_A on A could be represented by a curve decreasing exponentially through the first half of the system of elements, and running more or less horizontally for larger atomic weights. The problem was to integrate the system of equations (1) with A running from 1 to 238 (and up), and to find where there is a value of the constant in the expression for S for which theoretical values of N_A coincide with the observed abundances of the elements in the universe. The latter curve, obtained by exhaustive geological and astronomical studies, is similar (or rather, antisimilar) to the neutron capture curve: the abundance of elements decreases exponentially through the first half of the element-sequence, and runs more or less horizontally for larger atomic weights.

Since, at the time this work was done, electronic computers were in the early stage of development and not yet available for purely scientific work, Alpher had to do the computations by less advanced equipment and could not possibly carry out the integration of over two hundred confluent differential equations. Thus the entire interval from hydrogen to uranium was divided into a dozen sections and the results were averaged over each section. In spite of this crude approximation, the results were very interesting. The theoretical abundance curve followed the general features of the observed one with a sharp drop in the beginning and a horizontal plateau at the second half of the system of elements. The value of the constant in Eq. (2) necessary to achieve that fit was found to be about 10^{-3} g/cm³.†

† More exact calculations of that problem were made later by R. Alpher and R. Herman on the electronic computer of the National Bureau of Standards in Washington, D.C., and confirmed the original crude results.

In writing up the preliminary communication of this work, I was unhappy that the letter β was missing between α and γ. Thus, sending the manuscript for publication in *Phys. Rev.*, I put in the name of Hans Bethe (in absentia) between our names. This was planned as a surprise to Hans when he would unexpectedly find his name as co-author and I was sure that, being my old friend, and having a good sense of humor he would not mind.

What I did not know was that at that time he was one of the reviewers for *Phys. Rev.* and that the manuscript was sent to him for evaluation. But he did not make any changes in it except to strike out the words "in absentia" after his name, thus endorsing the idea and the results.

In its further development, the original α, β, γ theory ran on the rocks when E. Fermi and A. Turkévich decided to use a different calculational approach, and, instead of covering the entire system of elements in an approximate way, concentrated on the detailed study of the reactions pertaining to the first few steps of the building-up process and involving one H, D, T, He^3, and He^4 nuclei.†

They found that, under the originally assumed temperature and density conditions [Eq. (2) with the constant $= -10^{-3}$], the building-up process would result in about equal amounts of left-over hydrogen and built-up helium (He^4) with the admixture of about 1% of D, T and He^3, from which the heavier elements had to be formed. But their calculations also led to the result that the formation of nuclei heavier than He^4 was inhibited by the nonexistence of stable (or, at least, sufficiently long living) nuclei with the mass 5. Thus, while the expected relative abundances of hydrogen and helium came out to be in perfect agreement with the observational data, the calculated relative abundances of all heavier elements fell short of the observed values by a factor of about a hundred. Various ingenious proposals, one of them made by E. Wigner‡ to cross the "crevasse 5" in the continuous building-up of elements by neutron capture, failed to solve the difficulty, and it seemed for a while that the α, β, γ theory should be abandoned.

An alternative explanation of the origin of heavy elements was proposed by F. Hoyle and developed in some detail by him, W. Fowler,

† These authors never published their calculations, but their results are described in detail by R. Alpher and R. Herman in their review article in *Rev. Mod. Phys.*, **22**, 153 (1950).

‡ Private communication.

and the Burbages.† According to this proposal, heavy elements were formed later in the history of the galaxy in the processes of violent stellar explosions (supernovae) which took place in a distant past, and scattered their material through interstellar space, forming the tenuous, rarified medium from which the new stars were later formed. It would follow from this theory that our Sun, as well as all other stars of the Milky Way, are, so to speak, "second hand" stars formed from the material ejected by previous generations of stars which existed and exploded a long time ago. This point of view which led to the Sun's Song:‡

> I'm a second-hand star, and I love it!
> My origin's lowly—what of it?
> > Though born from some scraps
> > Of old stellar collapse
> I'm rising (and setting) above it.

is, however, also not free from difficulty. In fact, according to observations, supernovae appear in galaxies at the rate of about one in a few centuries and as the age of the Milky Way is a few billion years, only 10^7 supernovae must have exploded during its existence. Since the total number of stars in the Milky Way is about 10^{11}, the maximum possible contribution of supernovae produced heavy elements would be only 0.01 of a per cent, i.e., one hundred times smaller than actually observed. One way of circumventing this difficulty is the hypothesis of "painted stars". According to it, spectroscopically observed abundances of heavier elements pertain only to the thin layers of stellar atmospheres and are much lower in their interior, being accreted when the stars pass through the clouds of material ejected by supernovae in the past history of the Milky Way. Another possibility is, of course, that in the early history of galactic evolution supernovae were much more common phenomena and appeared in each galaxy almost yearly. A new development in the conflict between the two theories of the origin of the heavier elements took place some years ago when W. Baade showed that, in contrast to earlier beliefs, there are two rather different types of stellar populations in various galactic communities: *Population I*, forming the arms of the spiral galaxies, as well as all irregular galaxies which represented until recently the main subject of astronomical studies, since our Sun is located in an arm of the Milky Way and *Population II*, forming

† It is summarized in an extensive review by these authors in *Rev. Mod. Phys.*, **29**, 547 (1957)

‡ Barbara Gamow, Collected Verses (unpublished).

the central bodies of spiral galaxies (including the globular clusters) and all elliptical galaxies deprived of spiral arms.

Population I is characterized by a large amount of interstellar material (about 50% by mass) and very hot and bright stars (blue giants) which must be of comparatively new origin, presumably condensed from that material. On the other hand, the regions inhabited by stellar Population II are completely deprived of the interstellar material and contain no blue giants at all. The studies of M. Scharzschield and L. Spitzer have also shown that spectra of the stars belonging to this population are deprived of metal lines, thus indicating that the abundance of heavier elements in them is at least one hundred times smaller than that in the stars of Population I. Summing up the above described theoretical considerations, and the observational results, one may come to the following plausible picture. During the very early prestellar stage of the expanding universe; about one-half of the original proton-neutron mixture (ylem) was turned into helium nuclei with only a negligible amount of heavier elements being formed. Thus the stars which condensed inside of the original protogalaxies belonged all to what we call now Population II, being deficient in the heavier elements. Very little can be said at present about the properties of these stars except that, due to a practically complete absence of carbon and nitrogen, they must have been drawing their energy supply from H—H thermonuclear reactions:

$$H + H \rightarrow D + e^+$$

$$D + D \begin{array}{c} \nearrow T + H \\ \\ \searrow He^3 + n \end{array} \tag{3}$$

It is possible that during the life of these early stars the process of successive neutron capture (similar to the α, β, γ process) led to some increase of the originally meager amounts of heavier elements. Those primeval stars that were very massive have used up their original hydrogen supply and exploded, throwing their material containing a certain percentage of heavier elements into the surrounding space, thus making it available to less massive stars which still could exist for a much longer time on the thermonuclear H—H reactions.

Why then did the accretion of that material not take place in the central body of the Milky Way, but rather occur only in the spiral arms?

Here we come to the mystery of the origin of the spiral arms themselves, a problem closely connected with the formation of gaseous proto-galaxies and their subsequent condensation into individual stars. There is hardly any doubt that the formation of stars in the originally gaseous protogalaxies was the result of Jeans' gravitational instability and that their sizes and masses were essentially determined by the temperature and density of gas. One should not forget, however, that the original galaxies were in different states of rotation, and that the spiral arms were developed only in those galaxies whose ellipticity exceeded the value 0.6 in Hubble's classification. Thus it is entirely possible that, whereas the inner parts of these galaxies condensed completely into stars, the formation of stars in the outer parts was inhibited by a conflict between gravitational forces and the effect of differential rotation (just as in the case of Saturn rings in Maxwell's theory) so that a considerable fraction of the material remained in the gaseous form.

Such an assumption would permit us to understand the difference of chemical constitution of the stars forming the inner and outer regions of the spiral galaxies. Indeed, the gases ejected in the explosions of the stars located in the galactic interior were moving at very high speed through a complete vacuum and had little chance to be captured by the stars located in this region. On the other hand, entering into the outer galactic envelopes containing still uncondensed masses of hydrogen and helium, these gas streams were slowed down, becoming an easy prey for the stars already condensed in these regions thus increasing the percentage of heavy elements in their atmospheres. This picture of the origin of the characteristic galactic features is, of course, rather tentative and vague, and detailed mathematical studies are necessary for the evolution of its validity.

In conclusion a few words must be said about the relation of the above described views with the newly discovered distant objects known (tentatively) as "quasars". If the observed very large redshifts in the spectra of these objects are interpreted as the result of the Doppler effect, quasars must be considered as galaxies located many billions of light years away from us. Since looking far away in space is equivalent to looking far back in time, observation of quasars should tell us about the properties of the galaxies at the early stages of their evolution. But probably one should wait until more observational material is accumulated concerning these unusual objects.

On a Theory of Quasars

EDWARD TELLER

University of California

Introduction

The possibility is discussed that quasi-stellar radio sources (quasars) are due to collisions between a galaxy and an antigalaxy. The variable light near the visible region as well as the high-frequency radio waves are emitted by chance collisions between a star from one galaxy with a dense gas cloud from the other. The low-frequency radar and the visible wisps of faint luminosity may be due to electrons escaping along magnetic lines of force from the active region.

If antigalaxies indeed exist, it seems reasonable to postulate that the amounts of matter and antimatter in the universe are equal. Some consequences of this assumption are discussed.

I. The Distance and Variability of Quasars

It is most natural to assume that the observed redshifts[1] in the spectra of quasars are due to a great distance of these objects and the corresponding velocities of recession. The assumption of a gravitational redshift has been disproved[2], and the assumption of a local explosion[3] raises great difficulties. If, for instance, one assumes that a few million years ago a great explosion occurred in our galaxy which hurled out quasars with observed velocities ranging from $0.1c$ to more than $0.5c$, one can hardly understand that matter in an individual quasar remained concentrated to a region little more than one light year. The original explosion should have amply sufficed to tear the quasars themselves apart.

From the great distances of quasars, which range from 0.1 to more than 0.5 times the radius of the universe, it follows that these objects emit approximately an energy of $M_\odot c^2$ per year where $M_\odot$ is the mass of the sun. The extension of the wisps near the quasars indicates a lifetime of 10^6 years resulting in a total emission of $10^6 M_\odot c^2$.

On the other hand, the variability of quasars limits the size of an individual radiation source to approximately one light year. Indeed, the visible light and the high-frequency component of the radar emission show marked irregular intensity fluctuations in periods comparable to one year. If one attempts to pack a million or more solar masses into the confines of one light year, one obtains conditions in which gravitational collapse seems imminent. It has often been asserted that the phenomenon of quasars is actually due to such a collapse.

The hypothesis of a simple, spherical gravitational collapse leads, however to extremely short periods of active radiation. One can use a dimensional argument to estimate this period t, and one obtains the Schwarzschild-radius divided by the light velocity c, so that

$$t = GM/c^3,$$

where G is the gravitational constant and M the collapsing mass. For $M = 10^6 M_\odot$ one obtains a few seconds and for $M = 10^{11} M_\odot$ (which is the mass of a galaxy), a few days. One should compare this with the lifetime of a quasar which is about a million years.

It may be argued that these short periods are valid only for a local observer and that great time dilatations will appear to one standing outside the quasar. However, really big time dilatations can affect only a small fraction of the emitted radiation.

If one wants to maintain the idea of a gravitational collapse, it may be best to invoke a turbulent process in which one local region after another slides down into the abyss of gravity. Such a model seems to be in constant danger of early and sudden termination, either by a collapse of most of the mass or by the production of sufficient energy to disperse the material which has, as yet, not collapsed.

It would be most difficult to rule out the collapse hypothesis, particularly if it is presented in conjunction with hydromagnetic or thermonuclear processes. But the concentration of enormous masses into a limited space seems to be connected with so many difficulties that it may appear to be justified to explore radically different possibilities.

Direct visual observation and conclusions from radar-interference phenomena do not permit localization of the quasi-stellar source with a much higher accuracy than an arc of 1″. Even at the location of the closest quasar (3C 273), this permits an extension of 5000 light years. Since 3C 273 was observed for almost a century, a systematic proper motion can be ruled to very high accuracy[4] (0.01″/year). But irregular displacements of 0.1″ and maybe 1″ would lie within the errors of observation. Indeed, there are indications that the high-frequency variable radar source is not necessarily single.

It is, therefore, possible that the phenomenon of a quasar consists of individual processes, each lasting approximately one year, each releasing an energy of approximately $M_{\odot}c^2$ in a region of less than a light year but each proceeding at a different location in an independent manner. The fluctuations are then of a statistical nature. It is reasonable that cyclotron emission from electrons should outlast the visual emission, thus leading to more than one pointlike radar source.

If one assumes such a scintillating model, then in addition to slight spacial displacements one would expect changes in the spectral appearance. This is verified at least to the extent that visual and radar intensities may change in opposite directions.

One theory of the scintillating variety was based on the assumption that quasars consist of a series of supernova outbursts imbedded in a relatively dense interstellar gas[5]. Though a detailed explanation as to how the proper conditions get established has not yet been presented, this model seems to account for the observations in a reasonably successful manner.

It is possible to construct a different scintillating model that explains the properties of quasars. This model shall now be presented.

II. Collision of a Galaxy and an Antigalaxy

Our galaxy consists predominantly of matter. Antiprotons seem to be absent from primary cosmic rays, and these rays are probably a good sample of the material in our galaxy.

One could hardly have expected a different situation. The lifetime of coexistence of protons and antiprotons in an interstellar gas of one particle per cubic centimeter is less than 3×10^7 years. Individual stars might well consist of antimatter, but there is a continuous exchange of material between stars and interstellar gas. Old and inactive stars might be made of antimatter. But recently condensed stars of big mass which may rapidly develop into supernovae will contain no antimatter. It is probable that cosmic rays are produced by the exceedingly strong shock appearing in the surface layers of a supernova[6] unless they are generated by the Fermi mechanism from interstellar gas. Thus, directly or indirectly, cosmic rays are derived from the tenuous interstellar material which most probably does not contain antimatter.

But if our galaxy consists of matter, other galaxies may be built from antimatter[7]. Should one expect spectacular effects when a galaxy collides with an antigalaxy?

Two facts are obvious. The collision will last about one million years, which is a satisfactory time span for a quasar. If all material is annihilated, one produces much more energy than has been observed in the emission from a quasar. The total available energy is $10^{11} M_{\odot} c^2$ while the observed energy is less by a factor 10^5.

At this point it is desirable to consider the detailed mechanism of energy release. One will think of three possibilities: Collisions between stars, collisions between atoms (or nuclei), and collisions between stars and nuclei.

Collisions between a star and an antistar are very rare. Only a few will occur in the million years while the galaxies interpenetrate. Furthermore, the total energy released in such an encounter is not particularly great. The first contact will produce a high concentration of energy. This will send shock waves into the collision partners, and the intermingling of the main stellar masses will be prevented. The energy produced will be of the same order of magnitude as the relative kinetic energy of the colliding stars. This may be not much more than $10^{-6} M_{\odot} c^2$. At the distance of 10^9 light years, the event will not be observable.

Collisions between protons and antiprotons in interstellar space may produce a total energy of $3 \times 10^9 M_{\odot} c^2$ in 10^6 years provided that matter and antimatter intermingle in a free and intimate way. Most of this energy would be emitted in the form of hard gamma-rays (~ 50 MeV) obtained from the decay of neutral π mesons. Additional energy will be produced by annihilation of original electrons and positrons which gives much softer gamma-radiation (< 1 MeV). Finally electrons and positrons carrying a few times 10 MeV appear as a result of the two-step decay of negative and positive π mesons. Apart from additional annihilation radiation, cyclotron radiation and bremsstrahlung will be emitted. These radiations are, however, not to be connected with the radar emissions and visible light of the quasars. The radio emission has a low frequency and insufficient intensity to explain the observations. The bremsstrahlung has more than sufficient total intensity, but the energy of the multi-MeV electrons gets distributed among all particles, and since radiation is slow, a temperature of several MeV results. Thus most of the bremsstrahlung is in the x-ray region, and there may not be enough visible emission. Furthermore, the observed emission lines cannot be explained if these high temperatures and the low densities in galaxies (one particle per cm^3) prevail.

Actually the energy release of $3 \times 10^9 M_\odot c^2$ in the form of ~ 50 MeV gamma-rays is sharply contradicted by experimental observation[8]. From the nearest quasar, 3C 273, alone we should obtain 0.2 quanta/cm^2-sec. Summation over all quasars would give several quanta/cm^2-sec. This is many thousand times as high as a reasonable experimental upper limit. We must conclude that in an actual collision between a galaxy and antigalaxy the materials from the collision partners do not intermingle in an intimate manner. Indeed we can exclude such intermingling on a galactic scale from the gamma-ray experiments alone, no matter how quasars are to be explained. The development of shock waves in the interstellar gases furnishes a sufficient limitation to the interpenetration of matter and antimatter. The presence of interstellar magnetic fields will further reduce the zone of any mixing.

As a result, the energy release and the gamma-ray emission due to the gas-phase reaction must be reduced at least by a factor 10^{-3}, and none of the emissions from the starlike radio objects are likely to be explained in a quantitative manner by such a reaction.

Finally, the phenomenon of the quasars might be blamed on collisions between a star and the gaseous antimatter from the collision partner. Because of the extremely dilute nature of interstellar matter, this releases less energy per area of a bombarded star than is received on the surface of the earth from the sun. Most stars will increase their brightness by less than one part in a million. Quasars certainly cannot be explained in this fashion.

Therefore, the straightforward methods by which annihilation of matter and antimatter may explain quasars must be rejected. But only a fraction 10^{-5} of the available energy need be made available. Therefore, it is permissible to consider some exceptional configuration of matter within a galaxy which contains only a small fraction of the total mass. The most plausible configuration is a gas cloud held together by gravity.

There is ample evidence for the existence of gas clouds. They are observed as dark clouds in which the dust content is responsible for the lack of transparency. A gas cloud surrounding a hot star produces the phenomenon of a planetary nebula. The spectrum of such a nebula is actually similar to that of a quasar in that it contains emission lines of hydrogen and also other, often multiply ionized, elements. Finally, the formation of new stars indicates the previous existence of protostars, that is, gasmasses. An interesting case is the Orion nebula[9] in which new stars seem to be forming.

To consider the collision of a star from one galaxy with a gas cloud from the other galaxy has the following simple consequences: The number of collisions becomes large due to the great number of stars on the one hand and the large cross section of the gas cloud on the other. Random collisions give rise to the phenomenon of scintillation which we discussed in Sec. I in connection with the variability of quasars. Finally, the collision with a gas cloud does not release energy in as sudden a manner as collision between two stars of an opposite kind; the gas cloud cannot be rapidly dispersed, and there may be sufficient time for the annihilation process to release considerable amounts of energy.

We shall focus our attention on gas clouds of an appropriate size. If a cloud is too small, it will probably not be hit during the galactic collisions. Very big clouds may exist in limited numbers, but there may not be enough of them to account for the several hundred thousand individual flareups that seem to take place during the life of a quasar. If the gas cloud has a radius of 0.1 light years, its cross section is 10^{-11} times the cross section of the galaxy. Since this cloud is exposed to a bombardment by 10^{11} stars, it probably will be penetrated by one of them. A much smaller cloud is likely to escape a direct hit. A much larger cloud will certainly participate in the annihilation process but can do so only once. The first penetration may not consume all the material in the cloud but will certainly release enough energy to disperse it and to render it incapable of any further effective collision.

A gas cloud should contain at least one solar mass in order to give rise to a fully effective outburst. If we combine this with a radius of 0.1 light year, we obtain approximately 2×10^5 hydrogen atoms per cm^3. Estimates based on the intensity of emission lines[10] yield similar densities for the gas within which the light phenomena of quasars must be produced. We shall see in the next section that the actual densities have to be somewhat higher, perhaps 10^8 atoms per cm^3. This might still be compatible with the spectroscopic evidence which in some of its essential parts is based on the intensity of forbidden lines. Too high a density would quench these lines prior to optical emission. It is sufficient, however, that some parts of the gas cloud should have a low density in order to obtain the observed intensity of these forbidden lines. All this leads to the conclusion that relevant gas clouds should probably contain several solar masses, and masses as high as $10^5 M_\odot$ may be encountered. Since we need more than 10^5 clouds and since the galaxy has a mass of $10^{11} M_\odot$, the mass of $10^5 M_\odot$ and the radius of 10 light years may be upper limits for gas clouds which are to explain the majority of fluctuations in the radiation of a quasar.

Is it reasonable to assume that a galaxy contains more than 10^5 massive gas clouds? In answering this question, we should remember that gas clouds not containing enough dust and not excited to light emission by a neighboring star should be invisible. We must also estimate the lifetime of an extended gas cloud.

Calculating the velocities within gas clouds by setting the kinetic energy approximately equal to the gravitational potential, one obtains values not greatly in excess of $10^{-6}c$. Thus a gas cloud cannot easily collapse in a time shorter than 10^5 years. There may be several reasons by which the lifetime could be greatly extended. For instance, the presence of angular momentum may prevent further condensation. Or the gas cloud may consist almost exclusively of atoms (rather than molecules or small condensed aggregates); the atoms, however, do not radiate except for the improbable emissions that occur during the collisions of atoms. Thus the cloud retains its energy and may live for many millions of years. Alternatively, the cloud may contain a great accumulation of dust which renders it opaque so that radiation is emitted but will be slow to escape. (This possibility requires the presence of an unusually high percentage of heavy atoms.) Finally, the cloud may be heated by a bright central star, and a steady state lasting for a long period may be established.

One may conclude that the presence of numerous gas clouds within a galaxy is an assured fact and a number in excess of 10^5 is a reasonable possibility. Closer investigation of the occurrence of gas clouds will have an important bearing on the explanation of quasars which we are discussing.

III. Collision and Disintegration of Star and Cloud

We shall now discuss the detailed processes which occur when a star consisting of ordinary matter enters a gas cloud composed of antimatter. In order to obtain a considerable initial energy production, we assume a rather high gas density of 10^8 atoms per cm³. The collision velocity shall be 3×10^7 cm/sec.

Under these conditions, 10^{13} erg/cm²-sec will be released on the surface of the star which is more than 10^2 times the energy flux emitted by the sun. This energy will be released in a markedly nonuniform manner because only one side of the rotating star will be exposed and probably even more because the star may very well carry a magnetic field. For lack of a better example, we may consider a star, like our sun, on whose surface bunches of magnetic field lines are anchored in areas similar to the sunspots.

In the neighborhood of the star, the gas cloud will be ionized, and the ions cannot reach the surface of the star except in the regions where magnetic lines enter. As is shown by the terrestrial aurorae, intense ionic streams will indeed reach the surface along the magnetic lines. That this happens is probably due to hydromagnetic turbulence originating in the region, where $(1/2)\rho v^2$ of the impinging gas is comparable with $(1/8\pi)H^2$ of the stellar magnetic field.

The resulting local heating will give rise to most intensive jets along the magnetic lines of force. This extends the effective stellar surface, thus causing a further increase in the total rate of energy release. At the same time magnetic lines will be stretched initiating large-scale hydromagnetic turbulent motion. It is to be noted, however, that the gas cloud is essentially transparent to all the disintegration radiations. Thus no shock is generated, and the gas is not prevented from reaching the star. In contrast to the collision of two stars, the encounter between star and cloud should be called soft.

The actual evaporation of the star may take a time long compared to a year, and it is difficult to predict in precisely what manner the stars will be torn apart due to the stream of antimatter that impinge upon it. On the other hand, little radiation will be emitted in this phase compared to the total brilliance of a quasar. The main effects of disintegration will not occur until matter and antimatter are thoroughly mixed which requires the expansion of the stellar material to a radius of 0.1 light years. (That thorough mixing occurs at all is probably due to hydromagnetic turbulence.) It is possible to describe in a simple way the process of the stellar expansion.

Let us call r_0 the radius of a sphere which contains an amount of the gas cloud equal to the mass of the star. As an example, we may consider this mass to be $M_\odot$. We shall see that the stellar expansion takes many years. If the radius r to which the star has expanded is small compared to r_0, then the density of the star is still great compared to the density of the gas cloud. Due to the turbulence, matter and anti-matter will mix and the material of gas cloud that has been swept up will be promptly annihilated. Thus the energy released, up to the time the expansion reached the radius r, will be $2M_\odot c^2(r/r_0)^3$. Half of this energy will probably escape through the gas cloud while the other half, emitted inward, will pass through the expanding star. The neutrino component (approximately one-half of the total) will of course escape. Thus an amount $\frac{1}{2}M_\odot c^2(r/r_0)^3$ will be deposited in the star.

During the early phases ($r \ll r_0$) the radiation loss from the surface of the star is not essential and most energy (as is also the case for supernovae) appears as kinetic energy. This leads to the estimate

$$(1/2)M_\odot \dot{r}^2 = (1/2)M_\odot c^2(r/r_0)^3$$

or

$$\dot{r} = (r/r_0)^{3/2}c$$

The time required for a two-fold expansion t_2 will be

$$t_2 = r/\dot{r} = (r_0/c)(r_0/r)^{1/2}$$

If r_0 is 10^{-2} light years and if at an early phase we set $r = 3$ light seconds $= 10^{-5}r_0$, then at that time $t_2 = 3$ years. Toward the end of the expansion, for r approaching r_0, the time t_2 becomes 3 days. At this time disintegration will become relatively slow, and our simple equations are no longer valid. But the qualitative situation is probably well described by the statement that radiation becomes important in a period that may be shorter than a year and that this event follows the entry of the star into the gas cloud by several years.

For $r \sim r_0$ matter and antimatter will annihilate in a few months[11] provided both are present at a density of 10^8 atoms per cm^3. The assumption of a much lower density would not explain the relatively rapid rise in intensities occasionally observed in quasars. A density of 10^7 atoms per cm^3 would still be compatible with observations.

It has been stated that the observed continuous visible spectrum is due to bremsstrahlung. This is in agreement with the observation that over extended parts of the spectrum the energy emitted is constant per unit frequency interval. On the other hand the emission of bremsstrahlung will not prevent the gas from reaching a temperature beyond an MeV. The result is that a considerable amount of gamma-rays will be emitted, but the emission in the visible will be so small as to leave the observed spectrum unexplained. Thus a different mechanism is needed.

Such a mechanism is the cyclotron radiation emitted by high-energy electrons as they spiral around magnetic fields. For energies $E \gg mc^2$ the approximate value of the emitted angular frequency is $\omega \approx (eH/mc)(E/mc^2)^2$ and the energy radiated in unit time will be

$$-\dot{E} \approx (e^4 H^2/m^2 c^3)(E/mc^2)^2 \qquad (1)$$

According to a famous suggestion of Fermi[12] individual fast particles will be accelerated by successive collisions with plasma streams which carry magnetic fields. On the average the particle increases its energy by a fraction v^2/c^2 in each collision. Fermi applied this idea to the acceleration of protons in cosmic ray production. He did not apply it to electrons because in our galaxy energy loss by cyclotron radiation exceeds the energy gained due to the collisions.

We are considering here a much more violently agitated and more turbulent region in which the energy gain per collision is greater and in which collisions are very much more frequent. Thus electrons may be accelerated up to a rather high energy. In fact, we shall assume magnetic fields and an upper limit of electron energies sufficient to emit radiation at $\omega \sim 10^{16} \sec^{-1}$. In the following we shall assume that a small fraction of the released energy $2M_O c^2$ is equally divided (according to Alfven) into magnetic energy and the kinetic energy of turbulence while the bulk of the released energy has been radiated away. In the following, we shall give a set of consistent values for a steady state.

If we assume 80 gauss for the root mean square average of the magnetic field, then the magnetic energy will be 260 ergs/cm^3 or a kinetic energy 1.3×10^{-6} for each of the 10^8 protons and antiprotons. This amounts to a fraction $.8 \times 10^{-3}$ of the self energy of one proton. The energy, available as the random energy in the turbulent motion, leads to a value $v^2/c^2 = 1.6 \times 10^{-3}$. Therefore 600 collisions will be needed for the e-folding of the energy of an electron by the Fermi mechanism.

To attain a frequency $\omega \sim 10^{16}$ sec^{-1}, electrons must be accelerated to $2.6 \times 10^3 \, mc^2 = 1300$ MeV. If this is accomplished, the accelerating electrons will indeed extract all available energy from the plasma and only a fraction of the energy released will be left in the form of hydro-magnetic turbulence. It should be incidentally noted that electrons rather than protons will be injected into mechanism of acceleration with sufficiently high initial energy and therefore essentially only electrons (and of course positrons) will be accelerated. It will be noted that this is an extreme case of the Fermi mechanism in which the high energy particles succeed in depleting the original energy sources.

It follows from Eq. (1) that the energy of an electron is lost by cyclotron radiation in a time $t_{\text{loss}} = [(mc^2)^4/e^4 H^2 cE]$. For 80 gauss and $E = 2.6 \times 10^3 mc^2$ one obtains $t_{\text{loss}} = 16$ seconds. Thus we require that an electron make a collision once every 16 seconds and the size of the turbulent elements will be 16 light seconds. The e-folding time therefore becomes $16 \times 600 = 10{,}000$ seconds $= 3$ hours. This is 10^{-3} times the duration in which the annihilation process occurs and it is consistent to state that during this time, which is equal both to the essential portion of the electron acceleration period and to the period in which the electrons lose their energy, a fraction 10^{-3} of the total annihilation energy is available in the hydromagnetic turbulence. Thus we have indeed a consistent set of numbers according to which the energy released in three hours will accelerate the gas to turbu-lent motions of $v^2/c^2 \sim 10^{-3}$ and in which this energy is transferred into radiation ranging from the radar region into the visible spectrum.

The form of the spectrum depends on the energy distribution of the electrons. We deal here with a form of acceleration in which no important energy loss is encountered until one reaches the top of the spectrum. If an electron of initial energy E_0 has been exposed to the Fermi energy-gain mechanism for t seconds then the energy will be $E = E_0 e^{t/t_0}$, where t_0 is the e-folding time. Since equal numbers of electrons are found in equal time intervals dt the number of electrons in the energy interval dE will be $(dt/dE) \, dE = t_0(dE/E)$. (Fermi's formula (dE/E^m) is based on a mechanism of loss of particles which remains constant during the process of energy gain.) The flux emitted by particles of energy E is, according to Eq. (1), proportional to E^2.

It must also be proportional to the number of particles in the energy interval dE/E. Thus the flux varies as dE/E. But the frequency of emission ω is proportional to E^2 and therefore the flux is proportional to $d\omega$. This is the same as for the bremsstrahl spectrum and agrees with experiment. At the same time the spectrum does not need to extend far beyond the ultraviolet.

There are two difficulties. One is that electrons should accumulate near the upper end of their energy range. In this region the electrons constantly lose energy and regain it again. This should produce a peak of flux near the upper end of the frequency spectrum and such a peak is not observed. Fluctuations involving, among other things, the energy distribution between the high energy electrons and the hydromagnetic motion is likely to broaden and maybe wash out this maximum. The same effect may be obtained by the transfer of the turbulence out of the region of annihilation, that is, to distances beyond r_0. Compton collisions of gamma rays and possibly escaping electrons may serve as the injections into the Fermi acceleration at these greater distances. The observed emission lines are probably generated in these or even more remote positions where velocities are smaller, corresponding to the limited breadth ($\delta\nu/\nu < 0.01$) of the emission lines.

The second difficulty arises when we attempt to apply our results to the lower end of the spectrum, in particular to the radar region. Here the spectrum will be modified by the reabsorption of the cyclotron radiation. The effect becomes important for waves longer than a millimeter. For longer waves the flux should drop rapidly with decreasing ω values. That this is not the case is at least in part due to the fact that electrons escape from the gas cloud and radiate at a later time in more distant regions of lower density and of much smaller magnetic field strengths. The long-wave radio component which should be due to electrons produced at earlier times should not show intensity fluctuations. This, indeed, seems to be the case below a kilomegacycle. This radiation is primarily to be found in 3C 273 in the "comet tail" in a region 10^5 light years removed from the quasi-stellar object. It is less clear what happens at frequencies between $\nu = 10^9$ sec^{-1} and $\nu = 10^{11}$ sec^{-1}. These frequencies might be emitted within a year after escape from the gas cloud. It may be significant that in one example the radar signal was seen to increase while the visible emission was fading. This might happen toward the end of an individual collision. Hot plasma masses may emerge from cooler surroundings.

IV. Cosmological Considerations

One piece of astronomical evidence strongly suggests that quasars can not be due to collisions between galaxies and antigalaxies[13]. A considerable fraction of galaxies occur in clusters. No quasar has ever been seen in a cluster.

It is nevertheless possible to maintain the annihilation hypothesis if one assumes that galaxies and antigalaxies are as a rule quite far apart. Then their collisions are strongly impeded by the fact that the universe is expanding and collisions require a motion of the galaxy strongly different from the one associated with its location. It is plausible that such "runaway" galaxies should not be part of a cluster. If, furthermore, the irregular motions of the galaxies have a Gaussian distribution it is much more easy to produce a strong relative motion if each collision partner possesses an irregular velocity. If, for instance, the relative motion is 6 times the normal random velocity then the probability is e^{-36} in case the whole value is contributed by one galaxy but only $e^{-9} \times e^{-9}$ if each partner moves with three times the normal speed toward the other. Thus neither galaxy should belong to a cluster.

Since our galaxy happens to be in a cluster we should in no case expect to turn into a quasar. The possibility here discussed (if it should correspond to reality) we may contemplate from a safe distance.

Why should galaxies and antigalaxies generally be distant? The answer to this question is to be sought nearer to the origin of the universe.

It is an appealing possibility to extend the validity of natural laws as far as possible. Since the number of nucleons is conserved one will like to assume that the algebraic sum of all nucleons is and always has been zero. That is the number of nucleons and antinucleons is equal. There is just as much matter as antimatter.

Alfven and Klein[14] have proposed that in an early state the universe consisted of an ambiplasma that is a mixture of ionized matter and antimatter. They proposed mechanisms by which matter and antimatter might have been separated. Whether or not this special proposal holds, simultaneous presence of matter and antimatter must have led to some annihilation in the early mixed stages.

One expects (and experiment seems to indicate) that for kinetic energies well below 100 MeV the annihilation cross section varies as $1/v$. This leads to a situation where the lifetime of a mixture is independent of the velocities.

But the $(1/v)$ law holds only down to $v = c/137$. Below this limit the Coulomb attraction between nucleon and antinucleon produces a $1/v^2$ dependence. Thus for low velocities lifetimes become short. It may be that matter survived the early days of creation only whenever its velocity differed from antimatter by more than $c/137$.

Early velocity differences translate themselves into positional differences in later stages. We may expect that in general matter and antimatter have distances of about the radius of the universe (10^{10} light years) divided by 137. One may expect a mosaiclike structure, collisions become rare and are as a rule limited to galaxies moving with unusual velocities. All of this might give a consistent picture.

Whether the annihilation hypothesis is tenable does not appear clear at present. But whether this or another explanation of quasars is correct, whatever we learn will give information about early stages of the universe. This is true because the brilliant quasars can be seen at long distances and therefore at early times. What we see, however, is of limited value unless it is accompanied by a proper explanation.

Archeology whether in human history or in astronomy becomes really interesting only if we go beyond the process of digging and advance to understanding.

References

1. Schmidt, M., *Nature*, **197**, 1040 (1963).
2. Greenstein, J., and M. Schmidt, *Astrophys. J.*, **140**, 1 (1964).
3. As suggested by F. Hoyle.
4. Jefferys, W. H., *Astrophys. J.*, **69**, 255 (1964).
5. Colgate, S. A., and A. G. W. Cameron, *Nature*, **200**, 870 (1963).
6. Colgate, S. A., and M. H. Johnson, *Phys. Rev. Letters*, **5**, 235 (1960).
7. The statement is not new; see, e.g., Harold Furth, *New Yorker*, 1956, and E. Teller, ibid.
8. Kraushaar, W. L., and G. W. Clark, *Phys. Rev.*, **8**, 106 (1961).
9. A review is given by P. O. Vandervoont, *Scientific American*, February 1965, p. 91.
10. Greenstein and Schmidt, loc. cit.
11. For the relevant cross sections see Cook et al., *Nuovo Cimento*, **25**, 497 (1962).
12. Fermi, E., *Phys. Rev.*, **75**, 1169 (1949).
13. I am indebted for this argument to Dr. Greenstein.
14. Alfvén, H., and O. Klein, *Arkiv Fysik*, **23**, 187 (1962); H. Alfvén, *Rev. Mod. Phys.*, **37**, 652 (1965). Radio emission due to annihilation products was discussed by A. G. Ekspong, N. K. Yamagdi, and B. Bonnevien, *Phys. Rev. Letters*, **16**, 664 (1966).

Dimensionless Ratios and Stellar Structure

E. E. SALPETER*

Cornell University

1. Introduction

Our sun contains an "astronomically large" number of hydrogen atoms, about 10^{57}. And yet, objects whose mass differ from that of the sun by mere factors of 10^3 either way have quite different properties. Why? Stellar structure theory abounds with other large ratios, such as evolution times of the order of 10^{10} years compared with pulsation periods measured in hours. We shall see that these ratios can be expressed in terms of a very small gravitational dimenisonless coupling constant α_G, equivalent to the Sommerfeld fine-structure constant α of electrodynamics. The results we shall derive are of course not new but merely represent simplified qualitative versions of well-known results, obtained essentially from dimensional analysis. In recent years speculations have become popular about possible time-variations of the gravitational coupling constant. Simple dimensional analysis is particularly useful to get a qualitative insight into such time-dependent theories.

If the equation of state for stellar material followed the perfect gas law, we would not have any preferred units for density and temperature. In fact we shall have to consider the possible importance of radiation pressure (which involves Planck's constant h), of electron degeneracy (which involves h and the electron's rest mass m), and of special relativity (which involves the velocity of light c). Our natural units for length, time, energy, and temperature are then

$$\hbar/mc = 0.386 \times 10^{-10} \text{ cm}, \; \hbar/mc^2 = 1.28 \times 10^{-21} \text{ sec},$$

$$mc^2 = 0.511 \text{ MeV} = 8.2 \times 10^{-7} \text{ erg}, \; mc^2/k = 5.93 \times 10^9 \text{ }^\circ\text{K} \quad (1)$$

where $\hbar = h/2\pi$ is the rationalized Planck's constant.

* This work was supported in part by the National Science Foundation under Grant GP-3488.

463

As unit gravitational mass we choose the mass H of the hydrogen atom (an atomic mass unit). Density ρ we shall reexpress in terms of a dimensionless parameter x,

$$H = 1837m = 1.67 \times 10^{-24} \text{ gm},$$

$$\rho = (Hx^3/3\pi^2)(mc/\hbar)^3 = x^3 \times 9.74 \times 10^5 \text{ gm/cc} \qquad (2)$$

The parameter x equals the electron Fermi momentum (in our units of mc) in hydrogen gas at this density and the radius (in our units of $\hbar/mc$) of a sphere containing one hydrogen atom equals $(4/9\pi)^{1/3}x^{-1}$. The mass M and radius R of a star can be expressed in terms of x and the number N of atomic mass units in the star,

$$M = NH, \qquad R = (4/9\pi)^{1/3}(N^{1/3}/x)\hbar/mc \qquad (3)$$

In quantum electrodynamics the Sommerfeld fine structure constant α plays the role of a dimensionless coupling constant for the Coulomb force. We can define a completely equivalent gravitational fine-structure constant α_G,

$$\alpha^{-1} \equiv \hbar c/e^2 = 137.04, \qquad \alpha_G^{-1} \equiv \hbar c/GH^2 = 1.75 \times 10^{38} \qquad (4)$$

where G is the gravitational constant. This constant measures the smallness of the gravitational force between two hydrogen atoms, just as α measures the smallness of the Coulomb force between two electrons. Some fractional powers of α_G will enter our discussions. We define

$$N_0 \equiv 0.49\alpha_G^{-3/2} = 1.20 \times 10^{57} \qquad (5)$$

where the factor 0.49 is introduced purely for convenience, since N_0H then equals the solar mass $M_\odot$.

In Sec. 2 we discuss the Virial theorem, which can provide a qualitative short-cut to the solution of differential equations, and the equation of state as modified by radiation pressure and electron degeneracy. In Sec. 3 we apply the work of Sec. 2 to show how radiation pressure puts an upper limit and electron degeneracy a lower limit on the mass of a hydrogen-burning main sequence star. In Sec. 4 we estimate evolutionary lifetimes and dynamic time scales for a star in terms of α_G. In Sec. 5 we discuss thermonuclear reaction rates and estimate interior and surface temperatures. Some numerical coincidences in observational cosmology are discussed in Sec. 6.

2. Equations of State and the Virial Theorem

The key to our dimensional arguments will be the Virial theorem, a consequence of the fact that a star must be (almost) in hydrostatic equilibrium. This theorem can be stated in a very general form, which holds for *any* equation of state for the matter making up the star, based only on the assumptions of (1) complete equilibrium and (2) Newtonian gravitational theory: The condition of equilibrium implies that the net external work required for an infinitesimal (virtual) change in the star's configuration cancel the gravitational energy release to first order. Applying this principle to an infinitesimal uniform change in scale for all distances in the star one finds

$$3 \int P \, dV = -\Omega_G, \qquad (6)$$

where P is the total pressure in a volume element dV and Ω_G is the total gravitational potential energy for the whole star.

Let ϵ_K be the average (positive) internal kinetic energy, ϵ_G the average (negative) gravitational potential energy and $\epsilon_{tot} = \epsilon_K + \epsilon_G$ the average total energy, each per free particle (including electrons and ions) expressed in our units of $mc^2 = 0.51$ MeV. We define next a dimensionless

$$\Gamma \equiv 3P\mu H/\rho\epsilon_K \qquad (7)$$

where μ is the mean molecular weight and ρ is the density. Our Virial theorem can then be expressed as

$$\Gamma\epsilon_K = -\epsilon_G; \qquad \epsilon_{tot} = -(\Gamma - 1)\epsilon_K \qquad (8)$$

where averages over the whole star are implied.

The quantity Γ equals 2 for a perfect classical gas, but is also of order unity even for other equations of state where the expressions for P and ϵ_K individually differ drastically from those for a perfect gas. For a partially degenerate but fully ionized gas one also has $\Gamma = 2$ as long as all particles are nonrelativistic. It is amusing (but not very useful) to note that an equation like Eq. (8) with $\Gamma = 2$ still holds even when some neutral atoms or molecules (or solids) are present, if internal molecular kinetic energy is included in ϵ_K and internal Coulomb energy in ϵ_G. This equation can be derived from nonrelativistic quantum mechanics by means of the variational principle[1]. For pure radiation pressure, on the other hand, $(\Gamma - 1)$ is zero exactly and it is almost zero for a highly relativistic electron gas.

The total gravitational potential energy $\Omega_G \equiv (N/\mu)\epsilon_G$ is of order $-GM^2/R$. Using the definitions in Eqs. (3)–(5), we can derive from Eq. (8) an order of magnitude relation

$$\epsilon_K \sim (G\mu HM/\hbar c)(x/N^{1/3}) \sim \mu \times \alpha_G N^{2/3} \sim \mu x(N/N_0)^{2/3}, \tag{9}$$

which relates ϵ_K under equilibrium conditions to the density (or radius) parameter x and the mass of the star.

We wish to discuss next the possible equations of state, i.e., explicit expressions for ϵ_K in terms of x and of τ, the temperature T expressed in units of (mc^2/k). For a perfect classical gas we have simply

$$\epsilon_{K,\mathrm{pg}} = 1.5\tau,$$

but we are also interested in radiation pressure of pure blackbody radiation and in Fermi pressure of a partially degenerate electron gas. Instead of quoting the well-known exact expressions in our units, it may be instructive to rederive order of magnitude relations from dimensional arguments.

Let us start with blackbody radiation at temperature $\tau(mc^2/k)$. In our "natural units" the energy of a "typical" photon is of order τ and its wavelength of order τ^{-1}. Equilibrium blackbody radiation contains about one photon per cubic wavelength and the energy density of the photons is then of the order of τ^4 per unit volume. Comparison with the perfect gas law for particles of number density $\sim x^3/\mu$ and average energy 1.5τ gives

$$\epsilon_{K,\mathrm{rad}}/\epsilon_{K,\mathrm{pg}} \sim (\tau/x)^3 \mu \tag{10}$$

The effects of electron degeneracy can be estimated as follows. One free electron occupies an average volume of linear dimensions about $\mu_e^{1/3} x^{-1}$ (where $\mu_e = A/Z$) and the Heisenberg uncertainty momentum p_0 is simply the inverse of this linear dimension (in our units where $\hbar = 1$). The Fermi momentum for the electron gas is close to p_0 and the average energy per electron at zero temperature (slightly less than the Fermi energy) is close to ϵ_0, the kinetic energy corresponding to p_0. If $p_0 \ll 1$ the electrons are nonrelativistic and $\epsilon_0 \approx p_0^2/2m \sim (x\mu_e^{1/3})^2$; if $p_0 \gg 1$ the electrons are highly relativistic and $\epsilon_0 \approx p_0 c \sim x\mu_e^{-1/3}$. The zero-temperature energy per electron $\epsilon_{K,\mathrm{deg}}$ is then of the order

$$\epsilon_{K,\mathrm{deg}} \sim x\mu_e^{-1/3} \frac{x\mu_e^{-1/3}}{1 + x\mu_e^{-1/3}} \tag{11}$$

and the actual kinetic energy per particle is of the order of $\epsilon_{K,\mathrm{deg}}$ or $\epsilon_{K,\mathrm{pg}} = 1.5\tau$, whichever is larger.

If the perfect gas law held for all x and τ, the Virial theorem in Eq. (9) would read

$$\tau/\mu x \sim (N/N_0)^{2/3}, \tag{12}$$

but there would be no important qualitative features which depend on the numerical value of N/N_0. However, such a dependence is introduced by radiation pressure and electron degeneracy.

Neglecting degeneracy at the moment, Eqs. (10) plus (12) show that radiation pressure (and energy) is negligible only if $N/N_0 \gg 1$. If we call β the ratio of $\epsilon_{K,\mathrm{pg}}$ to the total $\epsilon_K = \epsilon_{K,\mathrm{rad}} + \epsilon_{K,\mathrm{qg}}$, then Eqs. (9) and (10) (including a factor 20 from actual models) give the more general relation

$$\frac{1-\beta}{\beta^4} \sim \left(\frac{\mu^2 N}{20 N_0}\right)^2, \tag{13}$$

independent of the value of the density parameter x. For $N/N_0 \gg 1$ this reduces to

$$\beta \sim (20 N_0/N)^{1/2}\, \mu^{-1} \ll 1, \qquad \tau/x \sim (N/20 N_0)^{1/6}. \tag{14}$$

Let us return to the question of electron degeneracy. Because of the onset of special relativity when $x \gtrsim 1$ (μ_e is of order unity) we have $(\epsilon_{K,\mathrm{deg}}/x) \lesssim 1$ at all densities, as shown explicitly by Eq. (11). If $N/N_0 \gg 1$ we have $\tau/x \gg 1$ from Eq. (14) and thus $\epsilon_{K,\mathrm{deg}} \ll \epsilon_{K,\mathrm{pg}} = 1.5\tau$, so that degeneracy can be neglected and Eq. (14) used at all densities. On the other hand, if $N/N_0 \ll 1$ radiation pressure and also relativity can be neglected (we shall see that $x \ll 1$). Then ϵ_K on the left-hand side of Eq. (9) can be approximated by

$$\epsilon_K \sim 1.5\tau + x^2 \mu_e^{-2/3}, \tag{15}$$

and this equation solved for τ as a function of increasing x: For small enough x the second term in Eq. (15) is smaller than the first and Eq. (12) still holds, but τ reaches a maximum value $\tau_{\max}$ when the two terms in Eq. (15) become comparable and τ actually goes to zero at a slightly larger value $x_{\max}$ of x,

$$\tau_{\max} \sim (\mu_e^{-1/2}\, x_{\max})^2 \sim (\mu_e^2\, N/N_0)^{4/3} \ll 1. \tag{16}$$

Since the temperature cannot be negative, no stellar models are possible at all for a density parameter x exceeding $x_{\max}$. Actual calculations[2] show that $x_{\max}$ tends to infinity at a finite value N_{Ch} of N, the so-called "Chandrasekhar limiting mass",

$$\mu_e^2 N_{\mathrm{Ch}} = 5.76 N_0 \tag{17}$$

3. Stellar Masses

In Sec. 1 we had defined a large dimensionless number N_0 in terms of the fundamental constants of nature GH^2, $\hbar$ and c, which also "happens" to equal the solar mass (in atomic mass units H). The work of Sec. 2 now provides the explanation why common stars lie in a rather narrow mass range around N_0. For masses near N_0, neither radiation pressure nor electron degeneracy are of overwhelming importance (except possibly at high density). For the mass and radius of the sun, for instance, the pressure is given by the perfect classical gas law to within better than 10%.

For $N \gg N_0$ we have seen that electron degeneracy is negligible and that for $N \geq N_{\text{Ch}} = (5.76/\mu_e^2)N_0$ stellar models are possible for arbitrarily high density (and temperature). Physically speaking, as the density is increased the electrons become relativistic before they become degenerate and the degree of degeneracy then remains independent of density and small. On the other hand, we have seen that, for $N \gg N_0$, radiation pressure predominates and this can have some marked effects which tend to make a very massive star unstable: For instance, the effective value of surface gravity for atoms in the photosphere is lowered drastically by the upward thrust due to scattering of the escaping radiation and this effect could lead to enhanced mass loss by means of corpuscular radiation. However, the most important effect of predominant radiation pressure seems to be an indirect one connected with the fact that $\Gamma - 1$ in Eq. (8) is then much less than unity (it would be zero for pure radiation pressure). A moderate change in the total energy ϵ_{tot} of the star can then lead to a large change in $\epsilon_K \approx -\epsilon_G$ and hence in the structure of the star. Temperature-sensitive nuclear reactions in a star's interior can feed energy into pulsations which can become unstable (amplitude increasing with time) if $\Gamma - 1$ is sufficiently small. Detailed calculations[3] predict that this instability should set in for "main-sequence" stars (see Sec. 4) of mass exceeding about $60N_0$. In fact no stars of mass exceeding $100N_0$ have been observed.

For $N < N_0$, on the other hand, we have seen that radiation pressure and relativity are unimportant but that nonrelativistic degeneracy puts upper limits on the temperature and density the star can reach. "White dwarfs" (with masses mainly in the range of 0.4 to $0.8N_0$) are in fact thought to be stellar remnants which are highly degenerate and are cooling off at almost constant radius and density to the final zero-temperature configuration. The finite value of $\tau_{max} \propto N^{4/3}$ has the following consequence: As discussed in the next section, the release of thermonuclear energy from hydrogen-burning requires $\tau \sim 10^{-3}$ to 10^{-2} and this can be reached only for stars more massive than a critical mass $N_{crit} \propto N_0 \tau^{3/4}$. Actual calculations give a value of $N_{crit} \approx 0.08 N_0$. For smaller masses stellar models are still possible but they have to rely on gravitational contraction for their energy source which lasts a much shorter time than nuclear energy would.

Conventional stars consist of almost completely ionized matter and "atomic forces" (i.e., Coulomb potentials plus quantum mechanics) are usually not very important. Atomic forces become important, however, for smaller masses still: For hydrogen, at least, the ionization potential I in our units is about α^2 and the density parameter x for the zero-pressure solid is about $\alpha = 1/137$. According to Eq. (16), for $N_{at} \equiv \alpha^{3/2} N_0 \sim 10^{-3} N_0$ hydrogen would be just barely temperature-ionized and pressure-ionized when reaching the star's maximum temperature. The neglect of atomic forces is justified for $N \gg N_{at}$, but not for objects with $N \lesssim N_{at}$, such as planets or rocks, where one has to deal with solids (or liquids) and whose density is almost independent of N for $N \ll N_{at}$. It is interesting to note that the mass of Jupiter is close to N_{at}.

4. Luminosity and Time Scales

We have discussed the thermal energy content of a star with average temperature τ, but not yet its luminosity L, i.e., the steady outward heatflow caused by the star's radial temperature gradient. If convection is absent and if the electrons are not extremely degenerate most of the heatflow is carried by the blackbody radiation rather than by the particles. To calculate the luminosity L properly one has to solve a heat-transport equation, but we shall merely estimate it by obtaining the order of magnitude for the average time t_{ph} blackbody photons take to escape from the star's interior.

Let σ be the average cross section (in our units of $\hbar^2/m^2 c^2$) per electron or ion for the scattering or absorption (followed quickly by reemission) of a typical blackbody radiation photon at temperature τ. For pure Thomson scattering from free electrons $\sigma \sim \alpha^2$, whereas σ can be as large as α^{-1} in hydrogen under favorable conditions of temperature and density (and even larger if heavier atoms are present). Thus σ can deviate from unity by factors of the order of 10^4 in either direction.

The mean free path for a photon is of order $(x^3\sigma)^{-1}$ and the number n of mean free paths in a stellar radius R is, according to Eq. (3),

$$n \sim \sigma x^2 N^{\frac{1}{3}} \gg 1. \tag{18}$$

The escape from the interior of a typical photon can be thought of as a random walk process with total path length of order nR, so that the time taken (in our units of $\hbar/mc^2$) is

$$t_{\text{ph}} \sim nR \sim \sigma x N^{\frac{2}{3}} \sim \sigma \epsilon_K \alpha_G^{-1} \equiv \sigma \epsilon_K t_0. \tag{19}$$

We have used the Virial theorem of Eq. (9) to obtain the last expression (replacing μ by unity) and have defined

$$t_0 \equiv \alpha_G^{-1}(\hbar/mc^2) \approx 7 \times 10^9 \text{ years.} \tag{20}$$

The luminosity L is then of the order of $N\epsilon_{K,\text{rad}}/t_{\text{ph}}$ where $\epsilon_{K,\text{rad}}$ is given by Eq. (10).

We can now easily estimate time scales for stellar evolution under various circumstances. Consider first fairly massive stars with $N \gtrsim 20N_0$ so that the blackbody radiation represents an appreciable fraction of the total thermal energy content $N\epsilon_K$ and the time taken to radiate away half, say, of that total energy is simply of order t_{ph}. In the absence of any potential energy source other than gravitation, the star must contract by a factor of 2 (the "Kelvin contraction time scale") in about this time t_{ph}. If the star is using thermonuclear energy production, the available energy reservoir per particle is of order unity (1 MeV being a characteristic energy release in a nuclear reaction) compared with the much smaller thermal energy content ϵ_K ($\epsilon_K \sim 10^{-3}$ for the sun, for instance). The thermonuclear evolution time is then

$$t_{\text{thn}} \sim \sigma t_0, \tag{21}$$

where $\sigma \sim 10^{-4}$ for a very massive star and $t_{\text{thn}} \sim 10^6$ years. For stars of lower mass only a small fraction $(1 - \beta)$, given by Eq. (13), of the thermal energy content ϵ_K is radiated away in time t_{ph}, so that t_{thn} in Eq. (21) is increased by a factor of order $(20N_0/N)^2$. Typical values of σ are also larger for stars of low mass, so that evolution times increase rapidly with increasing mass (for $N \gg 20N_0$).

To within factors of about 10^4, stellar evolution times are of the order of t_0. This contrasts sharply with typical dynamic time scales t_{dyn}.

One might at first sight expect two different kinds of dynamic timescales; (1) a "free-fall time" in which a star would collapse under its own gravitational field if internal pressure were suddenly turned off, (2) a "communication time" in which a soundwave could travel from one end of the star to the other. If neither radiation pressure nor electron degeneracy are of overwhelming importance, these two times are comparable, however: The sound speed is always comparable to the thermal velocity v_i of the ions and the kinetic energy acquired by a free-falling ion would be comparable with its gravitational potential energy. Because of the Virial theorem the soundspeed and the free-fall velocity are then both of order $v_i \sim (2\tau m/H)^{\frac{1}{2}}$ and

$$t_{\text{dyn}} \sim R/v_i \sim N^{\frac{1}{3}}(1836/\tau)^{\frac{1}{2}}x^{-1}.$$

Using once more the Virial theorem in Eq. (12) we have

$$(x/10)^{\frac{3}{2}}t_{\text{dyn}} \sim N_0^{\frac{1}{3}} \sim \alpha_G^{-\frac{1}{2}}(\hbar/mc) \sim \alpha_G^{\frac{1}{2}}t_0. \tag{22}$$

Pulsational periods for stars are also of the order of t_{dyn}.

For typical stars $(10/x)^{\frac{3}{2}} \sim 10^5$ so that $t_{\text{dyn}}/t_0 \sim 10^5\alpha_G^{\frac{1}{2}} \sim 10^{-14}$. Stars are in hydrostatic equilibrium to a very good approximation, since deviations from it are of the order of the very small ratio of t_{dyn} to stellar evolution times. If a portion of a star is unstable against convection, a very minute superadiabatic gradient can provide sufficient heat transport, since an appreciable degree of superadiabaticity would transport the heat content in short times of order t_{dyn} rather than the required t_{ph}. The strong inequality $t_{\text{dyn}} \ll t_{\text{ph}}$ also prevents small temperature fluctuations from leading to nuclear explosions under normal stellar conditions, since appreciable superheating would require times only somewhat shorter than t_{ph} whereas cooling by adiabatic expansion takes only times of about t_{dyn}.

5. Temperatures and Thermonuclear Reactions

It has been known[4] for about thirty years that "main-sequence stars" (the most common stars, including the sun, Sirius A and α-Centauri) utilize thermonuclear reactions involving hydrogen as an energy source. We have stated that thermonuclear reaction rates in stars are very temperature sensitive and typical temperatures τ are less than 0.01 (in our units). Instead of reproducing the actual formulas for these rates we shall merely show how some inequalities are related to H/m, α, and α_G.

We have already indicated that the luminosity of a star is determined largely by photon opacity and not by the energy source. If a star is using nuclear fuel it had to adjust its internal temperature τ so that the characteristic reaction time for the thermonuclear reactions coincides with the photon-controlled time in Eq. (21). If we consider factors like 10^4 as "of order unity" this required reaction time is of order $t_0 = \alpha_G^{-1}(\hbar/mc^2)$ compared with intrinsic nuclear collision times which are roughly of order $\hbar/mc^2$.

The required "slowing down factor" $e^{-\gamma} \sim \alpha_G \approx e^{-87}$ in a thermonuclear reaction rate is made up of the product of two exponentially small factors. One is the Gamow barrier penetration factor $e^{2\pi\eta}$ for the Coulomb collision between a pair of nuclei with relative kinetic energy ϵ, the other is the Boltzmann factor $e^{-\epsilon\tau}$. For a fixed temperature τ one can show that the optimum energy ϵ is given by

$$2\pi\eta \equiv 2\pi \sqrt{\frac{H}{m}} \, \alpha \, \frac{Z_1 Z_2 A}{\epsilon^{1/2}} = \frac{2}{3}\gamma, \qquad \frac{\epsilon}{\tau} = \frac{1}{3}\gamma$$

where Z_1 and Z_2 are the atomic charges of the reacting nuclei and A is the reduced mass (in atomic units). This gives

$$\tau \sim (27\pi^2\alpha^2 H/m)Z_1^2 Z_2^2 A\gamma^{-3} \sim (20 Z_1^2 Z_2^2 A)\gamma^{-3}, \qquad (23)$$
$$\gamma \sim \ln \alpha_G^{-1} \sim 87$$

We thus see that the smallness of α_G has as one consequence fairly small temperatures τ (i.e., thermal energies that are nonrelativistic even for the electrons) for a nuclear-fueled star, unless the only remaining nuclear fuel has fairly high Z and A (for stars using $H^1 + C^{12}$ and $O^{16} + O^{16}$, respectively, $\tau \sim 10^{-3}$ and 0.5). The logarithmic derivative of reaction rate versus temperature is about $\gamma/3$ which explains the great temperature sensitivity of the rates.

We have seen the reason for interior temperatures τ of the order of 10^{-3} ($\sim 10^7$ °K). How about surface temperatures τ_S which are generally factors of 10^3 or 10^4 smaller? This ratio τ/τ_S can be estimated as follows. Because of the random walk process discussed in Sec. 2 the effective net speed with which the blackbody radiation from the interior (energy density $\sim \tau^4$) leaks out is only about $n^{-1}c$ with n given by Eq. (18). On the other hand, the final escape of the same heat flux is accomplished by the blackbody radiation in the star's photosphere (energy density $\sim \tau_S^4$) escaping with practically the full light velocity c. For a star with $N \sim N_0 \sim \alpha_G^{-3/2}$ we then have

$$\tau/\tau_S \sim (\sigma x^2)^{1/4} N^{1/12} \sim (\sigma x^2)^{1/4} \alpha_G^{-1/8} \gg 1, \qquad (24)$$

where $\alpha_G^{-1/8} \sim 10^{4.5}$ but the multiplying factor is usually less than unity.

The inequality in Eq. (24) also explains why the outer boundary of a star is so well defined, i.e., why the gravitational scale height h_s near the star's photosphere is so much smaller than its radius R. The local scale height at some radial distance is inversely proportional to the local value g of the gravitational acceleration and proportional to the local temperature. The value of g at a "typical" point in the star's interior (some distance out from the center with temperature $\sim \tau$) is not very different from its surface value and it follows from the Virial theorem that the scale height at this point is also comparable with the radius R. It thus follows that R/h_s is comparable with $\tau/\tau_S \gg 1$ as given by Eq. (24).

6. Stellar Evolution and Cosmology

We have made use of the Virial theorem to derive various in-equalities in terms of the very small dimensionless constant of nature $\alpha_G \equiv GH^2/\hbar c$ (and other constants like α and H/m). In particular we have seen that an object of mass near $N_0 H$, where $N_0 \equiv 0.49\alpha_G^{-3/2}$, remains a "main sequence" star burning hydrogen into helium for a time t_{thn} of about $t_0 \equiv \alpha_G^{-1}(\hbar/mc^2)$, preceded by a shorter period of contraction (and followed by a more rapid star death). We have also seen that a star's lifetime t_{thn} increases with decreasing mass, but that in practice t_{thn} nevertheless lies in a reasonably narrow range of values, since stellar masses fall in a rather narrow range: Stars with $N > 100N_0$ are unstable because of effects of radiation pressure and stars with $N < 0.05N_0$ cannot become hot enough (because of effects of electron degeneracy) to burn nuclear fuel at all.

One observational fact of cosmology is the redshift–distance relation which is interpreted in terms of an expansion of the universe. One can then define an "observation radius of the universe" R_u as the distance from us whose relative expansion velocity is an appreciable fraction (say 80%) of c. The density of matter averaged over large distances in the universe is also known (although to poor accuracy) and hence the mass $N_u H$ of the "observable universe", i.e., the mass contained in a sphere of radius R_u. There are two numerical coincidences between these observed cosmological quantities and the fundamental constants discussed above. They can be put in the following form (treating factors like 100 as order unity)

$$\left.\begin{array}{l} c^{-1} R_u \sim t_0 \equiv \alpha_G^{-1}(\hbar/mc^2) \\ GN_u H/R_u c^2 = \alpha_G N_u(\hbar/HcR_u) \sim 1 \end{array}\right\} \tag{25}$$

so that the "number of hydrogen atoms in the universe" N_u is about $(H/m)\alpha_G^{-2} \sim 10^{79}$.

The question arises whether the two numerical relations in Eq. (25) are merely chance coincidences or have a deeper reason. This is not merely a philosophical question and can be rephrased in operational terms by asking if the coincidences persist as a function of time or not. In the steady-state cosmology this question is automatically answered in the affirmative (since everything is postulated to be in a steady state). For any evolving cosmological model it is an open question, however, since even a specific model does not specify the constancy or time dependence of the fundamental dimensionless ratio α_G.

If α_G is time independent it is easy to see that one cannot satisfy *both* inequalities in Eq. (25) throughout all time for any evolving cosmology which allows no creation of matter (unlike the steady-state model): The ratio $R_u mc/\hbar$ is observed to be of order α_G^{-1} at the present epoch but the universal expansion implies that this ratio will increase with time for any given receding galaxy. R_u as a function of time is not defined in terms of a given shell of galaxies, however, but in terms of a fixed fraction of the light speed and depends on the acceleration parameter of the cosmology. One can therefore find a cosmological model in which the expansion velocities are accelerated in such a manner that $R_u mc/\hbar$ remains constant. For the same reason, however, the number N_u of hydrogen atoms in the "observable universe" (i.e., inside R_u) decreases with time for such an accelerating model and the second inequality in Eq. (25) cannot hold at epochs other than the present. A more fashionable class of cosmological models with constant α_G satisfies the second inequality at all times, but the first inequality only at the present epoch.

It is possible, however, that the fundamental "constants" vary with time so that α_G is a function of time (only the variation of dimensionless ratios such as $N \equiv M/H$, H/m, $Rmc/\hbar$, α_G, α, etc. is operationally significant). The evolution of an individual star is rather complicated[5] under such circumstances since the stellar structure depends on the value of $N\alpha_G^{3/2}$, as we have seen, and the number N of nucleons in a given star presumably does not change.

An interesting possibility suggested by Dirac[6] is a cosmological model with a law of deceleration where N_u and $R_u mc/\hbar$ increase with time in such a way that $N_u(\hbar/mcR_u)^2$ remains constant. If one allows α_G^{-1} to increase with time in the appropriate manner, then both relations in Eq. (25) are satisfied at all times.

The first relation in Eq. (25) guarantees that the evolutionary lifetimes of "typical" stars (with $N\alpha_G^{3/2} \sim 1$) are comparable with the "age of the universe" $c^{-1}R_u$. If this relation is violated very strongly in either direction, one could not have stellar systems similar to our galaxy, since stars would either not have had time to contract to the main sequence, or would already have burned out, in the available time of $c^{-1}R_u$.

References

1. Bethe, H. A., and E. E. Salpeter, *Quantum Mechanics of One- and Two-Electron Atoms* (§ 36e), Academic Press, New York (1957).
2. Chandrasekhar, S., *Astrophys. J.*, **74**, 81 (1931).
3. Schwarzschild, M., and R. Härm, *Astrophys. J.*, **129**, 637 (1959).
4. Bethe, H. A., *Phys. Rev.*, **55**, 434 (1939).
5. Dicke, R. H., *The Theoretical Significance of Experimental Relativity*, Gordon and Breach, New York (1964).
6. Dirac, P. A. M., *Proc. Roy. Soc.*, **A165**, 199 (1938).

Phase Transitions

R. BROUT

Université Libre de Bruxelles

Introduction

That a chapter on phase transitions should occur in a volume which honors Hans Bethe is natural for the scholar of statistical mechanics and the solid state. It is a tribute to the breadth and versatility of this remarkable man, however, that such a contribution might seem rather out of place to most of his present colleagues: high-energy and nuclear physicists. The facts are that the early investigations in the quantum theory of magnetism were in large measure Bethe-inspired and that in the latter 1930's and early 40's, it was the "Bethe approximation" which was most talked about in order-disorder phase transitions.

Our understanding of phase transitions has advanced somewhat since Professor Bethe's contributions and it is the purpose of this article to present some of these advances. At the present time, the theory is primarily developing along four different tracks:

(1) Crude molecular field methods (crude referring to the statistical mechanical element): these generally provide adequate descriptions of both phases outside the critical region. Among these are the ancient, but very much alive theories of Weiss (magnetism), Bragg Williams (order-disorder-formally identical to Weiss) and van der Waals (liquid-gas condensation). And then there are the more erudite newcomers like the Bardeen-Cooper-Schrieffer theory of superconductivity. A great advantage of molecular field theories is that most of the phase transitions are understandable in a common light—no mean accomplishment in view of the diversity of the physical phenomena involved.

(2) A qualitative and semiquantitative understanding of the fluctuations which result in dramatic precursor phenomena on either side of a critical phenomenom: historically speaking, it was Ornstein

and Zernicke who first developed the theory of long-range correlations from a macroscopic point of view, thereby explaining critical opalescence in fair detail. It was in the category of fluctuation theory that Bethe made the famous Bethe approximation in which by an ingenious physical argument, he was able to estimate the residual energy left in the disordered phase after the long-range order vanished. In the same way, he was able to estimate that amount of energy in the ordered phase which was not accountable for by the molecular field (long-range order). Bethe never pushed his methods far enough to get the long range correlations. However his methods and those of Ornstein and Zernicke were joined neatly by Elliott and Marshall in order to get a reasonable picture of the correlation function over the whole range of distance. In present day theory, there has been considerable effort in using modern many-body techniques, [graphology, equations of motion, response functions, Green's functions, etc.] to get a more complete theory of the precursor fluctuations.

(3) The precise nature of critical singularities: within the past few years, a theoretical, numerical and experimental science has blossomed forth, in which the precise nature of the critical singularities have been investigated. The primary theoretical and numerical impetus has been supplied by the King's College group of Domb, Fisher, and Sykes. These authors by dint of fantastic calculational ingenuity as motivated by physical thinking, have supplied a set of numerical answers for a large variety of spin transitions, the spins being confined to a given lattice. It is most probable that the critical behavior which is deduced is the correct answer. Apart from certain general thermodynamic and stability arguments, which relate singularities of different thermodynamic functions to each other, there has been absolutely no theoretical advance of an analytic nature on this subject. However, experimentation both on spin systems and on liquid-gas critical systems is keeping up with calculation. The degree of accord is very impressive indeed.

(4) Finally, we mention "special techniques." Most notable among these is Onsager's solution of the two-dimensional Ising model, which has now been duplicated in a variety of ways by a number of authors. Unfortunately, every method of evaluation breaks down on the attempt at generalization. The example seems to be a solvable freak. One must therefore exercise considerable caution when trying to learn "interesting" facts from this model. The very solvability may well lead to spurious effects which are not representative of any other system.

We also mention the technique of functional integration introduced by Kac, which has now been used to investigate some questions concerning liquid gas condensation, and magnetism.

Naturally, I cannot in these few pages review all of these different facets of the subject. I will therefore try to pick a few examples and review our present knowledge in terms of items 1, 2, and 3. Item 4 (special techniques) will not be reviewed.

Molecular Field Methods

1. Magnetism and Order-Disorder

For a lattice of spins localized on sites, there are two models in current use corresponding to Hamiltonians

$$H = \tfrac{1}{2} \sum v_{ij} S_i^z S_j^z - \mathscr{H} \sum S_i^z \qquad \text{(Ising model)} \qquad (1.1)$$

$$H = \tfrac{1}{2} \sum v_{ij} \mathbf{S}_i \cdot \mathbf{S}_j - \mathscr{H} \sum S_i^z \qquad \text{(Heisenberg model)} \qquad (1.2)$$

$\mathbf{S}_i$ is the spin operator of the ith spin and S_i^z its zth component. $\mathscr{H}$ is an external field measured in units of energy.

The Heisenberg model provides a reasonable description of crystalline antiferromagnets (e.g., MnF_2), ferrites and rare-earth metallic ferromagnetism (the f electrons being well localized). Of course, suitable modifications must be incorporated to take into account various sources of anisotropy (dipolar, crystalline field, spin–orbit coupling, etc.). Such complications will not be explored here since they are not of general interest to phase-transition theory.

The Ising model rarely serves as a model of ferromagnetism, an exception being a set of substances called cobalt tutton salts. However, this model does provide a description of order-disorder phenomena through a redefinition of the symbol S. Namely, consider a 50–50 solution of A atoms and B atoms, where the AB force is more attractive than AA or BB. At low temperatures, the favored state is a superlattice in which A atoms are surrounded by B's and conversely. At high temperatures the distribution is random. Fix one atom in the crystal. Then at zero temperature the type of atom which occupies a given site is uniquely determined. If at a higher temperature the other kind of atom is sitting on this site, one calls this a bad site. Otherwise it is a good site. At high temperatures there is equal probability of sites being good or bad. But below a certain critical temperature there is an unequal probability. In Ising-model language on uses Eq. (1.1) where S_i^z takes on values $+1$ (good site) and -1 (bad site). The effective "spin–spin" interaction is easily deduced to be

$$v_{ij} = v_{AB} - \tfrac{1}{2}(v_{AA} + v_{BB}),\tag{1.3}$$

where we have limited ourselves to near-neighbor interactions [i.e., (ij) are near neighbors] and the v_{AB}, v_{AA}, and v_{BB} are the respective, near-neighbor potentials of interaction between the various kinds of atoms.

Another use of the Ising model is as a model of condensation. Here a good site is one which is occupied by an atom and a bad site is one which is empty. Multiple occupation is not allowed, thereby simulating a hard-core potential.

The molecular field theories of both Ising and Heisenberg models is identical; the differences are manifest only in the fluctuations. We therefore develop the Ising-model molecular field for simplicity and take spin $1/2$. S_i^z takes on values ± 1 and we will adopt the symbol μ_i for this special case. The long-range order is defined

$$R = \langle \mu_i \rangle = (1/N) \sum \mu_i = (N_{\text{up}} - N_{\text{down}})/N \tag{1.4}$$

The Weiss or Bragg Williams idea is that in some approximation the thermodynamic state of the system is completely determined by R. The Hamiltonian [Eq. (1.1)] implies the existence of a field of interaction on site i given by

$$V_i = -\sum v_{ij}\mu_j + \mathscr{H} \tag{1.5}$$

The mean field is

$$\langle V_i \rangle = -\sum v_{ij}\langle \mu_j \rangle + \mathscr{H} \tag{1.6}$$

If the condensed phase is ferromagnetic [or a superlattice] then $\langle \mu_j \rangle$ is independent of the index j, by translation symmetry, so that

$$\langle V_j \rangle = -v(0)R + \mathscr{H}, \tag{1.7}$$

where we have used the Fourier transform $v(q)$ at $\mathbf{q} = 0$

$$v(\mathbf{q}) = \sum_j v_{ij} \exp\left[i\mathbf{q}\cdot(\mathbf{R}_i - \mathbf{R}_j)\right] \tag{1.8}$$

The Weiss approximation is that the field at i is to be approximated by $\langle V_i \rangle$. This is obviously in error in that if a spin is up at i then the neighboring spins will be polarized preferentially up. However, this effect clearly becomes diluted if the range of the force becomes long. In fact we will show that the approximation is exact for infinite-range forces. The Weiss description may then be construed as a zeroth order

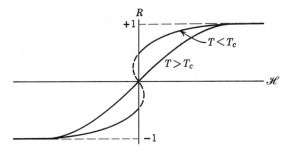

Fig. 1 Plot of R vs. $\mathcal{H}$ at fixed T.

approximation in $(1/z)$ where z is the number of atoms within the range of the potential.

We now use Eq. (1.7) to get the magnetic equation of state through

$$R = \langle \mu_i \rangle = \frac{\text{tr}\,[\exp\,(-\beta \mu_i \langle V_i \rangle)\mu_i]}{\text{tr}\,[\exp\,(-\beta \mu_i \langle V_i \rangle)]} = \tanh\,[-\beta(v(0)R - \mathcal{H})] \quad (1.9)$$

where $\beta = (kT)^{-1}$ and tr means trace over the spin states. The ferromagnetic case is $v(0) < 0$, and in this case the solution for R vs. $\mathcal{H}$ at given T is given in Fig. 1 for $T \leq T_c$ where

$$kT_c = v(0) \quad (1.10)$$

is the critical temperature. The dotted lines are thermodynamically spurious for reasons which will be discussed below. However, they may represent metastable regions so long as $dR/d\mathcal{H} > 0$ such as seen in hysteresis. The spontaneous magnetization is given in Fig. 2. This is found by reading off the intercepts in Fig. 1 at $\mathcal{H} = 0$.

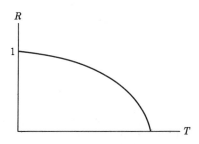

Fig. 2 Plot of R vs. T at $\mathcal{H} = 0$.

In the antiferromagnetic case or ferrite case, one deals with several sublattices and an order parameter must be introduced for each sublattice. For example, an antiferromagnet of two sublattices requires R_A and R_B, where $R_B = -R_A$. Then the molecular field on an A site is (for $\mathscr{H} = 0$)

$$\langle V \rangle_A = \sum_{j \text{ on } B} v_{ij} R_B + \sum_{j \text{ on } A} v_{ij} R_A = -\langle V \rangle_B, \qquad (1.11)$$

and the Weiss equations become

$$\begin{aligned} R_A &= \tanh\left[-\beta V_A\right] \\ R_B &= \tanh\left[-\beta V_B\right], \end{aligned} \qquad (1.12)$$

which in general are coupled equations, being uncoupled for symmetry reasons in the present case.

To see how well such methods represent the facts, we compare theory and experiment for MnF_2 in Fig. 3. It is seen that up to about 5% of the critical temperature, Weiss theory is good. (At very low temperatures spin-wave effect precludes a comparison.)

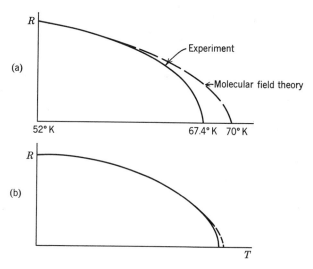

Fig. 3   (a) Sublattice magnetization of MnF_2 according to the data of Heller and Benedek. The dashed line is the molecular field curve with $T_c \cong 70°K$. (b) The same data extrapolated to $0°K$ assuming the validity of molecular field theory at low temperature.

To see how a theory of condensation comes out of these considerations we adopt the lattice gas interpretation. The potential is attractive [ferromagnetic] between the sites. To see the details of the connection, we introduce the symbol $\varepsilon_i = (1 + \mu_i)/2$. We then have for the density

$$\rho \equiv (N/N_0) = \sum \varepsilon_i = (1 + R)/2, \tag{1.13}$$

where N is the number of particles and N_0 the number of sites. The Hamiltonian [Eq. (1.1)] becomes

$$H = \tfrac{1}{2} \sum (4v_{ij})\varepsilon_i \varepsilon_j - 2N(v(0) + \mathscr{H}) + \text{constant.} \tag{1.14}$$

The complete trace over all states includes a sum on R from -1 to $+1$ and hence on N from 0 to N_0. We then have a grand ensemble of chemical potential μ given by

$$\mu = -2[v(0) + \mathscr{H}] \tag{1.15}$$

The interaction between particles is the attractive force $4v_{ij}$.

The Weiss equation in this language becomes

$$(2\rho - 1) = \tanh\left[(\beta/2)(+4v(0)\rho + \mu)\right] \tag{1.16}$$

Differentiating and using the thermodynamic equation $d\mu = v\,dp$ at fixed T and integrating back yields

$$p + a\rho^2 = -(kT/b) \log\left[1 - (v/b)\right], \tag{1.17}$$

where $v = \rho^{-1}$ and for dimensional reasons we have introduced the volume of the cell, b. a is given by $-2v(0) > 0$. Equation (1.17) is very much like the van der Waals equation but with $(kT/v - b)$ replaced by the log term. The latter is probably closer to the truth than the original van der Waals guess.

Equation (1.17) gives the familiar van der Waals loops for $T < T_c$ (Fig. 4) which are again thermodynamically spurious.

The method of Bragg Williams is to treat the problem more globally. The free energy is

$$-\beta F = \log Z = \log \operatorname{tr} e^{-\beta H} = \log \sum_{R = -1}^{+1} (\operatorname{tr})_R \, e^{-\beta H} \tag{1.18}$$

The trace is divided into two pieces, the sum on R and the sum on configurations for a given R. By standard statistical arguments, the former is concentrated around $R_{\text{equil.}}$ with fluctuation $\mathcal{O}(1/\sqrt{N})$. Therefore for thermodynamic purposes

$$-\beta F = \log\left[(\operatorname{tr})_{R_{\text{eq.}}} e^{-\beta H}\right] + \mathcal{O}[\log(N)] \tag{1.19}$$

It is convenient to write Eq. (1.19) as

$$-\beta F = \log\left[(\mathrm{tr})_R\, e^{-\beta H}/(\mathrm{tr})_R 1\right] + \log\left[(\mathrm{tr})_R 1\right] \qquad (1.20)$$

$(\mathrm{tr})_R 1$ is the number of configurations available for a given R. Thus

$$(\mathrm{tr})_R 1 = W(R) = \binom{N}{N(1 + R)/2} \qquad (1.21)$$

$$\log W(R) = -N\left[\frac{(1 + R)}{2} \log\left(\frac{1 + R}{2}\right) + \left(\frac{1 - R}{2}\right) \log\left(\frac{1 - R}{2}\right)\right]$$
$$+ \mathcal{O}\left[\log N\right] \quad (1.22)$$

If the term in $e^{-\beta H}$ is expanded in Eq. (1.20) and one stops at the first order, the evaluation is

$$-\beta F = -N \frac{\beta v(0) R^2}{2} + \log W(R) - N\beta R\mathcal{H} \qquad (1.23)$$

This is the Bragg Williams form of the free energy. The value of R, which is needed is found by picking out the largest term in Eq. (1.18). Thus one maximizes Eq. (1.23). The result is Eq. (1.9).

We now come to the point where the spurious loops are eliminated. From Eq. (1.18), the free energy is

$$\log \int_{-1}^{+1} dR\, e^{-\beta F(R)} \qquad (1.24)$$

There is a very tight saddle point which dominates this integral which is at R_{Weiss} as given by the solid lines in Fig. 1. At $\mathcal{H} = 0$, the saddle takes a jump and eliminates the loops. This is easily seen by just drawing $F(R)$ as a function of R at given $\mathcal{H}$ and going to the limit $\mathcal{H} \to 0$, above and below. The peaking is clearly on the side with the sign of $\mathcal{H}$.

In the lattice-gas interpretation, these arguments establish the Maxwell construction and the elimination of the van der Waals loops.

Finally we show that Eq. (1.23) becomes exact as $z \to \infty$. The interaction energy is

$$V = \tfrac{1}{2} \sum v_{ij}\mu_i\mu_j \qquad (1.25)$$

Take a square-shaped potential of size $v(0)/z$ and go to limit $z \to N \to \infty$. Then

$$V \to \frac{1}{2} \frac{v(0)}{N} \sum_{i \neq j} \mu_i\mu_j = \frac{1}{2} \frac{v(0)}{N} \left[(NR)^2 - N\right] = \tfrac{1}{2}Nv(0)R^2 + \mathcal{O}(1) \quad (1.26)$$

Thus in this limit the energy is a function of R alone and Eq. (1.23) becomes an exact evaluation.

We mention briefly how these methods are adapted to a quantum gas of electrons (itinerant model of ferromagnetism). Such a model is probably more characteristic of transition metal magnetism. The theory in its present form is far too crude to be at all realistic since no one has as yet produced a band model which takes into account the important correlation effects which play an essential role in a heavy yet mobile band. Nevertheless, the general Hartree–Fock ideas to be sketched below will probably be reflected in the ultimate form of the theory.

The Weiss approximation [essentially, replacing $\langle \mathbf{S}_i \cdot \mathbf{S}_j \rangle$ by $\langle \mathbf{S}_i \rangle \cdot \langle \mathbf{S}_j \rangle$ in the energy] is in this scheme replaced by the Hartree–Fock approximation. The exchange energy is then given by

$$-\frac{1}{2} \sum_{\mathbf{k}, \mathbf{k}', \sigma} v(\mathbf{k}, \mathbf{k}') \langle n_{\mathbf{k}\sigma} \rangle \langle n_{\mathbf{k}'\sigma'} \rangle \, \delta_{\sigma\sigma'}, \tag{1.27}$$

where $\mathbf{k}$ labels the Block momentum and σ the spin. $v(\mathbf{k}, \mathbf{k}')$ is the exchange matrix element due to a screened Coulomb interaction. For simplicity (and for lack of any reliable potential) we will take $v(\mathbf{k}, \mathbf{k}') =$ constant $= V$. The entropy is given by

$$-\sum \langle n_{\mathbf{k}} \rangle \log \langle n_{\mathbf{k}} \rangle - \sum \langle 1 - n_{\mathbf{k}} \rangle \log \langle 1 - n_{\mathbf{k}} \rangle$$
$$\text{(sum on } \mathbf{k} \text{ and } \sigma) \quad (1.28)$$

The sum of Eqs. (1.27) and (1.28) is the counterpart of Eq. (1.23) for bands. Minimizing then gives the Stoner equation of state

$$R = \sum_{\mathbf{k}} \left[\frac{1}{\exp\left[\beta(\varepsilon_{\mathbf{k}} - VR)\right] + 1} - \frac{1}{\exp\left[\beta(\varepsilon_{\mathbf{k}} + VR)\right] + 1} \right] \tag{1.29}$$

This equation has met some success in the interpretation of metallic ferromagnetism, but it is nowhere like on the sound theoretical grounds of the previous development.

2. Theory of Condensation

From the above considerations, a more realistic theory of condensation is easily drawn. In the lattice gas interpretation Eq. (1.23) says that the entropy $(\log W(R))$ is that of a noninteracting hard-core gas and the energy that of the attractive tail taken in a hard-core medium. We therefore write the potential between two atoms in a fluid as

$$v_{ij} = v_{ij}^{\mathrm{HC}} + v_{ij}^{\mathrm{att}} \tag{2.1}$$

and

$$\exp\left[-\beta v_{ij}\right] = \eta_{ij} \exp\left[-\beta v_{ij}^{\mathrm{att}}\right], \tag{2.2}$$

where $\eta_{ij} = 0$, $|\mathbf{r}_{ij}| < c$ and $\eta_{ij} = 1$, $|\mathbf{r}_{ij}| > c$. This is clearly an idealization of the potential which has a "soft" core. There is as yet no theory which has estimated the error in this procedure. However, the physical potential in all probability rises sufficiently fast that there is some effective core distance which does not vary significantly with temperature. The free energy is then written in the form

$$-\beta F = \log \left[\frac{\int \prod \eta_{ij} \exp\left(-\beta V_{\text{att}}\right) dr_1 \cdots dr_N}{\int \prod \eta_{ij}\, d\mathbf{r}_1 \cdots d\mathbf{r}_N} \right] + \log Z_{HC}, \quad (2.3)$$

where Z_{HC} is the denominator in the first term of Eq. (2.3). The last term is the hard-core free energy, which becomes identified with the entropy. It is the analog of $\log W(R)$ in Eq. (1.23). Unfortunately it cannot be evaluated analytically in the present case. However, there are well-known reliable approximation methods available over the whole fluid range so this presents no problem. Again, we will expand to first order in the potential, V_{att}. The result is

$$-\beta F = -\beta \langle V_{\text{att}} \rangle_{HC} + \log Z_{HC}$$
$$= \frac{-N}{2}\beta\rho \int v_{\text{att}}(r) g_{HC}(r)\, d^3 r + \log Z_{HC} \quad (2.4)$$

$g_{HC}(r)$ is the radial distribution of a hard-core fluid at density ρ. The equation of state is then found from $p = -(\partial F/\partial V)_{N,T}$. The resulting isotherms present van der Waals loops for $T < T_c$ which are eliminated as previously mentioned. [For this, recourse to the grand ensemble is required]. The isotherms are drawn in Fig. 4. The critical parameters were calculated by using a potential whose core is at c where $v(c) = 0$. The potential parameters (depth $= \varepsilon$, and c) are determined by comparison with dilute gas phase data. In Table I, the critical parameters

TABLE I. Comparison of Critical Parameters

Parameter	Based on Eq. (2.4)	Van der Waals	Experiment
kT_c/ε	1.42	0.30	1.28
v_c/c^3	3.04	8.88	3.09
$\beta_c p_c v_c$	0.418	0.375	0.292

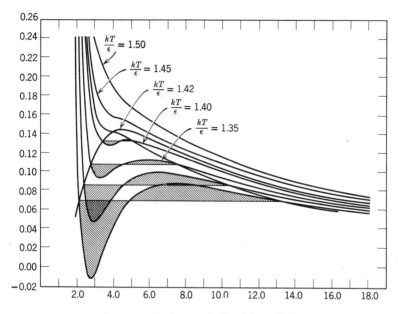

Fig. 4 p–v isotherm calculated from (2.4).

are compared with experiment and those of the usual van der Waals theory. p_c is very sensitive to the calculation. For example lowering T_c by 10%, lowers p_c by 40%. The order of magnitude of the error in the estimate of the critical parameters is probably of the order of the error in the intermolecular potential so that further work in this direction is pointless until better potentials are available.

3. Superconductivity

The most spectacular recent success of molecular field theory is that of the BCS theory of superconductivity. We sketch below the relevant physical ideas and the mathematical formalism.

The provocative remark is that of Cooper, who pointed out that any attractive force no matter how small causes a bound state between two electrons in states above the Fermi sea of a metal. This is because the Pauli principle provides a barrier to the low-momentum states. Since only the high-momentum states are available, the electrons may increase their kinetic energy by only a very small fraction in order to bring about sufficient localization to take advantage of the attraction. The potential in a metal is caused by mutual polarization of the lattice [an electron polarizes the lattice ions in its vicinity for the order of a lattice vibrational period; another electron "senses" this polarization and is attracted to it]. Such a potential causes S-wave bound states. The Pauli principle then causes the spins to be antiparallel. The minimum of energy is when the total momentum of the pair is zero. The momentum space wave function is then of the form $\sum A_{\mathbf{k}} a^{\dagger}_{-\mathbf{k}} a^{\dagger}_{\mathbf{k}} |0\rangle$ where $a^{\dagger}_{\mathbf{k}}$ is a creation operator and $|0\rangle$ is the state of the filled Fermi sea. $A_{\mathbf{k}}$ is the amplitude of finding the kth component in the Cooper bound state.

The full statistical theory must treat all the electrons together and not just one pair at a time. The above considerations indicate that at low temperatures there will develop a correlation between populations in states $(\mathbf{k}\sigma)$ and $(-\mathbf{k} - \sigma)$. (From now on $-\mathbf{k}$ will designate $-\mathbf{k} - \sigma$.) Thus one may adopt an order parameter

$$\langle n_{\mathbf{k}} n_{-\mathbf{k}} \rangle - \langle n_{\mathbf{k}} \rangle \langle n_{-\mathbf{k}} \rangle = |b_{\mathbf{k}}|^2 \qquad (3.1)$$

In a conventional Fermi gas such a fluctuation is of $\mathcal{O}(1/N)$. It is the essential BCS idea to admit $b_{\mathbf{k}} = \mathcal{O}(1)$ at low temperatures.

We remark at this point that in the Weiss theory of ferromagnetism at $\mathscr{H} = 0$, the free energy [Eq. (1.23)] is a function of R^2 alone (and in the Heisenberg model, $|\mathbf{R}|^2$). Nevertheless, we could in all correctness isolate our considerations to a fixed $\mathbf{R}$. The meaning of the direction in $\mathbf{R}$ is the residual direction of an external field as the magnitude of the latter goes to zero. This is the subject of broken symmetry in phase transitions, to which we will turn our further interest in the chapter on fluctuations. Our main point here is that in spite of the fact that the free energy can depend only on fluctuations like Eq. (3.1), it is nevertheless useful to introduce the symbol $b_{\mathbf{k}}$, a complex quantity. The free energy can only depend on $|b_{\mathbf{k}}|$. Mathematically, one can add an external field to the Hamiltonian

$$\sum h^{*}_{\mathbf{k}} b_{\mathbf{k}} + \text{c.c.} \qquad (3.2)$$

and go to the limit $h_{\mathbf{k}} \to 0$ at the end of the calculation.

With this introduction we now present BCS theory. The complete Hamiltonian (with Eq. (3.2)) is

$$H = \sum e_{\mathbf{k}} n_{\mathbf{k}} + \tfrac{1}{2} \sum v(\mathbf{k}_3, \mathbf{k}_4; \mathbf{k}_2, \mathbf{k}_1) a^{\dagger}_{\mathbf{k}_3} a^{\dagger}_{\mathbf{k}_4} a_{\mathbf{k}_1} a_{\mathbf{k}_2} \, \delta(\mathbf{k}_1 + \mathbf{k}_2 - \mathbf{k}_3 - \mathbf{k}_4$$
$$+ \sum h^{*}_{\mathbf{k}} b_{k} + \text{c.c.} \qquad (3.3)$$

$e_{\mathbf{k}}$ is the kinetic energy and v the interaction potential. The term responsible for Cooper pair formation is $a_{\mathbf{k'}}^{\dagger} a_{-\mathbf{k'}}^{\dagger} a_{\mathbf{k}} a_{-\mathbf{k}}$. The *operator* $b_{\mathbf{k}}$ is identified from Eq. (3.1) as $a_{\mathbf{k}} a_{-\mathbf{k}}$. Thus the interesting part of H is

$$H_{\text{reduced}} = \sum e_{\mathbf{k}} n_{\mathbf{k}} + \tfrac{1}{2} \sum v(\mathbf{k}, \mathbf{k'}) b_{\mathbf{k}}^{\dagger} b_{\mathbf{k'}} + \sum h_{\mathbf{k}}^{*} b_{\mathbf{k}} + \text{c.c.} \quad (3.4)$$

Weiss field methods are easily adapted to Eq. (3.4) (and in fact are rigorous, the approximation being the reduction to Eq. (3.3) to Eq. (3.4)). A pair in $\mathbf{k}$ has a "pair" field upon it which is

$$\mathscr{H}_{\mathbf{k}} = h_{\mathbf{k}} + \sum v(\mathbf{k}, \mathbf{k'}) \langle b_{\mathbf{k'}} \rangle \quad (3.5)$$

(Here we distinguish the operator $b_{\mathbf{k}}$ from its expectation value $\langle b_{\mathbf{k}} \rangle$.) The complete pair Hamiltonian is

$$H_{\text{pair}}(\mathbf{k}) = e_{\mathbf{k}} (n_{\mathbf{k}} + n_{\mathbf{k}}) + (b_{\mathbf{k}} \mathscr{H}_{\mathbf{k}}^{*} + \text{c.c.}). \quad (3.6)$$

[This is the analog to the Weiss Hamiltonian of a single spin $= S_i \cdot (\mathscr{H} + v(0)R)$.] $\langle b_{\mathbf{k}} \rangle$ is calculated from

$$\langle b_{\mathbf{k}} \rangle = \text{tr} \exp \left[-\beta H_{\text{pair}}(\mathbf{k}) \right] b_{\mathbf{k}} / \text{tr} \exp \left[-\beta H_{\text{pair}}(\mathbf{k}) \right], \quad (3.7)$$

where the trace extends over the four states $n_{\mathbf{k}}, n_{-\mathbf{k}} = 0, 1$. The result is

$$\langle b_{\mathbf{k}} \rangle = (-\mathscr{H}_{\mathbf{k}}/2E_{\mathbf{k}}) \tanh \left[\beta E_{\mathbf{k}}/2 \right], \quad (3.8)$$

where

$$E_{\mathbf{k}} = (e_2^{\mathbf{k}} + |\mathscr{H}_{\mathbf{k}}|^2)^{\frac{1}{2}} \quad (3.9)$$

$e_{\mathbf{k}}$ is measured from the Fermi surface. For simplicity, we take $v(\mathbf{k}, \mathbf{k'}) = \text{const} = -V$ for a set of states about the Fermi surface. Going to the limit $h_{\mathbf{k}} \to 0$ and summing (3.8) on $\mathbf{k}$ then gives

$$1 = \frac{V}{2N} \sum_{\mathbf{k}} \frac{\tanh \left[(\beta/2)(e_{\mathbf{k}}^2 + \varDelta^2)^{\frac{1}{2}} \right]}{(e_{\mathbf{k}}^2 + \varDelta^2)^{\frac{1}{2}}} \quad (3.10)$$

$$\varDelta = -V \sum \langle b_{\mathbf{k}} \rangle.$$

$\varDelta$ is now a single-order parameter; the solution of Eq. (3.10) for $\varDelta$ vs. T is a Weiss type curve (Fig. 2). The critical temperature is obtained by setting $\varDelta = 0$ in Eq. (3.10). This gives a relation between kT_c and the gap in the quasi-particle spectrum at $\varDelta = 0$ which is confirmed in a wide class of superconductors. The function $\varDelta(T)$ can be measured with great accuracy by tunnel experiments and the ideas expressed in the BCS theory are amply confirmed. There are dynamical details which can and have been included. This brings about an agreement which is very impressive indeed.

Whereas in magnetic experiments, Weiss theory is expected to break down within ten or twenty percent of T_c (for reasons discussed below), the same is not true of the superconductor. The region of intense critical fluctuation is within the order of (Δ/e_F) of the critical temperature and hence is essentially unobservable. Thus the statistical theory of superconductivity is on a more rigorous footing than that of ferromagnetism. In this case, it is the dynamics which is more difficult.

Fluctuation Theory

4. Magnetism: Ising Model

The ideas of Ornstein and Zernicke (OZ) effectively extend the Weiss idea from a global to a local consideration. We introduce the idea of a correlation function $\langle \mu_1 \mu_2 \rangle$ which in Weiss approximation was set to $\langle \mu_1 \rangle \langle \mu_2 \rangle = R^2$. $\langle \mu_1 \mu_2 \rangle$ may be interpreted as the mean value of μ_2 *if* 1 is up at the origin, and we use this interpretation to develop the OZ approximation. Consider the field on spin 2 due to 1 up at the origin as well as the surrounding spins. This is

$$V_2 = v_{12} + \sum_{3 \neq 1} v_{23} \mu_3$$

The average value of the field V_2 contains $\langle \mu_3 \rangle$ in the ensemble where μ_1 is up. This is $\langle \mu_3 \mu_1 \rangle$. Therefore,

$$\langle V_2 \rangle = v_{12} + \sum_{3 \neq 1} v_{23} \langle \mu_3 \mu_1 \rangle. \tag{4.1}$$

The OZ approximation is to take V_2 to be equal to its mean $\langle V_2 \rangle$ and so extend the molecular field concept. In that case $\langle \mu_1 \mu_2 \rangle$ is given by $-\tanh \langle \beta V_2 \rangle$, where $\langle V_2 \rangle$ is given by Eq. (4.1). In the nonmagnetic phase the fluctuation is assumed to be small and hence the tanh may be linearized. This gives

$$\langle \mu_1 \mu_2 \rangle = -\beta v_{12} - \beta \sum v_{23} \langle \mu_3 \mu_1 \rangle \quad \text{(noncondensed phase)} \tag{4.2}$$

The solution is best given in terms of Fourier transforms. One defines

$$\mu_q = (1/\sqrt{N}) \sum \mu_i \, e^{i q \cdot R_i} \tag{4.3}$$

Equation (4.2) becomes simply

$$\langle |\mu_q|^2 \rangle = 1/1 + \beta v(q) \tag{4.4}$$

The fluctuation $\lim\limits_{q \to 0} \langle |\mu_q|^2 \rangle$ is equal to the susceptibility

$$\chi = \frac{\partial R}{\partial \mathscr{H}} = \frac{1}{\beta} \frac{\partial^2}{\partial \mathscr{H}^2} \left\{ \log \operatorname{tr} \exp \left[-\beta (V - \mathscr{H} \sum \mu_i) \right] \right\}$$

$$= \sum_{i,j} [\langle \mu_i \mu_j \rangle - \langle \mu_i \rangle \langle \mu_j \rangle].$$

Thus in the approximation (4.4)

$$\chi = \beta/1 + \beta v(0) = (T/T - T_c) \tag{4.5}$$

which is precisely that obtained in the Weiss approximation [Eq. (1.9)] in the limit $\mathscr{H} \to 0$ and $T > T_c$. The reason for this identity is that the approximation for the response of the system to the perturbation caused by placing spin 1 up at the origin is taken to be linear. Hence the qth component of the exciting field effects only $\langle |\mu_q|^2 \rangle$ [Eq. (4.4)]. Since the $q = 0$ component is treated in the same molecular field approximation as was used to get the Weiss theory, the response to this Fourier component of the field (i.e., χ) must be the same in both treatments.

The energy in the uncondensed phase is immediately calculated through

$$\langle V \rangle = \tfrac{1}{2} \sum v_{ij} \langle \mu_i \mu_j \rangle = \tfrac{1}{2} \sum v(\mathbf{q}) \langle |\mu_q|^2 \rangle$$

$$= \frac{N}{2(2\pi)^3} \int_{\text{first zone}} d^3q \, \frac{v(\mathbf{q})}{1 + \beta v(\mathbf{q})} \tag{4.6}$$

For a force with a range $z^{1/3}$, the integral is of the order of $[v(0)/z]$. Hence as expected the residual energy per particle is $(1/z)$ of the ground-state energy. This is what is not taken into account in the Weiss theory, where the energy vanishes in the uncondensed phase.

The specific heat is found by differentiation. This gives a denominator $[1 + \beta v(\mathbf{q})]^{-2}$ in Eq. (4.6). At $T = T_c$ (i.e., $1 + \beta v(0) = 0$) this gives rise to a square root singularity ($v(\mathbf{q}) = v(0) + \alpha q^2 + \cdots$). Hence $C_V \sim [T - T_c]^{-1/2}$. Finally we observe that the blowing up of $\langle |\mu_q|^2 \rangle$ for small $\mathbf{q}$ and T near T_c is manifested in abundant neutron scattering (critical opalescence) and this has been observed.

In this way we see how a simple refinement of the Weiss idea yields critical precursor phenomena, which if one does not look too closely are in rather good accord with experiment. Actually experiment now is convincing in showing a breakdown within 10 or 20% of the Curie point so that the above ideas are applicable only in the analysis of the precursor to the precursor.

An interesting question now arises. What happens to these wild fluctuations in the condensed phase? The answer is obtainable when one realizes that the linearization procedure mentioned in connection with OZ theory must be in the difference between $\langle V_2 \rangle$ and $\langle V_2 \rangle_{Weiss}$, i.e., one must linearize in $\langle V_2 \rangle - v(0)R$. This results in

$$\langle |\mu_q|^2 \rangle = \frac{1 - R^2}{1 + \beta v(q)(1 - R^2)}; \quad q \neq 0 \quad T < T_c \qquad (4.7)$$

For $q \to 0$ this again becomes χ_{Weiss} for $T < T_c$. By χ_{Weiss} we mean the initial slope at $\mathcal{H} = 0$ of R vs. $\mathcal{H}$ in Fig. 1. Since this is >0, Eq. (4.7) is always >0. The factor $(1 - R^2)$ in the denominator damps the singularity and it is completely squelched for $T \lesssim 0.8 T_c$ where Weiss theory takes over completely. Thus the singularity is accommodated by the system in that the latter condenses, thereby giving rise to Eq. (4.7) rather than Eq. (4.4).

All of these results are obtainable by graphical cluster methods. It can be shown that the OZ, Weiss theories give the free energy and energy correctly to $\mathcal{O}(1/z)$. However, when one more derivative is taken, the series diverges at the critical point. Consequently, a classification in a parameter is useless. It is perhaps of interest to indicate the origin of the difficulty. A graph consists of a number of connected interaction lines, each of weight βv_{ij} and hence of weight $(1/z)$ near T_c. A classification of the order of magnitude of a given topological structure is immediate. Thus trees are $\mathcal{O}(1)$; rings are $\mathcal{O}(1/z)$. These are the molecular field and OZ approximations, respectively. However, for a graph with n bonds ($n > z$), the number of graphs which are not rings, exceeds the number which are. Hence in spite of each graph being smaller, the nonring graphs contribute. Now the order of magnitude of nth order is $[\beta v(0)]^n \sim [T_c/T]^n$. For $T > T_c(1 + 1/z)$ and $n \gtrsim z$, these terms are negligible. However for $T_c < T < T_c(1 + 1/z)$, these n's are important in C_V and χ but not in F and E. In fact this is what causes the divergence in C_V and χ. Thus within $(1/z)$ of T_c, the Weiss OZ method breaks down in second derivative thermodynamic functions. There is no known cure for this ailment.

5. Condensation

The suppression factor $(1 - R^2)$ in Eq. (4.7), in the lattice gas reads $\rho(1 - \rho)$. Hence in the "liquid" phase the factor $(1 - \rho)$ is the effective suppressor. In the real liquid gas transition this factor finds its counterpart. As the reasoning is a bit lengthy, but not different in content from the above we simply quote the result. We introduce the density fluctuation

$$\rho_q = \frac{1}{\sqrt{N}} \sum \exp [i\mathbf{q} \cdot \mathbf{r}_i] \qquad (5.1)$$

$$\langle |\rho_q|^2 \rangle = 1 + \rho \int [g(\mathbf{r}) - 1] \exp [i\mathbf{q} \cdot \mathbf{r}] \, d^3r, \qquad (5.2)$$

where $g(r)$ is the radial distribution function $= (1/\rho^2)\langle \rho(\mathbf{r}_1)\rho(\mathbf{r}_2)\rangle$. We assumed the distribution $g_{HC}(r)$ in the hard-core fluid to be known (and hence also $\langle |\rho_q|^2 \rangle_{HC}$) and we look for its perturbation. The result is

$$\langle |\rho_q|^2 \rangle = \frac{\langle |\rho_q|^2 \rangle_{HC}}{1 + \beta \tilde{v}(\mathbf{q}) \langle |\rho_q|^2 \rangle_{HC}}; \quad \tilde{v}(q) = \rho \int v(r) g_{HC}(r) \exp [i\mathbf{q} \cdot \mathbf{r}] \, d\mathbf{r} \quad (5.3)$$

One can prove that $\lim_{q \to 0} \langle |\rho_q|^2 \rangle = \rho kT\kappa$, where κ is the isothermal compressibility so that Eq. (5.3) as $q \to 0$, reads

$$\kappa = \frac{\kappa_{HC}}{1 + \beta \tilde{v}(0) \kappa_{HC}} \qquad (5.4)$$

The van der Waals equation, obtained from Eq. (2.34) gives

$$p = p_{HC} + [v(0)/2]\rho^2 + \text{term in } (\partial g_{HC}/\partial \rho) \qquad (5.5)$$

The last term is negligible in the limit of a long range attractive force. A second derivative yields Eq. (5.4) with $\kappa^{-1} = \rho(\partial p/\partial \rho)$. Thus Eq. (5.3) goes over to the van der Waals equation for small q, just as in the magnetic case the fluctuation went over into the Weiss equation.

Equation (5.3) thus gives critical opalescence at the van der Waals critical point, as well as divergent $C_V \sim [T - T_c]^{-\frac{1}{2}}$ and compressibility $\sim [T - T_c]^{-1}$. In the liquid phase $\langle |\rho_q|^2 \rangle_{HC}$ becomes very small $\sim 10^{-2} - 10^{-3}$ at small q and the fluctuations become those of the hard core liquid. The only role of the attractive forces is to fix the density at a given pressure through the term in $v(0)$ in Eq. (5.5).

Experiments follow the Ornstein-Zernicke behavior to within about 5% of the critical point.

6. Magnetism—Heisenberg and Band Models

A special feature arises in the theory of fluctuations in a condensed phase characterized by a broken symmetry, the latter being characterized by a continuous group. It has been pointed out after Eq. (3.1) that for the Heisenberg model the condensed phase is characterized by a fixed **R**, whereas at zero field the free energy is a function of $|\mathbf{R}|^2$. The latter is a consequence of the rotational symmetry of the Hamiltonian, which contains, only scalar quantities $\mathbf{S}_i \cdot \mathbf{S}_j$. The same is true of a band-model ferromagnet. That the condensed phase is describable in terms of a given **R** has as profound consequence that at low temperatures, fluctuations are much easier to produce than in the case of a broken discrete symmetry (Ising model). These come about through collective modes, spin waves in the present case. Thus, whereas in the Ising model at low T, the fluctuations damp exponentially [Eq. (4.7) gives $\langle |\mu_\mathbf{q}|^2 \rangle \rightarrow$ $(1 - R^2) \xrightarrow[T \ll T_c]{} e^{-2T_c/T}$], in the Heisenberg model the transverse fluctuations at low T obey $\langle S^-_{-q} S^+_q \rangle \xrightarrow[T \gg T_c]{} (T/T_c)^{3/2}$.

The case is best put by examining the ground state. For example for spin 1/2, the ground state is N-fold degenerate corresponding to $-N/2 \le Sz \le N/2$. We pick out some one of these. However, any linear combination will do. Suppose we begin with $S_z = N/2$ (called $|0\rangle$ in what follows). Then the state $(\sum S^-_i |0\rangle)$ is another of the same energy. In other words there is a mode of macroscopic motion, corresponding to normal coordinate $\sum S^-_i$ which has zero frequency; $[H, \sum S^-_i] = 0$. This has the following immediate implication. Divide the crystal in two. Then turn half the spins one way and half the other. Except on the border between the two halves, no energy is expended. The width of the border in which energy is expended is given by the range of the potential and this we consider finite. (For infinite-range forces, spin waves do not exist and the Weiss theory becomes exact.) If many parts of the crystal are turned with respect to one another the energy expended is proportional to the number of turning points provided these are well separated compared to the range of the force. Now translational symmetry requires that the excitations be classified by wave number. The number of turning points is proportional to wave number, from which we deduce: *there are excitations whose energy is proportional to wave number and have zero energy at zero wave number.* All of this for nothing—broken symmetry alone.

Mathematically, the theory at zero temperature is simple. Given the Hamiltonian $\frac{1}{2} \sum v_{ij} \boldsymbol{\sigma}_i \cdot \boldsymbol{\sigma}_j$, it is trivial to establish

$$[H, \sigma^-_\mathbf{q}]|0\rangle = -2[v(0) - v(\mathbf{q})]\sigma^-_\mathbf{q} |0\rangle; \qquad v(0) < 0 \qquad (6.1)$$

$$\sigma^-_\mathbf{q} = \frac{1}{\sqrt{N}} \sum \sigma^-_i \exp [i\mathbf{q} \cdot \mathbf{R}_i] \qquad (6.2)$$

Therefore the energy excitation of the **q**th spin wave is $2[v(\mathbf{q}) - v(0)]$. Though $\sigma_q^-\sigma_{q'}^-|0\rangle$ is not quite an exact eigenstate it misses by only $\mathcal{O}(1/N)$. In general, at low temperatures, it is possible to prove that the state $\prod_q[\sigma_q^-]^{n_q}/n_q!$ is a good state except for an error which is proportional at most to $(\sum n_q/N)$. Therefore at low temperatures there is an effective description in terms of numbers of bosons

$$\langle S_q^+ S_{-q}^-\rangle = \langle n_q\rangle = [e^{\beta\omega_q} - 1]^{-1}$$
$$\omega_q = 2[v(\mathbf{q}) - v(0)]; \quad S = 1/2 \tag{6.3}$$

The magnetization is then found as follows [we take spin $1/2$]. The number of wrong spins is equal to

$$\sum_i \langle \sigma_i^+ \sigma_i^-\rangle = \sum_q \langle \sigma_{-q}^+ \sigma_q^-\rangle$$
$$= \frac{N(1 - R)}{2} = \sum_q [e^{\beta\omega_q} - 1]^{-1} \tag{6.4}$$

from which it follows that R falls off like $(T/T_c)^{3/2}$ at low T. This is a consequence of $\omega_q \sim q^2$, for small q.

The question is now to be posed: how does this neat low temperature description break down and become a description of critical fluctuations at high temperatures. A fairly good answer is provided by what is called the random phase approximation (RPA) an idea due to Tiablakov in Russia and Englert, Haken, and the author in the United States. At finite temperature, the commutator Eq. (6.1) which has nonlinear terms can be considered on the average. The only difference is a factor of the magnetization

$$[H, \sigma_q^-] \simeq 2[v(q) - v(0)]R\sigma_q^- \tag{6.5}$$

Thus the spin wave frequencies become reduced on the average by a factor of R. It is easy to show that the modification of Eq. (6.4) is

$$\frac{N(1 - R)}{2} = \sum_q \frac{R}{\exp(\beta\omega_q R) - 1} \tag{6.6}$$

This new magnetic equation of state has some remarkable properties which suggest that it is in fact quite a good extrapolation formula over a wide range of physical situations.

(*1*) As the range of the force goes to infinity, Eq. (6.6) become $R = \tanh \beta v(0)R$, precisely the Weiss formula as required.

(2) On this basis, it is possible to show that for a physical model ($z = \mathcal{O}(10)$ to $\mathcal{O}(100)$), that for $T \gtrsim 0.2T_c$ the magnetic equation of state is dominated by spin wave behavior. For $T \gtrsim 0.2T_c$, the condensed phase is approximately describable in terms of a Weiss like theory.

(3) Equation (6.6) presents a critical point somewhat below the Weiss value [$T_c = 0.75(T_c)_{\text{Weiss}}$ for a f.c.c. lattice with near neighbor interactions]. This correction is physical and is quite close to that predicted by accurate numerical extrapolation methods [$T_c = 0.70(T_c)_{\text{Weiss}}$]. Above T_c, one must pass to the limit $R \to 0$ in Eq. (6.6) in a special way. First put on a magnetic field. The argument of the exponential becomes modified to $\omega_q R + 2\mathcal{H}$. For $T > T_c$, one goes to the limit $R \to 0$, $\mathcal{H} \to 0$; $R/\mathcal{H} \to \chi$. There results a theory which is called the spherical model. This theory joins onto the Ornstein-Zernicke theory for $T \gtrsim (T_c)_{\text{Weiss}}$. For $T_c \gtrsim T \gtrsim (T_c)_{\text{Weiss}}$, there is considerable modification. For example, the susceptibility χ goes to infinity like $[T - T_c]^{-2}$. Whereas this is a movement in the right direction, the correction is too extreme. Numerical calculations of Domb et al. indicate that the correct behavior is $[T - T_c]^{-4/3}$.

The limits of the theoretical validity of Eq. (6.6) are fairly well understood. At very low T, Dyson has made a rigorous theory of spin wave interaction, provided terms in $\exp(-T_c/T)$ are negligible. One finds that a description in terms of spin waves with an effective frequency does exist, however the frequency does not scale with R but with $\Delta E/E(0)$, a result due to Keffer and London. Thus $\omega_q(T) \simeq \omega_q(0)[(1 - (T/T_c)^{5/2}]$ rather than $[1 - (T/T_c)^{3/2}]$. The error in R scaling is completely understood and corresponds to a neglect of spin wave exchange terms. Dyson's analysis is valid only as long as spin wave behavior dominates the problem i.e. for $(T/T_c) \gtrsim 0.2$. In this range all of these effects are negligible in so far as the magnetic equation of state is concerned. However, neutron spectroscopy is now available to measure $\omega_q(T)$. At low T, Dyson's behavior should prevail. On the other hand, for reasons given in the next paragraph for $T \gtrsim 0.2T_c$, R scaling should become predominant.

Stinchcombe, Howitz, Englert and Brout, in order to find out what really goes on, did a complete graphical analysis of the Heisenberg model. It was found that in physical models, for $T \gtrsim 0.2T_c$, there was a graph which modified RPA and converted it into Dyson's result (this is the spin exchange term). However, once this range of temperature is exceeded, the extra graph was smaller than the RPA graphs by $0(1/z)$, so that the RPA results obtain in the temperature range $0.2T_c \leq T \leq (1 - 1/z)T_c$. Within $(1/z)$ of T_c, critical fluctuations dominate as in the Ising model and an analytic treatment appears to be impossible.

Finally we mention that the real physics of the situation is probably best expressed in terms of spectral distribution functions, the Fourier transform of $\langle \sigma^-_q(t)\sigma^+_q(0)\rangle$. At low temperatures this distribution approaches a δ function: $\delta(\omega - \omega_q(T))$, where $\omega_q(T)$ is Dyson's value. The width of the line is readily estimated and shrinks to zero in some known way as a function of q and T. At higher temperature the spectrum widens. What RPA does is to approximate the integral $\langle \sigma^-_q(0)\sigma^+_q(0)\rangle = \int d\omega S(\omega)[e^{\beta\omega} - 1]^{-1}$ by setting the spectral density $S(\omega)$ to a δ function about its central value $\omega \simeq \omega_q R$. This probably is no great mistake in estimating the magnetization curve in the undelicate region. However, it is a far cry from a complete description of the physical phenomenon. Important efforts have been made in this direction by Martin and Gottfried.

7. Fluctuations in Superconductors

In all transitions but that of magnetism in the Heisenberg model, theoretical work has been carried out only in RPA. In superconductivity this work is due to Anderson, Bogoliubov, Thouless, and others.

We only announce the results, as the techniques are profoundly analogous to those discussed in the previous section, though algebraically much more complicated.

In the uncondensed phase, one looks for the fluctuations in the operators $a_{-k}a_{k+q} \equiv b^q_k$. In the case $v(\mathbf{k}, \mathbf{k}') = -V$ [Eq. (3.10)], the results are easily expressed in terms of the fluctuations of $b^q \equiv \sum_k b^q$. b^q is the analog of the spin–wave operator σ^+_q in the Heisenberg model. One finds for small q ($q \ll k_F$)

$$\langle |b^q|^2\rangle = \frac{\sum_{\mathbf{k}} \dfrac{1 - n(\mathbf{k}) - n(\mathbf{k} + \mathbf{q})}{\exp\left[\beta(\varepsilon_{\mathbf{k}} + \varepsilon_{\mathbf{k}+\mathbf{q}})\right] - 1}}{1 - (V/N)\sum \dfrac{1 - n(\mathbf{k}) - n(\mathbf{k} + \mathbf{q})}{\varepsilon_{\mathbf{k}} + \varepsilon_{\mathbf{k}+\mathbf{q}}}}. \tag{7.1}$$

The singularity occurs when $\langle |b^{q=0}|^2\rangle \to \infty$. This is identical with the BCS condition Eq. (3.10) at $\Delta = 0$. One then expands the denominator about small q. The interaction energy is $V\sum |b^q|^2$. It then follows that all the results of OZ obtain. However, the increase in specific heat no longer occurs within $(1/z)$ of the critical point, but rather within (Δ/ε_F) of T_c. This makes experimentation almost impossibly difficult.

In the condensed phase, a collective mode exists. This is because the phase is described in terms of $\langle b_k \rangle$. Anderson remarked that this is a broken symmetry of the gauge group. The collective mode at $q = 0$, corresponds to the rotation of the gauge angle. At higher q the normal modes are linear combinations of density fluctuations ρ_q and pair fluctuations b_k^q. These are very complicated modes which unfortunately in a metal become irrelevant since the collective behavior becomes completely dominated by the density fluctuation. In this case, because of the long-range Coulomb repulsion, the mode is a simple plasma wave. However if a neutral superconductor ever is found (He^3 at very low temperatures is the only candidate) these Anderson modes will exist and will be observable. They are the exact, but fancy analogs of spin waves.

8. Exact Numerical Results and Experimental Situation

In the accompanying table we set out some of the results of the King's College group based on their numerical calculations of critical temperature, and thermodynamic singularities the Ising model as compared to the Weiss-OZ prediction on one hand and experiment (liquid-vapor condensation) on the other.

Table II.

	Below T_c			Above T_c	
	α'	β	γ'	α	γ
Weiss–OZ	$0_{\text{discont.}}$	$1/2$	1	$0_{\text{discont.}}$	1
Ising model	≥ 0	$\simeq 5/16$	$\geq 5/4$	$\geq 0, \leq 0.2$	$5/4$
Experiment	$\geq 0_{\log}$	0.33–0.36	≥ 1.27	$\simeq 0.2$	> 1.1

From M. Fisher, *J. Math. Phys.*, **5**, 944 (1964).
Definition of symbols: $C_V \sim |T - T_c|^{-\alpha}$; R or $(\rho_{\text{liq}} - \rho_{\text{gas}}) \sim (T_c - T)^\beta$
$\qquad$ x or $\kappa \sim |T - T_c|^{-\gamma}$

In addition we quote Fisher's result that the long range part of the distribution function in the critical region is

$$e^{-Kr}/r^n; \quad K \sim (T - T_c)^{0.65}; \quad n = 1.06 \qquad (8.1)$$

as compared to OZ theory $K = (T - T_c)^{0.5}$; $n = 1$. (This being the Fourier transform of $[1 + \beta v(q) \simeq [(T - T_c) + \alpha q^2]^{-1}$.)

The experimental situation is in general accord with these findings Liquid–gas condensation follows Ising model behavior for most of the singularities, though some deviations have shown up. The reason for the general accord doubtless lies in the lattice gas interpretation of the Ising model. Thus the Ising model on the low temperature side predicts $R \sim (T_c - T)^{0.32}$; in condensation this is translated into $[\rho_{\text{liq}} - \rho_{\text{gas}}] \sim (T_c - T)^{0.32}$ on the line of coexistence. [In the lattice gas the condition $\mathscr{H} = 0$ is translated into $\mu_{\text{liq}} = \mu_{\text{gas}}$.] The coefficient 0.32 has now been confirmed to within a few per cent by many experiments on many substances. The only thing lacking is the analytic theory. The susceptibility in the Ising model diverges like $[T - T_c]^{-5/4}$. In Fig. 5 we display the experiment of Habgood and Schneider on xenon for the analogous quantity—the compressibility along the critical isochore. One sees how at a few per cent above T_c, the Ornstein-Zernicke $[T - T_c]^{-1}$ behavior takes over. The specific heat has now been measured with great accuracy by Voronel and Bagatskii. It is found that C_V diverges like $[T - T_c]^{0.2}$ for $T_c \leq T \leq 1.2 T_c$. On the low-temperature side the divergence is more logarithmic. This again accords with Ising model calculations. Equation (8.1) is more difficult to confirm. Light scattering gives Ornstein-Zernicke behavior with signs of deviation leaning towards Eq. (8.1) very near the critical point. Precise quantitative results are still in the waiting.

The situation in magnetic substances is equally impressive. Figure 4 represents the experiment of Benedek and Heller on MnF_2 and gives

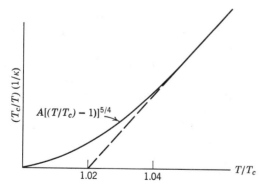

Fig. 5   Compressibility data of Habgood and Schneider. The solid line is the data. The dashed line is the extrapolation of the high-temperature data.

$R \sim (T_c - T)^{0.33}$ as predicted by the calculation. One also sees how the experimental and Weiss curves join outside the critical region. [In this case the range of the force is expected to extend to second neighbors as indicated by observed spin wave behavior. This is why the Weiss description becomes valid only at 5% below T_c instead of the expected 20% for near neighbor interactions. It is somewhat more of a mystery to explain the Habgood-Schneider data in Fig. 5, where the joining to OZ behavior is expected more at $1.2T_c$ rather than the observed $1.04T_c$.] Susceptibility measurements on Heisenberg model like substances confirm the calculated $[T - T_c]^{-\frac{4}{3}}$ behavior and hence show up the distinction between Heisenberg and Ising models. Specific heat data indicate a logarithmic behavior on both sides, which is not inconsistent with the calculations.

The general situation is a wide range of agreement between experiment and calculated critical singular behavior. Outside of a region which straddles T_c by between five and twenty per cent, depending on the substance, the Weiss-Ornstein-Zernicke behavior takes over. The gap to fill is the creation of an analytic theory within the critical region itself. At the moment, this seems of insurmountable difficulty.

We finally mention the efforts primarily of Fisher and Rushbrooke which relate some of the critical singular indices to each other. These appear as rigorous inequalities which in some cases lead to a conjecture of equality. In terms of Table II, one finds as a consequence of thermodynamic stability arguments

$$\alpha' + 2\beta + \gamma' \geq 2$$

This inequality becomes an equality in the molecular field case and present calculations tend to support this as a general equality.

This article is a condensed informal résumé of the book by the author entitled *Phase Transitions*, W. A. Benjamin, New York, 1965. The interested reader will find details and bibliography therein. This explains the absence of all references in the present work.

In addition, we recommend the reprint volume *Classical Theory of Fluids*, Ed., H. Frisch and J. Lebowitz, W. A. Benjamin, New York, 1965. As the title indicates, this volume contains many pertinent references on the liquid–gas condensation.

A Mathematical View of the Theory of
Phase Changes

M. KAC

The Rockefeller University

1. The first statisticomechanical theory of phase changes is that of van der Waals. An essentially equivalent (mathematically) theory of spontaneous magnetization is associated with the names of Curie and Weiss and we owe an almost identical theory of transition phenomena in binary alloys to Bragg and Williams. It is to the Bragg–Williams theory that Hans Bethe made a significant and penetrating contribution and it therefore seemed appropriate to include in the volume honoring him a brief essay on a subject closely related to one of his early scientific interests.

2. The van der Waals and the Curie–Weiss theories are based on the assumption that the attractive interactions are *weak* and of *long range*. Since it became known that this is not the case these theories have naturally enough been somewhat neglected. Perhaps the strongest blow against these theories has come from Onsager's famed exact solution of the two-dimensional Ising model, mainly because the rigorously established fact that the specific heat has a logarithmic singularity was in direct contradiction with predictions of theories based on the assumption of weak, long-range forces (even when modified by the Bethe correction, the first step toward bringing "short-range order" into the theories).

In recent years Brout originated a revival of interest in the older theories by an attempt to construct, in a systematic way, corrections to the molecular field theory of Curie and Weiss. This led to so called $1/Z$ expansion, where Z is the number of elementary magnets (or spins) with which a given elementary magnet interacts significantly.

For high temperatures (well above the Curie point) this is a valid procedure but the expansions surely break down near the critical point and it is already difficult, without bringing in extraneous thermo-dynamic arguments, to construct $1/Z$ expansions below the Curie point.

A somewhat different line was taken by Uhlenbeck, Hemmer, and myself. By starting with a specific interaction we were able to exhibit the analogs of the $1/Z$ expansions both above and below the critical temperature. We could also study (for our model) what happens in the critical region where these expansions fail.

As a result of this and some farther studies there begins to emerge a view of a mathematical mechanism of phase transitions which may well prove to be general.

While much of what I shall say is tentative and speculative, I believe that a dimly-lit bridge between the old theories based on ideas of van der Waals and the new ones based on those of Onsager is beginning to emerge on the horizon.

3. Let me begin by reviewing briefly a special one-dimensional model. The model is an array of N "spins" μ_k ($k = 1, 2, \ldots, N$)

$$E = -\alpha\gamma \sum_{1 \le i < j \le N} e^{-\gamma|i-j|} \mu_i \mu_j. \tag{3.1}$$

Each spin can, of course, be either $+1$ or -1.

It was shown elsewhere [see e.g., Kac[1] or Kac and Helfand[2]] that, in the thermodynamic limit $N \to \infty$, the free energy per spin is given by the formula

$$-(\psi/kT) = \log 2 - (\nu\gamma/2) + \log \lambda_{\max}, \tag{3.2}$$

where

$$\nu = \alpha/kT \tag{3.3}$$

and $\lambda_{\max}$ is the maximum eigenvalue of the integral equation

$$\int_{-\infty}^{\infty} [\cosh(\sqrt{\nu\gamma}x)]^{\frac{1}{2}}[W(x)/W(y)]^{\frac{1}{2}}P_\gamma(x \mid y)[\cosh(\sqrt{\nu\gamma}y)]^{\frac{1}{2}}\psi(y)\,dy$$
$$= \lambda\psi(x). \tag{3.4}$$

Here and henceforth we use the notation

$$W(x) = (1/2\pi)^{\frac{1}{2}} \exp(-x^2/2) \tag{3.5}$$

and

$$P_\gamma(x \mid y) = \frac{\exp[-(y - xe^{-\gamma})^2/2(1 - e^{-2\gamma})]}{[2\pi(1 - e^{-2\gamma})]^{\frac{1}{2}}}. \tag{3.6}$$

The integral operator in Eq. (3.4) is equivalent to the operator

$$\exp[(1/2)\log\cosh(\sqrt{\nu\gamma}x)] \exp\left[\gamma\left(\frac{d^2}{dx^2} - \frac{1}{4}x^2 + \frac{1}{2}\right)\right]$$
$$\exp[(1/2)\log\cosh(\sqrt{\nu\gamma}x)] \tag{3.7}$$

which for small γ and to $O(\gamma)$ can be shown to be simply

$$\exp\left[\gamma\left(\frac{d^2}{dx^2} - \frac{1}{4}x^2 + \frac{1}{\gamma}\log\cosh(\sqrt{v\gamma}x) + \frac{1}{2}\right)\right]. \qquad (3.8)$$

Thus to order γ

$$\lambda_{\max} \sim \exp(-\gamma E_0), \qquad (3.9)$$

where E_0 is the lowest eigenvalue of the Schroedinger equation

$$\frac{d^2\bar{\psi}}{dx^2} + \left\{E + \frac{1}{2} - \frac{1}{4}x^2 + \frac{1}{\gamma}\log\cosh(\sqrt{v\gamma}x)\right\}\bar{\psi} = 0 \qquad (3.10)$$

[I use $\bar{\psi}$ to distinguish it from the *rigorous* eigenfunctions ψ of Eq. (3.4) or (3.7).]

To find where the potential

$$V(x) = (1/4)x^2 - (1/\gamma)\log\cosh(\sqrt{v\gamma}x) \qquad (3.11)$$

in Eq. (3.10) has its minima we must solve the equation

$$\sqrt{\gamma}x/2 = \sqrt{v}\tanh\sqrt{v\gamma}x,$$

or setting

$$x = \eta\sqrt{2}/\sqrt{\gamma} \qquad (3.12)$$

the equivalent equation

$$\eta/\sqrt{2v} = \tanh\sqrt{2v}\eta, \qquad (3.13)$$

which is easily recognized as the equation determining the mean field in the Curie–Weiss theory.

If $2v < 1$ (high temperatures) the only solution of Eq. (3.13) is $\eta = 0$ but if $2v > 1$ the potential has two minima at $\pm\eta\sqrt{2}/\sqrt{\gamma}$ at which the potential attains its maximal depth

$$(1/2)\eta^2 - \log\cosh\eta\sqrt{2v}.$$

Correspondingly, to lowest order in γ

$$\log\lambda_{\max} = \begin{cases} 0, & 2v < 1 \\ (-\eta^2/2) + \log\cosh\eta\sqrt{2v}, & 2v > 1 \end{cases} \qquad (3.14)$$

and we have the Curie–Weiss phase transition.

4. As is well known there is no phase transition for $\gamma > 0$, in the sense that the *exact* $\lambda_{\max}$ is an *analytic* function of $v\ (= \alpha/kT)$. Only in the limit $\gamma \to 0$ do we detect nonanalytic behavior.

In spite of this there are highly suggestive analogies with the two-dimensional Ising model.

The most striking and the most obvious is that in both cases the free energy is related to the largest eigenvalue of a linear operator.

The next is more subtle, and is connected with what is called *asymptotic degeneracy* of the eigenvalues.

In the case of the two-dimensional Ising model one starts with a $N \times M$ square lattice, say, and one expresses the partition function $Q_{N,M}$ as a trace of the Nth power of a certain $2^M \times 2^M$ matrix K_M

$$Q_{N,M} = \text{Trace } \{K_M\}^N \tag{4.1}$$

It therefore follows that

$$\lim_{N \to \infty} (1/N) \log Q_{N,M} = \lambda_{\max} \text{ of } K_M. \tag{4.2}$$

For temperatures above the critical the eigenvalues of K_M are all simple. Below the critical temperature there are *two* such spectra and they *are shifted with respect to each other by an amount of the order* $\exp(-cM)$ where c is a positive constant.

An analogous situation obtains for our one-dimensional model.

For $2\nu < 1$ (i.e., above the critical point) we can replace, to first order in γ,

$$(1/\gamma) \log \cosh (\sqrt{\nu\gamma}x)$$

by

$$\nu x^2/2$$

and thus from Eq. (3.10)

$$E_n \sim -\tfrac{1}{2} + (n + \tfrac{1}{2})(1 - 2\nu)^{1/2}$$

or

$$\lambda_n \sim \gamma[\tfrac{1}{2} - (n + \tfrac{1}{2})(1 - 2\nu)^{1/2}], \qquad (\lambda_0 = \lambda_{\max}). \tag{4.3}$$

In other words, the spectrum consists of simple eigenvalues spaced roughly γ apart.

For $2\nu > 1$ the situation changes drastically because the potential now has two minima (at $\pm\eta\sqrt{2}/\sqrt{\gamma}$).

For small γ the wells are deep and set far apart. Each can be approximated (to first order in γ) by a parabolic well and each contributes a set of identical harmonic oscillator eigenvalues. But there is no *strict degeneracy* [although, remarkably enough, the apparent degeneracy persists to all orders of γ!]. We again have two sets of eigenvalues each set consisting of points spaced roughly

$$\frac{\gamma}{2}\left[1 - 2\nu(1 - \tanh^2 \eta\sqrt{2\nu})\right]^{1/2}\dagger$$

apart but the corresponding members of the two sets are *shifted* with respect to each other by quantities of the order

$$\exp\left(-c/\gamma\right)$$

While this can be established by a rigorous discussion of the integral equation (3.4) it can also be seen intuitively as follows. Consider, for the sake of brevity only the maximum eigenvalue.

It is seen that both

$$\bar{\psi}_0[x - (\eta\sqrt{2}/\sqrt{\gamma})] \quad \text{and} \quad \bar{\psi}_0[x + (\eta\sqrt{2}/\sqrt{\gamma})] \tag{4.4}$$

where

$$\bar{\psi}_0(x) = (\sqrt{\omega}/\sqrt[4]{2\pi})\exp\left(-\omega x^2/4\right), \quad \omega^2 = \nu - 2\nu(1 - \tanh^2 \eta\sqrt{2\nu}) \tag{4.5}$$

are approximate eigenfunctions corresponding to the two (approximate) parabolic wells.

The "overlap" integral

$$\int_{-\infty}^{\infty} \bar{\psi}_0[x - (\eta\sqrt{2}/\sqrt{\gamma})]\bar{\psi}_0[x + (\eta\sqrt{2}/\sqrt{\gamma})]\, dx \tag{4.6}$$

is an approximation to the separation of the two largest eigenvalues and can easily seen to be of the order $\exp\left(-c/\gamma\right)$.

The intuitive argument is dangerous because $\exp\left(-c/\gamma\right)$ is outside the range of perturbation calculations and yet we use $\bar{\psi}_0(x \pm \eta\sqrt{2}/\sqrt{\gamma})$ which is obtained from a perturbation argument.

5. The significance of asymptotic degeneracy of the highest eigenvalue can be best appreciated (as is indeed also the case with the Ising model) by considering the correlation $\langle\mu_k\mu_{k+r}\rangle$, in the limit $N \to \infty$, with k of order N and r of order unity (i.e., both spins "well within" the lattice but separated by a finite distance).

† The reason why $1 - 2\nu(1 - \tanh^2 \eta\sqrt{2\nu}) > 0$ for η satisfying Eq. (3.13) is that slope of the straight line $y = \eta/2\nu$ is greater than the slope of the curve $y = \tanh \eta\sqrt{2\nu}$ at the point the two intersect.

One finds [see ref. (2)] that

$$\rho(r) = \lim_{N \to \infty} \langle \mu_k \mu_{k+r} \rangle = \sum_{j=0}^{\infty} \left(\frac{\lambda_j}{\lambda_0}\right)^r \left(\int_{-\infty}^{\infty} \psi_0(x)\psi_j(x) \tanh \sqrt{\nu\gamma}x \, dx\right)^2 \quad (5.1)$$

and since the principal eigenfunction $\psi_0(x)$ is even the term with $j = 0$ is zero since $\tanh \sqrt{\nu\gamma}x$ is odd. However, $\psi_1(x)$ is odd and we have

$$\rho(r) \sim \left(\frac{\lambda_1}{\lambda_0}\right)^r \left(\int_{-\infty}^{\infty} \psi_0(x)\psi_1(x) \tanh \sqrt{\nu\gamma}x \, dx\right)^2 \quad (5.2)$$

Now, for $\nu > 1/2$,

$$\lambda_1/\lambda_0 = 1 - O[\exp(-c/\gamma)]$$

and hence the correlation persists over distances of order

$$\exp(c/\gamma)$$

while for $\nu < 1/2$ it persists only over distances of order

$$1/\gamma.$$

Moreover, if we approximate $\psi_0(x)$ by

$$(1/\sqrt{2})\bar{\psi}_0[x - (\eta\sqrt{2}/\sqrt{\gamma})] + (1/\sqrt{2})\bar{\psi}[x + (\eta\sqrt{2}/\sqrt{\gamma})]$$

and $\psi_1(x)$ by

$$(1/\sqrt{2})\bar{\psi}[x - (\eta\sqrt{2}/\sqrt{\gamma})] - (1/\sqrt{2})\bar{\psi}[x + (\eta\sqrt{2}/\sqrt{\gamma})]$$

[$\bar{\psi}$ is defined by Eq. (4.5)], we see that the residual correlation is approximately

$$(2 \tanh \eta\sqrt{2\nu})^2.$$

6. Consider, for example, an $N \times M$ (two-dimensional) system of spins $\mu_{k,l}$ with interaction energy

$$E = \sum_{\substack{1 \le k < k' \le N \\ 1 \le l < l' \le M}} v(k, l; k', l')\mu_{k,l}\mu_{k,l}, \quad (6.1)$$

where

$$v(k, l; k', l') = \alpha\gamma \exp(-\gamma|k - k'|)[(1/2)\delta_{l-1,l'} + (1/2)\delta_{l+1,l'} + \delta_{ll'}]\dagger. \quad (6.2)$$

† This is "model A" discussed by Kac and Helfand[2].

The analog of Eq. (3.2) is now

$$-(\psi/kT) = \log 2 - (v\gamma/2) + \lim_{M \to \infty} (1/M) \log \Lambda_{\max}, \qquad (6.3)$$

where again

$$\nu = \alpha/kT, \qquad (6.4)$$

but $\Lambda_{\max}$ is now the maximum eigenvalue of the M-fold integral equation:

$$\int \cdots \int \prod_{k=1}^{M} P_\gamma(x_k|y_k;1) \prod_{k=1}^{M-1} \cosh \sqrt{\frac{v\gamma}{2}} (y_k + y_{k+1}) \varphi(y_1, \ldots, y_M)$$
$$\times\, dy_1 \cdots dy_M = \Lambda \varphi(x_1, \ldots, x_M). \qquad (6.5)$$

If one couples the Mth row with the first, the $M - 1$ in the product above can be replaced by M (one identifies, of course, y_{M+1} with y_1); this simplifies matters somewhat and we shall therefore adopt this simplification in the sequel.

The analog of Eq. (3.8) is

$$\exp\left\{\gamma\left[\nabla^2 - \frac{1}{4}\sum_1^M x_k^2 + \frac{M}{2} + \frac{1}{\gamma}\sum_1^M \log \cosh \sqrt{\frac{v\gamma}{2}} (x_k + x_{k+1})\right]\right\} \quad (6.6)$$

and the Bragg–Williams Curie point is that value of ν for which the quadratic form

$$\sum_1^M x_k^2 - \nu \sum_1^M (x_k + x_{k+1})^2$$

ceases to be positive definite. This is easily seen to be $1/4$ and for

$$\nu < 1/4 \qquad (6.7)$$

one obtains, for example, to first order in γ (after letting $M \to \infty$)

$$-\frac{\psi}{kT} = \log 2 + \frac{1}{2}\left(1 - \nu - \frac{1}{2\pi}\int_{-\pi}^{\pi} \sqrt{1 - 2\nu \cos \theta}\, d\theta\right)\gamma + \cdots. \quad (6.8)$$

For

$$\nu > 1/4$$

the potential

$$V(x_1, \ldots, x_M) = \frac{1}{4}\sum_1^M x_k^2 - \frac{1}{\gamma}\sum_1^M \log \cosh \sqrt{\frac{v\gamma}{2}} (x_k + x_{k+1}) \quad (6.9)$$

can be seen to have again *exactly two minima* one at

$$(\eta\sqrt{2}/\sqrt{\gamma}, \eta\sqrt{2}/\sqrt{\gamma}, \ldots, \eta\sqrt{2}/\sqrt{\gamma})$$

and the other at

$$(-\eta\sqrt{2}/\sqrt{\gamma}, -\eta\sqrt{2}/\sqrt{\gamma}, \ldots, -\eta\sqrt{2}/\sqrt{\gamma}),$$

where η now is obtained by solving the analog of Eq. (3.13) which is

$$\tanh 2\sqrt{\nu}\eta = \eta/2\sqrt{\nu}. \tag{6.10}$$

The analog of the overlap integral (4.6) yields a number of the order

$$\exp(-cM/\gamma) \tag{6.11}$$

and if this were indeed the rigorous order of the separation of the two highest eigenvalues then we would have an asymptotic degeneracy exactly like in the two-dimensional Ising model.

Letting $M \to \infty$ (which is part of taking the thermodynamic limit) would then alone suffice to produce the residual correlation at infinity, and hence long-range order.

We have not yet succeeded in finding a rigorous proof that the desired separation is of order (6.11) but have little doubt that the result is correct.

In this way we see that the one-dimensional and the two-dimensional models are quite similar and that the origins of the *apparent singularity* in the former and the *real singularity* in the latter are essentially the same.

References

1. Kac, M., *Statistical Mechanics of Some One-Dimensional Systems*, Studies in Mathematical Analysis and Related Topics, Stanford University Press, 1962.
2. Kac, M., and E. Helfand, "Study of Several Lattice Systems with Long-Range Forces", *J. Math. Phys.*, **4**(8), 1963, pp. 1078–1088.

Phonon Physics

J. A. KRUMHANSL

Cornell University

I. Introduction

The physics of the solid state is a subject of long standing interest, to which Hans Bethe made numerous contributions in the early years of its development. The subject continues to develop, not because of the search for new elementary phenomena as on the ultra-microscopic or high-energy scale, but because of the richness which can be found in the collective behavior of extended many-particle systems. For the most part the subject has been explored to date only in well-ordered, structurally-stable systems, i.e., crystalline solids.

Topics of particular interest in solids have been electronic excitations, magnetic properties, and lattice properties. The description of physical phenomena involving the elementary excitations of the solid—such as superconductivity, ferromagnetism, charge and heat transport, and nuclear and electron spin resonance—has profited considerably in recent years through the introduction of the methods of quantum field theory and formal scattering theory. The concepts of quasi-particles, self-energy correction and lifetimes, as well as resonance and collective behavior are now commonplace in solid-state physics. The subjects of superconductivity and ferromagnetism have received the major attention. But the topic of lattice excitations, under the general appellation of phonon physics, has also received considerable attention and I would like to review some of the recent viewpoints. These will be brief descriptions of the types of problems which are receiving attention, some at Cornell. The discussion will be divided into three sections: The free phonon field, phonon interactions, and selected applications to phenomena involving phonons. Wherever standard or obvious notation is used it will be defined explicitly. No treatment of the subject would

509

be complete without mention of the classic papers of one of Bethe's close contemporaries, Rudolf Peierls[1]; much of the modern development is based on his 1929 paper, and in the next section his approach to the quantized phonon field is used.

II. The Phonon Field

II.1. We begin by considering the atomic motions in a perfectly periodic crystal. Several considerations are (*1*) the system has translational periodicity, (*2*) it is assumed to be stable so that small displacement excitations are harmonic in first approximation, and (*3*) the many-electron interactions actually occurring in a real solid may be replaced (adiabatic approximation) by effective potentials dependent on the displacements from equilibrium (quantum effects such as exchange of particles between sites are neglected).

The properties of the free phonon field then may be described (*1*) in terms of a representation appropriate to periodic systems, (*2*) in terms of the dynamics of the harmonic oscillator, and (*3*) conditional on the nature of the effective potentials.

The periodic lattice may be described by means of a set of indicial vectors (Born and Huang[2])

$$\mathbf{x}(l, s) = \mathbf{x}(l) + \mathbf{x}(s),$$

where $\mathbf{x}(l)$ locates the *l*th unit cell and $\mathbf{x}(s)$ is the location of the *l*th atomic species in the unit cell. The notation details are not fundamental to the physics so we will abbreviate to $\mathbf{x}(l)$.

For the $\mathbf{x}(l)$ labeled particles we denote the dynamic variables by a karat to explicitly indicate their dynamic nature, i.e.,

$$\hat{\mathbf{u}}(l) = \text{displacement of } l\text{th atom}$$
$$\hat{\mathbf{p}}(l) = \text{momentum of } l\text{th atom}$$

The vector fields $\hat{\mathbf{u}}(l)$ and $\hat{\mathbf{p}}(l)$ may be treated by either classical or quantum dynamics; only the latter is strictly correct. In either case the dynamics is found from a Hamiltonian containing the physics of the system. In particular, in the harmonic approximation

$$\hat{H} = \sum_l \frac{\hat{\mathbf{p}}(l)^2}{2m} + \sum_{l,l'} \tfrac{1}{2}\varPhi(l, l')\hat{\mathbf{u}}(l)\cdot\hat{\mathbf{u}}(l')$$

in "$\hat{\mathbf{u}}(l)$, $\hat{\mathbf{p}}(l)$ representation".

The consequences of translational symmetry appear by noting that [we assume periodic boundary conditions throughout the rest of the discussion; standard references (Ziman[3]) may be consulted] the translation group is reduced by the representation

$$\hat{u}(l) = \hat{b}(k) \exp [ik \cdot x(l)]/\sqrt{Nm(l)}$$

$$\hat{p}(l) = \hat{c}(k) \exp [ik \cdot x(l)]/\sqrt{Nm(l)}.$$

In this representation, the Hamiltonian will become diagonal in k. For S atoms per unit cell the potential matrix Φ transforms to a series of $3S \times 3S$ matrices, for each k. A further unitary transformation to a set of polarization vectors $w(k, \nu)$ $(\nu = 1, \ldots, 3S)$ yields the representation

$$\hat{u}(l) = \hat{b}(k, \nu)w(k, \nu) \exp [ik \cdot x(l)]/\sqrt{N}$$

$$\hat{p}(l) = \hat{c}(k, \nu)w(k, \nu) \exp [ik \cdot x(l)]/\sqrt{N}$$

By definition, the w are the orthonormalized eigenvectors of the matrix equation

$$L(k, k')\{w(k', \nu)\} = \omega^2(k, \nu)\{w(k, \nu)\}.$$

Here $(L)_{ll'} = \Phi(l, l')/(m_l m_{l'})^{1/2}$ is the dynamic matrix in ll' representation, while

$$L_{k, k'} = \sum_{l, l'} \frac{\exp [-ik \cdot k(l)]}{\sqrt{N}} \frac{\Phi(l, l')}{(m(l)m(l'))^{1/2}} \frac{\exp [ik' \cdot x(l')]}{\sqrt{N}}$$

is its transformed k, k' representation; it is in fact diagonal in k, k'. Also

$$w(-k, \nu) = w^*(k, \nu)$$

and

$$[w^*(k, \nu)] \cdot \{w(k', \nu)\} = \delta(k, k') \delta(\nu, \nu')$$

and

$$\omega^2(k, \nu) = \omega^2(-k, \nu).$$

There is a long history since Born and von Karman, and Brillouin, of the study of the eigenvalues of the dynamical matrix for different lattice types and potentials. Those differences which distinguish various solid types are now more in the nature of solid state chemistry; the current interest is directed toward dynamic properties.

II.2. First, attention may be called to some present day viewpoints on effective potentials for atom displacements. Cochran[4] has unified several approaches by emphasizing that the proper quantity to consider in the potential lattice motion is the excitation energy produced by an atomic "density fluctuation" characterized by $\mathbf{k}$ and $\omega(\mathbf{k}, \nu)$. That is, the dynamic matrix L in $\mathbf{k}, \mathbf{k}'$ representation is more fundamental than the traditional model of pairwise (e.g., Coulomb, Born-Mayer, etc.) potentials between ion pairs expressed in l, l' representation. This is particularly apparent in two tractable limiting cases: ionic crystals where the electronic polarization of the ions is assumed to be dynamically determined by the motion of the ions themselves, and metals where the free electron gas participates intimately and responds dynamically and *nonlocally* to ion motions.

In the case of an ionic or covalent lattice the electronic polarization may sometimes be regarded (Dick and Overhauser[5]) in terms of a "shell model" of electronic charge which can displace with respect to its ion core and with respect to shells of other ions; the "shell model" has found considerable use. However, the concept has been made considerably more precise by Cochran's formulation.

The essential quantities involved are the Coulomb and non-Coulomb energies $\Phi^{(C)}$ and $\Phi^{(R)}$. It is then postulated that one may introduce an internal "shell displacement" electronic coordinate $\hat{\mathbf{v}}(l)$ for each ion to which its electronic dipole moment is proportional. The energy is then expressed to quadratic terms in $\hat{\mathbf{v}}(l)$ and the atomic displacement $\hat{\mathbf{u}}(l)$:

$$V = \tfrac{1}{2}[\hat{\mathbf{u}}\Phi^{(C)}_{\hat{u}\hat{u}}\hat{\mathbf{u}} + \hat{\mathbf{u}}\Phi^{(C)}_{\hat{u}\hat{v}}\hat{\mathbf{v}} + \hat{\mathbf{v}}\Phi^{(C)}_{\hat{v}\hat{u}}\hat{\mathbf{u}} + \hat{\mathbf{v}}\Phi^{(C)}_{\hat{v}\hat{v}}\hat{\mathbf{v}}]$$
$$+ \tfrac{1}{2}[\hat{\mathbf{u}}\Phi^{(R)}_{\hat{v}\hat{u}}\hat{\mathbf{u}} + \cdots + \cdots \qquad \qquad]$$

The condition of minimization of the electronic energy with respect to the internal coordinate $\hat{\mathbf{v}}$, i.e., $\partial V/\partial \hat{\mathbf{v}} = 0$ is used to eliminate terms in the shell displacements $\hat{\mathbf{v}}(l)$. In lattice representation l, l' the Coulomb matrices are quite complicated; in $\mathbf{k}, \mathbf{k}'$ representations they may be evaluated using Ewald's method (Kellerman[6]) and are easily computed. There remains a certain amount of arbitrariness in the division of the energy into the contributions indicated; but using this procedure it is remarkable how well experimental neutron inelastic scattering data has been explained. Extensive tests and tabulations of phonon dispersion relations have been carried out along these lines (Cochran, Cowley, Brockhouse, and Woods[7], Karo and Hardy[8]).

Turning to metals, the response of the free-electron gas to ion motions is particularly illustrated by the Kohn effect (W. Kohn[9]). In addition to $\Phi^{(R)}$ and $\Phi^{(C)}$ one now has an electron gas contribution $\Phi^{(E)}$. The electron gas responds to the ion motion through a dielectric constant $\varepsilon(\mathbf{k}, \omega)$; phonon frequencies are so low compared to metal plasma frequencies that effectively $\omega \simeq 0$. In the $\omega = 0$ limit and at high electron densities (RPA) the k-dependent screening length defined by $\varepsilon(\mathbf{k}, 0)$ is given by

$$\lambda(\mathbf{k}, 0) \simeq \frac{2}{\pi} \frac{k_f}{a_0} \left[1 + \frac{1}{kk_f} \left(k_f^2 - \frac{k^2}{4} \right) \ln \left| \frac{k + 2k_f}{k - 2k_f} \right| \right],$$

and this determines the behavior of $\Phi^{(C)}$ in $\mathbf{k}, \mathbf{k}'$ representation.

The point of particular physical interest is that when $|\mathbf{k}| \simeq 2k_f$ where k_f is the electron Fermi surface wave number, $|d\lambda/dk|_{k=2k_f} \to \infty$ and the phonon dispersion relation $\omega(\mathbf{k})$ will have an infinite slope as a function of $\mathbf{k}$ (but will be continuous). This effect, known as the Kohn anomaly, has now been seen in a variety of systems after having first been seen by Brockhouse et al.[10] in lead.

Thus, the understanding of the physics underlying the choice of effective displacement potentials in both nonmetals and metals has improved significantly during the past several years.

II.3. Following Peierls, the dynamics may be discussed in terms of the $\hat{b}(\mathbf{k}, \nu)$. By transformation of the l, l' representation the Lagrangia in $\mathbf{k}, \mathbf{k}'$ representation is

$$\mathscr{L} = T - V = \sum_{\mathbf{k}, \nu} \frac{\dot{\hat{b}}(\mathbf{k}, \nu)\dot{\hat{b}}(-\mathbf{k}, \nu) - \omega^2(\mathbf{k}, \nu)\hat{b}(\mathbf{k}, \nu)\hat{b}(-\mathbf{k}, \nu)}{2},$$

where k ranges over a Brillouin zone in k space. For the generalized coordinate $\hat{b}(\mathbf{k}, \nu)$, the conjugate momentum is $\dot{\hat{b}}(-k, \nu)$, i.e., $\partial\mathscr{L}/\partial\dot{\hat{b}}(\mathbf{k},\nu)$ The equations of motion are easily found to be

$$\ddot{\hat{b}}(\mathbf{k}, \nu) = -\omega^2(\mathbf{k}, \nu)\hat{b}(\mathbf{k}, \nu)$$

from the Hamiltonian

$$\mathscr{H} = T + V = 2T - \mathscr{L}.$$

For brevity we usually omit the index ν.

The dynamic variable $\hat{b}(\mathbf{k})$ is physically a displacement and $\dot{\hat{b}}(-\mathbf{k})$ a momentum for which the quantum commutation conditions would be

$$[\dot{\hat{b}}(-\mathbf{k}), \hat{b}(+\mathbf{k})] = \hbar/i$$

These coordinates lack in one important respect for application to extended lattices—the fields $\hat{\mathbf{u}}(l)$ and $\hat{\mathbf{p}}(l)$ given in the $\hat{b}(\mathbf{k})$ representation are standing-wave fields. For this reason it is customary to make a further transformation to the action (momentum) and angle (coordinate) variables $\hbar j_k$ and $\hat{\phi}_k$, respectively:

$$\hat{b}(\mathbf{k}) = \left[\left(\frac{\hbar j_k}{2\omega_k} \right)^{\frac{1}{2}} e^{i\hat{\phi}_k} + \left(\frac{\hbar j_{-k}}{2\omega_{-k}} \right)^{\frac{1}{2}} e^{-i\phi_{-k}} \right]$$

$$\dot{\hat{b}}(-\mathbf{k}) = i\left[\left(\frac{\hbar\omega_k j_k}{2} \right)^{\frac{1}{2}} e^{i\phi_k} - \left(\frac{\hbar\omega_{-k} j_{-k}}{2} \right)^{\frac{1}{2}} e^{-i\hat{\phi}_{-k}} \right]$$

These expressions may be used in both the classical and quantum cases, though in the former case the constant $\hbar$ is to be regarded only as a unit for j_k.

The variables

$$\hat{a}_k^+ = (j_k^{\frac{1}{2}} e^{i\hat{\phi}_k}) \qquad \hat{a}_k = (j_k^{\frac{1}{2}}) e^{-i\hat{\phi}_k}$$

are thus suggested. Their meaning is clear in the classical case; but Susskind and Glogower (1964) have pointed out that the angle operator cannot be defined in the quantum case. The definition

$$\hat{b}(\mathbf{k}) = \left(\frac{\hbar}{2\omega_k} \right)^{\frac{1}{2}} [\hat{a}_k^+ + \hat{a}_k]$$

$$\dot{\hat{b}}(-\mathbf{k}) = i\left(\frac{\hbar\omega_k}{2} \right)[\hat{a}_k^+ - \hat{a}_k]$$

may be used in either the classical or quantum case. The Hamiltonian may be written generally as

$$\mathscr{H} = \sum_k \frac{\hbar\omega_k}{2} (\hat{a}_k^+ \hat{a}_k + \hat{a}_k \hat{a}_k^+)$$

and the displacement and momentum fields are

$$\hat{\mathbf{u}}(l) = \sum_k \left(\frac{\hbar}{2Nm_l\omega_k} \right)^{\frac{1}{2}} [\mathbf{w}^*(\mathbf{k})\hat{b}_k^+ \exp\left[-i\mathbf{k}\cdot\mathbf{x}(l)\right] + \mathbf{w}(\mathbf{k})\hat{a}_k \exp\left[i\mathbf{k}\cdot\mathbf{x}(l)\right]$$

$$\hat{\mathbf{p}}(l) = \sum_k \left(\frac{\hbar m_l\omega_k}{2N} \right)^{\frac{1}{2}} i[\hat{a}_k^+ \mathbf{w}^*(\mathbf{k}) \exp\left[-i\mathbf{k}\cdot\mathbf{x}(l)\right] - \hat{a}_k\mathbf{w}(\mathbf{k}) \exp\left[i\mathbf{k}\cdot\mathbf{x}(l)\right]$$

The dynamics in the classical case follows from these expressions, since $\hat{a}_k^+ \hat{a}_k = \hat{a}_k \hat{a}_k^+ = j_k$. Then

$$\mathscr{H}_{\text{class}} = \sum_k \hbar\omega_k j_k$$

and

$$j_k = \frac{\partial \mathcal{H}}{\partial \hat{\varphi}_k} = 0; \qquad j_k = \text{const}$$

$$\dot{\varphi}_k = \frac{\partial H}{\partial(\hbar j_k)} = \omega_k; \qquad \varphi_k = \omega_k t + \varphi_{k0}$$

The equation of motion for $\hat{a}_k^+$ and $\hat{a}_k$ follows from the brackets

$$\dot{\hat{a}}_k = \frac{\partial \hat{a}_k}{\partial(\hbar j_k)}(\hbar \dot{j}_k) + \left(\frac{\partial \hat{a}_k}{\partial \hat{\varphi}_k}\right)\dot{\hat{\varphi}}_k = -i\omega_k \hat{a}_k$$

$$\dot{\hat{a}}_k = i\omega_k \hat{a}_k^+$$

yielding the classical time-dependent variables

$$\hat{a}_k^+(t) = \exp(i\omega_k t)\hat{a}_k^+(0), \qquad \hat{a}_k(t) = \exp(-i\omega_k t)\hat{a}_k(0).$$

Substitution in the expression for the displacement fields shows immediately that for positive $\mathbf{k}$

$$\hat{\mathbf{u}}(l, t) = \sum_k \left(\frac{\hbar}{2Nm_l\omega_k}\right)^{\frac{1}{2}}[\mathbf{w^*}(\mathbf{k})\hat{a}_k^+(0)\exp[i(\omega_k t - k \cdot x(l))] + \text{conjugate}]$$

corresponds to a right-going wave, while for $-\mathbf{k}$ since $\omega_{-k} = \omega_k$ the excitation is left going.

The dynamics in the quantum case begin with the commutation relations found by substitution for $\hat{\mathbf{u}}(l)$ and $\hat{\mathbf{b}}(l)$ to be

$$[\hat{a}_k, \hat{a}_{k'}^+] = \delta_{k.k'}$$

$$[\hat{a}_k, \hat{a}_{k'}] = 0 \qquad [\hat{a}_k^+, \hat{a}_{k'}^+] = 0.$$

The states of this system (Dirac[12]) then follow from the Hamiltonian

$$\mathcal{H} = \sum_k \hbar\omega_k(\hat{a}_k^+\hat{a}_k + \tfrac{1}{2}) = \sum_k \hbar\omega_k(\hat{n}_k + \tfrac{1}{2}),$$

where $\hat{a}_k^+\hat{a}_k$ is the number operator $\hat{n}_k$, whose stationary states $|n_k\rangle$ have eigenvalue $\hat{n}_k|n_k\rangle = n_k|n_k\rangle$, with $n_k = 0, 1, 2, \ldots$, and have the well-known properties of creation and annihilation operators:

$$\hat{a}_k^+|n_k\rangle = (n_k + 1)^{\frac{1}{2}}|n_k + 1\rangle,$$

$$\hat{a}_k|n_k\rangle = n_k^{\frac{1}{2}}|n_k - 1\rangle.$$

The time-dependent Schrödinger states are

$$|n_k(t)\rangle = \exp(-in_k\omega t)|n_k\rangle,$$

while in Heisenberg representation the operators $\hat{a}_k^+$, $\hat{a}_k$, and $\hat{u}(l)$ are

$$\hat{a}_k^+(t) = \exp{(i\hat{H}_0 t/\hbar)}\hat{a}_k(0)\exp{(-i\hat{H}_0 t/\hbar)} = \hat{a}_k^+ \exp{(i\omega_k t)}$$
$$\hat{a}_k(t) = \hat{a}_k \exp{(-i\omega t)},$$

which exhibits explicitly the traveling-wave nature of the representation.

II.4. It is of some interest to develop the quantized-field form of the phonon system.

To begin with recall that in the quantization of field we may discuss a scalar field $\hat{\psi}^+(\mathbf{r})$, $\hat{\psi}(\mathbf{r})$ associated with creation and annihilation operators, or the vector field (e.g. $\hat{\mathbf{E}}$, $\hat{\mathbf{H}}$, $\hat{\mathbf{A}}$, $\hat{\boldsymbol{\phi}}$ in the electromagnetic case) which define the Hamiltonian in the space-time coordinates $\mathbf{r}$, t. Here the scalar field is that of the phonon creation and annihilation operators, while the role of $\hat{\mathbf{E}}(\mathbf{r}, t)$ and $\hat{\mathbf{H}}(\mathbf{r}, t)$ is assumed by the dynamic variables $\hat{\mathbf{u}}(l, t)$ and $\hat{\mathbf{p}}(l, t)$. Then the Hamiltonian comparable to

$$(1/8\pi) \int (\hat{\mathbf{E}}^2 + \hat{\mathbf{H}}^2)\, d\tau$$

is

$$\mathcal{H} = \sum_l \frac{\hat{p}_l^2}{2m} + \sum_{l,l'} \frac{\hat{\mathbf{u}}(l)\varphi(l, l')\hat{\mathbf{u}}(l')}{2}$$

Actually it is possible formally (Krumhansl[13]) to place this Hamiltonian in integral representation, using a method equivalent to Bloch-Wannier transformations for electronic problems. One may define a field on a (fictitious) continuous space $\mathbf{R}$ by the unitary transformation

$$\hat{\mathbf{u}}(\mathbf{R}) = \sum_e \hat{\mathbf{u}}(l)(m_l)^{-\frac{1}{2}} S(\mathbf{R} - \mathbf{x}(l))$$

It is found that $\hat{\mathbf{u}}(\mathbf{R}) = \hat{\mathbf{u}}(l)$ for $\mathbf{R} = \mathbf{x}(l)$; thus defined, $\hat{\mathbf{u}}(\mathbf{R})$ has Fourier integral components spanning only the lattice Brillouin zone. The transformation function $S(\mathbf{R} - \mathbf{x}(l))$ is a "sampling function" localized around $\mathbf{x}(l)$; the method is convenient if there is only one atom per unit cell but may be carried out more generally. The transformed Hamiltonian then becomes

$$\mathcal{H} = \int d\mathbf{R} \left[\frac{\hat{\mathbf{p}}(\mathbf{R})^2}{2} + \tfrac{1}{2}V(\hat{u}, _R\hat{u}, _R{}^2\hat{u}, \dots) \right]$$

and the effective potential for the continuous field depends on *all orders of derivatives*, which arises from the transformation of the difference operator $\Phi(l, l')$ to a continuous representation. This somewhat amusing contrast to the usual dependence of field Hamiltonian functions on only the first derivatives is, of course, due to the discrete lattice.

The continuous representation might appear to be of formal interest only. Actually, it may be applied in the long wavelength limit to relate continuum elasticity to lattice theory. If one neglects ∇^2 terms and higher the result is the usual uniform strain continuum elasticity, where if terms ∇^3 and higher are dropped the more general couple–stress elasticity discussed by Toupin[14] and Mindlin[15] is obtained. The method not only provides a systematic method for relating lattice to continuum elasticity, but also may be used to determine the limits of the continuum approximation.

We now discuss the scalar field representation, then the Heisenberg equations of motion for the vector fields $\hat{\mathbf{u}}(l)$, $\hat{\mathbf{p}}(l)$. The development is based on that of Jensen[16].

The basic states are denoted in many particle form

$$|N_p\rangle = |n_{k_1}, n_{k_2}, \ldots\rangle = \frac{\hat{a}_{k_1}^{+n_1} \hat{a}_{k_2}^{+n_2} \cdots}{(n_1! \, n_2! \cdots)^{\frac{1}{2}}} |0\rangle$$

In the "vacuum state" $|0\rangle = |0, 0, 0, \ldots\rangle$ all oscillators are in the $n_k = 0$ state. Defining $\hat{N}_p = \sum_k \hat{a}_k^+ \hat{a}_k$ as the "number" operator for phonons, $|N_p\rangle$ is an eigenfunction of $\hat{N}_p$ with eigenvalue $\sum_k n_k$, as though the phonons were Bose particles without restriction on the number occupying any state k. The $\hat{n}_k = \hat{a}_k^+ \hat{a}_k$ commute with each other $[\hat{n}_k, \hat{n}_{k'}] = 0$ and so are each constants of motion of the non-interacting free field. In particular, $|N_p\rangle$ is simultaneously an eigenstate of

$$\hat{H}|N_p\rangle = \left[\sum_k \hbar\omega_k(\hat{n}_k + \tfrac{1}{2})\right]|N_p\rangle$$

and

$$\hat{\mathbf{\Pi}}|N_p\rangle = \left[\sum_k \hbar_k \hat{n}_k\right]|N_p\rangle$$

where the quantity $\mathbf{\Pi}$, which clearly commutes with the Hamiltonian, plays the role of the field momentum for phonons. It is an important constant of the motion, being related to the heat current (Peierls[1]).

Just as the operator $\hat{a}_k^+$ "creates" a phonon in the kth state, it is possible to define a scalar field creation operator $\hat{a}^+(l)$ which "creates a phonon" at the position $\mathbf{x}(l)$ in the lattice,

$$\hat{a}^+(l) = \sum_k \hat{a}_k^+ \exp\left[-i\mathbf{k}\cdot\mathbf{x}(l)\right]/\sqrt{N}$$

$$\hat{a}(l) = \sum_k \hat{a}_k \exp\left[i\mathbf{k}\cdot\mathbf{x}(l)\right]/\sqrt{N}$$

along with the obvious inverse relations. Then the commutators are

$$[\hat{a}(l), \hat{a}^+(l)] = \delta_{l,l'}$$

$$[\hat{a}(l), \hat{a}^+(l')] = 0 = [\hat{a}^+(l), \hat{a}^+(l')]$$

and

$$\sum_l \hat{a}^+(l)\hat{a}(l) = \sum_k \hat{a}_k^+ \hat{a}_k = \hat{N}_p$$

as usual, whence one may define $\hat{n}_l = \hat{a}^+(l)\hat{a}(l)$.

The equation of motion, generalizing to time dependent $\hat{a}^+(l, t)$, is given directly by

$$\frac{\partial \hat{a}^+(l, t)}{\partial t} = \sum_k \frac{\exp\left[-i\mathbf{k}\cdot\mathbf{x}(l)\right]}{\sqrt{N}} \frac{\partial \hat{a}_k^+}{\partial t} = \sum_k \frac{i\omega_k \exp\left[-i\mathbf{k}\cdot\mathbf{x}(l)\right]}{\sqrt{N}} \hat{a}_k^+$$

$$= \sum_k \left[\sum_{l'} i\omega_k \frac{\exp\left[-i\mathbf{k}\cdot(\mathbf{x}(l) - \mathbf{x}(l'))\right]}{\sqrt{N}}\right]$$

$$\hat{a}^+(l', t) = \sum_{l'} \frac{1}{i\hbar} \hat{H}_{l,l'} \hat{a}_k^+(l', t),$$

where

$$H_{ll'} = -\sum_k \hbar\omega_k \frac{\exp\left[-i\mathbf{k}\cdot(\mathbf{x}(l) - \mathbf{x}(l'))\right]}{\sqrt{N}}.$$

This equation is not as convenient as that for the second derivative with respect to time. [In fact it is not possible to take a simple, long-wavelength limit of $\hbar\omega_k$; acoustic branches are nonanalytic, at $\mathbf{k} = 0$, i.e., $\omega_k = c|\mathbf{k}|$.] However,

$$\frac{\partial^2 \hat{a}^+(l, t)}{\partial t^2} = -\frac{1}{\hbar^2} \sum_{l',l''} \hat{H}_{l,l'} \hat{H}_{l'l''} \hat{a}^+(l'', t)$$

$$= -\frac{1}{\hbar^2} \sum_{l''} (\hat{H}^2)_{l,l''} \hat{a}^+(l'', t)$$

Here

$$(\hat{H}^2)_{l,l''} = \sum_k \hbar^2 \omega_k^2 \exp\left[-i\mathbf{k}\cdot(\mathbf{x}(l) - \mathbf{x}(l''))\right]/\sqrt{N},$$

and since ω_k^2 is given by the dynamic matrix the difference operator $(\hat{H}^2)_{l,l''}$ is defined directly as the Fourier transform (over the Brillouin zone) of the dispersion relation.

The above is for a single phonon branch; the generalization $\psi_\nu(l, t)$ to each of $\nu = 1, \ldots, 3S$ branches is straightforward.

Thus, completely localized excitations in "l representation" complementary to the extended pure phonon states and having Hamiltonian $\hat{H}_{l,l'}$ may be defined through the unitary transformation

$$|l'\rangle = \sum_k \hat{a}_k^+ \exp\left[-i\mathbf{k}\cdot\mathbf{x}(l)\right]/\sqrt{N}|0\rangle$$

whence

$$\hat{n}_l|l'\rangle = \hat{a}_l^+ \hat{a}_l|l'\rangle = \delta(l, l')|l'\rangle$$

with the expected orthonormality $\langle l|l'\rangle = \delta(l, l')$. A general phonon state may then be constructed in localized representation.

Single phonon Schrödinger state functions may be written either in $\mathbf{k}$ or l representation

$$|\psi\rangle = \sum_k \psi(\mathbf{k}, t)\hat{a}_k^+ |0\rangle = \hat{\psi}^+(\mathbf{k}, t)|0\rangle$$

$$|\psi\rangle = \sum_l \psi_l(\mathbf{x}(l), t)\hat{a}_l^+ |0\rangle = \hat{\psi}(\mathbf{x}(l), t)|0\rangle,$$

and it is readily verified that the appropriate Schrödinger equations are

$$i\hbar \frac{\partial \psi_s}{\partial t}(\mathbf{k}, t) = \hbar\omega_k\psi_s(k, t)$$

$$i\hbar \frac{\partial \psi_s}{\partial t}(\mathbf{x}(l), t) = \sum_{l'} (\hat{H})_{l,l'}\psi_s(\mathbf{x}(l'), t).$$

Further physical insight is obtained by defining operators which may act to label the effective $\mathbf{k}$ or $\mathbf{k}(l)$ of a state. These are

$$\hat{\mathbf{x}} = \sum_k \mathbf{k}\hat{a}_k^+ \hat{a}_k$$

$$\hat{\mathbf{x}} = \sum_l \mathbf{x}(l)\hat{a}_l^+ \hat{a}_l.$$

Then $\hat{a}_{k'}^+ |0\rangle$ is an eigenfunction of $\mathbf{k}$ with eigenvalue $\mathbf{k}'$, while $\hat{a}_{l'}^+ |0\rangle$ is an eigenfunction of $\hat{\mathbf{x}}$ with eigenvalue $\mathbf{x}(l')$. From the commutation relation

$$[\hat{x}_\alpha, \hat{k}_\alpha] = i\delta_{\alpha,\beta}$$

it follows that for a general state

$$\langle \dot{\hat{x}}_\alpha \rangle = \left\langle \frac{\partial \omega}{\partial k_\alpha} \right\rangle; \qquad \langle \dot{\hat{k}}_\alpha \rangle = 0$$

which is relevant to the phonon Boltzmann equation, where it provides the free field drift term $\mathbf{v}_g \cdot \nabla_x$.

We now proceed to the Heisenberg equations of motion for $\hat{\mathbf{u}}(l)$, and $\hat{\mathbf{p}}(l)$. Starting from

$$\hat{\mathbf{u}}(l, t) = \sum_k \left(\frac{\hbar}{2Nm_l\omega_k}\right)^{\frac{1}{2}} [\mathbf{w}^*(\mathbf{k})\hat{a}_k^+(t) \exp[-i\mathbf{k}\cdot\mathbf{x}(l)] + \text{h.c.}]$$

$$\hat{\mathbf{p}}(l, t) = \sum_k i\left(\frac{\hbar m_l\omega_k}{2N}\right)^{\frac{1}{2}} [\mathbf{w}^*(\mathbf{k})\hat{a}_k^+(t) \exp[-i\mathbf{k}\cdot\mathbf{x}(l)] + \text{h.c.}],$$

and the inverse relations, the equations of motion may be obtained by repeated application of $i\hbar\dot{\hat{\theta}} = [\hat{\theta}, \hat{H}]$. There results

$$\dot{\hat{\mathbf{u}}}(l, t) = \hat{\mathbf{p}}(l, t)/m(l)$$

$$\dot{\hat{\mathbf{p}}}(l, t) = -\sum_{l'} \frac{1}{\hbar^2} (\hat{H}^2)_{l,l'} \sqrt{m(l)m(l')}\, \hat{\mathbf{u}}(l', t),$$

where

$$(\hat{H}^2)_{l,l'} = \sum_k \mathbf{w}^*(\mathbf{k}) \exp[-i\mathbf{k}\cdot(\mathbf{x}(l) - \mathbf{x}(l'))]\mathbf{w}(\mathbf{k})(\hbar\omega_k)^2/\sqrt{N}$$

is a tensor operator; in fact, it is $\hbar^2$ times the original dynamic matrix $(\mathbf{L})_{l,l'}$, expressed in terms of its eigenvalues ω_k^2 and eigenvectors $(\exp[i\mathbf{k}\cdot\mathbf{x}(l)]/(N)^{\frac{1}{2}})$. Thus

$$\dot{\hat{\mathbf{u}}}(l, t) = \hat{\mathbf{p}}(l, t)/m(l)$$

$$\dot{\hat{\mathbf{p}}}(l, t) = -\sum_{l'} (\mathbf{L})_{l,l'} \sqrt{m(l)m(l')}\, \hat{\mathbf{u}}(l', t),$$

or in terms of the potential matrix

$$\dot{\hat{\mathbf{p}}}(l, t) = -\sum_{l'} (\Phi)_{l,l'}\, \hat{\mathbf{u}}(l', t)$$

$$m\ddot{\mathbf{u}}(l, t) = -\sum_{l'} (\Phi)_{l,l'}\, \mathbf{u}(l', t).$$

Thus it is demonstrated that the Heisenberg variables $\hat{\mathbf{u}}(l, t)$, and $\hat{\mathbf{p}}(l, t)$ obey the same equations of motion as the classical fields. It follows that any quantum property of the free phonon field depending on $\hat{\mathbf{u}}$, $\hat{\mathbf{p}}$ may be found from the classical equations of motion with the understanding that the variables are Heisenberg operators.

This result may be applied in a variety of ways: to compute dynamic correlation functions which arise in neutron or light scattering by lattices, to relate the defect lattice problem which may be solved classically to the quantized defect lattice, and so forth.

III. Interacting Phonons

III.1. The phonon excitations of the perfect harmonic lattice do not, of course exist in real life. In the condensed state of matter phonons interact to a greater or lesser degree with almost any other type of excitation which one can conceive. Even within the phonon community itself interactions modify the phonon properties; and defects in the lattice, and anharmonic corrections to the potential of the perfect lattice have important effects.

Here there has been great activity during recent years (see particularly, *International Conference on Lattice Dynamics*, Copenhagen, 1963, Ed. R. F. Wallis[17]) stimulated by inelastic neutron scattering and optical measurements. I have chosen three current topics to review: localized modes and scattering from isolated defects, phonons in the anharmonic crystal, and the conservation rules for phonons interacting with each other or with external probes. These three cases may be visualized by writing the appropriate Hamiltonian in phonon representation. Graphically this may be depicted as shown in Figure 1.

Defect systems may be described by a harmonic Hamiltonian, but with masses or potential constraints differing from the normal lattice. Using the perfect crystal phonons as a basis set the quadratic Hamiltonian becomes

$$\hat{H} = \sum_{k,k'} [H_{k,k'}\hat{a}_k^+ \hat{a}_{k'} + H_{k'k}^* \hat{a}_k \hat{a}_{u'}^+],$$

whereas

$$\hat{H}_0 = \sum_{k,k'} \hbar\omega_k \delta_{k,k'}(\hat{a}_k^+ \hat{a}_k' + \hat{a}_k \hat{a}_{k'}^+).$$

Thus $\hat{n}_k$ no longer commutes with $\hat{H}$ and the phonons are scattered into other states. However, this quadratic Hamiltonian may be transformed to a set of proper excitation operators. When this is done it is found that not only may there be localized lattice excitations, but also that there may be resonant scattering with quasi-localized excitation. The problem is to achieve the proper transformation.

The second case, that of the anharmonic lattice, has Hamiltonian

$$\hat{H} = \hat{H}_0 + \hat{V}^{(3)} + \hat{V}^{(4)} + \cdots,$$

where $V^{(2)}$, $V^{(4)}$, etc., are third, fourth, etc. order potentials in the displacements $\hat{u}_{l_1}, \hat{u}_{l_2}, \ldots$. Again, transformation to phonon coordinates makes the nature of the problem apparent. Terms such as

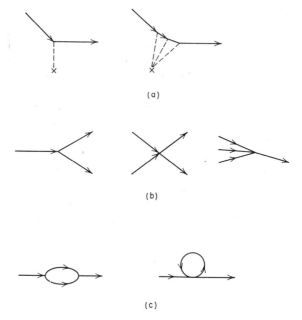

Fig. 1. (a) Single and multiple scattering of phonons. (b) Three and four phonon anharmonic processes. (c) Lowest order anharmonic contributions to self energy correction.

$V^{(3)} \propto \hat{a}_{k''}^{+}\hat{a}_{k'}^{+}\hat{a}_{k}^{+}$, $V^{(4)} \propto \hat{a}_{k'''}^{+}\hat{a}_{k''}^{+}\hat{a}_{k'}^{+}\hat{a}_{k}^{+}$, etc. state that phonons are created and destroyed by the anharmonicity; phonon number is not conserved, $[\hat{n}_{k}, \hat{H}] \neq 0$. This then becomes a field-theoretic, many-body problem; the phonons may be discussed as quasiparticles, and the concepts of lifetime and self-energy corrections apply. The thermodynamic Green's function method is used to treat this problem.

In the third case the lattice system interacts with other excitations. One important example is that of interaction of low-energy neutrons with the lattice, where the Hamiltonian is

$$\hat{H} = \hat{H}_0 + \hat{H}_{int}((\mathbf{r}, \hat{\mathbf{u}}_l) + \hat{H}_{lat}(\mathbf{r}),$$

and if $\mathbf{r}$ is the neutron coordinate, a good approximation to $\hat{H}_{int}$ is the Fermi psuedo-potential $\hat{H}_{int} = \sum_l b_l \, \delta(\mathbf{r} - \mathbf{v}_l)$, where b_l is an effective scattering length, generally spin dependent. In many cases the neutron and lattice do not couple strongly, and Born approximation may be used to describe the development of the system. We then examine two relevant properties: first, the space-time correlation functions of the lattice displacements; second, general conservation conditions.

We proceed to details of these three situations.

III.2. The vibrational properties of the defect lattice have been examined extensively beginning with Lifshitz' early work[18]. This subject is reviewed in detail by Maradudin[19], who together with Montroll and many others applied the Lifshitz Green's function method for the classical field to solve defect vibration problems.

The essentials are as follows. The Hamiltonian is

$$\hat{H} = \sum_l \frac{\hat{p}_l^2}{2M_l} + \sum_{l,l'} \frac{\Phi(l, l')}{2} \hat{u}_l \hat{u}_{l'},$$

where M_l are the masses, some of which differ from the normal lattice masses, and $\bar{\varphi}(l, l')$ may differ from $\varphi(l, l')$ near the defects.

The quantum mechanical problem may be solved by finding a linear transformation which diagonalizes the above Hamiltonian classically; this is obvious, of course. The actual solution requires a practical method to make use of the unperturbed lattice phonons.

The unperturbed modes were mass normalized to the normal lattice masses, i.e., $\hat{u}_\alpha \propto 1/\sqrt{m_l}$, $\hat{p}_\alpha \propto \sqrt{m_l}$, and the basic dynamic matrix was similarly mass normalized

$$L_{l,l'} = \varphi(l, l')/\sqrt{m_l m_{l'}}.$$

To use the normal lattice phonons as a basis, rather than coordinates normalized to the actual masses we proceed as follows. A short-hand notation is convenient:

$|\hat{u})$ is a column matrix having elements $\hat{\mathbf{u}}_l$
$(\hat{u}|$ is the transpose row vector
$\mathbf{A}$ is a square matrix

The transformation

$$|\hat{u}) = (\mathbf{m}_l^{-\frac{1}{2}}\boldsymbol{\delta}_{\mathbf{l},\mathbf{l'}})|\hat{\xi})$$

$$|\hat{p}) = (\mathbf{m}_l^{\frac{1}{2}}\boldsymbol{\delta}_{\mathbf{l},\mathbf{l'}})|\hat{p}_\xi)$$

leads to the perfect lattice mass normalized potential, with "effective mass" M_l/m_l in the transformed Hamiltonian

$$\hat{H} = \tfrac{1}{2}(\hat{p}_\xi| \, \mathbf{m}_l/\mathbf{M}_l \, |\hat{p}_\xi) + \tfrac{1}{2}(\hat{\xi}| \, \mathbf{\overline{L}} \, |\hat{\xi})$$

$$\hat{H} = \sum_l \frac{\hat{p}_{\xi l}^2}{2(M_l/m_l)} + \sum_{l,l'} \frac{\Phi_{l,l'}}{\sqrt{m_l m_{l'}}} \hat{\xi}_l \hat{\xi}_{l'}$$

This classical Hamiltonian defines the equation of motion

$$(\mathbf{M_l}/\mathbf{m_l})\,|\ddot{\hat{\xi}}) = \overline{\mathbf{L}}\,|\hat{\xi})$$

which is solved by the eigenvalue solutions

$$\omega_s^2(\mathbf{M_l}/\mathbf{m_l})\,|\hat{\xi}_s) = \overline{\mathbf{L}}\,|\hat{\xi}_s)$$

while the perfect lattice was defined by

$$\omega_k^2\,|\hat{\xi}_s) = \overline{\mathbf{L}}\,|\hat{\xi}_k)$$

The latter may be used as a basis for defining the perturbed problem

$$\omega_s^2\,|\hat{\xi}_s) = (\mathbf{D} + \mathbf{L})\,|\hat{\xi}_s)$$

with the defect matrix $\mathbf{D}$ defined

$$
\begin{aligned}
(\mathbf{D})_{ll'} &= \left(1 - \frac{M_l}{m_l}\right)\omega_s^2\delta_{l,l'} + (\overline{L}_{l,l'} - L_{l,l'}) \\
&= -\frac{\varDelta M_l}{m_l}\,\omega_s^2\delta_{l,l'} + \frac{\overline{\varPhi}_{l,l'} - \varPhi_{ll'}}{\sqrt{m_l m_{l'}}}
\end{aligned}
$$

The virtue of this particular transformation is now apparent: this representation has the property that mass defects correspond to a strictly diagonal change in the dynamic matrix, while at the same time the defect potential change appears separately in a symmetric potential matrix. Other common representations are complicated by nondiagonal mass contributions to the defect potential matrix and similar difficulties. These eigenvectors have the orthonormal properties

$$\left(\hat{\xi}_{s'}\left|\frac{\mathbf{M_l}}{\mathbf{m_l}}\right|\hat{\xi}_s\right) = \delta_{s,s'}$$

whence the eigenvectors

$$|\hat{\eta}_s) = \left(\frac{M_l}{m_l}\right)^{1/2}|\hat{\xi}_s)$$

have the more convenient property $(\hat{\eta}_{s'}|\hat{\eta}_s) = \delta_{s,s'}$.

The solution of the classical defect problem will be given shortly. It may be used to reduce the quantum mechanical problem as follows. Define $\mathbf{S}$ to be a matrix whose columns are the $|\eta_s)$. With the transformation

$$|\hat{u}) = \left(\frac{1}{\mathbf{m_l^{1/2}}}\right)\left(\frac{\mathbf{m_l^{1/2}}}{\mathbf{M_l^{1/2}}}\right)\mathbf{S}\,|\hat{Q})$$

$$|\hat{p}) = (\mathbf{m_l^{1/2}})\left(\frac{\mathbf{M_l^{1/2}}}{\mathbf{m_l^{1/2}}}\right)\mathbf{S^\dagger}\,|\hat{P})$$

the Hamiltonian becomes

$$\hat{H} = \frac{(\hat{P}|\hat{P})}{2} + \frac{(\hat{Q}|\,\omega_s^2\delta_{s,s'}\,|\hat{Q})}{2}$$

$$= \sum_s \left(\frac{\hat{P}_s^2 + \omega_s^2\hat{Q}_s^2}{2}\right)$$

The transformation to action-angle variables is

$$\hat{Q}_s = \left(\frac{\hbar}{2\omega_s}\right)^{1/2}(\hat{b}_s^+ + \hat{b}_s)$$

$$\hat{P}_s = i\left(\frac{\hbar\omega_s}{2}\right)^{1/2}(\hat{b}_s^+ - \hat{b}_s)$$

which may be quantized with the result

$$[\hat{b}_s, \hat{b}_s^+] = \delta_{s,s'}, \quad [\hat{b}_s, \hat{b}_{s'}] = 0, \quad [\hat{b}_s^+, \hat{b}_{s'}^+] = 0$$

$$\hat{H} = \sum_s \frac{\hbar\omega_s}{2}(\hat{b}_s\hat{b}_s^+ + \hat{b}_s^+\hat{b}_s)$$

The displacement and momentum variables $\hat{u}$ and $\hat{p}$ may be expressed in terms of either $\hat{a}_k^+$ and $\hat{a}_k$ or $\hat{b}_s^+$ and $\hat{b}_s$. Again the Heisenberg operators $\hat{u}(l, t)$ and $\hat{p}(l, t)$ will be found to obey the classical (defect lattice) equations of motion. Thus the classical defect lattice equations determine the quantum states and energy levels of the perturbed crystal, the definition of defect phonon field operators, and the motion of the Heisenberg operators for the atomic displacements and momenta.

We now give the solution of the defect problem by the classical Green's function method due to Lifshitz. To solve

$$\omega^2|\hat{\xi}) = (\mathbf{D} + \mathbf{L})|\hat{\xi})$$

consider the auxiliary inhomogeneous problem

$$(\omega^2 - \mathbf{L})|\hat{\xi}) = \mathbf{D}|\hat{\xi}) + |\hat{J})$$

where $|\hat{J})$ is a generating "force" applied to the lattice. When $\mathbf{D} \to 0$ this equation is solved by $\mathbf{G}_0 = (\omega^2 - \mathbf{L})^{-1}$

$$|\hat{\xi}) = \mathbf{G}_0|\hat{J}) \qquad (\mathbf{D} \to 0)$$

With the defect,

$$|\hat{\xi}) = \mathbf{G}_0\mathbf{D}|\hat{\xi}) + \mathbf{G}_0|\hat{J})$$

$$|\hat{\xi}) = \frac{1}{1 - \mathbf{G}_0\mathbf{D}}\mathbf{G}_0|\hat{J})$$

and the modified Green's function is

$$\mathbf{G} = \frac{1}{1 - \mathbf{G}_0 \mathbf{D}} \mathbf{G}_0$$

The perfect lattice classical Green's function $\mathbf{G}_0$ is given directly from the classical normal modes,

$$(\mathbf{G}_0)_{l,l'} = \sum_k \frac{\mathbf{w}(\mathbf{k}) \exp(i\mathbf{k}\cdot\mathbf{x}_l)\mathbf{w}^*(\mathbf{k}) \exp(-i\mathbf{k}\cdot\mathbf{x}_l)}{N\sqrt{m_l m_{l'}} (\omega^2 - \omega_k^2)}$$

thus employing the unperturbed lattice solutions.

These equations have been solved in detail for many cases, the mass defect being the simplest. Two important types of behavior result: first, there may be localized modes at frequencies outside of the normal phonon spectrum; or second, that resonances may occur within the normal phonon spectral region. Rather than concentrating on one particular situation we show how these may occur in general (Maradudin[19], Krumhansl[13], Wagner[20]).

A distinguishing feature of most defect problems is the finite range of the matrix $\mathbf{D}$, which is concentrated around the defect and is a small finite matrix which may be denoted by $\mathbf{d}$. It is then possible to reduce the general problem (for one defect) to that of finding the eigenfunction and eigenvalues of

$$\mathbf{g}_0 \mathbf{d} |\gamma) = \lambda_\gamma |\gamma),$$

where $\mathbf{g}_0$ is the submatrix of $\mathbf{G}_0$ which lies on $\mathbf{d}$ (the left-hand eigenvector must be determined separately). The λ_γ depend implicitly on ω through $\mathbf{g}_0$.

Most defect objects have high symmetry and the $|\gamma)$ are then symmetry coordinates, which may be constructed by group theoretical methods. This facilitates greatly the application of the methods discussed.

The equations may then be partitioned (Krumhansl[13], Lehman and de Wames[21], Wagner[20], and Maradudin[19]) denote the subspace of the defect by 1, the rest of the lattice by 2 so that

$$|\hat{\xi}) = \begin{vmatrix} \hat{\xi}_1 \\ \hat{\xi}_2 \end{vmatrix} \quad \text{and} \quad \mathbf{G}_0 = \begin{bmatrix} \mathbf{g}_0, & \mathbf{G}_0(1, 2) \\ \mathbf{G}_0(2, 1), & \mathbf{G}_0(2, 2) \end{bmatrix}$$

Thus

$$|\hat{\xi}_1) = \mathbf{g}_0 \mathbf{d} |\hat{\xi}_1) + \mathbf{g}_0 |\hat{J}_1) + \mathbf{G}_0(1, 2)|\hat{J}_2)$$

$$|\hat{\xi}_2) = \mathbf{G}_0 \mathbf{d} |\hat{\xi}_1) + \mathbf{G}_0(2, 1)|\hat{J}_1) + \mathbf{G}_0(2, 2)|\hat{J}_2)$$

and $|\hat{\xi}_1)$ may be expressed in $|\hat{\gamma})$ representation leading to expressions for the displacements both in the subspace of the defect and outside.

$$|\xi_1) = \left[\sum_\gamma |\gamma) \frac{1}{1 - \lambda_\gamma} (\gamma|\right] \mathbf{G}_0 |J)$$

$$|\xi_2) = \mathbf{G}_0 \left[\mathbf{d} \sum_\gamma |\gamma) \frac{1}{1 - \lambda_\gamma} (\gamma| \mathbf{G}_0 + 1\right] |J)$$

The perturbed lattice classical Green's function is then

$$\mathbf{G} = \mathbf{G}_0 \left[1 + \mathbf{d} \sum_\gamma |\gamma) \frac{1}{1 - \lambda_\gamma} (\gamma| \mathbf{G}_0\right]$$

The two important consequences of the defect now appear. If λ_γ is real, and as a function of ω any $\lambda_\gamma \rightarrow 1$ a "bound state" occurs. This can occur only if ω lies outside of the continuous spectrum and is a discrete mode which is easily shown to be localized in space. These states are called "localized modes."

On the other hand, as may be made particularly apparent if $|\hat{J})$ is chosen to produce a normal lattice phonon, i.e., $\mathbf{G}_0|\hat{J}) = |\xi_{k_0})$ one obtains (by choosing a scattering Green's function $\mathbf{G}_0^+$)

$$|\xi^+) = \left[1 + \mathbf{G}_0^+ \mathbf{d} \sum_\gamma |\gamma) \frac{1}{1 - \lambda_\gamma} (\gamma|\right] |\xi_{k_0})$$

$$|\xi^+) = [1 + \mathbf{T}^+] |\xi_{k_0})$$

which formally defines a T-matrix; this provides a convenient solution of the scattering problems. Asymptotic forms of $\mathbf{T}^+$ may be obtained. For many years phonon scattering was computed only to Born approximation; the general method just given was indicated by Lifshitz and exact solutions have been developed in detail during the past few years. Interesting features appear for ω in the continuous spectrum where $\lambda_\gamma = \text{Re } \lambda_\gamma + i \text{ Im } \lambda_\gamma$. When $\text{Re } \lambda_\gamma \rightarrow 0$, a resonance may occur. (Brout and Visscher[22], Wagner[20], Takeno[23], Klein[24], Elliott and Taylor[25], and Krumhansl[13].) Most recently Klein[24] has made a thorough study of the formal properties, including the optical theorem for phonon scattering.

Experimentally, both localized modes and resonances have been observed in the low temperature thermal conductivity of nonmetals, in the study of lattice vibrations by inelastic neutron scattering, and by infrared spectroscopy—particularly of ionic crystals. In fact it is no surprise that phonon scattering at low temperatures is almost never described accurately by Born approximation, in spite of its common use. Experimental and theoretical work is continuing, with an increasing emphasis on realistic models made possible by modern computers. Of much greater interest, and difficulty, is the situation with interacting defects. The ultimate "defect lattice" is the disordered state, such as may be found in alloys, amorphous materials, liquids and glasses. Although some progress has been made (Dyson[26], Langer[27], Dean[28] Lifshitz[29]) the description of these systems presents perhaps the most challenging problem of low energy physics today.

III.3. The lattice with point defects, but still harmonic, represents a special case of interacting phonons since it can in principle still be described in terms of noninteracting excitations as just shown. However, this is not generally true and methods for arbitrary interactions are needed; specifically, anharmonic interactions may be present and, though small, when treated by perturbation theory will in turn contribute in all orders.

As the subject of anharmonicity developed a method to handle these many interactions was needed, which in recent years has been provided to many body problems by the techniques of quantum field theory. The phonon system is tractable for another reason—the interactions between the phonons are usually small and do not exhibit the singularities found in most field theories. The results are now familiar: often it is possible to define "quasi-particle" excitations in some sense with characteristic self-energy and lifetime.

The method of thermodynamic Green's functions has been applied to the phonon problem by Baym[30], Mermin and Baym[31], Maradudin and Fein[32], Cowley[33], Langer[27], and Elliott and Taylor[25], and by now is standard. Cowley has presented an extensive development for the anharmonic crystal, with application to thermodynamic properties, elastic properties, optical absorption, dielectric properties, and scattering (neutron) properties. Horie and Krumhansl[34], and Martin and Kwok[35] have discussed the phonon Boltzmann equation. The attenuation of sound has been discussed by Maris[36], and by Kwok, Martin, and Miller[35].

In the present discussion we simply illustrate the principal points of Green's function method. By way of introduction we may examine the point defect problem of the previous section by this general method, following Elliott and Taylor[25].

The retarded Green's function is directly related to the measurable properties of a system (Zubarev[37]); the response of field operator $\hat{A}$ to an externally applied force having field operator $\hat{B}$ is given by

$$G^R(\hat{A}\hat{B}, t) = -i\theta(t)\langle\langle[\hat{A}(t), \hat{B}(0)]\rangle\rangle,$$

where the double averaging is over quantum and thermal states; $\theta(t) = 1$, $t > 0$ and vanishes for $t < 0$. The retarded Green's function is closely related to the thermodynamic Green's function

$$G(\hat{A}\hat{B}, it) = \langle\langle T\hat{A}(t)\hat{B}(0)\rangle\rangle,$$

which (Kadanoff and Baym[38]) may be computed more directly than G^R. In particular the Fourier transforms of G^R and G may be related by analytic continuation in the transform variable. The spectral representation provides direct information, through its poles, of the frequency (self-energy) and lifetimes of the quasi-particle phonon excitations.

Two common methods for computing the Green's function may be employed. First, the equations of motion for the Green's function may be obtained; usually these comprise a chain of increasingly higher order Green's functions which are terminated by some physically guided approximation. Second, the Green's function may be developed in a perturabtion series, e.g., in interaction representation, and the various contributions classified and summed according to their order in extensive or intensive parameters. The former may be applied to the defect lattice; the latter has been applied to the anharmonic crystal.

For the defect lattice a relevant Green's function is that for displacements, in cartesian components α, β,

$$G(\hat{u}_\alpha(l)\hat{u}_\beta(l'), t) = \langle\langle T\hat{u}_\alpha(l, t)\hat{u}_\beta(l', 0)\rangle\rangle$$

The equation of motion for G is found by commuting with the Hamiltonian

$$\frac{i\hbar^2}{2\pi}\frac{dG}{dt} = \hbar\,\delta(t)\langle[\hat{u}_\alpha(l, t), \hat{u}_\beta(l', 0)]\rangle + \langle\langle[\hat{u}_\alpha(l, t), \hat{H}]\hat{u}_\beta(l', 0)\rangle\rangle$$

and the second term on the right-hand side is another Green's function [it is $(i\hbar M_i^{-1})\langle\langle\hat{p}_\alpha(l, t)\hat{u}_\beta(l', 0)\rangle\rangle$]. Fortunately, differentiating again terminates the chain giving an equation entirely in G itself (adopting a short-hand notation):

$$M_l\frac{d^2}{dt^2}G_{\alpha\beta}(l, l') = -2\pi\delta_{\alpha\beta}\delta(l, l')\delta(t) - \sum_{\gamma, l''}\Phi_{\alpha\gamma}(l, l'')G_{\gamma\beta}(l'', l')$$

This is, of course, a consequence of the harmonic nature of the problem. Most important is that the Green's function has simply the *classical equation of motion*. Thus everything done in the previous section is directly applicable, so it need not be repeated. The time-dependent Green's function under consideration here is found, of course, by Fourier transforming $(\mathbf{G}(\omega))_{l,l'}$ given there.

A major virtue of the method is that one may proceed in particularly direct fashion to the observable properties of the system. For example, neutron scattering or optical absorption are related to displacement—displacement correlation functions. But these may be computed directly from the Green's function

$$\langle \hat{u}_\alpha(l, t)\hat{u}_\beta(l', 0)\rangle = \frac{i\hbar}{2\pi} \lim_{\varepsilon \to 0} \int_{-\infty}^{\infty} dw \, \frac{e^{i\omega t}}{e^{\beta\omega} - 1} \, [\mathbf{G}(\omega + i\varepsilon) - \mathbf{G}(\omega - i\varepsilon)]_{l,l'}$$

As an example, the result for the equal-time displacement-displacement self-correlation function (Elliott and Taylor[25]) for a simple mass defect $(\Delta M/m = \varepsilon)$ is

$$\langle u_\alpha(0)^2\rangle = \frac{\hbar}{2M} \int_0^\infty \frac{\coth\left(\frac{\beta\omega}{2}\right)\gamma(\omega)\,d\omega}{\omega\{(1 - \omega^2 I_1)^2 + I_2^2\}}$$
$$+ \frac{\hbar \coth\left(\frac{\beta\omega_l}{2}\right)}{2\omega_l M}\left[\varepsilon^2\omega_l^4 \int \frac{\nu(\omega')\,d\omega'}{(\omega_l^2 - \omega'^2)} - \varepsilon\right]^{-1}$$

The first term may show resonant behavior in the continuum if the frequency dependent (self-energy) integral I_1 is positive and large enough. The second term is indicative of localized modes if $\mathbf{G}(\omega)$ has poles on the real ω axis at ω_l lying outside of the continuum. Resonances and localized modes have been seen in a variety of neutron and optical experiments.

The anharmonic case may be handled by perturbation methods. Using the similarity between imaginary time and temperature dependence, the thermodynamic Green's function may be developed from the Hamiltonian

$$\hat{H} = \hat{H}_0 + \hat{H}_A,$$

where $\hat{H}_A$ is the anharmonic contribution. In terms of an interaction representation, with $\tau = (it/\hbar)$

$$\hat{A}_I = e^{\tau\hat{H}_0} \, \hat{A} \, e^{-\tau\hat{H}_0}$$

it is found by using the Bloch equation that

$$G(\hat{A}\hat{B}, \tau) = \langle\langle T\hat{A}_I(\tau)\hat{B}_I(0) \sum_{n=0}^{\infty} \frac{(-1)^n}{n!} \int\int \cdots \int H_{A_I}(\tau_1) \cdots H_{A_I}(\tau_n)$$
$$\times \, d\tau_1 \cdots d\tau_n \rangle\rangle$$

This may be computed using the phonon representation $\hat{n}_k$, $\hat{a}_k$, $\hat{a}_k^+$. The authors cited have carried this out in terms of diagrams where each phonon is represented by a line and the H_{A_I} are the vertices: Wick's theorem is applied. The development parallels that of Goldstone and Hugenholtz. The summation must be restricted to connected diagrams with external lines to $\hat{A}$ and $\hat{B}$. Moreover, the disconnected diagrams must be summed exactly otherwise one obtains an incorrect dependence on the volume of the crystal. Actual calculations are carried out on the Fourier transform of G rather than the time domain Green's function.

The anharmonic part of the Hamiltonian usually is taken to include only cubic and quartic terms $\hat{H}_A = \hat{V}^{(3)} + \hat{V}^{(4)}$, whence

$$\hat{H}_0 = \sum_k \frac{\hbar\omega_k}{2} (\hat{a}_k \hat{a}_k^+ + \hat{a}_k^+ \hat{a}_k)$$

$$\hat{H}_A = \sum_{k_1, k_2, k_3} V^{(3)}(k_1, k_2, k_3)[\hat{a}_{k_1}\hat{a}_{k_2}\hat{a}_{k_3} + \cdots]$$
$$+ \sum_{k_1, k_2, k_3, k_4} V^{(4)}(k_1, k_2, k_3, k_4)[\hat{a}_{k_1}\hat{a}_{k_2}\hat{a}_{k_3}\hat{a}_{k_4} + \cdots]$$
$$+ \cdots$$

and one examines Green's functions for the phonon field operators $\hat{a}_k^+$, $\hat{a}_{k'}$, or combinations of them. In the harmonic approximation the Fourier transform $[G(\tau) = \sum_n G(i\omega_n) \exp(i\hbar\omega_n\tau)$ becomes

$$G(k, k'; i\omega_n) = \frac{2\omega_k}{\beta\hbar} - \frac{1}{\omega_n^2 + \omega_k^2}\delta_{k,k'}$$

which has poles at the unperturbed phonon frequency. However, when the anharmonic terms are included this is modified in an essential way. Thus, Maradudin and Fein, and Cowley employ the Dyson equation to sum improper diagrams and then obtain renormalized one-phonon Green's functions. The Green's function is now found to have poles at

$$\omega = \omega_k + \Sigma_k(\omega, T) + i\Gamma_k(\omega, T)$$

where both the self-energy and lifetime corrections are frequency and temperature dependent. The leading diagrams which contribute to the self-energy correction have been indicated in Fig. 1c. Cowley and Maradudin have used phonon spectra from neutron scattering data, together with force constant models, to estimate self energy and lifetime corrections. For alkali halides the theoretical values are quite small and lead to the conclusion that, at least as far as single quasi-particle excitations are concerned, phonons have a well-defined meaning even in the presence of anharmonic interactions. However, in computing thermodynamic properties it is quite incorrect to treat them as independent excitations. There is general agreement with the experimental frequency and widths in neutron inelastic scattering spectra, but measured lifetimes are often significantly shorter than theoretically predicted.

III.4. We turn next to some different aspects of phonons interacting with each other, and with external probes. The previous discussion has related only to phenomena occurring entirely within the crystal, and the phonon coordinates are "internal" coordinates. To treat both internal and external interactions we must also include the center of mass coordinate and momentum $\hat{\mathbf{R}}$ and $\hat{\mathbf{P}}$. We may then see whether there are any symmetry conditions which may be applied to obtain conservation relations for general interactions. This is the principal subject of this section, following Süssman[39], Jensen[16], and Prohofsky[40].

Invariance properties and conservation conditions are obtained generally by discovering operators which commute with the Hamiltonian. We use the representation

$$\hat{\mathbf{r}}(l) = \hat{\mathbf{R}} + \mathbf{x}(l) + \sum_{k}' \left(\frac{\hbar}{2mN\omega_k}\right)^{\frac{1}{2}} [w^*(k) \exp [-i\mathbf{k}\cdot\mathbf{x}(l)]\hat{a}_k^+ + \text{h.c.}],$$

$$\hat{\mathbf{p}}(l) = \frac{\hat{\mathbf{P}}}{M} + \sum_{k}' \left(\frac{\hbar m\omega_k}{2N}\right)^{\frac{1}{2}} i[w^*(k) \exp [-i\mathbf{k}\cdot\mathbf{x}(l)]\hat{a}_k^+ - \text{h.c.}],$$

(where M is the total mass of the crystal) which explicitly exhibits the position and momentum of the crystal as a whole. In this represetation

$$\hat{H} = \hat{H}(\hat{P}, \hat{R}; \hat{a}_{k_1}, \hat{a}_{k_1}^+, \hat{a}_{k_2}, \ldots).$$

For the free crystal in the absence of external fields, the potentials (the anharmonic case included) depend only on the relative position of the atoms and

$$\hat{H} = \frac{\hat{\mathbf{P}}^2}{2M} + \hat{H}_c(\hat{a}_{k_1}^+, \hat{a}_{k_1}, \hat{a}_{k_2}, \ldots).$$

The variables $\hat{a}_k^+$, $\hat{a}_k$ satisfy the usual commutation relations; in addition $[\hat{a}_k, \hat{P}) = 0 = [\hat{a}_k, \hat{a}]$ and $[\hat{R}, \hat{P}] = i\hbar$. Thus, in this case, from

$$[\hat{H}, \hat{P}] = 0$$

the center-of-mass momentum is a constant of the motion for the free crystal.

Suppose now the crystal interacts with some external probe. The principles are illustrated by examining the interaction with a neutron which we may approximate by the interaction Hamiltonian $H_{\text{int}} = \sum_l v_0 \, \delta(\hat{\mathfrak{r}}(l) - \hat{\mathfrak{r}})$. Denoting by $\hat{\mathfrak{r}}$ (and $\hat{\mathfrak{p}}$) the neutron dynamic variables the Hamiltonian becomes

$$\hat{H} = \frac{\mathbf{p}^2}{2\mu} + \frac{\hat{\mathbf{P}}^2}{2M} + \sum_l v_0 \, \delta(\hat{\mathfrak{r}}(l) - \hat{\mathfrak{r}}) + \hat{H}_c(\hat{a}_{k_1}, \ldots).$$

Since $\hat{\mathbf{R}} = \sum_l \hat{\mathfrak{r}}(l)$, $\hat{\mathbf{P}} = \sum_l \hat{\mathfrak{p}}(l)$ it is easily demonstrated that

$$[\hat{\mathfrak{p}} + \hat{\mathbf{P}}, \hat{H}] = 0$$

as expected, i.e., the momentum of the probe plus system is conserved. This will be true regardless of any internal excitations (harmonic or anharmonic) which are produced, as it must be. The next step, that of computing the scattering of the probe particle and the resulting excitations of the system is also the subject of an extensive recent history and literature, distinguished by the pioneering work of George Placzek[41], to whom the enormous evolution based on his ideas is a fitting memorial. In collaboration with van Hove, the meaning and use of correlation functions has been studied in detail; an excellent review has been given by Sjölander[42]. Basis states $|\mathbf{p}, \mathbf{P}, \hat{n}_{k_1}, \hat{n}_{k_2}, \ldots\rangle$ may be used to show that in first Born approximation a neutron may scatter with a change in momentum $\varDelta\mathbf{p} = \hbar\varkappa = -\varDelta\mathbf{P}$ and energy loss $\hbar\omega$, and that the cross section for this process depends on the Fourier transform of a correlation function

$$S(\varkappa, \omega) = \frac{1}{2\pi} \int_{-\infty}^{\infty} e^{-i\omega t} \, dt \langle\langle \exp\left[-i\varkappa \cdot \hat{\mathfrak{r}}(l, t)\right] \exp\left[i\varkappa \cdot \hat{\mathfrak{r}}(l, 0)\right]\rangle\rangle$$

This correlation function which does not contain the time ordering may be obtained from the system Green's function as noted in the previous section. Upon studying the properties of this function in detail it is found that scattering may take place:

(*1*) Elastically with $\varkappa = 2\pi n\mathbf{b}$, i.e., Bragg scattering with reciprocal lattice vector **b**.

(*2*) Inelastically, with creation or annihilation of one, two, three, etc. phonons. In particular selection rules are found:

$$\hbar\omega + \sum_k \hbar\omega_k \, \varDelta n_k = 0$$

$$\hbar\varkappa + \sum_k \hbar\varkappa \, \varDelta n_k = 2\pi n\mathbf{b}$$

The second of which is of some curiosity since $\hbar\varkappa$ is really a mechanical momentum while $\hbar\varkappa$ is a phonon field quantity.

Is there any general underlying principle involved? The answer is yes, and it may be demonstrated by finding appropriate symmetry operators.

To begin with we know how to construct a translation operator which mechanically translates the crystal itself by a displacement **a**; this is

$$\mathscr{T}_c(\mathbf{a}) = \exp\left[\frac{i}{\hbar}\mathbf{a}\cdot\sum_l \hat{\mathbf{p}}(l)\right] = \exp\left[\frac{i}{\hbar}\mathbf{a}\cdot\hat{\mathbf{P}}\right]$$

For the free crystal $[\mathscr{T}, \hat{H}] = 0$ and $\mathscr{T}$ is a constant of the motion with value $\exp[i/\hbar a \cdot \mathbf{p}]$. With the interaction present this will no longer be a constant of the system. Of course this may easily be taken into account for the crystal plus neutron by translating the neutron also, whence

$$\mathscr{T}_n(\mathbf{a})\,\mathscr{T}_c(\mathbf{a}) = \exp\left[\frac{i}{\hbar}\mathbf{a}\cdot(\mathbf{p} + \hat{\mathbf{P}})\right]$$

commutes with $\hat{H}$ and $\hat{\mathbf{p}} + \hat{\mathbf{P}} = $ constant. This much is trivial.

However, there are phonon field symmetry operators which have nontrivial implications. Define the "phonon field translation operator" in terms of

$$\hat{\mathbf{\Pi}} = \sum_k \hbar\mathbf{k}\hat{a}_k^+ \hat{a}_k$$

by the relation

$$\hat{Y}(\mathbf{a}) = \exp\left[\frac{i}{\hbar}\mathbf{a}\cdot\hat{\mathbf{\Pi}}\right],$$

where now **a** is restricted to be any multiple of the lattice primitive vectors. It may be readily verified that in the defect-free lattice this shifts the phonon field by the amount **a**, that is

$$\hat{Y}\hat{u}(\mathbf{l}, t)\,\hat{Y}^+ = \hat{u}(l + \mathbf{a}, t)$$
$$\hat{Y}\hat{p}(l, t)\,\hat{Y}^+ = \hat{p}(\mathbf{l} + \mathbf{a}, t)$$

This has important implications—first, for the free but arbitrarily anharmonic defect-free lattice; second, for interaction with probes.

In a periodic, defect-free lattice the energy depends only on the relative displacements of the particles, thus whether harmonic or anharmonic and in spite of the complexity of the state of the system except for end effects, which can be neglected, the energy is unchanged by rigid translation of the phonon field. Therefore, for the free crystal, $[\hat{H}, \hat{Y}] = 0$ and the quantity

$$\mathbf{\Pi} = \text{const.} + 2\pi n\mathbf{b},$$

where the additive Bragg constant $2\pi n\mathbf{b}$ results from the periodicity. This may immediately be written out for phonon interactions, say due to anharmonic forces,

$$\varDelta\Pi = \sum_{\mathbf{k}} \hbar\mathbf{k}\,\varDelta n_{\mathbf{k}} = 0 + \varDelta(2\pi n\mathbf{b}),$$

which is a familiar selection rule first noted by Peierls. If the right-hand side is zero the process is said to be normal, i.e., N-processes, otherwise it is an "umklapp" process, i.e., U-process. The virtue of the derivation just given is that it is perfectly general and eliminates any concern that selection rules found by perturbation approximations might have limited validity. The relation is in essence an internal conservation condition for phonon "field momentum".

Finally, we may generalize to the situation of neutron and crystal interacting. First, for a stationary crystal move the phonon field and the neutron by the same amount, whence

$$\exp\left[\frac{i}{\hbar}\mathbf{a}\cdot(\hat{\mathbf{p}} + \hat{\mathbf{\Pi}})\right] = \mathscr{T}_n(\mathbf{a})\hat{\psi}(\mathbf{a})$$

commutes with $\hat{H}$ of the *interacting* system. Thus

$$\mathbf{P} + \sum_{\mathbf{k}} \hbar\mathbf{k}n_{\mathbf{k}} = \text{const.} + (2\pi n\mathbf{b})$$

and the selection rule

$$\varDelta\mathbf{p} + \sum_{\mathbf{k}} \hbar\mathbf{k}n_{\mathbf{k}} = 0 + \varDelta(2\pi n\mathbf{b})$$

includes Bragg and inelastic scattering, with the previously found conservation between neutron momentum and phonon "field momentum."

But it is also possible to find another invariant. If the phonon field is moved by $\mathbf{a}$, and the crystal is translated back by $-\mathbf{a}$ again the Hamiltonian is unchanged, thus

$$-\mathbf{P} + \sum_{\mathbf{k}} \hbar \mathbf{k} n_{\mathbf{k}} = \text{const.} + (2\pi n\mathbf{b})$$

Thus the center-of-mass motion of a crystal and the phonon field may be coupled through the intervention of a fixed and localized external interaction. This result is provocative—for example, as a possible coupling between the normal (phonon) and super-fluids in liquid helium—but as yet no direct experiments have examined such effects.

III.5. In closing, a brief description of one very exciting current problem in interacting phonons may be cited. The thermal conductivity and other transport properties of the phonon excitations may be described by the phonon Boltzmann equation

$$\frac{\partial \hat{n}(\mathbf{k}, \mathbf{x}, t)}{\partial t} + \mathbf{v}_g(\mathbf{k}) \cdot \nabla_x \hat{n}(\mathbf{k}, \mathbf{x}, t) = -\dot{\hat{n}}_{\text{coll}}.$$

which though limited to properties which do not vary too rapidly in space, and which are primarily diagonal in phonon number representation does properly describe many situations.

A very special situation occurs in very pure systems at low temperatures. Here the lattice scattering by N-processes dominate. Then there are two "moments" of the equation

$$\sum_{\mathbf{k}} \hbar \omega_{\mathbf{k}} \hat{n}(\mathbf{k}, \mathbf{x}, t) = E(\mathbf{x}, t)$$

and

$$\sum_{\mathbf{k}} \hbar \mathbf{k} \hat{n}(\mathbf{k}, \mathbf{x}; t) = \mathbf{\Pi}(\mathbf{x}, t),$$

which are strictly conserved by the collision term. In fact although the term "collision" is used, the discussion just preceding shows that these are strictly conserved quantities, however generally the interactions are treated. Under these circumstances the two moments of the Boltzmann equation may be shown to be quite analogous to hydrodynamic equations

$$\frac{\partial E}{\partial t} + \nabla \cdot (\mathbf{v}E) = 0$$

$$\frac{\partial \mathbf{\Pi}}{\partial t} + \nabla \cdot (\mathbf{v} \cdot \mathbf{\Pi}) = 0.$$

These solutions predict hydrodynamic behavior in a phonon gas, even with anharmonic interactions, as long umklapp, impurity scattering and phonon "viscosity" may be neglected. There is now reason to believe that steady state Poiseuille phonon flow has been observed experimentally in solid He^4 by Mezov-Deglin[43]. Meanwhile, "second sound" which is the name given to the wavelike solutions for a collective phonon excitation is being searched for experimentally. There has been an extensive theoretical literature on this subject also. (Ward and Wilks[44], Dingle[45], Prohofsky and Krumhansl[46], Guyer and Krumhansl[47], M. Chester[48], and Kwok, Martin and Miller[35].) There is every reason to believe that if Poiseuille flow is seen, second sound may also be observed when adequate high frequency thermometer techniques become available.[49]

IV. Conclusion

This has been a selected review of various topics in phonon physics. Omissions of important references probably have occurred, but it is hoped that some flavor of the very venerable and yet very current subject of phonon physics has been conveyed.

References

1. Peierls, R. E., *Ann. Phys. Lpz.*, **3**, 1055 (1929); cf. also R. E. Peierls, *Quantum Theory of Solids*, Oxford, 1955.
2. Born, M., and K. Huang, *Dynamical Theory of Crystal Lattices*, Oxford, New York, 1954.
3. Ziman, J. M., *Electrons and Phonons*, Oxford, New York, 1960.
4. Cochran, W., *International Conference on Lattice Dynamics, Copenhagen*, R. F. Wallis, Ed., Pergamon, London, 1965.
5. Dick, B. G., and A. W. Overhauser, *Phys. Rev.*, **112**, 90 (1958).
6. Kellerman, E. W., *Phil. Trans. Roy. Soc.*, **A238**, 513 (1940).
7. Cochran, Cowley, Brockhouse, and Woods, *Phys. Rev.*, **131**, 1030 (1963).
8. Karo, A. M., and J. R. Hardy, *Phys. Rev.*, **129**, 2024 (1963).
9. Kohn, W., *Phys. Rev. Letters*, **2**, 393 (1959).
10. Brockhouse, B. N., in *Phonons and Phonon Interactions*, T. Bak, Ed., Benjamin, New York, 1964.
11. Susskind and Glogower, in press.
12. Dirac, P. A. M., *Principles of Quantum Mechanics*, Oxford, New York, 1947.
13. Krumhansl, J. A., *International Conference on Lattice Dynamics, Copenhagen*, R. F. Wallis, Ed., Pergamon, London, 1965.

14. Toupin, R. A., *Arch. Rational Mech. Anal.*, **11**, 385 (1962).

15. Mindlin, R. D., and H. F. Tiersten, *Arch. Rational Mech. Anal.*, **11**, 415 (1962).

16. Jensen, H., in *Phonons and Phonon Interactions*, T. Bak, Ed., Benjamin, New York, 1964.

17. Wallis, R. F., ed., *International Conference on Lattice Vibrations, Copenhagen*, Pergamon, London, 1963.

18. Lifshitz, E. M., *J. Phys. U.S.S.R.*, **7**, 215 (1943); **7**, 249 (1943); *Nuovo Cimento* (*Suppl.* **10**), **3**, 716 (1956).

19. Maradudin, A. A., in *Repts. Progr. Phys.*, **28** (1965).

20. Wagner, M., *Phys. Rev.*, **131**, 2520 (1963); **133**, A750 (1964).

21. Lehman, G. and R. E. de Wames, *Phys. Rev.*, **131**, 1008 (1963).

22. Brout, R., and W. M. Visscher, *Phys. Rev. Letters*, **9**, 54 (1962).

23. Takeno, S., *Progr. Theor. Phys.* (*Kyoto*), **29**, 191 (1963); **30**, 144 (1963).

24. Klein, M. V., *Phys. Rev.*, **131**, 1500 (1963); *Phys. Rev.*, in press.

25. Elliott, R. J., and D. W. Taylor, *Proc. Phys. Soc.*, **83**, 189 (1964).

26. Dyson, F. J., *Phys. Rev.*, **92**, 1337 (1953).

27. Langer, J. S., *J. Math. Phys.*, **2**, 584 (1961); R. W. Davies and J. S. Langer, *Phys. Rev.*, **131**, 163 (1963).

28. Dean, P., *Phys. Soc. London*, 1960–61.

29. Lifshitz, E. M., *Advan. Phys.*, **13**, 483 (1964).

30. Baym, G., *Ann. Phys.*, **14**, 1 (1961).

31. Baym, G., and D. Mermin, *J. Math. Phys.*, **2**, 232 (1961).

32. Maradudin, A. A., and A. E. Fein, *Phys. Rev.*, **128**, 2589 (1962).

33. Cowley, R. A., *Advan. Phys.*, **12**, 421 (1963).

34. Horie, C., and J. A. Krumhansl, *Phys. Rev.*, **136**, A1397 (1964).

35. Kwok, P. C., Harvard Thesis, May 1965; P. C. Kwok, P. C. Martin, and P. B. Miller, *Solid State Comm.*, **3**, 181 (1965).

36. Maris, H. J., *Phil. Mag.*, **115**, 89 (1965).

37. Zubarev, D. N., *Soviet Physics Uspekhi*, **3**, 320 (1960).

38. Kadanoff, L. P., and G. Baym, *Quantum Statistical Mechanics*, Wiley, New York, 1962.

39. Süssman, G., *Z. Naturf.*, **11a**, 1 (1956).

40. Projofsky, E. W., Cornell Thesis, 1963.

41. Placzek, G., *Phys. Rev.*, **86**, 377 (1952); G. Placzek and L. van Hove, *Phys. Rev.*, **93**, 1207 (1954).

42. Sjölander, A., in *Phonons and Phonon Interactions*, T. Bak, Ed., Benjamin, New York, 1964.

43. Mezhov–Deglin, L. P., *JETP*, **49**, 66 (1965).

44. Ward, J. C., and J. Wilks, *Phil. Mag.*, **42**, 314 (1951); **43**, 48 (1952).

45. Dingle, R. B., *Proc. Phys. Soc.*, **A65**, 374 (1952).

46. Prohofsky, E. W., and J. A. Krumhansl, *Phys. Rev.*, **133**, A1403 (1964).

47. Guyer, R. A., and J. A. Krumhansl, *Phys. Rev.*, **133**, A1411 (1964).

48. Chester, M., *Phys. Rev.*, **131**, 2013 (1963).

49. Added in proof: Second sound in solid helium has been observed by Ackerman, Bertman, Fairbanks, and Guyer, *Phys. Rev. Letters*, May 1966.

Superconductivity and the Many Body Problem

H. FRÖHLICH

University of Liverpool

1. Introduction

The invitation by the editor of this volume to write an article on superconductivity for Bethe's sixtieth birthday reminds me of the days more than thirty years ago in which we discussed the errors of the latest attempts to deal with this problem[1]. The subject has of course changed drastically. At present—as in the whole of physics—development in breadth at enormous speed is coupled with progress in depth with a speed which has hardly changed (provocatively speaking). This poses the obvious question whether development in depth is still required in superconductivity. In the subsequent section I have, therefore, expressed my opinion on this point. This section is necessarily vague. It is followed by a discussion of questions which have arisen in course of applications of powerful new methods to electrons which attract each other: Before one studies these methods he has usually been taught that electrons repel each other. It is obvious, therefore, that the effective interaction plays a much more important role than is sometimes admitted. In fact prior to my introduction of phonon-induced electron interaction it seemed ridiculous to assume attractive forces between electrons—which is probably the reason why the theoretical treatment of superconductivity was held up for so long. Such historical questions are discussed in the final section. Throughout I have endeavoured to follow the editor's suggestion to make the article informal and provocative.

2. The Many-Body Problem

Frequently approximate treatments of N-body ($N \gg 1$) problems are introduced by words like "since the problem is too complicated for exact solution we ....." Would 'exact solution' be desirable? Definitely not. For these solutions would depend on all the constants of motion whose number is very large, of order N. What is desirable, therefore, is not to solve the equations of motion exactly but to find answers to certain questions in terms of concepts which usually will refer simultaneously to many (or all) of the particles. Some of these concepts are well known: thus finding the specific heat requires the density of energy levels of the whole system; the properties of long longitudinal oscillations require introduction of the long wave Fourier components of the density as "collective coordinates." A question which might be of fundamental importance (if answered positively) is whether we have so far not missed many of these many body concepts. Such concepts might be of great value in connecting physics with chemistry and biology both of which deal with materials which in terms of physics seem very complicated. Finding new concepts within the realm of very simple materials might, however, also be of importance. For they might open a way in pointing to methods by which such concepts can be found.

All this is very vague, but stimulated by the general idea one might recall the similarity of superconductors and superfluid liquid helium from a hydrodynamic point of view: both (with a few exceptions) have an energy gap for the setting up of transverse excitations, and it is this feature which is mainly responsible for their most striking properties. Yet the present-day microscopic theory of superconductivity differs vastly from the theory of superfluid helium. One might hope then that it should be possible to derive the common properties in a very general manner which does not require going into all the details which present theories contain. Such an attempt would naturally start in terms of a "collective coordinate" describing transverse displacements and motion. Yet such a quantity has never been presented.

To discuss this further consider first displacements in a simple crystalline solid. Here the well-known normal modes

$$\mathbf{q_k} = \frac{1}{\sqrt{N}} \sum_j \xi_j \exp\left[-i\mathbf{k}\cdot\mathbf{a}_j\right], \qquad \xi_j = \mathbf{x}_j - a_j \qquad (2.1)$$

represent, of course, collective coordinates. They are, however, based on the assumption of particular states in which the particle with coordinate $\mathbf{x}_j$ oscillates round the lattice point with coordinate $\mathbf{a}_j$. Now for the longitudinal modes the Fourier components ρ_k of the density operator,

$$\rho_k = \sum_j \exp\left(-i\mathbf{k}\cdot\mathbf{x}_j\right), \tag{2.2}$$

form more satisfactory collective coordinates because they are given through the $\mathbf{x}_j$ without reference to a particular state. Moreover, for the particular state for which $|\mathbf{x}_j - \mathbf{a}_j|$, is small, they lead to $\mathbf{g}_k$ because then

$$i\rho_k \simeq (\mathbf{k}\mathbf{q}_k)\sqrt{N} \quad \text{and} \quad k^2\mathbf{q}_k = \mathbf{k}(\mathbf{k}\mathbf{q}_k) \tag{2.3}$$

for longitudinal modes. The coordinate ρ_k can be used for noncrystalline materials as well. No such simple coordinate has been presented for transverse modes, however.

To understand the difference we note that the long-wave density ρ_k's are basically macroscopic coordinates. Microscopic properties like correlation between neighboring particles cannot be described by them; in terms of the density operator, such correlations depend on the short-wave Fourier components. Now transverse displacements in a solid lead to density changes with short-wave Fourier coefficients only, even if the wavelength of the normal mode is very long. One may conclude from this that while longitudinal displacement can be described by collective coordinates which are closely connected with a macroscopic description, transverse displacements necessarily contain a microscopic element. A sufficiently general transverse collective coordinate would, therefore, have to combine the long-wave (macroscopic) feature of the normal mode with a short-wave feature capable of expressing correlations between nearest neighbours.

Clearly, establishment of transverse collective coordinates would be desirable for the purpose of discussing the common properties of superconductivity and superfluidity without reference to details of the respective models.

It is of interest in this connection to note that macroscopic wave functions Ψ as they are often used in superconductivity as well as superfluidity automatically lead to an irrotational velocity field $\mathbf{v}$ in the absence of external fields—or to the London relation curl $\mathbf{v} \propto \mathbf{H}$ in the presence of a magnetic field $\mathbf{H}$. For in this case, the macroscopic density

$$\sigma = \Psi^*\Psi \tag{2.4}$$

can be assumed to fluctuate only weakly around its mean value σ_0. As a consequence one can define for $\mathbf{H} = 0$ (m = particle mass)

$$\mathbf{v} = \frac{\hbar}{mi} (\Psi^* \nabla \Psi - (\nabla \Psi^*)\Psi) \, \Psi^* \Psi = \nabla \varphi \qquad (2.5)$$

if

$$\Psi = \sqrt{\sigma} \, e^{i\phi}, \qquad (2.6)$$

and hence

$$\text{curl } \mathbf{v} = 0. \qquad (2.7)$$

This procedure would be impossible for the (microscopic) field operators ψ; for the exact density operator $\rho = \psi^+ \psi$ is highly singular and does not possess an inverse, so that a microscopic operator corresponding to $\mathbf{v}$ does not exist. One can, however, always form expectation values σ and $\mathbf{j}$ of the exact density and current density operators, and hence establish a macroscopic wave function with the help of the irrotational part $\mathbf{v}$ of $(\mathbf{j}/\sigma)$. These macroscopic σ and $\mathbf{v}$ usually will satisfy the equations of motion of classical irrotational hydrodynamics. The rotational part, however, from the above discussion may be expected to be determined not only by the macroscopic averages σ and $\mathbf{j}$, but also by the properties of short distance correlation. This is the origin of my earlier suggestion[2] of an extension of hydrodynamics into a nonlocal theory.

If it is at all possible to deal with these questions in a general manner (without reference to specific models) then the empirical observation by C. N. Yang[3] that the density matrices of both superfluids and superconductors contain long-range, off-diagonal elements must be of considerable importance for this concept could never be incorporated into a local hydrodynamics.

The conceptional difficulties of a local hydrodynamics can also be illustrated from a macroscopic point of view. Suppose we consider a friction-free fluid of a continuous, electrically neutral material. It is usually implied in hydrodynamics that such a fluid has only one specific property, namely density σ. How can we then observe a displacement field $\mathbf{P}$? Irrotational displacements are measured through the density because div $\mathbf{P} = -(\sigma - \sigma_0)$; but transverse displacements do not alter σ. To be consistent a further property should, therefore, be introduced even in macroscopic continuum theory.

Another question referring to very general properties concerns the specific heat, or entropy of Fermi liquids near the absolute zero of temperature T. It is known that in metals the "free electron model" works very well and leads to an entropy $\propto T$. If it is possible to consider this model as a valid approximation which in a higher order provides an appropriate further interaction between the "free electrons" then superconductivity arises and the entropy decreases much faster than T as $T \to 0$. It has been conjectured[4] that this faster decrease will always occur though not necessarily connected with the occurrence of super-conductivity. A being (computer or physicist) programmed to carry out some of the relevant calculations will reply that validity of the faster than T decrease of entropy depends on the chosen type of interaction. It is not possible, however, to choose this interaction freely. For establishment of the "free electron" model must have taken account of most of the interaction and by an appropriate choice of parameters, like lattice distance, must have led to a state of equilibrium. More exact solution might not change the qualitative properties and simply lead to a readjustment of these parameters. They might, on the other hand, lead to a different qualitative behavior as one finds in superconductivity. Whether this is the case must clearly depend on the type of corrections available in the higher approximation; the emphasis is on available.

3. The Importance of the Interaction

The particles composing a metal interact primarily through the Coulomb forces. These forces lead in the first place to the binding of the particles into a crystal and, in the case of a metal, to the behavior of some of the electrons as free. In the theory of superconductivity it is then considered that a fraction of the interaction has not been treated with sufficient accuracy, and that appropriate improvement may lead to superconductivity. Phrased in this manner, statements like "attractive interaction between electrons leads to superconductivity," lose their meaning. For we might in the first place have subtracted a small repulsive energy from interelectronic interaction, then after a solution by a method leading to the free electron model correct for these terms by adding a corresponding attractive interaction and treat it by a method "leading to superconductivity." One might argue that it would be more systematic to treat these terms as corrections to the total energy, lattice distance, etc. within the solutions in terms of the free electron model. The problem then clearly remains to discuss whether a further inter-action leading to superconductivity is still available.

Or to give another example, it is often stated that the attractive interaction $\int V(\mathbf{r} - \mathbf{r}')\rho(\mathbf{r})\rho(\mathbf{r}')d^3\mathbf{r}\,d^3\mathbf{r}'$ $[V(\mathbf{r} - \mathbf{r}') < 0; \rho(\mathbf{r})$ is the density operator] leads to superconductivity. But if V has its lowest value at $\mathbf{r} = \mathbf{r}'$, then it represents an unsaturated attractive interaction which normally would lead to a collapse in space if the total number of particles is very large.

These examples show that the "attractive interaction which leads to superconductivity" can only be considered in context with the total interaction responsible for cohesion, etc., and it would be necessary to prove that the methods leading to superconductivity are applicable. This is a difficult task; its solution has never been attempted.

The foregoing is meant to make clear that the choice of interaction, and the method used for solution are correlated. The phonon induced electron–electron interaction, which forms the basis for all subsequent developments was originally treated in a semiempirical way. I had shown then that the electron phonon interaction whose strength can be obtained from the high temperature electric resistivity must also lead to an electron–electron interaction. The free-electron model was thus taken for granted, which implies that most of the interelectronic Coulomb energy is already considered. Later applications of this interaction have explicitly added some further Coulomb interaction between the electrons. At present it seems quite unclear to what extent this should be done.

How would one formulate the task? In the first place one would restrict oneself to metals with complete inner shells which latter could then be treated as polarizable centers. One would then expect that solutions are obtainable if the ions are kept at rest at the lattice points, and the lattice parameters would be adjusted to equilibrium. Such solutions would thus take account of all interactions independent of the displacement of ions from the lattice points; they would refer to a whole range of electronic states and would lead to a "free electron" model although the single "free electron" would be a rather complex entity. Next one would introduce the lattice vibrations; displacement of an ion will lead to restoring forces partly due to interaction with other ions, but partly due to interaction with the "free electrons." This latter interaction must, of course, also lead to a redefinition of the concept of "free electrons." It is at this stage that the greatest conceptional difficulties may be anticipated. For we know semiempirically that one part of the corrections due to ion displacements leads to ionic vibrations, and to redefinition of "free electron" states, but another part leads to real scattering of "free electrons" on vibrations, and to an interaction relevant for superconductivity. This latter interaction must be extracted in such a manner that its influence on lattice distance or other equilibrium parameters is negligible.

The reason for discussing this scheme is to show that interactions "leading to superconductivity" cannot simply be postulated. In the case of metals with complete inner shells—apart from small magnetic interactions—the only available interaction is connected with lattice displacements provided one follows the above scheme.

The situation in metals with incomplete inner shells is radically different. These shells can now not be treated as polarizable centers. Already at the first stage when the ions are assumed fixed at the lattice points would one hesitate very much in accepting the "free electron" model for the inner shells. For in this case the treatment of interelectronic interaction in terms of plasma oscillations may be seriously at fault. Furthermore[5], the magnetic moment of the inner shells leads to magnetic interactions with "free electrons" which may no longer be negligible; and at the same level one might have to think of interactions connected with the quadrupole moment of the inner shells.

Turning to the influence of displacement of ions from the lattice points one finds that the situation is different from the case of complete inner shells already in the semiempirical treatment of electron phonon interaction. Thus the free-electron model leads to a description of a single electron in terms of a Bloch wave function which in zero order is independent of the lattice vibrations. Suppose for an inner shell we use the tight-binding approximation. Then if $\varphi(\mathbf{r}_{el} - \mathbf{a})$ represents a (say d-) wave function localized near $\mathbf{a}$, ($\mathbf{r}_{el}$ = electron coordinate), a Bloch wave function including the lattice vibrations can be written as

$$\psi_{\mathbf{k}, \text{Bloch}} = \frac{1}{\sqrt{N}} \sum_{j} \exp\left(i\mathbf{k} \cdot \mathbf{a}_j\right)\varphi(\mathbf{r}_{el} - \mathbf{a}_j)\chi(\mathbf{x}_1, \ldots, \mathbf{x}_j, \ldots, \mathbf{x}_N). \quad (3.1)$$

Here $\mathbf{a}_j$ represent the coordinates of the lattice points, χ is the vibrational wave function of the ions whose coordinates are denoted by $\mathbf{x}_j$. Clearly Eq. (3.1) describes an electron localized near any of the lattice points. Now when the lattice oscillates the parts of the electronic wave function near an ion should follow it adiabatically—in the tight binding approximation this implies the whole localized wave function.

Hence an improved one-electron wave function which contains already a considerable amount of electron–phonon interaction can be written as

$$\psi_{\mathbf{k}} = \frac{1}{\sqrt{N}} \sum_j \exp\left(i\mathbf{k}\cdot\mathbf{a}_j\right)\varphi(\mathbf{r}_{el} - \mathbf{x}_j)\chi(\mathbf{x}_i, \ldots, \mathbf{x}_N). \qquad (3.2)$$

This wave function can, of course, be developed in the displacement $\boldsymbol{\xi}_j = \mathbf{x}_j - \mathbf{a}_j$, assuming that $|\boldsymbol{\xi}_j|$ is small, i.e.,

$$\varphi(\mathbf{r} - \mathbf{x}) = \varphi(r - a) + \boldsymbol{\xi}\frac{\partial}{\partial \mathbf{r}}\varphi(\mathbf{r} - \mathbf{a}) + \tfrac{1}{2}\xi_l\xi_s\frac{\partial}{\partial r_e}\frac{\partial}{\partial r_s}$$

$$\varphi(\mathbf{r} - \mathbf{a}) + \cdots \qquad (3.3)$$

and the derivatives of φ can be developed in terms of the system of localized states φ_r; also the expressions $\xi_e\chi$, etc., can be written in terms of excited vibrational states. Wave function (3.2) thus is equivalent with the result of electron–phonon interaction in ordinary band wave functions (3.1) provided this interaction is formulated in terms of transitions between different bands. This type of interband interaction which normally is omitted thus is responsible for obtaining Eq. (3.2) in terms of ordinary band functions. Naturally one will avoid explicit treatment of these band to band transitions by starting with wave function (3.2) rather than with Eq. (3.1). In Eq. (3.2) an electron sits most of the time in the immediate neighborhood of one of the ions (i.e., it spends very little time between ions), and its interaction with the displacements of this particular ion has been considered with a high accuracy. Interaction with the displacement of neighboring ions then leads to the ordinary transitions within the band. The magnitude of this interaction is rather small compared with electron–phonon interaction acting on wave functions of type (3.1).

In considering a simple electron near $\mathbf{x}_j$, the coordinates $\mathbf{r}_{el}$ and $\mathbf{x}_j$ can be replaced by the relative and center of gravity coordinates; the latter in view of the small mass ratio can then again be replaced by $\mathbf{x}_j$. Considering more than one electron, however, does no longer permit this procedure when the two electrons sit near the same ion. One might argue that repulsive Coulomb interaction prevents this. If this were so then the band model would be invalid. For the simple case of a metal with one electron per ion would then lead to N instead of to $2N$ one particle states (N = number of ions). Thus assuming that the band model has some validity it follows that a reasonable chance must exist for having two electrons (coordinates r_1 and r_2) per ion. Their interaction with the displacements of neighboring ions will be larger than if they would sit at distant ions for each can 'benefit' from the displacement caused by the other. A localized wave function would then have the form $f(\mathbf{r} - \mathbf{x}_j, \mathbf{r}_2 - \mathbf{x}_j, \mathbf{r}_1 - \mathbf{r}_2)\chi_j$, where χ_j is the vibrational wave function modified in a self-consistent way by the two electrons sitting near $\mathbf{x}_j$. The corresponding two electron wave function

$$\Psi = \frac{1}{\sqrt{N}} \sum_j \exp(i\mathbf{k} \cdot \mathbf{a}_j) f(\mathbf{r}_1 - \mathbf{x}_j, \mathbf{r}_2 - \mathbf{x}_j, \mathbf{r}_1 - \mathbf{r}_2)\chi_j(\mathbf{x}_1, \ldots, \mathbf{x}_N) \quad (3.4)$$

would show a high correlation of the two electrons. It could be used as the basis of an N-electron wave function showing a strong correlation in the sense that an ion would either have two electrons or none near it.

It might well be that correlations of the type described above are relevant for the treatment of superconductivity in metals with incomplete inner shells. They depend on lattice displacements but are probably not connected with an isotope effect. This isotope effect exists in the case of metals with complete inner shells and there it is the main reason for the smallness of the relevant interaction; for only a fraction $(m/M)^{1/2}$ of electrons (m = electronic, M = ionic mass) take part in this interaction. In the present case when the modified tight-binding approximation [Eq. (3.2)] is supposed to hold all electrons take part in the interaction, but the relevant interaction is very much smaller than in the previous case because most of the interaction of electron and lattice displacements is already accounted for by replacing wave function (3.1) by (3.2) or (3.4).

A realistic treatment would, of course, require simultaneous consideration of inner shell and outer electrons; and it would involve consideration of the principal interactions connected with the two electron wave function f. These are Coulomb interactions and one might ask, therefore, why treatment through plasma oscillations is valid in some cases but not in others. There is no doubt that the long-range part of Coulomb interaction can always be treated in terms of plasma; however—if ω_p is the well-known plasma frequency—the question is whether the frequency of long longitudinal electric waves is $(\omega_0^2 + \omega_p^2)^{1/2}$ rather than ω_p, where the ω_0 term arises from the short-range part of the interaction. If the band model is valid, then of course $\omega_0 = 0$. This has been proved, however, only in the high-density limit. In this limit the kinetic energy of the electrons is large compared with the magnitude of the total Coulomb interaction energy. Unfortunately this is a totally unrealistic limit because according to the virial theorem the ratio of the two is always $1:2$ if the system is in equilibrium.

Not having seen a quantum mechanical discussion of this theorem, I suggest the following treatment. Consider a system of particles with charge e_j, mass m_j, coordinate $\mathbf{q}_j$, and momentum $\mathbf{p}_j$, where p_{jk} and q_{jk}, $k = 1, 2, 3$ are the three space components, and

$$(p_{jk}, q_{j'l}) = \frac{\hbar}{i} \delta_{jj'} \delta_{ke}. \tag{3.5}$$

Assume that the magnetic interaction can be neglected so that the Hamiltonian is

$$H = T + V, \quad T = \sum_j \frac{p_j^2}{2m_j}, \quad V = \sum_{j,l} \frac{e_j e_l}{|\mathbf{q}_j - \mathbf{q}_e|}. \tag{3.6}$$

We then have

$$\dot{\mathbf{q}}_j = \frac{i}{\hbar}(H, \mathbf{q}_j) = \frac{\partial T}{\partial \mathbf{p}_j} = \frac{1}{m_j} \mathbf{p}_j, \tag{3.7}$$

and

$$\dot{\mathbf{p}}_j = \frac{i}{\hbar}(H, \mathbf{p}_j) = -\frac{\partial V}{\partial \mathbf{q}_j}. \tag{3.8}$$

Hence if we define an operator $Z(t)$ by

$$Z(t) = \frac{1}{2} \sum_j (\mathbf{p}_j \mathbf{q}_j + \mathbf{q}_j \mathbf{p}_j) = \frac{1}{2} \frac{d}{dt} \sum_j m_j \mathbf{q}_i^2, \tag{3.9}$$

then using Eqs. (3.7) and (3.8)

$$\dot{Z}(t) = \frac{d^2}{dt^2} \frac{1}{2} \sum m_j \mathbf{q}_j^2 = \sum \left(\mathbf{p}_j \frac{\partial T}{\partial \mathbf{p}_j} - \mathbf{q}_j \frac{\partial V}{\partial \mathbf{q}_j} \right). \tag{3.10}$$

According to a theorem by Euler on homogeneous functions this expression is equal to $2T + V$. Thus we have the operator equation

$$\frac{d^2}{dt^2} \sum_j \frac{1}{2} m_j \mathbf{q}_j^2 = 2T + V. \tag{3.11}$$

Now in equilibrium the expectation value of the left-hand side vanishes ($\sum m_j \mathbf{q}_j^2$ is the moment of inertia). Hence

$$2\langle T \rangle = -\langle V \rangle = +\langle |V| \rangle. \tag{3.12}$$

This contradicts the basic assumption of the high density approximation.

The discussion in this section should show that although the interaction of electrons with phonons doubtlessly leads to an attractive force between electrons, treatment in terms of one of the methods "leading to superconductivity" has so far only been justified semi-empirically. It is unlikely that these methods may be applied to "any" attractive interaction because they do not include the possibility of readjusting the principal parameters (e.g., lattice distance) of the substance. In metals with complete inner shells if one assumes that the "free-electron" model holds on the assumption that the ions are fixed to the lattice points then the only available forces must be connected with the displacement of ions. This is confirmed by the isotope effect. In metals with incomplete inner shells the situation is very different; I consider it doubtful that the methods used for the case of metals with complete shells are applicable.

4. Historical Remarks

A sixtieth birthday provides a stimulus for looking into the past. Superconductivity today is a subject within solid state physics like many others. It was not so thirty years ago, and still less so twenty years ago when every other important phenomenon in solids was understood at least qualitatively. What was it that for so long frustrated all attempts, and how was this deadlock broken? To understand this it is not sufficient to look at the latest detailed theories and to trace the general treatment which they follow. For frequently in physics decisive new ideas are not presented at first in the form which they finally take. It is of considerable interest to see how these developments leading to the present highly specialized state took place, for they are a strong indictment against fragmentation and overspecialization in theoretical physics. In presenting this story I shall not give any explicit references but refer for this to a previous article[2]; an impartial account of the most important steps in the microscopic theory up to 1957 can also be found in Bogoliubov's[6] introduction to a series of reprints.†

† I wish to take this opportunity to fulfill a promise given to a number of colleagues, by referring to complaints about lack of acknowledgment of the origin of new steps in various branches of physics. Partly this arises simply from the habit of quoting only those papers which one has read and used; they are not always the ones in which the first steps were made. There exists, however, doubtlessly in some physicists a regrettable trend to acknowledge only what has been published by their compatriots.

Present-day formulations of the theoretical framework of super-conductivity express in one way or another the idea of electron pairing which was introduced by Schafroth and independently by L. N. Cooper on the basis of an attractive interaction between electrons. Formal proof for this pair formation is simple, and the only answer to the question why this was not found twenty years earlier would be that now people are more imaginative. But this is obviously not true—the opposite might hold. The reason rather is that no origin for an attractive inter-action could be seen though the desirability of such an additional interaction was frequently discussed. One used of course the free-electron model in which all interaction is supposed to be included already. This was criticized, at times, but the interactions resulting from improved treatments were always found to be repulsive. Even possibilities of the need for modification of basic laws of interaction were discussed in a serious manner. Obviously the problem was one of finding an additional interaction compatible with the successful free-electron model. Phenomenological theories were well developed by that time, and the analysis by F. London indicated what microscopic properties were relevant.

The separation of theoreticians concerned with field theory from those interested in solid state physics was already considerable twenty years ago. I personally had been connected with the early development of meson theory, but was disappointed with the basic difficulties (infinities, ambiguities, etc.) which one met. Earlier, however, I had been interested in the interaction of an electron with an ionic crystal and I had considered the idea of treating the ions not as individual particles but in terms of the polarization of the material. Later it occurred to me that this polarization could be treated as a field just like in field theories. Absorption and emission of vibrational quanta by the electron which one had considered in solid state physics formed simply one aspect of such a field theory; the other was a self-energy (now not divergent) and in the case of more than one electron, an interaction.

It is difficult at present to realize the impact of this simple idea because it is so obvious. The impact arose because solid state physicists were so self-centered that the concept of field had been connected with elementary particles and electromagnetic theory but nothing else. The first try out on ionic crystals (now widely developed as polaron theory) indicated the importance of dynamic rather than static properties in spite of the high ionic mass. Its application to metals at once revealed the existence of the small but sensitive attractive force which is the origin of the isotope effect.

It must be remembered that the isotope effect was derived as a consequence of the theory before it was discovered although the first experiments were made before publication of the theory. To most physicists it came as a great surprise; in fact I know of one laboratory which earlier had rejected an offer of isotopes for low-temperature investigations. For theoreticians it provided a welcome confirmation of the basic idea. The main reason for accepting it was in the first place, however, the fact that an attractive interaction had been derived as a direct consequence of the semiempirical free electron model as applied by F. Bloch to the theory of normal electric resistivity.

It is well known that the first success did not lead at once to the complete theory. It was soon realized that perturbation theory was insufficient; and that a further idea was lacking. The problem, however, was completely transformed. A definite Hamiltonian stood where before there was emptiness; a definite mathematical problem was posed.

Solution required considerable ingenuity which was provided by Schafroth, Blatt, and Butler and by Bardeen, Cooper, and Schrieffer who developed their theories—different in form, but equivalent in main content. The rest is well known. The BCS formulation proved more popular and easier to follow. It became the background to much further work and is usefully employed in many applications. B. Matthias has indicated, however, that the theory in its present form does not agree well with the behavior of superconductors with incomplete inner shells, in particular with respect to the isotope effect.

People were quick to point out that beside phonon-induced electron attraction any other force (independent of the ion mass) could be used. I have shown for this reason in Sec. 3 that it is not permissible simply to postulate such a force. On the other hand, metals with incomplete inner shells are much more complicated than other metals and the present disagreement might resolve itself when one has improved one's ability to deal with these metals. At this stage one should, however, also recall the conjecture presented at the end of Sec. 2 in connection with the temperature dependence of entropy at low temperatures. If one believes in this conjecture then one would regard existing theories as so specialized that they refer to specific materials only. One would then argue that they contain features which are much more general than is known at present and which should be extracted. For the time being this is a challenging question.

References

1. Bethe, H., and H. Fröhlich, *Zeits. f. Phys.*, **85**, 389 (1933).
2. Fröhlich, H., *Rept. Progr. Phys.*, **24**, 1 (1961).
3. Yang, C. N., *Rev. Mod. Phys.*, **34**, 694 (1962).
4. Casimir, H. B. G., *Zeits. f. Phys.*, **171**, 246 (1963); H. Fröhlich, *Phys. Rev. Letters*, **7**, 346 (1963); B. Matthias and K. Mendelssohn, *Rev. Mod. Phys.*, **36**, 156 (1964).
5. Matthias, B. T., *Physics Today*, **16**, 21 (1963).
6. Bogoliubov, N. N., preface to *The Theory of Superconductivity*, International Science Review Series, New York, 1962.

The Emergence of Economic Nuclear Power

H. HURWITZ, JR.

General Electric Co.

Introduction

There is general agreement that we are entering the era of economic fission power. The threshold that we are crossing is, by its nature, a broad one. Each electric utility must decide on the basis of its own special circumstances when it is appropriate to incorporate nuclear generating capacity into its system. Several major utilities have already made the decision to purchase nuclear plants from commercial suppliers. The decisions have not been primarily motivated by the desire to obtain experience with a new type of plant, but have instead been based on well-considered analyses that show the nuclear plants to be the most favorable means of fulfilling immediate needs for additional generating capacity. As of the end of 1965, the commercial nuclear power plants in operation and committed in the United States alone constituted a total generating capacity of 8.7 million kilowatts, approaching 4% of the total national central station generating capacity of 250 million kilowatts.

Of possibly greater immediate significance than the nuclear capacity now on line is the competitive impact that nuclear power exerts on the conventional generation industries. This has stimulated an average reduction of one mill per kilowatt hour in the generation costs of fossil-fueled plants ordered in 1965 as compared to that of plants ordered in 1962.

The fact that it is not possible to define a particular point in time that should henceforth be commemorated as marking the nascence of economic nuclear power does not detract from the importance of the achievement. It is perhaps fair to say that the implications of this milestone have not been as broadly recognized as they should. Therefore a discussion of these implications is of particular pertinence at this time.

There are perhaps two main reasons why the advent of commercial nuclear power has been relatively unheralded outside the power industry. The first is that the water moderated reactors that are dominating the present commercial market are not breeders. Their conversion ratio from U-235 to Pu-239 is in the range of 0.5 to 0.7, so that plutonium recirculation could only multiply the effective available amount of thermally fissionable material by a factor of two to three as compared to over one hundred with a breeding cycle. As will be later discussed, this is not apt to impair the utility of the water moderated reactor types for many decades. Indeed, with sufficiently favorable future experience in uranium prospecting and extraction, the water reactors could continue to be commercially important for a still longer span of time.

The second reason that the advent of economic nuclear power has gone somewhat unnoticed is that the scope of the underlying discoveries and accomplishments is not fully appreciated. It is true that some of the progress might be characterized as the expected result of an extensive development program ably planned and carried out. Nevertheless, even granted the amazingly favorable physics of the fission reaction itself, there have been many scientific and technological hurdles to surmount, any one of which could have postponed economic nuclear energy for a substantial period of years. Indeed, these obstacles have in the past been cited as reasons for doubting that fission power would become economically attractive prior to the depletion of fossil-fuel reserves. In the following paragraphs, some of the crucial developments in fission power will be discussed briefly with particular reference to the light water moderated and cooled reactor type that is now dominating the nuclear industry.

Fuel and Material Problems in Light-Water Power Reactors

The concept of using light water to perform the combined functions of moderation and heat removal has obvious attractions that resulted in its early consideration for power producing reactors.† Although light

† Light water-cooled and moderated reactors have been considered for plutonium production during World War II, but the concept was not pursued because lattice experiments with light water and natural uranium demonstrated insufficient reactivity. Engineering studies of a water-cooled and moderated power producing reactor were made at Oak Ridge (then Clinton Laboratories) circa 1946 by E. Wigner, A. Weinberg, G. Young, S. Untermyer, and others. These

water is the strongest practical neutron moderator, the relatively high thermal-neutron absorption of hydrogen precludes its use with unenriched uranium. This was at one time considered to be a major disadvantage of the light-water moderated system. Now, however, it has been recognized that the other systems also require, or can benefit by, the use of enriched uranium. This is because it is not sufficient to merely render a power reactor chain reacting, but substantial reactivity margin must be provided for compensating temperature coefficients, fuel burnup, structural material absorption, and fission product poisoning. Fortunately, the great progress that has been made in the development and construction of gaseous-diffusion uranium enrichment plants has eliminated the need to stringently minimize the fuel enrichment.

The major uranium enrichment plants throughout the world have been constructed primarily to fulfill military needs, and hence details of their operation are still largely classified. Nevertheless, public testimony, such as given at the Joint Committee on Atomic Energy hearings in June 1964,† makes it clear that the present AEC charge for separative work is based on full cost recovery in existing plants. Additional separative capacity will probably be needed by the late 1970's, and it is anticipated that the new privately operated plants, optimized to nuclear power requirements, could furnish enrichment services at a continually decreasing cost. Even at the present cost, the enrichment service constitutes a relatively minor portion of the fuel-cycle costs‡ (typically about 25%) so that the moderate enrichment (2 to 3%) required in the light-water power reactors is economically tenable.

studies centered around extensions of the highly enriched Material Testing Reactor designed at Oak Ridge. Slightly enriched light-water moderated and cooled power reactors were also proposed by E. Teller and K. Cohen at almost the same time.

† Joint Committee on Atomic Energy Hearings, June 9, 10, 11, 15, and 25, 1964, "Private Ownership of Special Nuclear Materials."

Proposed criteria for toll enrichment of privately owned uranium to begin after December 31, 1968 were filed by the AEC in the Federal Register on October 1, 1965.

‡ In broad terms, the light-water reactor fuel-cycle cost, which is roughly half of the total power cost, is divided approximately equally between fissionable isotope depletion charges and other components such as fabrication, recovery, and inventory. The depletion charge is in turn divided roughly equally between ore cost and enrichment cost.

A second major problem in the light-water reactor system has been that of developing structural materials and fuel elements that can survive the corrosive environment of water heated to a temperature in the range 550°F and above, and still further chemically activated by the high ambient neutron flux. A great boon in this connection has been the discovery of zirconium alloys that not only fulfill the material requirements but also, by virtue of the nuclear shell structure, have exceptionally low thermal and resonance neutron capture cross sections. (The most abundant zirconium isotope has 50 neutrons.)

Zirconium was cited as a possible power reactor structural material by G. Young and S. Untermyer in 1946. The first measurement of the absorption cross section of hafnium-free zirconium by H. Pomerance and J. Hoover[1] shortly thereafter greatly stimulated interest in this material. Untermyer continued to study the use of zirconium in water-moderated power reactors at Oak Ridge National Laboratory and then at Argonne National Laboratory where, in 1949, the naval reactor program was gathering momentum[2]. The Naval Reactors Branch of the AEC instituted a major program involving several laboratories for finding zirconium alloys that would be stable in high-temperature water, and for developing economic processes for the elimination of hafnium and the fabrication of high-purity zirconium alloys into ingots.[3] It was found that the addition of tin to zirconium eliminated erratic performance of the pure material that was ascribed to the effect of nitrogen on the water corrosion rate. The zirconium–tin composition, known as zircaloy, is not sensitive to trace impurities. Hence it was possible to replace the expensive crystal bar process for reduction of feed material to ingot by the less costly Kroll process. Although reactor–grade zircaloy is still relatively expensive, its excellent demonstrated performance as a core structural material and as fuel element cladding adequately justifies its use in commercial power reactors. Indeed, even in cases where thin stainless steel has proven to be a satisfactory fuel element cladding material, it now appears advantageous to substitute zirconium cladding.

Most of the development work on zirconium alloys was carried out with reference to applications in the pressurized-water reactors which formed the basis of the AEC Naval Reactors Branch program. Fortunately it has turned out that the zirconium technology could be readily adapted to boiling-water reactors. In particular, the presence of in-core boiling has not been found to affect deleteriously the zirconium performance.

The development of the fuel elements themselves has been another difficult materials problem in reactor technology. Because of the inevitably high-fabrication and fuel-reprocessing costs, it is essential that substantial burnup be achieved in each cycle. The uranium metal fuel elements used in early reactors were subject to serious distortion and rupture at exposure levels of a few thousand megawatt days per ton of uranium. The fact that the attainment of far longer fuel-element lifetimes was recognized to be an economic necessity has in the past been a primary source of pessimism with regard to economic nuclear power.

The innovation that has dramatically increased fuel-element lifetimes is the use of ceramic materials, particularly UO_2. An early application of oxide fuel was made in the naval power reactor program at the Knolls Atomic Power Laboratory. The oxide was produced *in situ* by oxidation of uranium metal foil in hollow steel pins. Subsequently it has been found possible to use the oxide in the form of compacted ceramic pellets placed loosely in zircaloy tubing. This approach was used in the Shippingport reactor designed by Bettis Laboratory in the early 1950's. Although the thermal conductivity of the ceramic is less than that of metallic uranium, the resulting high thermal gradients within the ceramic fuel elements are acceptable.

Below the oxide recrystallization temperature of 1700°C, the ceramic maintains its structure through repeated temperature cycling. Exceeding the recrystallization temperature or even the oxide melting temperature in the center of the fuel element does not cause serious deterioration and may become acceptable operating practice. The portion of the fission product gases that is normally released from the oxide can be accommodated by virtue of porosity in the ceramic structure or by additional void spaces provided within the cladding. Consequently, manufacturers are now able to provide fuel elements with warranted performance of about 20,000 MWd/ton average burnup, corresponding to about 2% fissioning of the uranium.

A surprisingly favorable discovery has been that, because of the compatibility of UO_2 and water, rupture of the fuel-element cladding does not lead to disintegration of the oxide. Operating power reactors have been used extensively for the testing of fuel elements of advanced design, and in certain of these tests fuel element failure has been encountered. Some of the failed elements were allowed to remain in the core for a substantial length of time, but because of the remarkable ability of the ceramic to contain nonvolatile fission products, no serious problems of radioactive contamination were encountered.

The absence of serious radioactive contamination from failed fuel has been a particular boon to the direct cycle boiling water reactor concept. The large decontamination factor provided by water vaporization has also turned out to be highly effective in preventing carry-over of radioactivity to the turbine. Consequently, no significant deviation from normal turbine maintenance procedures has been necessary in the direct-cycle plants.

The migration of radioactivity in the liquid phase as a result of surface corrosion in the reactor core has been recognized as a potentially serious operating problem in large water moderated reactors. Nevertheless, it has been found, on the basis of the extensive operating experience that has now been obtained that careful attention to water chemistry and the use of effective demineralizers enables system contamination to be maintained at gratifyingly low levels.

Physics of Light-Water Power Reactors

In addition to solving the metallurgical and chemical problems that are clearly crucial in achieving economic nuclear power, it has also been necessary to make substantial advances in the physics of reactor design. The large and complex cores of modern power reactors are a far cry from the relatively simple structures considered in earlier years. The reactor design must take into account numerous requirements such as maintaining a suitable power distribution at all times, optimizing the fuel cycle, and providing control system reactivity for compensating changes in temperature, xenon poisoning, and fuel burnup, with a minimum number of control elements. Machine calculation methods have proved to be very helpful in nuclear design, but in many instances significant refinements in the underlying analysis have also been required. Measurement techniques have also proved important, and the development of reliable in-core flux monitors has proved to be of great value in the operation of the large reactors.

The two major types of light-water power reactors—pressurized-water reactors (PWR) and boiling-water reactors (BWR)—have many physics features in common because of the rather similar core composition and operating temperature. Substantial differences arise, however, because of the different heat removal principles employed in the two systems. In the PWR's, the core pressure is maintained at a level about 50% higher than the exit coolant vapor pressure (about 2250 psia) so that coolant boiling in the core is suppressed. BWR's, on the other hand, operate with core pressure equal to the exit coolant vapor pressure (about 1000 psia). Steam generated in the core is separated from the unvaporized portion of the coolant in steam separators and then fed directly to the turbine. This eliminates the need for providing separate steam generators, and also eliminates the temperature difference of about 85°F which exists between the exit coolant and the secondary steam in PWR's. The PWR's are designed to have higher average core power densities than BWR's, so that smaller, albeit thicker, pressure vessels can be employed for a given total power rating. A major factor in determining the net economic effect of this trade-off is the power density at which the BWR cores can be operated. The maximization of this power density has therefore constituted a reactor physics and engineering problem of continuing interest and importance. Since the rate of coolant circulation in a reactor core is limited by pumping-power considerations, the achievement of high core power density in a BWR requires substantial coolant vaporization in each pass through the core. Consequently, modern boiling-water reactor designs call for average core void fractions in the range of 30% with exit void fractions above 75%.

When boiling-water power reactors were seriously studied by Untermyer and others in the late 1940's, there was some concern that even small void fractions in the core would introduce unacceptable operating problems in the form of "noise" in the fission rate or actual instability. It was therefore considered to be a significant milestone when a small water moderated assembly known as LITR was successfully operated with core boiling at Oak Ridge National Laboratory[4]. Subsequently, tests of the boiling mode were made at higher power levels and with actual steam generation in the BORAX facility operated by Argonne National Laboratory. These tests showed that when the void fraction became excessive, there was considerable noise in the power level, and at still higher void fractions the system became overstable and exhibited nonlinear oscillations known as "chugging". Nevertheless, the investigations of the boiling mode were sufficiently favorable to excite widespread interest in the boiling-water reactor concept[5].

As a result of the General Electric Company study of commercial central station nuclear power in 1953 to 1954 it was concluded that the boiling-water reactor concept had great economic promise. It was further recognized that a conservative approach could be taken to the stability problem by employing the dual-cycle concept in which the void fraction is kept low by removing some heat from the core through a secondary heat exchanger that could feed steam to the lower temperature turbine stages. Accordingly, the first commercial boiling-water reactor, Dresden I, was designed as a dual-cycle plant with a core void fraction of about 20%.

Prior to completion of Dresden I, further successful operating experience with boiling-water reactors was obtained from the Argonne Experimental Boiling-Water Reactor and the GE Vallecitos BWR. Even so, there was some concern that instabilities might result from the fact that the Dresden core has a typical dimension large compared to the neutron migration length and therefore consists, in a sense, of many loosely coupled chain reacting systems.

There were, however, several theoretical grounds for believing that the Dresden reactor would be stable. First, a linearized one node analysis predicted a substantial stability margin. Secondly, the self-consistent calculations of static power distribution in a large boiling core converged rapidly with no tendency for oscillation. Thirdly, various approximate analyses of time-dependent power distribution variations exhibited no instabilities. Nevertheless, the observation that the Dresden reactor exhibited no tendency for instability, even under special high-void test conditions, was highly gratifying and served to dispel lingering concern that something had been overlooked in the analyses.

Although stability problems can no longer be considered as jeopardizing the boiling-water reactor concept, this subject is still of great importance because of the incentive to further increase the core power density, and hence the average void fraction. A major test program on boiling-water stability and transients is being carried out at the Consumers Power Company Big Rock Point plant for the purpose of providing detailed information for the design of boiling reactors with enhanced core power density.

A typical one-node linearized closed-loop frequency response curve for a boiling reactor is shown in Fig. 1. The key parameter is the power coefficient of reactivity due to changes in void content. Although the power coefficient is intrinsically negative, instability can, in principle,

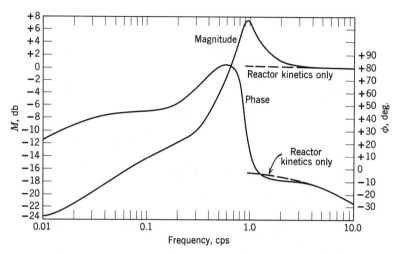

Fig. 1. Illustrative response of a BWR to small sinusoidal oscillations in a control element. M is equal to $20 \log_{10} \left\{ (|\Delta N|/N) \Big/ \frac{\Delta k}{k\beta} \right\}$ where $|\Delta N|/N$ is the amplitude of the fractional change in average neutron flux and $\Delta k/k\beta$ is the amplitude of the fractional applied change in reactivity divided by the effective delayed neutron fraction. The phase angle φ is that between the resulting oscillation in neutron flux and the applied oscillation in reactivity. These curves were obtained from a constant pressure analytical model under more responsive conditions than would exist in normal power reactor operation. Similar curves have been obtained experimentally in operating boiling water reactors. For high frequencies (several cycles per second) the reactor response is determined by reactor kinetics without reactivity feedback, whereas for low frequencies (0.1 cycles per second) the negative reactivity feedback due to Doppler and void coefficients reduces the response. In the frequency range near one cycle per second, the phase lag between reactor power and the resulting reactivity change is sufficiently large to cause a peak in the response. This peak is usually limited to about 3 db at the normal operation design point in order to insure an adequate margin of stability.

result because of phase shifts associated with the reactor kinetics, thermal time constants, and hydraulic characteristics. These considerations place an upper limit on the acceptable magnitude of the power coefficient. Since, from safety considerations, the power coefficient must not be too positive in the overmoderated cold-core condition, it is necessary to choose lattice parameters with great care.

The reactor response shown in Fig. 1 is by no means the whole story since system interactions are of extreme importance, particularly

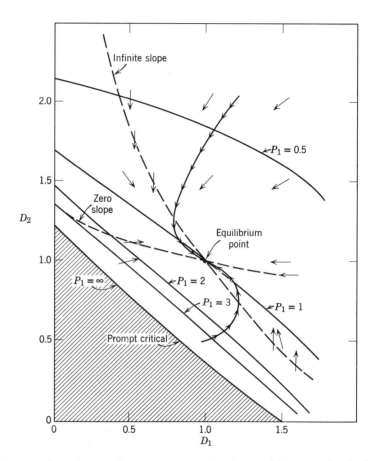

Fig. 2. Phase-plane trajectory representation for spacial power distribution transients in a BWR on the basis of a simplified nonlinear model. The terms D_1 and D_2 represent the delayed-neutron-progenitor inventories of the upper and lower parts of the reactor respectively. These are also proportional to the fuel-element temperatures. The dashed lines indicate the loci of zero and infinite trajectory slope. The sheath point at $D_1 = D_2 = 1$ represents stable equilibrium. Two trajectories approaching the equilibrium point are shown. Contours labeled with various values of P_1 refer to the power in the upper part of the reactor. For the assumed parameters, the decrease in prompt multiplication associated with an increase in fuel-element temperature outweighs the increase in delayed-neutron-source strength in the region of interest. Therefore P_1 decreases as D_1 or D_2 increase. [From article by Hurwitz in *Nuclear Sci. and Engineering*, **23**, 183–187 (1965).]

in abnormal transient situations. Accordingly, extensive systems analysis studies with analogue simulators and numerical prognoses are required to verify design of advanced reactors.

Operating experience has thus far exhibited no problems with regard to maintaining proper power distribution in the cores of large boiling-water reactors. This subject is, however, still receiving attention. One question, for example, is whether or not control-rod insertion in the bottom of the core could cause transient power peaks in the top of the core due to reduction in the local void fraction. With suitable simplifying assumptions, this problem can be treated graphically as shown in Fig. 2[6]. The analysis agrees with operating experience in predicting no severe power distribution transients of this type. Far more detailed models are now being employed to assure the absence of undesirable power distribution transients in reactors of advanced design.

Another problem that is sometimes encountered in large thermal neutron power reactors is the xenon instability. This instability can cause growing oscillations in power distribution because the increase in xenon burnout due to a local increase in neutron flux is not immediately counteracted by the increase in xenon production. (The xenon poisoning results from Xe^{135} which appears predominantly as a daughter of the fission product Cs^{135}.) The tendency for xenon instability is reduced by the existence of a large negative power coefficient such as that due to the void formation in a boiling-water reactor. Hence, pressurized-water reactors are intrinsically less immune to this instability than boiling-water reactors. The xenon instability problem can, however, be adequately handled by proper design principles such as choosing lattices with sufficient negative moderator temperature coefficient, and avoiding extended uncontrolled regions in the core.

Engineering Developments

Although resolution of the several key technical problems discussed above has been essential to achieving economic feasibility, an equally important factor has been the evolutionary engineering improvements associated with successive generations of similar plants. This has resulted in greater reliability, higher unit power, and substantial plant compaction. Consequently, nuclear power plants are now being sold commercially at a capital-cost-per-installed-kilowatt that is little, if any, in excess of that for a modern fossil-fuel plant. Careful attention has been paid to the electric utility requirements with regard to operation and maintenance. As a result of greater plant simplicity, streamlined reloading procedures, and improvements in load-following ability, nuclear plants are now fully compatible with traditional utility plant requirements.

Technological advances of particular importance to both PWR and BWR economics have occurred in regard to reactor pressure vessel construction, and in turbine design. A basic consideration in power-plant economics is that power costs vary much less than linearly with plant rating. Hence the capital investment per installed kilowatt can be substantially reduced by increasing unit size. The power ratings of 500 MWe and above that characterize present commercial designs are made possible by 2200 psia reactor vessels of over 12 feet internal diameter for the PWR's and 1000 psia reactor vessels of over 15 feet internal diameter for the BWR's. The fact that such vessels can now be constructed to the exacting standards of the nuclear industry has thus been of crucial importance in enabling nuclear-plant costs to be reduced to a level comparable to that of fossil-fuel plants.

The relatively low steam temperatures characteristic of PWR's and BWR's (typically 525°F and 545°F, respectively) have turned out not to seriously penalize the economics. This is because the low nuclear fuel-cycle costs that are now being achieved tend to reduce the importance of high thermal efficiency. By optimizing designs for the appropriate reactor steam conditions, it has been possible to develop turbines of the required large ratings which have thermal efficiencies well above 30% and also exhibit good operating reliability.

In the case of the BWR's, other features that are leading to more compact and hence lower cost plants are internal steam separators and dryers and jet recirculation pumps, all located within the reactor vessel itself. The jet pumps make it possible to obtain high-volume coolant circulation through the core by means of smaller capacity high-pressure pumps in the external loops. This reduces the number and size of the penetrations of the reactor vessel.

Nuclear Safety

The current nuclear plant designs reflect the great attention that has been paid to the matter of safety. This key subject in nuclear power is not one that can be treated in the abstract by, on one hand, viewing with alarm the large fission product burden of a power-reactor core, or, on the other hand, citing the inherent ease of reactor control and the engineering reliability of reactor components. Instead, it has been necessary to consider in detail what specific trains of events could conceivably lead to the escape of fission products from the core, and then to take specific measures to assure that these events cannot occur, or will not lead to dispersion of fission products outside the containment that is provided.

Government agencies such as the Advisory Council on Reactor Safety have adopted a properly conservative point of view with regard to public protection, and the reactor manufacturers have independently made nuclear safety a paramount requirement. These suppliers have fully recognized that a nuclear incident in a commercial plant might seriously impede progress of the entire nuclear industry.

Safety requirements in a nuclear plant are consonant with the requirements of plant operability. Before a deficiency in design, manufacturing, or maintenance could become a significant safety problem, it would in general manifest itself as an intolerable operating problem. Therefore, nuclear equipment standards are necessarily of extreme rigor.

The technologically implausible, but *a priori* conceivable, possibility of a rupture in the reactor primary coolant system has been taken into account by providing a containment barrier outside the reactor vessel itself. The dry containment scheme, first used at West Milton, N.Y., comprises a large pressure-tight structure of sufficient volume to contain the entire reactor coolant stored energy without exceeding code specifications. A recent advance in dry containment is the utilization of steel-lined reinforced-concrete structures instead of the earlier all steel spheres. For the large reactors that are now being offered commercially, steel containment would either be of extreme size or would require plate thicknesses too large for convenient construction in the field. In the composite structure, most of the mechanical strength and radiation shielding is provided by the concrete, while leak-tightness is assured by a welded carbon-steel plate liner. In a typical design such as the Connecticut Yankee PWR, the concrete is between $2\frac{1}{2}$ and $4\frac{1}{2}$ feet thick, while the steel liner thickness is $\frac{1}{4}$ to $\frac{1}{2}$ inch.

Another development in water-reactor containment is the pressure suppression system which has been a feature of recent BWR plants. In this system, the reactor vessel is enclosed in a relatively compact, but rugged, dry well that has a typical design pressure of about 90 psig (approximately twice the design pressure characteristic of dry containment). Steam that would be released to the dry well in the event of a primary coolant system rupture is vented through a large toroidal pool of water (cf. Fig. 3). This pressure suppression pool would absorb a major portion of the primary coolant stored energy and also the nonvolatile fission products that would be released if the postulated break in the primary coolant system were accompanied by gross fuel element disruption. Gas released from the surface of the suppression pool is retained by the pressure containing "wet well". Leakage from either the dry well or wet well would be further retained by the reactor building. The pressure suppression system not only makes it possible to accommodate the stored energy in a large BWR coolant system, but also, by virtue of the massiveness of the dry well, provides effective protection from possible missiles in a postulated reactor incident.

Both dry containment and pressure suppression containment include additional engineered safety features such as auxiliary spray systems that reduce the magnitude and duration of the pressure pulse on the containment vessel. Other engineered safety features being introduced in recent designs limit the magnitude and rate of reactivity increases that could occur in the event of gross mechanical failure of the control system. It is natural that as further experience and knowledge are obtained concerning nuclear system performance in both normal and abnormal situations, greater reliance can be placed on engineered safety features, particularly those designed to eliminate the conceivable causes rather than the effects of a nuclear incident.

Long-Range Prospects for Light-Water Reactors

In view of the striking scientific, technological, and economic progress that has been made with respect to light-water moderated and cooled reactors, it is pertinent to inquire as to the potential future role of this reactor type in supplying world power needs. First, it may be noted that logical extensions such as superheat, plutonium recycle and the use of thorium are now being investigated in existing test reactors. It can be expected that these features will be incorporated into the commercial plants on a time scale determined by the pace of the

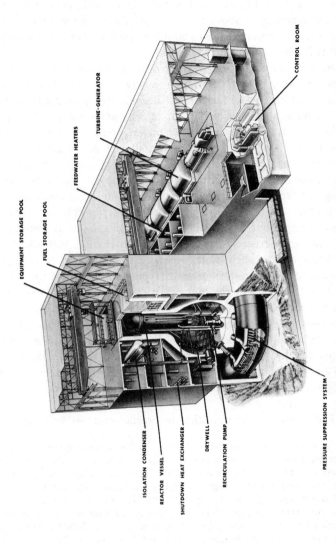

Fig. 3.   Schematic diagram of a BWR nuclear power plant employing pressure suppression containment.

needed technological developments and the magnitude of the economic incentives. The water moderated system thus provides an assured means for utilizing at good-to-excellent thermal efficiency the energy obtainable from the fissioning of about 1% of the uranium and thorium ore. (This assumes a conversion ratio of about 0.6 and a U-235 concentration of about 0.3% in enrichment plant tailings.)

Because the light-water reactor concept does not make complete utilization of the potentially available energy in the ore, it is frequently assumed that light-water reactors will become obsolete within a relatively few decades as a result of exhaustion of uranium resources. This simplified assessment will not necessarily prove correct. On the contrary, it appears that light-water reactors can play a dominant role in the commercial market until an alternative reactor type, such as the fast breeder, can be shown to provide lower cost power even in the absence of any substantial escalation in the price of uranium ore.† Assuming that another reactor type with markedly superior fuel economy does become competitive, there will still be a reluctance to abandon the hard-won water-reactor technology and experience. Instead, there is the likelihood that light-water reactors will continue to develop in symbiotic relationship with the newer type. As pointed out by K. Cohen and B. Wolfe[7], a nuclear industry based on both fast breeders and thermal nonbreeders may be able to produce power at lower cost than an industry based on either type alone. The fast breeders can effectively utilize the plutonium produced in the thermal-neutron reactors, and this demand could justify a higher plutonium price than would be appropriate if the plutonium were recirculated in a thermal-neutron spectrum. The firm plutonium price level would, in turn, aid the economy of the thermal reactors.

The timing of the transition to breeder reactors will depend not

† It is recognized that there is strong belief in some quarters that other reactor types such as gas-cooled or heavy-water moderated reactors can already compete favorably with light-water plants. This is particularly thought to be the case in circumstances where capital charges are low. However, expansion in world use of power is primarily limited by the availability of capital. Therefore, it would appear desirable to assign a high weighting to the capital cost comparison in evaluating alternative power-plant concepts; cf. L. H. Roddis, Jr., and E. Jones, Integration of Nuclear Reactors and Power Networks in the United States: Economic and Technical Aspects, Paper 216 of the *Proceedings of the Third International Conference on the Peaceful Uses of Atomic Energy*, Geneva, 1964, Vol. 1 (Progress in Atomic Energy), 206–215.

only on progress in reducing the capital and operating costs in these reactors but also on the cost trend of fissile ore. The latter depends both on the growth rate of the nuclear industry, and the success in finding sources of low to moderate price ore. Current estimates are that the installed, free-world nuclear capacity will reach 200 million kWe by the mid 1980's. At present thermodynamic efficiencies, this requires the generation of about 2×10^{16} BTU, or 0.02Q of nuclear heat per year. With the roughly 1% burnup of uranium that would characterize a converter-dominated economy with plutonium recycle, 1 Q requires the utilization of about 1.7 megatons of ore. Hence free-world nuclear-ore requirements would reach 50,000 tons per year by the mid 1980's. The role of nonbreeder reactors to the year 2000 and beyond therefore depends on the cost trend of ore in megaton quantities.

On the basis of current resource estimates, the free-market cost of ore may increase several-fold above the present $4 per pound figure before the cumulative requirements have reached the megaton level[8]. But since there is potential for further cost reductions in light-water nuclear technology, it is plausible that power costs could be maintained below 5 mills per kWh with ore costs as high as $30 per pound of U_3O_8.*

Present ore reserve estimates could be unduly pessimistic for various reasons. First, the period of intensive prospecting terminated about 1957 when ample reserves to fulfill weapons requirements had been assured. Up to the time when the U.S. incentive program was withdrawn, drilling productivity was steadily increasing, and the estimated ore reserves were approximately doubling each year (cf. Fig. 4). Secondly, there has been no strong incentive to prospect for any but the highest grade ores, nor to develop the technology required to economically extract fissile material from lower concentration sources. It is anticipated that an increase in ore price to the $15 to $20 per pound range would open the possibility of recovering megatons of uranium from shale deposits throughout the world, and it has been further suggested that a price increase to the $20 per pound range would allow the vast uranium supply in the sea to be tapped[9]. Thus while it can be anticipated that within a few decades the depletion of high-grade ore

* On the basis of 1% total burnup of uranium content and 32% thermal efficiency, a $30 per pound U_3O cost would correspond to 1 mill per kWhe. The impact of higher ore costs can be somewhat reduced by reoptimizing the enrichment cascade, but is increased by virtue of inventory charges.

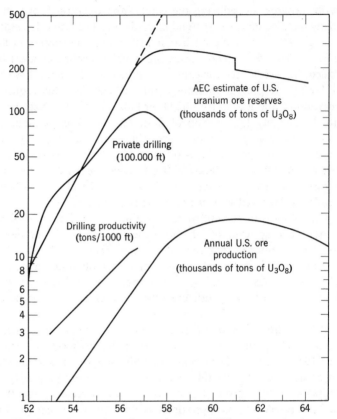

Fig. 4.   U.S. experience in uranium ore drilling and production.

reserves will heighten the economic competition between light-water reactors and reactors offering improved fuel utilization, it is entirely possible that the light-water systems will continue to be commercially viable well into the twenty-first century.

References

1. Pomerance, H., and J. I. Hoover, "Thermal Neutron Absorption Cross Sections of Separated Isotopes", *Phys. Rev.*, **73**, 1265(A) (1948).
2. Untermyer, S., "Zirconium, a Structural Material for Thermal Reactors", Clinton Laboratories report MonP-447, December 11, 1947.

3. Lustman, Benjamin, and Frank Kerze, Jr., Ed., *Metallurgy of Zirconium*, McGraw-Hill, New York, 1955.
4. Breazeale, W. M., T. E. Cole, and J. A. Cox, "Preliminary Boiling Experiments in the LITR", TID-5065, August 1952; W. M. Breazeale, T. E. Cole, and J. A. Cox, "Further Boiling Experiments in the LITR", AECD-3670, December 1952.
5. Dietrich, J. R., H. V. Lichtenberger, and W. H. Zinn, "Design and Operating Experience of a Prototype Boiling-Water Power Reactor", Paper 851 of the *Proceedings of the International Conference on the Peaceful Uses of Atomic Energy*, Geneva, 1955, Vol. 3 (Power Reactors), 56–68.
6. Hurwitz, H., Jr., "A Simplified Nonlinear Model for Qualitative Study of Reactor Power-Distribution Transients", *Nucl. Sci. & Eng.*, **23**, 183–187, October 1965.
7. Cohen, K., and B. Wolfe, "Development of the Fast Ceramic Reactor", *Nuclear News-ANS*, 11–15, February 1963.
8. Faulkner, R. L., and W. H. McVey, "Fuel Resources and Availability for Civilian Nuclear Power, 1964–2000", Paper 256 of the *Proceedings of the Third United Nations International Conference on the Peaceful Uses of Atomic Energy*, Geneva, 1964.
9. Davies, R. V., J. Kennedy, R. W. McIlroy, R. Spence, and K. M. Hill, "Extraction of Uranium from Sea Water", *Nature*, **203**, No. 4950, 1110–1115, September 12, 1964.

High Conversion High-Temperature Reactors

FREDERIC de HOFFMANN

General Dynamics Corporation

1. Resource Utilization, Fuel Cycles, and Reactor Systems

It is the hope of the author that this description of advanced graphite converter reactors and the one example given of their inter-relation with basic science illustrate the fundamental thesis that good science is indeed important in practical reactor design. This is a point of view Hans Bethe has often stressed and taught those who have had the privilege of working with him. With respect to the high-temperature graphite reactor (the HTGR), Hans Bethe[1] was one of the first to recognize its importance and to contribute detailed calculations and valuable advice during the course of development of such a reactor.

A. *Introduction*

Over the past 50 years electricity demand in the world has risen more than thirty-fold. There is every indication that this trend will continue due to population rise and continued mechanization of society.

The first generation of electrical power stations using nuclear reactors has been developed during the past two decades. They are often referred to as "burner" reactors because they principally burn uranium, but unfortunately only about 1 to 2% of the uranium fed into them. Since power demands will be so great beyond the year 2000, it can easily be shown that power production from burner reactors alone would not be a solution to the power problem of the world for very long. Thus, a more advanced class of nuclear power reactors, which make more efficient use of the total fissionable resources available to the world, is now coming into being—it places emphasis on the use of fertile materials that are converted into fissionable material, thereby considerably enhancing the total energy production.

573

The simultaneous requirements of better resource utilization and economical production of electricity from these reactors have required and continue to require the development of scientific and technical methods and scientific facts in a large number of basic fields.

B. *Fuel Resource Conservation*

We first turn to a general examination of the physical effects important in resource conservation. The ultimate resource consideration that counts in conservation is the kilowatt-hours of electricity obtained per pound of ore mined. This in turn involves three distinct considerations:

1. When a fissionable nucleus fissions and heat is generated, this heat must be converted as efficiently as possible into electricity since— from a resource conservation point of view—once this heat is dissipated without performing useful work, it is simply "lost". Thus, in a true sense, 45% efficiency of conversion from nuclear heat to electricity compared to a 30% conversion represents a 1.5 times better resource conservation.

2. Once a fission occurs we must make maximum use of the neutrons that are released during that fission. This implies three things:

Not losing the neutrons through absorption in parasitic material such as a high absorption moderator,

losing as few neutrons as possible by leakage from the reactor core, and

maximizing the capture of neutrons in fertile material, i.e., thorium or U-238, to create additional fissionable material, i.e., U-233 or Pu-239. (When more new fissionable atoms are created than are being consumed while the reactor operates we speak of the system as "breeding".)

In the simplest form of reactor one thinks of merely placing the fuel in the reactor and when it is discharged "throwing it away"—hence the use of the words "throw-away cycle" to describe this way of fueling reactors. From a resource conservation point of view it is clear that there will be both original fissionable material not yet used up and newly created fissionable material still in the fuel when it is discharged from the reactor. From the resource conservation point of view, therefore, it will always be valuable to reprocess the fuel, i.e., extract from the spent fuel the fissionable material for reuse. From the point of view of economics, however, a recycle mode of operation is not necessarily justified, although this turns out to be the case for the particular advanced reactor considered in Sec.1.E.

3. At first sight it would appear that any reactor that "breeds" is *a priori* a user of less fissionable material than one that does not breed. Actually, this is not necessarily so: The *total* average fissionable material used is the amount that is in the *total* system on the average— not just the fissionable material that is actually used in creating the heat. The total must include the amount of material in the fabrication, reprocessing, and refabrication stages and, more important, the amount of inventory in the reactor. The latter term is important in a world where there is such rapidly expanding demand for electricity because there is constant addition of new power plants, and thus fissionable material inventory additions in certain reactor systems can equal or exceed fissionable material burned to create energy. Thus, we must add a fourth criterion to our neutron criteria, namely,

> the system must have high specific power densities per unit of fissionable material used in the entire system.

In summary then, resource conservation dictates that one try to

(a) maximize thermal efficiency,

(b) maximize specific power,

(c) maximize creation of new fissionable material,

(d) minimize parasitic neutron absorption in the core, and

(e) minimize leakage from the core.

C. *Basic Fuel Cycle Considerations*

In order to have economical electricity production on a large scale, the total fuel cycle cost† must be minimized, and the considerations affecting this optimization are not necessarily the same as those involved in resource conservation. The goal of a good nuclear power system, then, is to have a low capital cost and to optimize both for low resource use and low fuel cycle cost. We can see immediately that we are dealing with an optimization problem with very many dimensions. In practice, the optimization is further complicated by the fact that "costs" are not a uniquely defined physical quantity but depend on the quantity of fuel or components being fabricated at any one time and equally important

---

† The total power cost consists of the capital cost portion, the fuel cycle portion associated with the burning of the fuel, and the maintenance and operating costs.

on money rates and accounting systems (which allocate costs incurred over the lifetime of a plant to the production cost per kilowatt-hour of electricity).

However, there are some generalized conclusions about the fuel cycle costs that one can draw regardless of these complicating factors. For this purpose, consider the separate terms of which the fuel cycle cost is made up; namely:

Fuel cycle cost = Depletion cost + Inventory cost

$$+ \text{Handling cost} \quad (1)$$

Depletion cost

$$= \alpha\left(\frac{1 - c}{\epsilon}\right) \tag{2}$$

Inventory cost

$$= \beta\left(\frac{\$ \text{ of fissile material}}{\text{kW}}\right) \cdot \frac{1}{\epsilon} = \beta'\left(\frac{1}{P_s \cdot \epsilon}\right) \tag{3}$$

Handling cost

$$= \gamma\left(\frac{\text{Fabrication} + \text{Shipping} + \text{Reprocessing} + \text{Working capital}}{\text{Burnup} \cdot \epsilon}\right), \tag{4}$$

where α, β, and γ are appropriate constants, c is the conversion ratio of the reactor (defined as the amount of fissionable nuclei created per number of fissionable nuclei consumed), ϵ is the thermal efficiency of conversion from heat to electricity, and P_s denotes the specific power. Furthermore, in Eq. (4) the term "Fabrication" includes the fabrication of fuel from new material as well as reprocessed material, shipping includes shipping of both fresh and spent fuel, and the working capital† is the working capital during all stages of fuel handling either in or out of the reactor. The burnup is usually expressed in fifa, i.e., fissions during the life of the fuel per initial fissile atom present, or more generally in terms of MW-days of heat produced per ton of fissionable plus fertile material placed in the reactor.

The obvious conclusions from Eqs. (1) through (4) are that for a *given* ore cost, fuel cycle costs will be minimized if we simultaneously

    (*a*) maximize the thermal efficiency,

    (*b*) maximize the specific power,

† That is, the interest charged on the value of the fissionable material and reactor core fabrication.

(c) maximize the conversion ratio,

(d) minimize the fabrication, reprocessing, and refabrication costs, and

(e) maximize the burnup.

Note that we have talked about optimizing the fuel cycle cost for a given ore price. Uranium and thorium ore, like any other mineral, can have widely fluctuating ore prices depending on supply and demand. For instance, in the United States at a time when the U.S. Government was the largest user of uranium (during the 1940's and 1950's), the U.S. Government was paying $8 per lb of U_3O_8. When this government demand subsided and the power reactor demand had not yet made itself felt in the world market, the price of uranium oxide dropped to the current world uranium ore price of $4 to $5 per lb of U_3O_8. While improved production methods and additional deposits will undoubtedly be found over the years, the long-term trend for uranium prices still must be considered as a likely upward one. In this connection, again, it is important to remind oneself that regardless of the system used it is not only the net consumption of fissionable material that counts but the *inventory* that will make such large demands on ore use.

The cost of the uranium ore enters the fuel cycle cost through terms in both Eqs. (2) and (3). A rise of ore price carries with it a rise in term (3); however, a rise in ore price does not carry an inevitable rise in the very important term (2), since we have means to offset the linear rise in the proportional factor. In particular, if we can devise a reactor system where the conversion ratio c can be increased without making the terms (3) and (4) rise unduly then we have a means of partially offsetting the rise in α because the product $\alpha(1 - c)$ will not rise linearly with the cost of ore. Thus, we see that another long-term demand that we wish to make on an advanced converter system is that

(f) the reactor can be run with fuel cycle modes that permit high conversion ratios c without an undue rise in inventory and handling costs of the fuel.

D. *Fast and Thermal Spectrum Reactors*

High conversion ratios in reactors can be achieved either by the use of systems operating in the thermal (or slightly epithermal) region or by the use of systems operating in the fast neutron region. Thermal or epithermal reactor systems of this type have been dubbed "advanced thermal converters" or more concisely "advanced converters". These advanced converters can reach conversion ratios as high as $c = 1.1$, but if we wish to obtain higher conversion ratios we need to turn to fast reactors. This paper is not intended to discuss fast reactors, but one general observation of their relationship to advanced converters may be of interest: Fast reactors *per se* do not necessarily result in better resource utilization even though their conversion ratio is higher than that of the advanced converters. This is simply bound up with the inventory question discussed in Sec. 1.A in an expanding electric economy. At the same time, fast reactor systems, just like the advanced converter systems, will have to meet the test of economic power costs. Several coolants can be considered for fast reactors—sodium, gas, and steam. Of these, a gas coolant such as helium leads to the least spectral degradation and thus the highest conversion ratio. In practice, sodium-cooled reactors have received the most attention, with helium-cooled reactors now beginning to be investigated intensely[2]. After practical considerations are taken into account, helium-cooled fast reactors promise the possibility of higher conversion ratios than sodium. In fact, helium reactors may achieve conversion as high as 1.6. Inasmuch as it is the quantity $(c - 1)$ that counts, this represents a substantial advantage in principle.

In the next section we shall describe a helium-cooled advanced converter system—the HTGR. Its development may bring with it a good deal of the technology—except for the fuel element technology, which is quite different in the two cases—required for the fast gascooled reactor.

E. *Characteristics of the HTGR Advanced Converter*

As shown in Sec. 1.A resource conservation requires good neutron economy, high specific power, and high efficiency. High thermal efficiency requires that the reactor coolant be at a high temperature, so that gases that do not undergo a phase transformation become a logical choice. Inasmuch as modern steam turbines operate with about 1000°F (535°C) steam, the reactor gas exit temperature must be considerably above this temperature to allow for temperature losses in the heat exchanger between the reactor cooling gas and the steam entering the steam turbine. Thus, gas temperatures of the order of 700° to 800°C suggest themselves.

1. *Coolant Choice*

The choice of a gas coolant is dictated by both heat transfer and material considerations. At the high temperatures under consideration, helium—since it is an inert gas—has been chosen for the first generation of high conversion gas-cooled reactors. With respect to the choice of coolant from a heat transfer point of view, this choice depends not only upon the reactor but also upon external systems such as heat exchangers and gas moving equipment. Generalized comparisons from the point of view of the reactor heat transfer only have been made by Fortescue[3] and more recently by Melese[4]. Melese finds that for given pressure and temperature conditions, where the maximum temperature of the fuel element as well as the ratio of internal pumping power to thermal power is fixed, the relative merit of gases is found to depend upon temperature more than upon pressure. Also, he notes that the condition for which coolants are compared alters the preference of gases. For example, at 535°C, CO_2 is better than helium for fixed flow area, but the inverse is true for fixed heat transfer area (these results are for smooth heat transfer surfaces rather than roughened heat transfer surfaces). On the other hand, material considerations dictate the choice of helium instead of CO_2 in certain reactor systems.

2. Moderator Choice

If we seek high-temperature moderators with good neutron economy (i.e., low parasitic absorption and good slowing-down properties), graphite suggests itself immediately. Furthermore, if a system can be devised in which the graphite instead of high-temperature metals (which do absorb neutrons parasitically) can act as the structural elements of the reactor core, then the neutron economy is considerably enhanced. One is therefore led to a system in which the graphite acts not only as moderator but also as the fuel-element structural material that holds the fissionable and fertile material.

3. Fuel-Moderator Arrangement

The next question to consider is how the fuel-moderator arrangement should be made. In the 1950's Peter Fortescue recognized that homogeneous or semihomogeneous distribution of the fuel throughout the moderator would mean that the moderator acts as heat transfer extension surfaces for the fuel particles, which in turn would lead to particularly good heat transfer properties for high-temperature reactor cores. Today, this principle is used in both the experimental "Dragon" reactor and in the class of HTGR power reactors.

4. Reactor Physics

The current class of HTGR reactors uses highly enriched uranium mixed with thorium as the fuel; for reactors of about 800 MW(t) [about 330 MW(e) production] the carbon-to-thorium ratio is about 200:1 and the C:U ratio is about 2500:1. The physics of such systems gives rise to very small core sizes, for a 330 MW(e) core the typical core diameter being only about 6 meters and that for a 1000 MW(e) core being only about 9.5 meters.

The good neutron characteristics of these reactors led to their extensive physics evaluation at General Atomic since 1957. One of the earliest comprehensive treatments written in 1957 is by Bethe (see ref. 1). A very recent evaluation of the neutron physics of high-temperature reactors can be found in the papers by Stewart and Jaye[5], which summarize the present state of knowledge of achieving high conversion ratios by means of high-temperature graphite-moderated reactors. It will be noted that in large sizes conversion ratios just below unity can be reached.

If the fuel is of a "fission-product-retaining" nature, i.e., most of the fission-product poisons stay in the fuel, if methods can be devised to use fission-product-releasing fuel where the fission-product poisons are continuously siphoned off, and if some beryllium is added to the core so that the resultant (n, $2n$) reaction will contribute to the neutron economy, then conversion ratios as high as $c = 1.1$ can be reached. In other words, from the point of view of neutron physics it *is* possible to conceive of thermal spectrum breeders. For a discussion of the economics and the fuel cycle lifetimes involved, the reader is referred to the two cited papers (see ref. 5). The second of these references also discusses low-enrichment systems as well as the substitution of plutonium for highly enriched uranium.

5. Fuel Elements

In practice, a modern HTGR fuel-moderator element is somewhat as described below. It consists of a tube or block of graphite with holes dispersed throughout, with some of these holes used to hold "coated" fuel particles and with the helium coolant stream flowing both on the exterior of the graphite tube or block and/or through some other holes within the graphite.

The coated fuel particles consist of a fuel-fertile particle kernel of the order of about 150-micron diameter which is then coated (by means of a simple chemical methane cracking process) with several differently oriented carbon layers, making the diameter of the whole fuel particle of the order of 200 to 250 microns. Such particles retain a large fraction of the fission products so that the coolant circuit is maintained at an activity level that can be technologically handled. It is probably simplest to think of each of these individual fuel particles as fuel with individual cladding around the particle.

Inasmuch as we are not dealing with metallic fuel bars, irradiation damage of a metal lattice does not set the limit to the mechanical integrity of the fuel. In fact, remarkably long burnups have been achieved with coated fuel particles without cracking the carbon coating. In one series of irradiations, triply coated uranium-thorium-carbide particles were irradiated up to 24% atom burnup without visible damage to the coating.

With respect to the economy of the fuel cycle cost, the fuel elements just described meet the tests laid down in Sec. 1.C: they give rise to a high specific-power system, a high conversion ratio, and a high burnup. There is every reason to believe that fabrication costs can be minimized, inasmuch as the fabrication of the fuel elements involves only simple hole-boring operations in the graphite and the fabrication of the fuel particles is a chemical rather than a precision mechanical process so that these fuel particles lend themselves to automated production on a large scale. With respect to reprocessing and refabrication, much work remains to be done on reprocessing, but there are no difficulties in principle that would lead one to expect unduly high reprocessing costs from large scale plants.

6. *Reactor Arrangement*

Having described the fuel elements and the coolant of the HTGR, a few short words regarding an actual physical reactor arrangement are perhaps of interest. Basically, the system consists of the reactor core, heat exchanger surfaces (without heat exchanger shells), and helium circulators, all contained within one enclosure. The cold inlet water on the one hand and hot steam on the other hand enter and leave the enclosure, respectively, and connect with the turbo-generator. It has been found that for compactness and ease of physical arrangement this enclosure is best made of concrete that has been made mechanically strong against the relatively low pressure (about 30 atmospheres) which it has to contain by means of placing the enclosure under compression through post-tensioning of this concrete enclosure. The advantages of such concrete enclosure (or pressure vessel) is that it can be assembled in the field without the necessity of transporting heavy pressure vessels, that it can be molded to most shapes the designer desires, and that it does not fail through brittle fracture as metals could conceivably do if strong irradiation damage were allowed to lower their brittle fracture critical temperature—and last but not least that its strength comes from a large number of individual tensioning devices, thereby increasing the safety of the pressure vessel.

2. Neutron Thermalization in High-Temperature Graphite Reactors†

A. *General*

Space does not permit discussion of the many recent physics advances that have contributed to accurate reactor calculations for graphite high conversion reactors. However, the reader is referred to the work on resonance absorption by Nordheim[6] and that on neutron thermalization in graphite both experimentally by Beyster and his coworkers[7], Poole[8], and others, and theoretically by Young and Koppel[9]. For a summary of earlier work, see Parks, Nelkin, Wikner, and Beyster[10]. As far as reactor calculations are concerned reactor physics has advanced markedly over the past two decades‡. The advent of high-speed computing machines led to today's multigroup multidimensional reactor calculations[11].

To give one illustration of recent physics advances of importance we now turn to an abbreviated view of the present situation in the graphite thermalization field.

Neutron thermalization is a field where the theoretical and experimental advances have been quite spectacular over the past decade—developments which have taken place none too soon from the point of view of their need in modern reactor calculations, and particularly for high-temperature reactors which operate in the epithermal neutron spectrum and which have moderator interfaces where one face is thermally much hotter than the other face.

† The author wishes to thank Dr. J. A. Young of the John Jay Hopkins Laboratory for Pure and Applied Science for discussions regarding the thermalization problem.

‡ The advances in theory of an analytical nature are treated, for instance, in A. M. Weinberg and E. P. Wigner, *The Physical Theory of Neutron Chain Reactors*, Univ. of Chicago Press, Chicago, 1958.

Let us look now at the case of the high-temperature graphite advanced converters. The graphite moderator in these reactor cores operates at about 1200°K (corresponding to a neutron energy of about 0.1 eV). The range of neutron energies of principal interest to us is from, say, thermal energies (0.025 eV) to about 2 eV. In this energy range, the various nuclei contained in the reactor have cross-section variations with energy which have anything but a simple $1/v$ energy dependence. In fact, U-235, Th-232, and U-233, which are the principal fissionable and fertile nuclei present in the system, all show complicated resonance phenomena in this energy region. Thus, it is important to know the prevailing energy spectrum in graphite at high temperatures quite accurately and to be able to predict them accurately from theory in order to be able to carry out accurate neutron physics reactor design. The reactor physics calculations must concern themselves not only with the core proper, which is at about 1200°K, but also with the neutron reflector made of graphite. In this graphite reflector there is of course no fission energy production and consequently the temperatures are considerably lower than in the reactor core, namely, on the order of 600°K.

The first physical question that suggests itself is to ask whether at these temperatures we need to concern ourselves with crystal effects or can consider the carbon atoms as a "free gas". We shall see below that at 1200°K we can indeed think of the carbon atoms as a "free gas" but that at 600°K this is not a good approximation. Furthermore, the critical experiments are of course most conveniently run at lower temperatures, i.e., room temperatures of around 300°K. Therefore, it is important to also understand the thermalization at 300°K to interpret these critical experiments as a proper source of reactor design information. At these room temperatures, crystalline effects become very important.

As the fission neutrons that are born in the 1 to 2 MeV region are slowed down in graphite, the neutrons first pass through an energy region in which the wavelength $\lambda_n = 0.287 \times 10^{-8}/\sqrt{E_0}$ cm (where E_0 is the incident neutron energy in electron volts) is considerably smaller than the interatomic distance in graphite, which is of the order of a few Angstroms. By the time neutrons are slowed down to thermal energies, say in a block of graphite at 300°K, then $E_0 \simeq 0.025$ eV so that the predominant neutron wavelengths are considerably longer than the interatomic distance and crystal effects become very important.

A more precise way of saying this is to note that one can compute the maximum crystal frequency of graphite[12] to be 0.2 eV. Clearly, below this frequency crystal effects will dominate the distribution of the scattering. Actually, the crystal effects extend above the region of 0.2 eV inasmuch as neutron scattering from the lattice can give rise not only to a single phonon emission or absorption but, in a certain fraction of the neutron-lattice scattering process, also give rise to multiple phonon emission.

The object of the theory, of course, is to find expressions for the inelastic-scattering cross section expressed in terms of the crystal dynamics, to calculate from it a spectral distribution at a given carbon temperature, and to compare this distribution with an experimentally measured one.

To calculate the double differential *inelastic* scattering cross section for graphite, two simplifying assumptions are made:

1. *The calculations assume that the scattered neutron waves do not interfere with each other, i.e., we treat the graphite crystal as though it gave rise to incoherent scattering.*

Actually, this is quite contrary to the physical facts since graphite is a coherent scatterer. It turns out in practice, however, that calculations ignoring this physical fact and proceeding as if graphite were an incoherent scatterer do give good results in the neutron energy region between, say, 0.02 and 2 eV—which is the region of principal interest for these reactors. The theoretical reason why the incoherent approximation does not introduce large errors in this neutron energy region relates to the fact that in this region the momentum transfer κ in a particular collision

$$\hbar^2\kappa^2/2M = E + E_0 - 2\sqrt{EE_0}\cos\theta \tag{5}$$

is generally large. Hence, many Brillouin zones contribute to the coherent scattering, and thus an effective averaging takes place which tends to eliminate interference effects.

It has been shown by Young and Koppel[13] that for neutron energies in the neighborhood of the first Bragg reflection distance of the crystal, if one properly describes the neutron scattering as coherent scattering, one can reproduce in first order the experimental results obtained at these very low energies for the case of beryllium. Calculations for graphite taking into account interference effects are in process at General Atomic.

2. *The calculations assume that we are dealing with an isotropic substance with one particle per unit cell.*

In actual fact, graphite is a highly anisotropic crystal structure so that this approximation would at first sight seem to be a poor one. Since we do not deal with single crystals of graphite, however, but with a large aggregate of many crystals, the net result is that in fact in practice we do deal with something like an isotropic medium, and, again, practice has shown this approximation to give very good results. Calculations taking this anisotropy into account show little difference from the isotropic approximation[14].

B. *The Double Differential Cross Section*

Under the two assumptions discussed above we may write the double differential cross section for neutron scattering from a harmonic solid as†

$$\frac{d^2\sigma}{d\epsilon\, d\Omega} = a^2 \left(\frac{E}{E_0}\right)^{\frac{1}{2}} \frac{1}{2\pi} \int_{-\infty}^{\infty} dt\, e^{i\epsilon t}$$
$$\exp\left[\frac{\hbar\kappa^2}{2M} \int_{-\infty}^{\infty} \frac{f(\omega)\, e^{-\omega/2T}}{2\omega \sinh(\omega/2T)} (e^{i\omega t} - 1)\, d\omega\right], \quad (6)$$

where ϵ = the energy transfer to the neutron,
κ^2 = the square of the momentum transfer,
a = the bound nuclear scattering length,
E_0, E = the initial and final neutron energies, respectively,
M = the atomic mass,
$f(\omega)$ = the phonon frequency spectrum, and
T = temperature of the crystal in units of k_B, where k_B is the Boltzmann constant.

The derivation of Eq. (6) is discussed for the one-phonon case by Placzek and Van Hove[15]. The treatment of the multiple-phonon case is given by Sjölander[16]. The variable t appearing in Eq. (6) is indeed a time. In fact, Wick[17] has shown that the physical meaning of t is the duration of time of the collision between the neutron and the scatterer.

C. *The Calculation of $f(\omega)$*

Graphite is a substance consisting of carbon atoms placed in sheets within which sheets the atoms are tightly bound in a hexagonal structure.

† This is the expression in the Born approximation using the Fermi pseudo potential which is very accurate because the scattering length has been matched to the angular cross section at zero energy.

The planes are weakly coupled and four carbon atoms describe a unit cell. This allowed Yoshimori and Kitano[18] to give a good description of the lattice dynamics in terms of only four force constants, as follows: (*1*) changes of bond length between nearest neighbors in a plane, (*2*) changes in bond angles in a plane, (*3*) changes in the bond length between nearest neighbors in two adjacent planes, and (*4*) changes due to bending of the hexagonal planes proportional to the relative normal displacement of any atom to its three nearest neighbors in the same plane. Using this description of the graphite crystal there are several ways to determine the four force constants. Of these, the one yielding most accurate results for our purposes is by Young and Koppel[19]; their method fits the force constants of the graphite crystal to the measured specific heats of graphite over a temperature range from 100° to 1000°K—a range of temperatures that covers the range of temperature of interest to our neutron thermalization calculations†. They then determined the phonon spectrum $f(\omega)$ by sampling the frequencies $\omega(\mathbf{k})$, where $\mathbf{k}$ is the phonon wave vector, for a large number of equally spaced points in an irreducible segment of the first Brillouin zone of a graphite crystal. This is shown‡ in Fig. 1.

With samples as large as 50,000 the function $f(\omega)$ is determined well enough to show excellent agreement with the measured specific heat of reactor-grade graphite at constant volume when C_v is calculated from

$$C_v = 3R \int_0^{\omega_{max}} d\omega \left(\frac{\omega}{T}\right)^2 \frac{e^{\omega/T}}{(e^{\omega/T} - 1)^2} f(\omega), \qquad (7)$$

where R is the gas constant[20].

D. *The Total Cross Section*

The first test to see whether the phonon spectrum $f(\omega)$ correctly describes neutron scattering is to consider the total scattering cross section for various neutron energies at a given graphite temperature, say 300°K. The total cross section consists of $\sigma_{total} = \sigma_{inel} + \sigma_{el} + \sigma_{a}$,

† It is true, as we shall see from Eq. (7), that the specific heat involves only the less sensitive $\int f(\omega)$ rather than $f(\omega)$ itself; however, this is partially offset by the fact that the force constants are not fitted to a single measured heat capacity but rather to six quite accurately measured specific heats over a wide range of temperature.

‡ It should be noted that the experimentally measured double differential cross section shows peaks at low neutron energies—primarily due to inelastic scattering. These peaks coincide in energy location with those of $f(\omega)$ shown in Fig. 1.

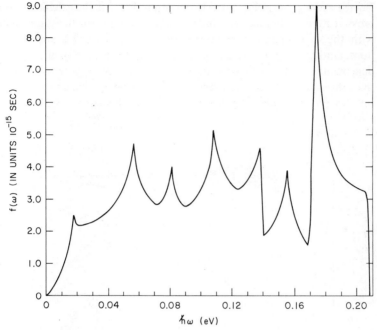

Fig. 1.   Phonon spectrum $f(\omega)$ of reactor-type graphite.

where σ_a is the absorption cross section, which is quite small; we shall compare the quantity σ_{total} for theory and for experiment. We may in turn write the elastic term

$$\sigma_{el} = \sigma_0 \sum_{|\tau|} \frac{e^{-\tau^2 W}}{\tau} |F_\tau|^2, \qquad (8)$$

where σ_0 is the bound-atom scattering cross section, τ are the reciprocal lattice vectors, F_τ is the structure factor, and where the Debye-Waller factor W is given by

$$W = \frac{\hbar}{2M} \int_0^{\omega_{max}} \frac{f(\omega) \coth (\omega/2T)}{\omega} \, d\omega. \qquad (9)$$

The region in which we want to compare the total cross section with experiment in order to test the accuracy of $f(\omega)$ is between, say, 0.02 and 3 eV. In Fig. 2 we have plotted the contribution of σ_{el} from

Eq. (8) and σ_{inel} from Eq. (6). Also shown in Fig. 2 is the calculated total cross section including σ_a, which is seen to be in excellent agreement with the experimentally measured cross section of Walton[21]. Predominantly, this agreement tests the correct form of $f(\omega)$ through the dependence of the inelastic-scattering cross section σ_{inel} on $f(\omega)$ rather than through the elastic-scattering cross section σ_{el}, inasmuch as σ_{el} is only weakly dependent on the form of $f(\omega)$ in this energy region. Thus,

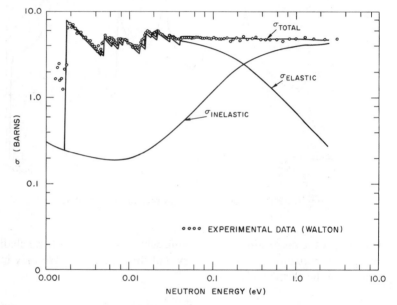

Fig. 2. Calculated and experimentally determined scattering cross sections of graphite.

this agreement between theory and experiment leads one to believe that one should be able to calculate the experimentally observed spectrum in graphite of various temperatures from Eq. (6).

E. *Neutron Spectra*

Figure 3 shows experimentally measured[22] neutron spectra resulting from the slowing down of fission-spectrum sources or sources closely simulating the fission spectrum. The spectra were measured in

samarium-poisoned graphite at three temperatures: 80°, 300°, and
600°K. For comparison, theoretical calculations performed by
numerical integration of Eq. (6) based upon the phonon spectrum of
Young and Koppel (see ref. 19) (indicated as Y-K on the figure) are
also shown (as solid lines). Calculation of the 300°K spectrum based
upon the phonon spectrum of Poole et al[23], is also shown as a solid
line. The dashed line for the 300°K case corresponds to the free-gas
approximation. From this we can see that the free-gas approximation is

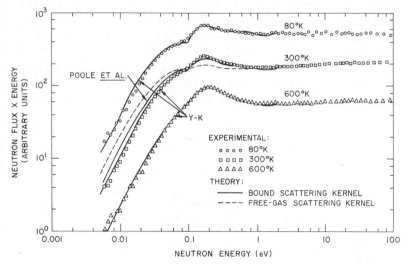

Fig. 3.   Theoretical and experimental neutron spectra in graphite poisoned with
samarium.

indeed not a good approximation for graphite at room temperature but
that calculations using Eq. (6) reproduce the experimental points
excellently for both the 300° and 600°K cases. This agreement has
resulted in application of the theory for the calculation of the actual
1200°K temperature situation in advanced converter reactors where
spectra have to be calculated for $C:U \approx 2500$, with the expectation
that the resultant spectra will indeed reproduce the physical situation
in the core.

F. *Neutron Spectra at Interfaces*

As noted in the beginning of Sec. 2, it is important to be able to product the neutron distribution at interfaces of graphite of different temperatures. This is a severe test of whether Eqs. (6) and (8) predict the angular distribution correctly, since angular current at the surface has to change abruptly. For the purpose of the HTGR one would preferably like to measure interface effects between 600° and 1200°K. In practice, however, the physical heating of graphite to such high temperatures would represent too difficult an experimental problem, and one therefore tests the theory on a 300°/600°K interface. Figure 4 shows the measurements of J. M. Neill et al. (see ref. 21), where curves 1 through 3 represent positions 1 in., 2 in., and 3.5 in., respectively, from the interface located in the room-temperature graphite and curves 4, 5, and 6 represent positions 1 in., 2 in., and 3.5 in., respectively, from the interface located in the 600°K graphite. On the high-temperature side samarium poison has been added to the graphite in order to simulate more nearly the conditions prevailing in the reactor core after some

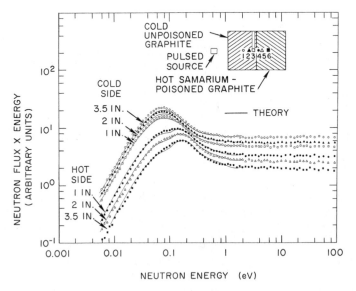

Fig. 4.   Neutron spectra across an interface dividing cold unpoisoned graphite from hot samarium-poisoned graphite.

time when fission-product poisoning has been built up. This also makes the experiment more sensitive to the scattering model, inasmuch as this adds to the neutronically different characteristics of the two sides and therefore leads to a sharper neutronic interface.

The solid lines represent the theoretical calculated neutron spectra for this situation. It is seen that very good agreement for the treatment of the interface is indeed obtained.

In summary, then, it can be seen that the thermalization problems in graphite at the moderator temperature and neutron energy region of interest to high-temperature reactors are well in hand.

References

1. Bethe, H. A., *Neutron Calculations on Homogeneous Graphite Reactors*, Report GAMD-221, General Atomic Division, General Dynamics Corporation, October 4, 1957.

2. Fortescue, P., R. T. Shanstrom, and H. Fenech, "Development of the Gas-Cooled Fast Reactor Concept", *Fast Reactor Technology: American Nuclear Society National Topical Meeting, Detroit, Michigan, April 26–28, 1965*, ANS-100, p. 89. See also P. Fortescue, et al., "Gas Cooling for Fast Reactors", *Proceedings of the Third International Conference on the Peaceful Uses of Atomic Energy, Geneva, 1964*, Vol. 6, United Nations New York, 1965, p. 80.

3. Fortescue, P., *Thermodynamic Aspects of Coolant Choice for Gas Cooled Reactors*, British Report AERE R/R-2153, Atomic Energy Research Establishment, 1957; or see *Nucl. Power*, **2**, 381 (1957).

4. Melese, G. B., *Comparison of Gases as Reactor Coolants*, unpublished data, General Atomic Division, General Dynamics Corporation, June 10, 1965.

5. Stewart, H. B., S. Jaye, and R. C. Traylor, *HTGR Fuel Cycle Assessment Studies*, USAEC Report GA-6146, General Atomic Division, General Dynamics Corporation, May 11, 1965; and S. Jaye, P. U. Fischer, and D. H. Lee, Jr., *The Use of Low-Enrichment Uranium and Plutonium in the HTGR*, USAEC Report GA-6367, General Atomic Division, General Dynamics Corporation, May 7, 1965. Both papers were presented at the EURATOM Symposium on Fuel Cycles of High-Temperature Gas-cooled Reactors, Brussels, June 10–11, 1965.

6. Nordheim, L. W., *Resonance Absorption*, Report GA-3973, General Atomic Division, General Dynamics Corporation, 1963. This paper was presented at A Symposium on Neutron Physics Related to Reactors, at the 1963 Southwestern Meeting of the American Physical Society, Houston, February 28, 1963.

7. See, for instance, J. R. Beyster, et al., "Neutron Thermalization and Reactor Applications", *Proceedings of the Third International Conference on the Peaceful Uses of Atomic Energy, Geneva, 1964*, Vol. 2, p. 14, United Nations, New York, 1965.

8. Poole, M. J., "Review of the Application of Pulsed Sources to the Measurement of Neutron Spectra in Moderators and Lattices", *Proceedings of the Symposium on Pulsed Neutron Research, held at Karlsruhe, 10–14 May 1965*, to be published by the International Atomic Energy Agency (IAEA SM-62/90).

9. Young, J. A., and J. U. Koppel, "Calculation of Thermal Scattering Kernels", *Proceedings of the Symposium on Pulsed Neutron Research, held at Karlsruhe, 10–14 May 1965*, to be published by the International Atomic Energy Agency (IAEA SM-62/66).

10. Parks, D. E., M. Nelkin, N. F. Wikner, and J. R. Beyster, *Slow-Neutron Scattering and Thermalization, With Reactor Applications*, forthcoming book now in preparation at John Jay Hopkins Laboratory, General Atomic Division, General Dynamics Corporation.

11. See, for instance, G. D. Joanou and H. B. Stewart, "Modern Techniques Used in Nuclear Design of Reactors", *Ann. Rev. Nucl. Sci.*, **14**, 259 (1964).

12. See Sec. 2.C, and J. A. Young and J. U. Koppel, "Phonon Spectrum of Graphite", *J. Chem. Phys.*, **42**, 257 (1965).

13. Young, J. A., and J. U. Koppel, "Coherent Inelastic Scattering from Polycrystalline Beryllium", *Phys. Letters*, **16**, 235 (1965).

14. Bell, J., *SUMMIT, An IBM-7090 Program for the Computation of Crystalline Scattering Kernels*, USAEC Report GA-2492, General Atomic Division, General Dynamics Corporation, February 1962.

15. Placzek, G., and L. Van Hove, "Crystal Dynamics and Inelastic Scattering of Neutrons", *Phys. Rev.*, **93**, 1207 (1954).

16. Sjolander, "Multi-phonon Processes in Slow Neutron Scattering by Crystals", *Arkiv Fysik*, **14**, 315 (1958).

17. Wick, G. C., "Scattering of Neutrons by Systems Containing Light Nuclei", *Phys. Rev.*, **94**, 1228 (1954).

18. Yoshimori, A., and Y. Kitano, "Theory of the Lattice Vibration of Graphite", *J. Phys. Soc. (Japan)*, **11**, 352 (1956).

19. Young, J. A., and J. U. Koppel, "Phonon Spectrum of Graphite", *J. Chem. Phys.*, **42**, 357 (1965).

20. Born, M., and K. Huang, *Dynamical Theory of Crystal Lattices*, Clarendon Press, Oxford, 1954, Chap. 2.

21. Walton, R. B., General Atomic, unpublished data.

22. Neill, J. M., et al., *Graphite Interface Studies, Technical Summary Report*, Part I, USAEC Report GA-6753, General Atomic Division, General Dynamics Corporation, November 1965.

23. Poole, M. J., P. Schofield, and R. N. Sinclair, "Some Measurements of Thermal-Neutron Spectra", *Exponential and Critical Experiments, Proceedings of the Symposium on Exponential and Critical Experiments held by the International Atomic Energy Agency in Amsterdam, Netherlands, 2–6 September 1963*, Vol. III, p. 87, IAEA, Vienna, 1964.

Thermonuclear Devices

S. M. ULAM

Los Alamos Scientific Laboratory

When Bethe's fundamental paper on the carbon cycle nuclear reactions appeared in 1939, few, if any, could have guessed or imagined that, within a very few years, thermonuclear reactions would become an object of most intensive theoretical studies—and that such reactions would be produced on Earth and enter decisively into the new technology of the nuclear age. The work of V. Weizsacker on the same problem and the papers by Atkinson and Houtermans on deuterium reactions have, together with Bethe's work, drawn attention to the schemata by which energy may be produced in the stars and in our sun; but it was hard to imagine that, in such a short time, human technology would successfully dare to imitate such processes on Earth. It is strange to realize now, some quarter of a century after those heroic times, how rapid was the tempo of the developments in both the theory and in the technological developments which now in these fields proceed at a more measured pace.

As often happens in the history of science, and of physics in particular, it was an additional and rather independent development, coming almost simultaneously, which combined with the theoretical ideas on thermonuclear reactions to make them realizable and applicable. The discovery of fission and the fact that more than one neutron is liberated in this process immediately suggested the possibility of a new type of a chain reaction leading to an enormous release of energy which, almost instantaneously, would appear in thermal form and produce situations where a small, terrestrial object would be instantly heated to temperatures orders of magnitude higher than any heretofore attained in a piece of matter in bulk. The story of the Manhattan District Project of the Metallurgical Laboratory in Chicago and of Los Alamos has been told in many accounts; but it is not perhaps

593

very well known that a small group of physicists, Bethe, Konopinski, Oppenheimer, Serber, and Teller, gathered in Berkeley during several weeks in the summer of 1942, before the Los Alamos Project was started, in order to discuss what could be done toward a design of a thermonuclear device. This was before the production of a nuclear fission chain reaction in Chicago; the courage of these physicists and their faith in theoretical thinking is, indeed, to be admired.

This article will attempt to sketch the subsequent history of the studies which were involved in the establishment of thermonuclear reactions and in the explosive release of their energy. We shall not attempt here to discuss the thermonuclear devices whose study forms the subject of the Project Sherwood, that is, the gradual release of confined thermonuclear energy and the various arrangements which have been proposed to this end.

The work at Los Alamos started in 1943 and was directed toward the design and construction of a fission bomb. The preoccupation with and the innumerable experiments on the fission process and the associated phenomena—the theoretical work on the process of the chain reaction—all had some good, if only general, background of previous work. Some of the most useful that existed in published form were the great papers on nuclear physics by Bethe (and Bacher and Livingston) which appeared in the *Reviews of Modern Physics* in 1936 and 1937. They became a true compendium of knowledge in this subject and were referred to as "The Bible" for information on nuclear reactions. Alongside of all this, a vast amount of work was going on, both theoretically and experimentally, on problems of chemistry and metallurgy vital to the construction of a device which, once initiated by neutrons, would explode yielding some meaningful fraction of the total energy available in the material. The study of the process of nuclear explosions with durations much shorter than any which were previously studied for such problems and involving the thermodynamical and hydrodynamical behavior of matter at temperatures and energy densities far outside those previously encountered on earth, preoccupied almost exclusively the scientists and engineers on the project. The task of constructing a fission bomb was not only one of immediate urgency and the primary assignment for the laboratory, but its solution was indeed a necessary condition for any attempts to conceive, design, and plan releases of energies which could be obtained from thermonuclear reactions. Nevertheless, from the very beginning of the Los Alamos project, a relatively small group of physicists devoted most of their time to specific work on a thermonuclear bomb. "Super" was the code word for this enterprise. It was Edward Teller who directed with enthusiasm and fantastic energy the thinking and the calculational work toward this end. It was realized from the beginning that temperatures of the order of tens of millions of degrees were necessary to provide an initiation for the thermonuclear reactions. Deuterium, which could be made available in sizable quantities, was, of course, the material primarily considered. The role of tritium as a product of the $D + D$ reactions was immediately noticed; and, as a matter of fact, the possibilities of using some tritium from the outset for facilitating the progress of the thermonuclear reaction were suggested already during the Berkeley Conference, mentioned above. The problems of igniting a mass of deuterium appeared very formidable. An understanding, in greatest detail, of the details of the preceding fission explosion was necessary for the establishment of the initial conditions for the explosion of deuterium. The subsequent interaction of the effects of the fission explosion had to be foreseen and calculated. As regards the process of the thermonuclear reaction itself, all the questions of behavior of the material as it heated and expanded—the changing time rate of the reaction; the hydrodynamics of the motion of the material; and the interaction with the radiation field, which "energy-wise" would be of perhaps equal importance to that of the thermal content of the expanding mass—had to be formulated and calculated.

Several schemata for the arrangement of the material were proposed by Teller and his collaborators, and these had to be scrutinized by extensive analytical and numerical work. It was realized very early that even to obtain a "yes" or "no" answer on the possibility of realizing a thermonuclear explosion depended crucially on being able to obtain accurate numerical descriptions of the extremely complicated processes referred to above. The schemata of "Super" appeared feasible, even though not certain of realization in the months preceding the first nuclear explosion in New Mexico in August of 1944. To realize nowadays the magnitude of the problems involved, one should remember that, even only mathematically, the problem of the start and explosion of a mass of deuterium combined a considerable number of separate problems. Each of these was of great difficulty in itself, and they were all strongly interconnected. The "chemistry" of the reaction, i.e., the production, by fusion, of new elements not originally present and the appearance of tritium, He_3, He_4, and other nuclei, together with the increasing density of neutrons of varied and variable energies in this "gas" influences directly the changing rate of the reaction; and it does so also by changing the values of the density and temperature. Simultaneously, the radiation field is increasingly present and influences, in its turn, the motion of the material. The work of the "Super" group on the visualization and on quantitative following of these processes constituted a veritable monument to the imagination and skill of theoreticians. We have to remember that electronic computing machines were not yet in existence in those days and daring simplifications and some, only intuitive, estimates had to be made. An account of some of this work by Teller and his collaborators was given in a series of lectures by *Fermi* toward the end of the war. Unfortunately, it still remains a classified document.

The work at Los Alamos on the "Super" continued after the end of the war. There were a few special meetings devoted to ascertaining the plausibility and feasibility of the arrangements and the devices as they were proposed during the war for the "Super". Following the directive issued by President Truman to proceed with the planning and construction of an H-bomb, the work at Los Alamos, which had been generally directed toward fundamental problems of feasibility, was stepped up considerably and reoriented toward the problems of specific device design. Even before, though, certain doubts had arisen about the practicability of the schemes outlined during the war and elaborated in subsequent work. A very detailed and comprehensive calculation was planned to be performed on the newly available electronic computing machines of the whole course of the ignition process of the thermonuclear reaction and its subsequent course. The plan was to do it as completely as possible, taking into account all the pertinent phenomena, and follow in a great number of time steps the interaction of the numerous variables. Von Neumann participated with Teller, the writer, and several other members of the Los Alamos Project in planning this gigantic calculation. Quite independently, however, the present writer, in collaboration with C. J. Everett, had undertaken the calculation of the ignition process and the following course of the thermonuclear reaction by using numerous simplifications and guesses as to the values of certain multidimensional integrals defining the distribution of neutrons and the products of reaction during the changing geometry of the mass of the active material. These calculations were performed with

TABLE I. Energy Sources and Maximum Exhaust Velocities

Source	v_{max} km/sec
Chemical reactions ($H_2 + \frac{1}{2}O_2$)	5
Stored thermal energy (high-temperature hydrogen)	~ 15
Metastable atomic and molecular states ($H_2^* \rightarrow H_2$)	20
Radioactive materials	
$\quad Po^{210}$	2×10^3
Fission	1.2×10^4
Fusion ($H^2 + H^2 = He^4$)	3.5×10^4
Complete annihilation of matter	3×10^5
Electromagnetic energy	3×10^5

It is interesting that, in principle, some chemical binding energies per unit mass are sufficiently large for reasonable transportation to the moon; the problem is to find a practical way to store atomic hydrogen at reasonably high density and low temperature.

Radioactive materials for propulsion should be produced in times which are not much greater than their half-lives, and their half-lives must be compatible with the time during which they will furnish energy for an engine. Very large pulsed reactors or controlled nuclear explosions are possible sources of neutrons for short-lived isotopes. A megaton thermonuclear explosion will furnish enough neutrons to produce enough energy in an alpha-emitting isotope to accelerate 200 tons to 100 km/sec. Although the values of v_{max} given will be very difficult to achieve, it should be noted that velocities of the order of 100 km/sec are achievable, in principle, from material containing a mass concentration of about 0.25% of a heavy radioactive isotope.

Fission energy can be supplied from a wide variety of continuous or pulsed solid, liquid, or gas core reactors and nuclear explosions. Modern nuclear explosions produce debris with average material velocities of several thousand km/sec, or more than 10% of v_{max}.

Controlled fusion energy cannot yet be effectively produced continuously, but most experts in the field agree that it will be possible in the foreseeable future. Thermonuclear explosions now provide exceedingly cheap sources of energy at material velocities greater than 10% of the v_{max} of 3.5×10^4 km/sec.

Antimatter cannot yet be produced in quantities relevant for applications, nor is it going to be easy to condense the components of a neutral gas, let alone a solid, in appreciable quantities. It appears likely that antimatter production and storage devices, if ever practical, would be best used in space. The equilibrium temperature of solid antimatter in a high earth orbit may be as low as a few hundred degrees, balancing energy production by incident nuclei against radiation from the surface. The problems of production and storage of antimatter are indeed formidable. But so are the requirements for energy for trips to the stars.

We include electromagnetic energy as a separate category of energy sources because it provides an exhaust velocity identical to light velocity and because there exist several natural sources which may be useful for propulsion. We arbitrarily include solar electromagnetic radiation in this category. Less directly traceable to some other energy source are the earth's magnetic field, interplanetary electric and magnetic fields, and possible interstellar fields. Even relatively weak fields may be useful for practical applications, since extremely large collection areas can, within limits, compensate for very low energy densities.

It is instructive to consider the idealized energy cost of different types of space transportation. These costs are defined as follows: We assume that the engine exhaust velocity is equal to the total velocity to be given to the payload, and that nonpropulsion energy losses are negligible. Assuming that the useful payload is about three-quarters of the final mass, the final kinetic energy of the payload is about half the total expended energy. We further assume that energy costs the equivalent of \$17/gram of ^{235}U or \$10/ton of coal. Some figures based on these assumptions are given in Table II.

The total cost of putting objects in orbit in 1965 ($\sim$ \$1000/lb) is approximately 10^5 times the cost shown in Table II. Of this cost, about 10^{-3} is the cost of chemical fuel. Approximately half the current cost is in the rocket, which is used only once, and the other half is in the supporting activities associated with a launch. The costs are extremely high because they are roughly equivalent to using supersonic aircraft to carry freight across the U.S., making one flight every several weeks, throwing away each aircraft after each flight, and including the entire operating costs of several major airports in the cost of the operation. The energy costs for both types of operations are of the same order of magnitude. Through developments not unlike those in commercial

TABLE II. Idealized Energy Costs for Various Types of Trips

Δv, km/sec	Type of trip	Energy costs ($1/kg of payload)
2.5	~75 km apogee above earth escape from moon's surface	1.5×10^{-3}
10	earth orbit	2.4×10^{-2}
30	round trip to Mars or Venus in less than 1 year	.2
100	~2 year round trip to Saturn satellites	2.4
1000	~6 day round trip to Mars ~4 mo round trip to Saturn	240
10,000	~2 mo round trip to Pluto ~600 year round trip to Alpha-Centauri	2.4×10^4
100,000	~60 year round trip to Alpha-Centauri	2.4×10^6
Relativistic	~20 year round trip to Alpha-Centauri	2.3×10^7

aviation, it does not appear unreasonable to expect that, eventually, the cost of transportation into cis-lunar space and even to the moon may approach that of commercial air transportation between points several thousand miles apart, and that transportation costs throughout the solar system will be largely determined by the idealized energy costs. For this to be true, however, propulsion systems which produce, efficiently, the required exhaust velocities are essential.

Finally, we note from Table II that the energy costs of even very long trips to the nearest star will be prohibitive until we have energy sources which are orders of magnitude lower in cost than any available today. Furthermore, the technical problems associated with high thrust engines with an exhaust velocity approaching light velocity are formidable indeed.

4. Outline of Classes of Propulsion Systems

All space engines require a source of energy, an expellant, a means for transferring energy to the expellant, and some method for directing its momentum. For an engine to be useful, it must operate in such a way that the payload and those parts of the space vehicle which must retain their structural integrity are protected from excessive pressures or temperatures. Given the large numbers of known types of energy sources, methods for storing and transferring energy, and possible types of constraints for directing momentum, it is to be expected that a very large number of classes of space propulsion systems should be technically feasible. It is therefore surprising that only a rather small number (perhaps a few dozen) of basically different space propulsion systems have been studied seriously during the last decade or so. Those concepts which have been examined seriously appear either to have been straightforward extrapolations of other concepts or, apparently, possibilities which have been picked more or less randomly, rather than as a result of systematic studies of those possibilities offered by our current knowledge of physics and engineering principles.

One way to make such a systematic study is by using a generalized outline of the components and processes required for a space engine. Such an outline is presented in Table III. The outline has been constructed in such a way that elements from each major category can be chosen at random and yet almost always suggest a class of propulsion systems which makes logical sense. Many other numbers and types of category headings could just as well have been chosen. Those in Table III were chosen in such a way as to yield roughly the amount of detail required to distinguish between "different" types of propulsion systems as they are now labeled by project names, contracts, etc.

The sun has not been specified as a separate class of energy sources because it is a source for several types of energy. The class of engines which uses the visible part of the solar spectrum could be specified by "electromagnetic field" as the energy source, and specifying that the energy source is external and further said to be the sun. Gravitational fields are included as an energy source because it is possible for space vehicles to pick up kinetic energy through gravitational interactions with astronomical bodies.

The energy source need not necessarily be carried along in the vehicle. Besides using the sun, an engine could be supplied with energy from a laser powered by a fixed energy source, confined explosions inside a fixed gun barrel, a series of explosions of devices propelled independently to the vicinity of the space vehicle, etc.

Similarly, part or all of the expellant may not be carried by the vehicle while it is accelerating. Besides the examples given above one can consider ramjets in planetary atmospheres or atmospheric breaking. One may argue that rendezvous with an expellant or energy supply is or is not a function associated with a particular type of propulsion system. For complete generality it should be included.

A pulsed energy source is one in which the rate of energy release changes considerably, and more than once, if the engine is operated at its maximum possible time-averaged thrust until a large fraction of the expellant is expended. All other energy sources are classed as continuous, rather than constant, to allow for moderate changes in energy release rates while the engine is operating.

An energy stage is defined as a step in the process of transfer of energy to the expellant. Each energy stage is characterized by the form of energy and the state of material directly associated with the stage. Whenever either of these changes, a new energy stage has been defined. The first stage is defined by specifying the primary energy source and the state of material associated with it. The last stage is the expellant, in some specified state, with some amount of kinetic energy. The number of possible energy stages can range from one to infinity. The category "more than seven" was chosen arbitrarily to allow detailed categorization of most of the propulsion systems which have been studied seriously so far.

It is difficult to be precise in the definition of an energy stage. For example, how far does one go in specifying all the energy forms associated with fission? Somewhat arbitrarily, we state that chemical or nuclear reactions (including fission) directly produce kinetic energy in one stage, whether the energy is in material or photons. We further state that the material associated with the energy in each stage is composed of those atoms, electrons, quanta, etc., which possess the kinetic or potential energy in each stage. Thus the heating of a liquid expellant by a solid core nuclear reactor proceeds through six stages: first, solid material, potential fission energy; second, charged particles, kinetic energy of fission fragments; third, solid, reactor core thermal energy; fourth, liquid, expellant thermal energy; fifth, gas, expellant thermal energy; sixth, gas, expellant kinetic energy. A solar sail engine consists of one stage: incident and reflected electromagnetic quanta. Transient states which are difficult to define and do not help specify the system are left out. For example, a conventional nuclear explosive is described as proceeding from a solid with potential fission or fusion energy to a plasma with thermal energy, rather than including a

TABLE III

Outline of Classes of Propulsion Systems

Outline element	Explanatory examples
1. Primary energy source	
1.1 Stored kinetic energy	rotating body, charged particle storage ring
1.2 Stored mechanical potential energy	spring, stressed solid
1.3 Stored thermal energy	hot solid core, compressed gas
1.4 Chemical energy	
1.4.1 Neutral atoms or molecules	$H_2 + \frac{1}{2}O_2 \rightarrow H_2O$
1.4.2 Free radicals	$H^+ + H^- \rightarrow H_2$
1.4.3 Metastable atomic or molecular states	$H_2^+ \rightarrow H_2, H + H \rightarrow H_2$
1.5 Nuclear energy	
1.5.1 Radioactive decay	^{238}Pu, ^{210}Po
1.5.2 Fission	^{235}U
1.5.3 Fusion	$D + D; D + T$
1.5.4 Antimatter annihilation	$e^+ + e^-$; $Li^6 + $ anti Li^6
1.6 Electromagnetic field	solar radiation
1.7 Gravitational field	near collisions with astronomical bodies
2. Placement of energy source with respect to vehicle	
2.1 Internal	nuclear reactor, chemical rocket
2.2 External	sun, beamed electromagnetic energy
3. Initial disposition of expellant	
3.1 Internal	chemical rocket
3.2 External	ramjet in earth's atmosphere
4. Time dependence of primary energy release	
4.1 Continuous	nuclear reactor, compressed gas
4.2 Pulsed	nuclear or chemical explosions

(continued)

TABLE III (continued)

Outline element	Explanatory examples
5. Number of energy stages from primary energy source to exhaust	
5.1 One	"solar sails" (reflected solar radiation)
5.2 Two	compressed gas (stored thermal energy to gas kinetic energy)
5.3 Three	solar heater of hydrogen (electromagnetic-thermal gas-kinetic)
5.4 Four	chemical rocket (stored chemical energy to kinetic to thermal energy to kinetic energy)
5.5 Five	nuclear rocket (stored fission energy to kinetic to thermal solid to thermal gas to kinetic energy)
5.6 Six	nuclear explosion (stored fusion energy to kinetic energy to thermal energy to thermal radiation to thermal energy of gas to kinetic energy)
5.7 Seven	nuclear magnetohydrodynamic electric engine (stored fission, kinetic energy, thermal solid, thermal gas, gas kinetic energy, electromagnetic field, charged particle kinetic energy)
5.8 More than seven	nuclear turbine—electric generator (stored fission, kinetic energy, thermal solid, thermal gas, gas kinetic energy, rotating solid, electromagnetic field, charged particle kinetic energy)
6. Time dependence of energy flow through each stage	
6.1 Continuous	—
6.2 Pulsed	—

(continued)

TABLE III (continued)

Outline element	Explanatory examples
7. State of material carrying energy at each stage, including first	
7.1 Solid	—
7.2 Liquid	—
7.3 Gas	—
7.3.1 Neutral atoms or molecules	—
7.3.2 Plasma	—
7.3.3 Charged particle beams	—
7.4 Electromagnetic field	—
8. Form of energy carried in each stage beyond first	
8.1 Kinetic energy	gas, elementary particles
8.2 Mechanical potential energy	spring, stressed solid
8.3 Thermal energy	hot gas
8.4 Chemical energy	batteries
8.5 Potential nuclear energy	
8.5.1 Radioactive decay	radioactive isotopes
8.5.2 Fission	^{239}Pu, ^{241}Pu
8.5.3 Fusion	$H^3 + H^2$
8.5.4 Antimatter	positrons
8.6 Electromagnetic field (photons included)	—
9. Method for preventing damaging heat transfer in each stage	
9.1 Acceptable stage temperature	—
9.2 Large spatial thermal gradient	—
9.3 Controlled ablation	—
9.4 Electromagnetic field	—
10. Method for controlling primary pressure	
10.1 Control of energy production rate	nuclear reactor
10.2 Control of rate of momentum transfer to engine	external explosions

(*continued*)

TABLE III (continued)

Outline element	Explanatory examples
11. Method for ejection of excess energy	
11.1 None (regenerative cooling)	—
11.2 Radiation	—
11.3 Heat dump without thrust	—
12. Type of constraint for directing momentum	
12.1 Mechanical	nozzle, reflection at flat surface
12.2 Hydrodynamic	shaped explosive charges
12.3 Electromagnetic field	particle accelerator
13. Time dependence of thrust	
13.1 Continuous	—
13.2 Pulsed	—

transient liquid stage. But the fission products, carrying kinetic energy, are included as a separate stage when considering a fissioning, low density gas, because their energy may be directly available for conversion to another form before heating the gas.

Distinctions between two types of time dependence of the energy flow in each intermediate stage are similar to those for the primary energy source. The reason this distinction is included is because pulsed operation of an energy storage stage is likely to be an important feature of space engines. Solar heating of hydrogen up to a high temperature and pressure before releasing the gas as exhaust is an example.

Excess energy is defined as any energy which interacts with the propulsion system which does not eventually appear as kinetic energy of the expellant. Heat dump without thrust includes any means other than radiation of disposing of excess energy. It might include, for example, the dissociation energy of a gas which does not recombine to supply energy which is useful for propulsion, or the heating of material which is ejected at a much lower velocity than the expellant.

The methods for preventing excessive heating of the solid structure and for keeping peak pressures below values which will damage the engine or payload are often basic to the practical use of a propulsion concept. Therefore an attempt has been made to categorize such methods, realizing that the methods chosen are arbitrary, and may not include all classes of methods.

The choice of types of constraints for directing the momentum of the expellant is also arbitrary. One might argue that all such types of constraints are electromagnetic because they use interatomic forces or generated fields to change the direction of motion of the exhaust. There appear to be rather fundamental differences between the classes of methods shown in the outline; undoubtedly further subdivision of this classification would be useful.

It is not necessarily true that a pulsed energy source is associated with pulsed application of thrust to the engine structure, or vice versa. A continuous energy source could be used to supply energy to a storage system which could generate pulses of thrust. Or pulses of energy, such as radiation, could be converted to expellant kinetic energy in such a way that the thrust is continuous.

5. Uses of the Propulsion System Outline

Among the possible uses of an outline of the general type as Table III are the following:

1. The outline, when permuted, demonstrates the exceedingly large number of possibilities to choose from.

2. It can be used as a basic concept generator for systematic searches for the "best" types of space engines for specific applications.

3. The outline can be used to study variants of well-known concepts in an effort to solve or alleviate problems which restrict the performance of a particular class of engines.

4. Certain particularly interesting classes of propulsion systems can be studied without involving very large numbers of concepts, for example, fission systems with only two energy stages.

5. It can be used for amusement or intellectual exercise by the examination of concepts which are randomly generated from the outline.

The number of possible permutations of the components of the outline is of the order of 10^{22}. Even using the specific form of this outline, this number is arbitrary, though perhaps instructive, because of the "seven or more" lumping of energy stages. One might expect to be able to reduce the number considerably by excluding classes of combinations which do not make logical sense. But one must be very careful to distinguish between what may not make sense and what may not be practical, e.g., too expensive, incapable of high thrust, etc. In many cases (perhaps in most) such distinctions may require rather careful study before they can be made definite.

In principle, the outline could be used for a systematic study of the "best" types of engines for a specific class of missions. First, the range of required mission velocities is used to exclude those types of energy sources which cannot provide an exhaust velocity at least equal to the mission velocity. (Note that this exclusion cannot be made for those types of engines for which the energy source is "external".) Then the remaining possibilities could be systematically examined in sufficient detail to condense the number of "projects" to a small enough number to be practical for detailed engineering studies. In practice, this looks exceedingly difficult, because of the large number of concepts which the outline can generate, even if restricted to one or two energy sources. It is possible that some type of computing machine sorting and exclusion of concepts may be useful, if only because a machine may be less likely than a human being to rule out good ideas because of preconceived notions of what is reasonable. But just such objectivity may be the machine's undoing, because of the immense number of possibilities to be considered.

Perhaps the best use of the outline is for studying variants of a specific class of propulsion systems. Let us very briefly consider the use of nuclear explosions for propulsion, as in the rather specific ORION concept[1,2]. Here a large number of nuclear explosives, stored inside the vehicle, are ejected one by one through a central hole in the engine, and detonated at a point directly below. Part of the debris of the nuclear explosion strikes a circular, flat, metal disk and drives it into a set of gas-filled shock absorbers, which relatively gently transfer momentum to the rest of the engine, the vehicle, and its contents. The concept has been studied in considerable detail since 1957 and appears to be a practical method for transporting payloads ranging from tens of tons to many thousands of tons or more throughout the solar system. The ORION concept, however, is just one example of many different ways of using nuclear explosions for propulsion. Prior to 1957 Ulam and Everett proposed a general class of concepts of propulsion by nuclear explosions[3]. Several proposals for enclosing the explosions inside a spherical "nozzle" have been made[4,5]. This considerably increases the engine's efficiency, but greatly decreases the maximum effective exhaust velocity which appears feasible. Van Dorn[5] has proposed using small nuclear explosions ejecting rugged objects from a cylindrical barrel in the ground. This method may be particularly good for ejecting material from the moon's surface into orbit around the earth. F. J. Dyson has proposed several variants of ORION, including some which expand the scale to masses of millions of tons or more, at exhaust velocities close to v_{max} for fission or fusion, which are described in classified reports.

Even a cursory study of Table III will show that many other variants of ORION are possible. These include the use of external nuclear explosions for radiatively heating a gaseous propellant which is ejected through a nozzle, systems which use the neutrons from nuclear explosions to heat a gas by neutron capture, and engines which use the thermal radiation from nuclear explosions to drive thermionic generators for acceleration of high-velocity charged particles, for example. As a class, systems which use nuclear explosions are especially interesting because the energy source produces *directly* large masses of material moving at velocities up to about 10% of v_{max} from fission or fusion.

Random generation of propulsion concepts from Table III is practically guaranteed to produce a concept that no one has ever thought of before. I have found it impossible to reject, as clearly nonsensical, any of the dozen or so concepts which I have seen derived this way, mostly by my children. But every one of them has been a strange idea indeed.

References

1. Nance, J. C., *Nuclear Pulse Propulsion*, General Atomic Report GA-5572, October 5, 1964.
2. Dyson, F. J., "Death of a Project", *Science*, **149**, 141 (1965).
3. Ulam, S. M., and C. J. Everett, *On a Method of Propulsion of Projectiles by Means of External Nuclear Explosions*, Los Alamos Scientific Laboratory Report LAMS-1955, August 1955, classified.
4. Teller, Edward, "BATO—A Method of Weight Lifting for Spaceflight", *Air Force Space Digest*, December 1965.
5. *Feasibility Study of a Gas Launched Payload Vehicle*, AVCO Corporation Report RAD 26-60-54, July 5, 1960, classified.

The Search for Extraterrestrial Technology

FREEMAN J. DYSON

Institute for Advanced Study

I owe to Hans Bethe both of the two most memorable experiences of my scientific life. The first was in 1947, when I came to Cornell University as a student and found Hans having just finished his pioneering calculation of the Lamb shift. He put me onto the job of making an improved calculation including relativistic effects, and this led directly to my taking part in the grand cleanup of quantum electrodynamics in the following year.

My second memorable experience was in 1958, when I went to work for a year on Ted Taylor's "Project Orion" at General Atomic in San Diego. This project to design a space-ship propelled by nuclear explosions[1] is now officially dead[2] but not declassified, and so there is not much glory attached to it. Still it was a splendid idea, and during the first year of the project's life we skimmed the cream off a multitude of technical problems in the most diverse branches of physics and engineering. It was Hans's willingness to vouch for our sanity that did most to persuade the authorities in Washington to spend money on a project which seemed at first glance so outrageous. In view of Hans's dedication to the Test Ban Treaty, nobody could accuse him of being bomb-happy.

Hans thus knows well both sides of my character, the eclectic physicist and the frustrated engineer. Since the rest of this book is mostly written by physicists, I have assigned my chapter to the frustrated engineer. I will write about ideas which arose, in the context of the work on Orion, when we tried to envisage the ultimate consequences of the things we were proposing to do.

There is a very fine book which I have in my study, called "Engineers' Dreams"[3]. It is about grandiose engineering projects which have been from time to time invented by engineers, studied by

641

committees, and finally killed by politicians for good or bad reasons. The Orion spaceship would make a good chapter for the next edition of that book. If they had allowed us to go ahead with the project, I would maybe now be helping to build it, instead of writing about even more gigantic and implausible undertakings.

I want to begin by emphasizing an important distinction. When one discusses engineering projects on the grand scale, one can either think of what we, the human species, may do here in the future, or one can think of what extraterrestrial species, if they exist, may have already done elsewhere. To think about a grandiose future for the human species ("la nostalgie du futur") is to pursue idle dreams, or science fiction. But to think in a disciplined way about what we may now be able to observe astronomically, if it should happen to be the case that technologically advanced species exist in our corner of the universe, is a serious and legitimate part of science. My discussion here will be entirely concerned with extraterrestrial phenomena which might be presently observable. In this way I am able to transpose the dreams of a frustrated engineer into a framework of respectable astronomy.

In recent years there has been much speculation among biologists, astronomers, and physicists concerning the probability of existence of extraterrestrial intelligent species. A good selection of writings on this theme is to be found in the book *Interstellar Communication* edited by Alastair Cameron[4]. Out of such writings there emerges a prevalent point of view[5] which I will call the "orthodox view". In grossly over-simplified form, the "orthodox view" may be summarized as follows. Life is common in the universe. There are many habitable planets, each sheltering its brood of living creatures. Many of the inhabited worlds develop intelligence, and an interest in communicating with other intelligent creatures. It makes sense then to listen for radio messages from out there, and to transmit messages in return. It makes no sense to think of visiting alien societies beyond the solar system, nor to think of being visited by them. The maximum contact between alien societies is a slow and benign exchange of messages, a contact carrying only information and wisdom around the galaxy, not conflict and turmoil.

This "orthodox view" is no doubt partly right. Certainly it was a brilliant idea of Cocconi and Morrison[6] to propose listening for signals on the 21 cm wavelength; it is to be hoped that Frank Drake's two-month period of listening [Project Ozma[7]] will be continued in future as a routine operation. However, my point of view is rather different, since I do not wish to presume any spirit of benevolence or community of interest among alien societies. I make a sharp distinction between intelligence and technology. It is easy to imagine a highly intelligent society with no particular interest in technology. It is easy to see around us examples of technology without intelligence, particularly when we eat lunch at the campus cafeteria in La Jolla and watch the bulldozers demolishing the eucalyptus trees†. When we look into the universe for signs of artificial activities, it is technology and not intelligence that we must search for. It would be much more rewarding to search directly for intelligence, but technology is the only thing we have any chance of seeing. So I was careful to call this chapter "The Search for Extraterrestrial Technology", rather than "Extraterrestrial Intelligence".

My argument begins with the following idea. If it is true, as many chemists and biologists believe[8], that there are millions of places in the universe where technology might develop, then we are not interested in guessing what an average technological society might look like. We have to think instead of what the most conspicuous out of a million technologies might look like. The technology which we have a chance to detect is by definition one which has grown to the greatest possible extent. So the first rule of my game is: think of the biggest possible artificial activities, within limits set only by the laws of physics and engineering, and look for those. I do not need to discuss questions of motivation, who would want to do these things or why. Why does the human species explode hydrogen bombs or send rockets to the moon? It is difficult to say exactly why. My rule is, there is nothing so big nor so crazy that one out of a million technological societies may not feel itself driven to do, provided it is physically possible.

There are two more rules of my game which I shall state explicitly. Others may like to choose different rules, but I think mine are reasonable and I shall defend them if anybody objects to them.

Second rule: I assume that all engineering projects are carried out with technology which the human species of the year 1965 A.D. can understand. This assumption is totally unrealistic. I make it because I cannot sensibly discuss any technology which the human species does not yet understand. Obviously a technology which has existed for a million years will be likely to operate in ways which are quite different

† Parts of this chapter are taken from a talk given at the University of California, San Diego, in April 1965.

from our present ideas. However, I think this rule of allowing only technology which we already understand does not really weaken my argument. I am presenting an existence proof for certain technological possibilities. I describe crude and clumsy methods which would be adequate for doing various things. If there are other more elegant methods for doing the same things, my conclusions will still be generally valid.

My third rule is to ignore questions of economic cost. I assume that if the physical resources of matter and energy for doing something are present, then the thing is possible. The reason why this rule is imposed is that economic costs operate on a short time scale. Suppose for example that a technical society has enough matter and energy available for building a large spaceship, but lacks the economic resources (industrial base) to do it. The necessary economic resources will be created automatically if the technology grows up to the limit set by its physical resources. We have no idea what the economic growth rate of an alien technology might be, but it is safe to assume that some alien technologies would have a growth rate as fast as ours, so long as their physical resources were not fully exploited. This means a growth rate of at least 1% per year,

i.e., a factor 20,000 growth per 1000 years,
i.e., a factor 10^{15} growth per 3500 years,

all times which are very short on an astronomical time scale. I assume, in other words, that the population explosion is out of control in at least one society besides our own.

The unanswerable question is: what would a very large and conspicuous technology be interested in doing? The orthodox view holds that it would send out radio messages for our enlightenment. Perhaps it would, or perhaps it wouldn't. I prefer to think instead of things that a big technology must do in order to exist at all. It must have lots of energy and lots of matter, and it must develop means of getting hold of both energy and matter.

Let us consider then the physical limits put on technological development within a single planetary system surrounding a single star. Here we have available roughly:

Sun power 4×10^{33} ergs/sec $= 4 \times 10^{26}$ watt,
Earth mass 6×10^{27} grams;

the ratio of mass to power is 15 kg/kW, which is reasonable for active biological systems, and also for electrical machinery. If we take the content of all nine planets but exclude hydrogen and helium, the amount of mass goes up by a factor of 30 or so. The present industrial base of the human species uses an energy flow of about 3×10^{19} ergs/sec operating on a mass of about 10^{17} grams. There is in principle available to us a growth by a factor of about 10^{12} in both energy and mass, without going beyond the solar system.

Now I make the main assertion of this chapter[9]. With only quantitative and no qualitative improvement of our present technology, a society expanding to the Malthusian limit would be able to use all of this 4×10^{33} ergs/sec and 6×10^{27} grams for biological and techno-logical purposes. How?

Point No. 1

It is possible to build large rigid structures in space. The formula for the maximum size D of such structures is

$$(gD)^2 = (gR)(T/\rho), \qquad g = GM/R^2,$$

where g is the local gravitational acceleration, and the limit is set by tidal forces from a mass M at a distance R. Here T is the tensile or compressive stress in the structural material, and ρ is its density. This is to be contrasted with the formula for structures built on the solid earth,

$$gD_E = T/\rho.$$

Tidal forces are a factor D/R smaller than the total gravitational force g.

For good structural materials like steel and Fiberglas, $T/\rho \approx 10^9$ (cm²/sec²), so that

$$D_E \cong 10 \text{ km},$$

which is correct for the height of the highest mountains on the earth. For a structure in a low orbit about the earth

$$D = \sqrt{D_E R} \approx 300 \text{ km}.$$

For a structure in an orbit around the sun at about the earth's distance,

$$g = GM/R^2 = 1, \qquad R = 1 \cdot 5 \times 10^{13},$$
$$D \cong 10^6 \text{ km}.$$

We can then imagine a shell or layer of rigidly built objects of diameter D arranged to move in orbits around the sun or earth, the orbits being arranged to avoid collisions. The minimum number of objects required to form a complete spherical shell is about

$$N = 4\pi R^2/D^2 = 4\pi(\rho/T)(GM/R) = 6000 \text{ (low earth orbit)}$$
$$= 2 \times 10^5 \text{ (shell around sun)}.$$

Point No. 2

It is possible to build light rigid structures. This is again a question of elementary engineering. Suppose we try to make a structure of size D as light as possible with building blocks of given properties. The unit building-block might be for example a rod of length 100 cm, diameter 1 cm made of steel. You can take 12 of these to form an octahedron of

$$\text{size } D_1 = 100 \text{ cm,}$$
$$\text{mass } M_1 = 10 \text{ kg.}$$

Now you can stick 100 octahedra together face-to-face to make the next size unit rod, and stick 12 of these rods together to make a bigger octahedron,

$$\text{size } D_2 = 10^4 \text{ cm,}$$
$$\text{mass } M_2 = 10^4 \text{ kg,}$$

and so on. Each generation multiplies the linear size by a factor $q = 100$ and the weight by a factor $qr = 900$, say $qr = 1000$ to allow for joints.

So the nth generation has

Size	$D_n = q^n \text{ cm,}$
Mass	$M_n = 10(qr)^n \text{ gm,}$
Volume	$V_n = q^{3n} \text{ cm}^3,$
Density	$\rho_n = 10(q^{-2} r)^n \text{ g/cm}^3.$

We have $r = \sqrt{q} = 10$ approximately. Hence at each generation

$$M = 10D^{3/2}, \qquad \rho = 10D^{-3/2};$$

the thing gets lighter as it gets bigger.

For example, for a 300 km structure near the earth,

$$D = 3 \times 10^7 \text{ cm } (n \sim 4),$$
$$M = 10^{12} \text{ gm} = 10^6 \text{ tons.}$$

For a 10^6 km structure in solar orbit,

$$D = 10^{11} \text{ cm } (n \sim 6),$$
$$M = 3 \times 10^{17} \text{ gm} = 5 \times 10^{-11} \text{ earth mass.}$$

So the minimum mass for 2×10^5 objects surrounding the sun is 10^{-5} earth mass.

The structures you build in this way with Eiffel-tower design are full of holes. The mass $M = 10D^{3/2}$ is only a minimum value. If you want to intercept all the sunlight crossing an area D^2, you must fill in the holes with additional structure and membranes. You will need a mass proportional to D^2 rather than to $D^{3/2}$. The point of this calculation is that the weight of the whole object is dominated by the g/cm^2 needed to collect sunlight, and not by the gram/cm$^{3/2}$ needed to build a rigid framework.

With the Earth's mass, 6×10^{27} gm, in a shell at the earth's distance from the sun, $4\pi R^2 = 2 \times 10^{27}$ cm^2, you have 3 gm/cm^2, which is quite adequate for building reflectors and supporting structure in an effective gravity field of $10^{-5} \times$ earth gravity.

I chose the octahedron as the basic structural unit only for illustrative purposes. The octahedron might in fact be a practical form for an extended framework in a place where gravitational stresses are small. If there are substantial gravitational or tidal stresses, the structure should be arranged so that units under compression lie parallel to the principal stress (as is customary when building sky-scrapers or suspension-bridges on the surface of the earth). Whether the overall design is octahedral or not, it remains true that the minimum mass of a rigid framework varies roughly as the three-halves power of the linear size.

Point No. 3

It is possible to take planets apart. The human species at present mines about 1 cubic kilometer of ore per year for industrial purposes. An expansion of industry by a factor 10^{12} would require the mining of a substantial fraction of the earth's total volume (10^{12} cubic km). To make this quantity of ore accessible for processing and to dispose of excess heat[10], it would be essential to remove the industrial machinery and the raw materials away from the earth and spread them out over a large volume of space. Either the earth itself, or preferably some other planet less well endowed with natural beauty and historic monuments, would have to be taken apart.

One can think of several feasible methods of disassembling a planet. I shall describe one method, using the earth as a numerical example to indicate the order of magnitude of the problem. I do not advocate that this, or any other[11], method be actually applied to the earth.

We begin by laying out metallic windings along lines of latitude on the earth's surface, the wires at latitude $(\pi/2 - \theta)$ carrying a current proportional to $\sin 2\theta$. This will give the earth a fixed quadrupole magnetic field, having a vertical component

$$H_z = H_0(1 - 3\cos^2\theta).$$

We could choose, for example, $H_0 = 100$ gauss without requiring excessively massive conductors. Next we produce a toroidal field, running horizontally along lines of latitude with intensity

$$H_x = H_0 \sin\theta.$$

The toroidal field must be generated by a uniform current of magnitude

$$J = cH_0/2\pi R = 2.5 \times 10^{-7} \text{ A/cm}^2,$$

where R is the radius of the earth, flowing through the body of the earth from the northern to the southern hemisphere. The return path of this current must be external to the earth, through orbiting metallic conductors and the magnetospheric plasma. We postpone for a moment the description of the return path, and discuss first the effect on the earth of the fields H_z and H_x.

The earth will be the armature of an electric motor. Its surface will experience a horizontal eastward stress equal to

$$P = \frac{1}{4\pi} H_z H_x = P_0 \sin\theta(1 - 3\cos^2\theta),$$

$$P_0 = (H_0^2/4\pi) = 800 \text{ dyn/cm}^2 = 8 \times 10^{-4} \text{ bar}.$$

Integrated over the earth's surface, this stress produces a net torque

$$T = \frac{4}{15} R^3 H_0^2.$$

The moment of inertia of the earth is numerically close to $4/3\rho R^5$, where ρ is the mean density. The angular acceleration is then

$$A = (H_0^2/5\rho R^2) = 9 \times 10^{-16} \text{ radians/sec}^2.$$

The present rotation speed (7×10^{-5} radians/sec) could be doubled, or the earth could be brought to rest, in 8×10^{10} sec = 2500 years.

Suppose that the torque T has been applied continuously for 40,000 years. Then the angular velocity is 10^{-3}, the rotation period is 100 minutes, and the equator is just ready to take off into space. From this point on, the process of disassembling the planet will proceed steadily as its angular momentum is increased. The power needed is approximately

$$W = T\omega = 6 \times 10^{26} \text{ ergs/sec.}$$
$$= 1.5 \times 10^{-7} \times \text{(total solar power)}$$
$$= 300 \times \text{(solar power intercepted by earth)}.$$

The complete machinery to take the earth apart must therefore consist of an arrangement of orbiting structures, to collect solar energy from an area extending about 100 earth-radii from the earth, to feed this energy into electric generators, to drive the current J around the return path from the southern to the northern hemisphere of the earth, and to dispose of excess angular momentum by using tidal effects of the sun.

I do not pretend to have solved all the design problems which the orbiting current generator poses. Its mode of operation is in principle identical with that of the recently proposed Alfvén Propulsion Engine[12]. As it moves through the earth's quadrupole field H, it experiences an induced emf in the direction $[V \times H]$ and a mechanical force in the direction $[I \times H]$, where V is the orbital velocity and I the current flowing through it. The current I is always maintained in such a direction as to contribute positively to the desired toroidal field H_x. This means that an object orbiting parallel to the earth's rotation will have current flowing parallel to the induced emf, while an object orbiting against the earth's rotation will have current flowing against the induced emf. The history of any one current generator will be roughly as follows. It will come into operation in a high orbit with large angular momentum parallel to the earth's rotation. It will then use the induced emf to generate current, the energy being derived from its gravitational potential, and will move gradually into a low orbit with less angular momentum. In the low orbit it will generate current transverse to the induced emf and so make the orbital plane precess until it is antiparallel to the earth's rotation. Finally it will generate current against the induced emf, lifting itself out of the earth's gravitation into a high orbit with large angular momentum directed oppositely to that of the earth. The net result of this cycle of operations is that angular momentum is transferred from the generator to the earth. A continuous stream of generators must be passing through these manoeuvers in order to maintain the torque accelerating the earth. Each generator, after emerging from the cycle to a great distance from the earth, can have its angular momentum reversed by solar tidal forces; it is then ready to go through the cycle again.

I do not need to emphasize the magnitude of the practical difficulties that would be involved in the implementation of this scheme. Two obvious difficulties are the avoidance of collisions between generators, and the formation of conducting paths through the insulating atmosphere of the earth. My object in discussing the scheme is only to prove feasibility in principle. It is noteworthy in this connection that the required electric fields (of the order of 1 volt per centimeter) and current densities (1 microampere per cm^2) are well within the range of conventional plasma physics.

We may conclude from the foregoing points 1, 2, and 3 that the mass of the planets is available for technological exploitation on a time scale of the order of 10^5 years or shorter. A technical society growing to the Malthusian limit can in a time of the order of 10^5 years harness completely the energy output of a star.

For us the important question is, can we detect such a technology? There is one obvious thing to look for, infrared radiation[9]. Independent of all engineering details, the second law of thermodynamics dictates that a technology exploiting 4×10^{33} ergs/sec must radiate away a substantial fraction of 4×10^{33} ergs/sec as waste heat at a lower temperature than the working parts of the machinery. If the star is surrounded with a shell of opaque objects, then presumably the outside surface of the entire shell would be used as radiator to dispose of waste heat. At least a major part of the 4×10^{33} ergs/sec would then be radiated at wavelengths in the range 3–10 microns. This radiation could not be hidden, whether or not the technical society were interested in revealing its existence to us.

Fortunately we can look for infrared sources in the 3–10 micron band using ground-based telescopes. The astronomers are of course professionally interested in looking for natural objects in this band. I am happy if they look for natural objects; this preserves their professional purity and serves my purpose just as well as an avowed search for artificial objects. The sort of natural object one expects to see is a protostar, a cloud of gas and dust in the process of condensing into a star and not yet hot enough to radiate in the visible. To observe such natural objects is important for the study of star formation, which is one of the central problems of astronomy. When such objects are found, I hope nobody will rush to the newspapers with claims that we have found something artificial. I say only that if highly expanded technologies exist then they are to be found among such objects.

There are at present at least two groups of astronomers searching for infrared sources with ground-based telescopes. Leighton[13] observes in the band 0.5–2.5 microns and Low[14] out to 10 microns and beyond. Leighton has found several interesting objects, but there is no reason whatever to consider them artificial. Their spectra are dominated by bands of vanadium oxide[15].

Other types of observation would be used to diagnose more completely any object which came under suspicion of being artificial. One would look in particular for irregular light variations due to starlight shining through chinks in the curtain, and for stray electromagnetic fields and radio noise produced by large-scale electrical operations (not necessarily carrying any "message"). The importance of the infrared observation is that it narrows down the search tremendously. If there is a big technology at all, then it must be in a place where an infrared source is found. After one has a list of infrared sources, then one will know where to look with optical and radio telescopes. Certainly one will not claim any object to be artificial unless it appears pathological in at least two independent modes of observation.

Next I want to venture briefly into considerably wilder extrapolations of the Malthusian principle. Is there any physical or engineering reason why a growing technology should remain confined to the neighborhood of a single star? The answer seems to me clearly negative.†

Professor Purcell[5] has given a proof that interstellar travel is impossible. His argument is correct in the sense that he did not make any arithmetical mistakes. But what he proved is only that interstellar travel going at 99% of the speed of light and making a round trip within a human lifetime is impossible. When we are discussing the

† A very illuminating discussion of the possible role of large-scale technology in the universe is contained in the concluding chapters of I. S. Shklovsky, "Universe, Life, Intelligence", in Russian, *Izd. Akad. Nauk SSSR*, Moscow, 1962. The idea that a technological society would naturally extend its activities into space in order to harness a greater fraction of the sun's energy is due to K. E. Tsiolkovskii, "Dreams of Earth and Sky" (in Russian), Goncharov, Moscow, 1895, paperback edition, *Idz. Akad. Nauk SSSR*, Moscow, 1959. Tsiolkovskii, besides being the first to formulate the laws of rocket propulsion in space, also anticipated many of the arguments used by the author in this chapter and in Reference 9.

growth of an unknown technological society, the human lifetime is an irrelevancy. So I will make the flat statement, which I think is a very conservative one,† that interstellar travel at 1% of the speed of light [1 light-year per century] is easily feasible. Any reasonably efficient nuclear-electric propulsion system, not to mention an Orion system, will take you to this kind of velocity. So the problem of interstellar travel is a problem of motivation and not of physics. If we assume a technology with a strong drive to expand, it will move from star to star in times at most of the order of 1000 years. It will spread from one end of a galaxy to another in 10^7 years, still a short time by astronomical standards. We are therefore confronted with a new order of questions. It is not enough to ask: what does a star look like when technology has taken it over? We must ask: what does a galaxy look like when technology has taken it over?

What would a technology do to a galaxy in order to expand its lebensraum as much as possible? First, the individual stars could be exploited, as we have already described. But it appears that a galaxy in the wild state has too little matter in the form of planets, too much in the form of stars, for efficient exploitation. A technology would try to get matter out of the stars and into interstellar space where it can be used. This sounds hard to do, but I know at least one brute-force way to do it. No doubt there are cleverer ways, but I will describe the one I know.

Suppose we rig up an electrical propulsion system squirting mass out of the solar system at a velocity of 2×10^8 cm/sec. Suppose the whole power output of the sun is used at 40% efficiency to do this. The mass of Jupiter used as propellant will last about 10^6 years, and in that time the sun's velocity has been changed by 2 km/sec, its position by 3 light-years. So the sun can be placed accurately at any desired point within a 3 light-year radius. But in our part of the galaxy (which is not particularly densely populated) another star comes through a circle of 3 light-year radius on the average about once every 10^5 years. So a technical society can arrange star-star collisions or near-collisions on a time scale of about 10^6 years all over the galaxy.

† It is not difficult to imagine a linear electromagnetic accelerator, looking like an immensely long gun barrel, which could accelerate large objects without expenditure of rocket propellant to 50% of light velocity. A rigid gun of the required length could be built in interstellar space using available planetary materials. However, this form of propulsion requires a second gun barrel for deceleration at the destination, and so it is useless for the initial voyages of colonization.

We do not know in detail what the effects of a star-star collision are. But it is clear that it is a good way of getting matter out of stars. One of two things must happen. Either the collision itself throws a substantial fraction of the star-masses out into space where it can be condensed and utilized, or the stars stick together and form a star of larger mass. In the second case the technical society can continue adding stars by successive collisions until the mass becomes many solar masses. A star of many solar masses is known to go through its evolution in 10^6 years and end up by blowing off most of its mass into space either gradually or explosively. So in either case the result of stellar collisions will be in the end (in times of the order of a few million years) to bring mass out of stars into the surrounding space.

So we may make a guess that the characteristic features of a "tame" galaxy as compared with a "wild" galaxy would be: (i) enhanced infrared emission, (ii) high ratio of interstellar to stellar mass, (iii) high frequency of star-star collisions, (iv) unusual abundance of short-lived giant stars and deficiency of ordinary dwarf stars. Seen from a great distance, the spectrum of a "tame" galaxy would probably be strong in the blue and infrared, weak in the red.

The subject of astrophysical engineering is an interesting one, but I have not explored the many other possible tricks that an advanced technology might use for manipulating stars. One possibility is to exploit the gravitational energy of a multiple star system directly, instead of using only the thermal radiation[16]. In principle the exploitation of gravitational energy would allow a technological society to convert a substantial fraction of the total Mc^2 energy of a system into useful work, compared with the 0.8% of Mc^2 that is available from nuclear reactions.

At the end of all these delightful speculations, we come back to the hard question, why do we not see in our galaxy any evidence of large-scale technology at work? In principle there might be two answers to this question. Either we do not see technology because none exists, or we do not see it because we have not looked hard enough. After thinking about this problem for a long time, I have come reluctantly to the conclusion that the first answer is the more probable one. I have the feeling that if an expanding technology had ever really got loose in our galaxy, the effects of it would be glaringly obvious. Starlight instead of wastefully shining all over the galaxy would be carefully dammed and regulated. Stars instead of moving at random would be grouped and organized. In fact, to search for evidence of technological activity in the galaxy might be like searching for evidence of technological activity on Manhattan Island. Nothing like a complete technological take-over has occurred in our galaxy. And yet the logic of my argument convinces me that, if there were a large number of technological societies in existence, one of them would probably have carried out such a take-over.

So in the end I am very skeptical about the existence of any extra-terrestrial technology. Maybe the evolution of life is a much less probable event than the molecular biologists would have us believe. Or maybe intelligence usually develops without technology. Whatever the truth may be, to be skeptical does not mean that one should not search. On the contrary, just because I am skeptical about extra-terrestrial technology being really there, I am all the more anxious that we should continue to search for it with all possible seriousness and scientific objectivity.

References

1. Nance, J. C., "Nuclear Pulse Propulsion", General Atomic Report No. GA-5572, October 5, 1964, unclassified.
2. Dyson, F. J., "Death of a Project", *Science*, **149**, 141 (1965).
3. Ley, W., *Engineers' Dreams*, paperback edition, Viking Press, New York, 1960.
4. *Interstellar Communication*, A. G. W. Cameron, Ed., W. A. Benjamin, New York, 1963.
5. This point of view is expressed most eloquently by Edward Purcell in "Radio-astronomy and Communication through Space", Chap. 13 of *Interstellar Communication*.
6. Cocconi, G., and P. Morrison, "Searching for Interstellar Communications", *Nature*, **184**, 844 (1959), Chap. 15 of *Interstellar Communications*.
7. Drake, F. D., Project Ozma, Chap. 17 of *Interstellar Communication*.
8. See, for example, Melvin Calvin, "Chemical Evolution", Chap. 5 of *Interstellar Communication*.
9. This statement was made, without any engineering details to support it, in F. J. Dyson, "Search for Artificial Stellar Sources of Infrared Radiation", *Science*, **131**, 1667 (1960), Chap. 11 of *Interstellar Communication*.
10. Fremlin, J. H., "How Many People can the World Support?", *New Scientist*, **24**, 285 (1964), describes in gruesome detail the fate of a species which fails to expand its habits in proportion to its numbers.
11. Another method is described by D. G. Brennan, Project Turnabout, unpublished memorandum, Ultra Secret, 1958.
12. Drell, S. D., H. M. Foley, and M. A. Ruderman, "Drag and Propulsion of Large Satellites in the Ionosphere; An Alfvén Propulsion Engine in Space", *Phys. Rev. Letters*, **14**, 171 (1965).

13. Neugebauer, G., D. E. Martz, and R. B. Leighton, "Observations of Extremely Cool Stars", *Astrophys. J.*, **142**, 399 (1965).
14. Low, F. J., and H. L. Johnson, "Stellar Photometry at 10 μ", *Astrophys. J.*, **139**, 1130 (1964).
15. Münch, G., and J. D. Scargle, "The Spectra of Two Extremely Red Objects", *Astrophys., J.*, **142**, 401 (1965).
16. Dyson, F. J., "Gravitational Machines", Chap. 12 of *Interstellar Communication*.

A Plastic Decoupling Zone in the Upper Mantle

FRANK PRESS

Massachusetts Institute of Technology

Preface

Hans Bethe's participation in the early negotiations for a Nuclear Test Ban Treaty led him to examine the physical basis of methods for separating explosions from naturally occurring events such as earthquakes. His treatment of excitation at the source, of effects of propagation for both underground and atmospheric explosions were models of clarity. His presentations at Geneva were lucid and authoritative, so much so, as to raise the level of discussions from controversy to scientific interchange. His efforts contributed much to the achievement of the partial treaty banning atmospheric tests. Should a comprehensive nuclear test ban be realized, Hans Bethe will certainly be counted among the architects of such a treaty.

Introduction

Geophysicists have often speculated about the occurrence of a plastic zone at a depth somewhere between 15 and 700 km in the earth. The evidence, although indirect, comes from diverse observations which can more readily be explained by its existence but which do not uniquely require it. In this paper, some of these observations are reviewed and some additional support is presented using a new measurement of the vertical extent of faulting for a great earthquake and new information on the dimension of the seismic source. The weak zone is placed at about 150 km where the low velocity, low Q region occurs.

Some Evidence for the Weak Zone

Earthquake foci do not occur at depths greater than about 700 km. Either flow occurs below these depths and strain cannot accumulate, or

657

the sources of stress which lead to the accumulation of strain are absent. The seismic energy release rate generally decreases with depth, but minima occur near 200 and 450 km. These may be associated with weak zones[7].

A basic observation of geophysics deals with the compensation of topographic loads such as continents, mountain systems, continental glaciers by roots of less dense crustal material projecting into the more dense mantle. The time constant as measured by postglacial uplift seems to be of the order of 25,000 years. A weak zone deeper than the base of the crust (35 km) has been suggested as the primary mechanism of isostatic compensation.

Paleomagnetic studies of the past decade have led many scientists to infer polar wandering and continental drift. Although these conclusions are not universally held, a zone of weakness which decouples an outer layer from the main body of the earth has been proposed to account for them. Polar wandering has an alternate mechanism involving a wavelike movement of the equatorial bulge.

Volcanism, laboratory studies of the melting of basalt, Q† and velocity-depth results from free oscillations and long surface waves yield a picture of the upper mantle suggestive of, but not uniquely requiring, a weak zone in the upper mantle. Studies of volcanoes such as Kilauea show that the basaltic magma enters the conduit system at a depth of about 60 km[6]. It erupts at a temperature about 1100°C which is appropriate for a depth of about 80 km by most theories of the thermal state of the earth. Laboratory melting-point data imply that temperatures at or near the melting point of basalt probably occur at depths of 100–200 km. Since basalt or its dense phase, eclogite, is probably a constituent (with lowest melting point) of the multicomponent silicate system which is the upper mantle, a state of partial melting is suggested.

The world-wide minima in shear Q and elastic velocity which occur between 50 and 150 km in the upper mantle[2,1] are among the important geophysical discoveries of recent years. (As an interesting aside, it may be mentioned that the shadow zone which occurs for seismic rays emerging in the range 500–2000 km results from the velocity reversal, and the absence of short period shear waves is due to the low shear Q. Both of these consequences are involved in the decision to base a nuclear test ban monitoring system on large arrays at distances beyond

† $1/Q$ is the specific dissipation function for elastic waves.

2000 km, the primary data being the compressional wave signatures.) The low Q and shear velocity is most probably a temperature effect with or without partial melting. In either case, one would expect a concomitant decrease in strength at these depths, although the connection between Q and shear velocity which are "high frequency" data and plasticity which involves response to long term stresses, is not clear.

The shear velocity and Q data of Anderson and Archambeau are summarized in Fig. 1. Also shown are the Yoder and Tilley[12] solidus for the basalt–eclogite system and temperatures estimated from MacDonald's[8] calculations for suboceanic models so as to yield the observed heat flow from the sea floor. The rapid decrease in Q and

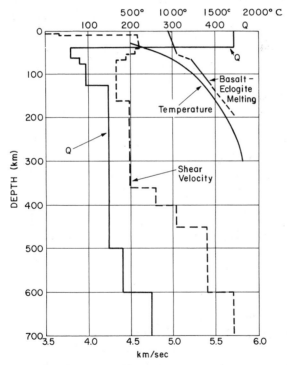

Fig. 1. Shear velocity and Q as a function of depth. Also shown are laboratory determined melting point–depth curves for the basalt–eclogite system and a theoretical temperature–depth curve for a "reasonable" model.

shear velocity seems to coincide with the approach of temperature to the initiation of melting.

New Evidence

The source-region mechanics of great earthquakes has long been a puzzle to earth scientists. A single large shock can cause movement of tens of feet along a fault over a horizontal distance as much as 1000 km. The cumulative displacement along major faults such as California's San Andreas fault is certainly tens if not hundreds of kilometers. Fault mechanics are simplified if a horizontal relaxation discontinuity is placed at depth, in which the material deforms continuously to keep up with the continuing elastic strain accumulation and release in the overlying slab[11,3]. The fracture should terminate in the relaxation zone, so that the vertical extent of faulting can be used to infer depth to this zone. Furthermore, this hypothesis implies that the energy release of large earthquakes would vary as the area of the source region whereas small ones with dimensions small compared to the depth of the relaxation zone would show energy depending on the source volume.

A disturbing feature of this hypothesis is that its proponents have placed the relaxation zone within the crust, at depths of about 10–20 km on the basis of very meager data. Seismic velocities and Q data show no evidence for such a zone. Crustal temperatures and pressures are amenable to duplication in the laboratory, and no plastic behavior of silicic rocks has been found. Recently, doubt has been cast on results implying shallow faulting depths for major earthquakes[3,10]. Based on data more abundant than previously available, Press and Jackson[10] showed that the fault for the great Alaskan earthquake of 1964 extended to depths of 130–200 km. The method makes use of the residual vertical displacements which were recoverable to distances of 200 km from the major fault from tide-gage records and shoreline changes. The displacements projected on a section normal to the strike of the fault are shown in Fig. 2. An interpretation of this pattern of uplift and subsidence can be made representing the fault as a vertical, rectangular dislocation sheet in a half-space. The displacement field can be computed and fitted to the observed displacements with the vertical extent of faulting as an adjustment parameter. Several attempts to fit the data are shown in Fig. 2, the best fit implying depths to the bottom of the fault sheet ranging from 130–200 km.

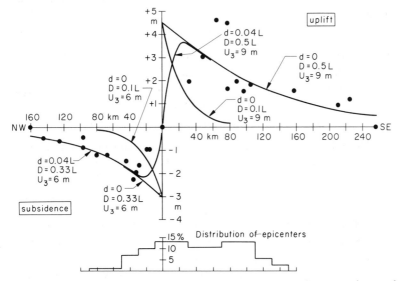

Fig. 2. Residual vertical displacements projected on a section normal to and bisecting the fault. Parameters for theoretical curves are d, depth to top of fault; D, depth to bottom of fault; L, half-length (400 km); U_3 vertical slip; index of seismicity, shown at bottom, is percentage of aftershocks in zone 20 km wide in the three days after main shock.

A theoretical relationship between magnitude and source dimension can be derived if the following are available: a magnitude–energy formula; the strain distribution in the source region; the efficiency factor for conversion of strain energy into seismic double waves.

We adopt De Noyer's[5] empirical magnitude–energy equation based on an integration of seismograms from eight earthquakes in the magnitude range $6\frac{3}{4}$–8

$$\log E_s = 7.76 + 1.87M, \tag{1}$$

where E_s is the seismic energy released.

We assume Tsuboi's hypothesis that strain-energy density is independent of magnitude, the latter being a function of the source volume only.

Assuming simple shear strain ϵ and linear source dimension L, the strain energy can be written as

$$E = 1/2\, \epsilon^2 DL^n, \tag{2}$$

where D is a constant with dimension L^{3-n} and μ is the rigidity. We guess an efficiency $E_s/E = 10\%$, and take $\mu = 3 \times 10^{11}$ dyn/cm^2, and $\epsilon = 10^{-4}$ which is consistent with the near displacement field of large earthquakes. Substituting Eq. (2) into Eq. (1) gives

$$M = -2.97 + (\log D)/1.87 + (n/1.87) \log L.$$

This relationship can be compared with experimental data on fault length as a function of magnitude. Tocher[11] developed such data using observations of surface faulting and his empirical relationship is shown in Fig. 3 by the heavy line. We have added the data shown by the points which support Tocher's earlier result, especially the slope of his curve. These data are derived from more recent earthquakes and are based on visual observations of faults where possible. Otherwise, after-shock zones, and radiation patterns of surface waves are used. This last method is a new development which recovers not only fault length but also rupture velocity[4].

Data for small shocks are difficult to obtain. These sources are never observable and most of the other methods are difficult to apply.

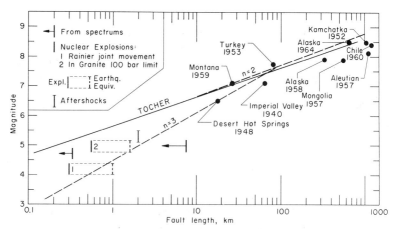

Fig. 3. Theoretical and experimental results for the magnitude–fault-length relationship.

We have used precision location of after-shocks, spectrum change with magnitude, and the source dimensions of nuclear explosions to infer the size of small-magnitude seismic sources. In the last method, we take a stress of 100 bars to define the beginning of the region of linear elasticity. The strength of rocks is about an order of magnitude higher and 100 bars is the approximate stress drop in the source region of earthquakes. Another indication of effective source dimension is that region beyond which movements along joints and bedding planes do not occur. The results are plotted in Fig. 3 along with the uncertainty in determining magnitude. For a more complete description of the methods used see Press[9].

Two theoretical curves are given in Fig. 3. The curve pertinent to large magnitude events takes $n = 2$ and $D = 10^6$ cm. This allows for horizontal source dimension $L \times (1/10)L$ and a depth of faulting of 10^7 cm, where the plastic zone is assumed to begin. The Alaskan earthquake was the model used in selecting these values. The small magnitude curve takes $n = 3$, $D = 1/10$ which implies the same horizontal source dimension $L \times (1/10)L$ and requires the vertical extent to be L. According to these values, small magnitude events show an L^3 dependence and are unaffected by the plastic zone which is at great depth compared to the source dimension.

The theoretical curve for $n = 2$ agrees with Tocher's large-shock data surprisingly well, especially since the efficiency factor was assumed (using the efficiency of explosions as a lower bound) without attempting to fit the data. Tocher recognized the L^2 dependence and inferred that the energy release is proportional to the surface area and is independent of the vertical extent of the strained region for all shocks. Our limited data on small and intermediate shocks seem to fit $n = 3$. This implies a transition dimension of about 100 km above which earthquakes are affected by the decoupling zone and below which they behave independently of it.

Discussion

Basalt–eclogite, a component of mantle rock is near or at its melting point at depths between 100 and 200 km in the earth. Basaltic lavas come from depths at least 60 km below Hawaii. Elastic velocity decreases to a minimum in this region as does the elastic quality factor Q. The best documented value for the vertical extent of faulting for a major earthquake is in this range. The epicentral region of shocks with horizontal fault dimensions larger than about 100 km behave as two-dimensional slabs, decoupled from the underlying material. These observations suggest that a weak or plastic zone occurs in the upper mantle. To speculate even further, this zone may be the source of the primary basaltic magma, and the region along which movements due to isostatic adjustment, polar wandering and continental drift occur.

References

1. Anderson, D. L., "Recent Evidence Concerning the Structures of the Upper Mantle from the Dispersion of Long-Period Surface Waves", in *Proc. Vesiac Conference on Variations of the Earth's Crust and Upper Mantle*, Inst. of Sci. and Tech., Univ. of Michigan, Ann Arbor, 1964.
2. Anderson, D. L., and C. B. Archambeau. "The Anelasticity of the Earth", *Jour. Geophys. Res.*, **69**, 2071–2084 (1964).
3. Benioff, H., "Movements on Major Transcurrent Faults", in *Continental Drift*, ed. S. K. Runcorn, Academic Press, New York, 1962, pp. 103–134.
4. Ben-Menahem, A., and M. N. Toksoz, "Source Mechanism from Spectra of Long-Period Seismic Surface Waves", *Bull. Seismol. Soc. Am.*, **53**, 905–919, 1963.
5. De Noyer, J., *The Energy in Seismic Waves*, Doctoral Dissertation, Univ. of California, Berkeley, 1957.
6. Eaton, J. P., and K. J. Murata, "How Volcanoes Grow", *Science*, **132**, 925–938 (1960).
7. Knopoff, L., "The Energy Release Rate-Depth Function for Earthquakes", *Proc. Nat. Acad. Sci.*, **51**, 1–3 (1964).
8. Mac Donald, G. J. F., "Dependence of the Surface Heat Flow on the Radioactivity of the Earth", *Jour. Geophys. Res.*, **69**, 2933–3946 (1964).
9. Press, F., "Dimensions of the Source Region for Small Magnitude Earthquakes", in *Proc. Vesiac Conference on Source Mechanism of Shallow Seismic Events in the 3–5 Magnitude Range*, Inst. of Sci. and Tech., Univ. of Michigan, Ann Arbor.
10. Press, F., and D. Jackson, "Alaskan Earthquake, 27 March 1964: Vertical Extent of Faulting and Elastic Strain Energy Release", *Science*, **147**, 1–2 (1965).
11. Tocher, D., "Earthquake Energy and Gound Breakage", *Bull. Seismol. Soc. Am.*, **48**, 147–153 (1958).
12. Yoder, H. S., Jr., and C. E. Tilley, "Origin of Basaltic Magmas", *Jour. Petrol.*, **3**, 342–532 (1962).

Hans Bethe, a Bibliography

Bethe, H., Theory of the Diffraction of Electrons by Crystals, *Ann. d. Physik*, **87.1**, 55 (1928).

Bethe, H., Passage of Cathode Rays through Electric Fields formed by Grids, *Zeits. f. Physik*, **54**, 703 (1929).

Bethe, H., Comparison of the Distribution of Electrons in the Helium Ground State as Calculated by Different Methods, *Zeits. f. Physik*, **55**, 431 (1929).

Bethe, H., Calculation of Electronic Affinity of Hydrogen, *Zeits. f. Physik*, **57**, 815 (1929).

Bethe, H., Term Separation in Crystals, *Ann. d. Physik*, **3.2**, 133 (1929).

Bethe, H., The Passage of Electrons Through the Electric Field of a Lattice, UCRL-Trans-917(1), *Zeits. f. Physik*, **54**, 703 (1929).

Bethe, H., Non-Stationary Treatment of the Photoelectric Effect, *Ann. d. Physik*, **4.4**, 443 (1930).

Bethe, H., Theory of Zeeman Effect in Salts of Rare Earth, *Zeits. f. Physik*, **60**, 218 (1930).

Bethe, H., Theory of Passage of Swift Corpuscular Rays through Matter, *Ann. d. Physik*, **5.3**, 325 (1930).

Bethe, H., Theory of Metals. Part I. Eigenvalues and Eigenfunctions of the Linear Atomic Chain, *Zeits. f. Physik*, **71**, 205 (1931).

Bethe, H., Scattering of Electrons, *Zeits. f. Physik*, **76**, 293 (1932).

Bethe, H., and Fermi, E., Interaction of Two Electrons, *Zeits. f. Physik*, **77**, 296 (1932).

Bethe, H., and Frohlich, H., Magnetic Interaction of Metallic Electrons. Criticism of Frenkel's Theory of Superconductivity, *Zeits. f. Physik*, **85**, 389 (1933).

Sommerfeld, A., and Bethe, Hans A., Elektronentheorie der Metalle, *Handbuch der Physik*, **24(2)**, Berlin, Springer, 1933.

Bethe, H., and Heitler, W., Stopping of Fast Particles and Creation of Electron Pairs, *Proc. Roy. Soc.*, **146**, 83 (1934).

Bethe, H., Theory of Supraconductivity, *Zeits. f. Physik*, **90**, 674 (1934).

Bethe, H., Influence of Screening on the Creation and Stopping of Electrons, *Cambridge Phil. Soc. Proc.*, **30**, 524 (1934).

Compton, A. H., and Bethe, H. A., Composition of Cosmic Rays, *Nature*, **134**, 734 (1934).

Bethe, H., Quantitative Calculation of the Eigenfunction of Electrons in Metals, *Helv. Phys. Acta*, **7**, suppl. 2, 18 (1934).

Bethe, H. A., and Peierls, R., Photoelectric Disintegration of the Diplon, *Int. Conf. on Physics*, London, **1**, 93 (1934).

Bethe, H. A. et al., Disintegration and Synthesis of Nuclei and Elementary Particles, *Int. Conf. on Phys.*, London, **1**, 162 (1934).

665

Bethe, H. A. et al., Natural Beta Decay, *Int. Conf. on Physics*, London, **1**, 66 (1934).

Bethe, H. A. et al., Cosmic Radiation, *Int. Conf. on Physics*, London, **1**, 247 (1934).

Bethe, H., and Peierls, R., Quantum Theory of the Diplon, *Proc. Roy. Soc.*, **148A**, 146 (1953).

Bethe, H. A., Ionization Power of a Neutrino and Magnetic Moment, *Cambridge Phil. Soc. Proc.*, **31**, 108 (1935).

Bethe, H. A., and Peierls, R., Scattering of Neutrons by Protons, *Proc. Roy. Soc.*, **149A**, 176 (1935).

Bethe, H. A., Annihilation Radiation of Positrons, *Proc. Roy. Soc.*, **150A**, 129 (1935).

Bethe, H. A., Theory of Disintegration of Nuclei by Neutrons, *Phys. Rev.*, **47**, 747 (1935).

Bethe, H. A., Statistical Theory of Superlattices, *Proc. Roy. Soc.*, **150A**, 552 (1935).

Bethe, H. A., and Bacher, R. F., Nuclear Physics I. Stationary States of Nuclei, *Rev. Mod. Physics.*, **8**, 82 (1936).

Weekes, D. F., Livingston, M. S., and *Bethe, H. A.*, Selective Absorption Regions of Slow Neutrons, *Phys. Rev.*, **49**, 471 (1936).

Bethe, H. A., Attempt to Calculate the Number of Energy Levels of a Heavy Nucleus, *Phys. Rev.*, **50**, 332 (1936).

Bethe, H. A., Nuclear Radius and Many-Body Problem, *Phys. Rev.*, **50**, 977 (1936).

Hoffman, J. G., Livingston, M. S., and *Bethe, H. A.*, Direct Evidence on the Magnetic Moment of the Neutron, *Phys. Rev.*, **51**, 214 (1937).

Rose, M. E., and *Bethe, H. A.*, Nuclear Spins and Magnetic Moments in Nuclei, *Phys. Rev.*, **51**, 205 (1937); *Phys. Rev.*, **51**, 993 (1937).

Bethe, H., Rose, M. E., Kinetic Energy of Nuclei in the Hartree Model, *Phys. Rev.*, **51**, 283 (1937).

Bethe, H. A., and Placzek, G., Resonance Effects in Nuclear Processes, *Phys. Rev.*, **51**, 450 (1937).

Bethe, H. A., Nuclear Physics. Part II. Nuclear Dynamics, Theoretical, *Rev. Mod. Phys.*, **9**, 69 (1937).

Bethe, H. A., and Spedding, F. H., Absorption Spectrum of Thulium Sulphate, *Phys. Rev.*, **52**, 454 (1937).

Livingston, M. S., and *Bethe, H. A.*, Nuclear Physics. Part III. Nuclear Dynamics, Experimental, *Rev. Mod. Phys.*, **9**, 245 (1937).

Bethe, H. A., Oppenheimer-Phillips Process (Nuclear Reactions), *Phys. Rev.*, **53**, 39 (1938).

Bethe, H. A., Binding Energy of the Deuteron, *Phys. Rev.*, **53**, 313 (1938).

Bethe, H. A., Rose, M. E., and Smith, L. P., Multiple Scattering of Electrons, *Am. Phil. Soc. Proc.*, **78**, 573 (1938).

Bethe, H. A., Order and Disorder in Alloys, *J. App. Phys.*, **9**, 244 (1938).

Konopinski, E. J., and *Bethe, H. A.*, Theory of Excitation Functions on Basis of Many-Body Model, *Phys. Rev.* **54**, 130 (1938).

Bethe, H. A., and Critchfield, C. L., Formation of Deuterons by Proton Combination, *Phys. Rev.*, **54**, 248 (1938).

Bethe, H. A., Coulomb Energy of Light Nuclei, *Phys. Rev.*, **54**, 436 (1938).

Bethe, H. A., Method for Treating Large Perturbations, *Phys. Rev.*, **54**, 955 (1938).

Bethe, H. A., Energy Production in Stars, *Phys. Rev.*, **55**, 434 (1939).

Rose, M. W. and *Bethe, H. A.*, Absence of Polarization in Electron Scattering, *Phys. Rev.*, **55**, 277 (1939).

Bethe, H. A., Meson Theory of Nuclear Forces, *Phys. Rev.*, **55**, 1261 (1939).

Bethe, H. A., and Kirkwood, J. G., Critical Behavior of Solid Solutions in Order-Disorder Transformation, *J. Chem. Phys.*, **7**, 578 (1939).

Bethe, H. A., and Marshak, R. E., Physics of Stellar Interiors and Stellar Evolution, *Phys. Soc. Reports*, **6**, 1 (1939).

Marshak, R. E., and *Bethe, H. A.*, Generalized Thomas-Fermi Method as Applied to Stars, *Astrophys. J.*, **91**, 239 (1940).

Bethe, H. A., Meson Theory of Nuclear Forces. Part II. Theory of the Deuteron, *Phys. Rev.*, **57**, 390 (1940).

Bethe, H. A., Meson Theory of Nuclear Forces. Part I. General Theory, *Phys. Rev.*, **57**, 260 (1940).

Bethe, H. A., Korff, S. A., and Placzec, G., Interpretation of Neutron Measurements in Cosmic Radiation, *Phy. Rev.*, **57**, 573 (1940).

Bethe, H. A., and Nordheim, L. W., Theory of Meson Decay, *Phys. Rev.*, **57**, 998 (1940).

Bethe, H. A., Recent Evidence on the Nuclear Reactions in the Carbon Cycle, *Astrophys. J.*, **92**, 118 (1940).

Bethe, H. A., Continuum Theory of the Compound Nucleus, *Phys. Rev.*, **57**, 1125 (1940).

Blanch, G., Lowan, A. N., Marshak, R. E., and *Bethe, H. A.*, Internal Temperature Density Distribution of the Sun, *Astrophys. J.*, **94**, 37 (1941).

Bethe, H. A., Theory of Diffraction by Small Holes, *Phys. Rev.*, **66**, 163MO (1944).

Bethe, H. A., and Oppenheimer, J. R., Reaction of Radiation on Electron Scattering and Heitler's Theory of Radiation Damping, *Phys. Rev.*, **70**, 451 (1946).

Bethe, H. A., Multiple Scattering and the Mass of the Meson, *Phys. Rev.*, **70**, 821 (1946).

Bethe, H. A., The Electromagnetic Shift of Energy Levels, *Phys. Rev.*, **72**, 339 (1947).

Barschall, H. H., and *Bethe, H. A.*, Energy Sensitivity of Fast Neutron Counters, *Rev. Sci. Instr.*, **18**, 147 (1947).

Von der Lage, F. C., and *Bethe, H. A.*, A Method for Obtaining Electronic Eigenfunctions and Eigenvalues in Solids with an Application to Sodium, *Phys. Rev.*, **71**, 612 (1947).

Marshak, R. E., and *Bethe, H. A.*, On the Two-Meson Hypothesis, *Phys. Rev.*, **72**, 506 (1947).

Bethe, Hans A., *Elementary Nuclear Theory*, New York, Wiley, 1948.

Alpher, R. A., *Bethe, H.*, and Gamow, G., The Origin of Chemical Elements, *Phys. Rev.*, **73**, 803 (1948).

Camac, M., and *Bethe, H. A.*, The Scattering of High Energy Neutrons by Protons, *Phys. Rev.*, **73**, 191 (1948).

Bethe, H. A., Remarks Concerning the Hydrogen Eigenfunctions in Dirac's Theory, *Z. Naturforsch.*, **3a**, 470 (1948).

Courant, E. D., and *Bethe, H. A.*, Electrostatic Deflection of a Betatron or Synchrotron Beam, *Rev. Sci. Instr.*, **19**, 632 (1948).

Bethe, H. A., Theory of the Effective Range in Nuclear Scattering, *Phys. Rev.*, **76**, 38 (1949).

Bethe, H. A., and Longmire, C., On the Experimental Value of the Fine Structure Constant, *Phys. Rev.*, **75**, 306 (1949).

Bethe, H. A., Fano, U., and Karr, P. R., Penetration and Diffusion of Hard X-Rays Through Thick Barriers. I. The Approach to Spherical Equilibrium, *Phys. Rev.*, **76**, 538 (1949).

Levinger, J. S., and *Bethe, H. A.*, Dipole Transitions in the Nuclear Photo-effect, *Phys. Rev.*, **78**, 113 (1950).

Bethe, H. A., The Range-Energy Relation for Slow Alpha Particles and Protons in Air, *Rev. Mod. Phys.*, **22**, 212 (1950).

Bethe, H. A., Brown, L. M., and Stehn, J. R., Numerical Value of the Lamb Shift, *Phys. Rev.*, **77**, 370 (1950).

Bethe, H. A., and Longmire, C., The Effective Range of Nuclear Forces. II. Photo-Disintegration of the Deuteron, *Phys. Rev.*, **77**, 647 (1950).

Bethe, H. A., Brown, L. M., and Walske, W. C., Stopping Power of K-Electrons, *Phys. Rev.*, **79**, 413 (1950).

Bethe, H. A., Tonks, L., and Hurwitz, H. J., Neutron Penetration and Slowing Down at Intermediate Distances Through Medium and Heavy Nuclei, *Phys. Rev.*, **80**, 11 (1950).

Bethe, Hans A., Kihss, Peter and Kaufmann, William W., *The H-Bomb and World Order*, New York, Foreign Policy Association, 1950.

Gluckstern, R. L., and *Bethe, H. A.*, Neutron-Deuteron Scattering at High Energy, *Phys. Rev.*, **81**, 761 (1951).

Hurwitz, H. Jr., and *Bethe, H. A.*, Neutron Capture Cross Sections and Level Density, *Phys. Rev.*, **81**, 898 (1951).

Walske, M. C., and *Bethe, H. A.*, Asymptotic Formula for Stopping Power of K-Electrons, *Phys. Rev.*, **83**, 457 (1951).

Bethe, H. A., and Wilson, R. R., Meson Scattering, *Phys. Rev.*, **83**, 690 (1951).

Beard, D. B., and *Bethe, H. A.*, Field Corrections to Neutron-Proton Scattering in a New Mixed Meson Theory, *Phys. Rev.*, **83**, 1106 (1951).

Heidmann, J., and *Bethe, H. A.*, Z-Dependence of the Cross Section for Photo-capture of Nuclei, *Phys. Rev.*, **84**, 278 (1951).

Salpeter, E. E., and *Bethe, H. A.*, A Relativistic Equation for Bound-State Problems, *Phys. Rev.*, **84**, 1232 (1951).

Levinger, J. S., and *Bethe, H. A.*, Neutron Yield from the Nuclear Photoeffect, *Phys. Rev.*, **85**, 577 (1952).

Bethe, H. A., and Rohrlich, F., Small Angle Scattering of Light by a Coulomb Field, *Phys. Rev.*, **86**, 10 (1952).

Bethe, H. A., and Butler, S. T., A Proposed Test of the Nuclear Shell Model, *Phys. Rev.*, **85**, 1045 (1952).

Bethe, H. A., and Austern, N., Angular Distribution of π^+ Production in n-p Collisions, *Phys. Rev.*, **86**, 121 (1952).

Maximon, L. C. and *Bethe, H. A.*, Differential Cross Section for Bremsstrahlung and Pair Production, *Phys. Rev.*, **87**, 156 (1952).

Bethe, H. A., Moliere's Theory of Multiple Scattering, *Phys. Rev.*, **89**, 1256 (1953).

Bethe, H. A., The Sign of the Phase Shifts in Meson-Nucleon Scattering, *Phys. Rev.*, **90**, 994 (1953).

Bethe, H. A., Maximon, L., and Low, F., Bremsstrahlung at High Energies, *Phys. Rev.*, **91**, 417 (1953).

Baranger, M., *Bethe, H. A.*, and Feynman, R. P., Relativistic Correction to the Lamb Shift, *Phys. Rev.*, **92**, 482 (1953).

Bethe, H. A., and Maximon, L. C., Theory of Bremsstrahlung and Pair Production I. Differential Cross Section, *Phys. Rev.*, **93**, 768 (1954).

Breit, G., and *Bethe, H. A.*, Ingoing Waves in Final State of Scattering Problems, *Phys. Rev.*, **93**, 88 (1954).

Davies, H., *Bethe, H. A.*, and Maximon, L. C., Theory of Bremsstrahlung and Pair Production II. Integral Cross Section for Pair Production, *Phys. Rev.*, 788 (1954).

Dyson, F. J., Ross, M., Salpeter, E. E., Schweber, S. S., Sundaresan, M. K., Vischer, W. M., and *Bethe, H. A.*, Meson-Nucleon Scattering in the Tamm-Dancoff Approximation, *Phys. Rev.*, **95**, 1644 (1954).

Bethe, H. A., Mesons and Nuclear Forces, *Phys. Today*, 7, 5 (1954).

Bethe, H. A., and de Hoffmann, F., Meson-Proton Scattering Phase Shift Analysis, *Phys. Rev.*, **95**, 1100 (1954).

de Hoffmann, F., Meteropolis, N., Alei, E. F., and *Bethe, H. A.*, Pion-Hydrogen Phase Shift Analysis between 120 and 217 MeV, *Phys. Rev.*, **95**, 1586 (1954).

Bethe, H. A., A General Survey of π-Mesons, *Nuclear and Meson Physics* (Glasgow) 236 (1955).

Bethe, Hans A., and Morrison, Philip, *Elementary Nuclear Theory*, 2d ed., New York, Wiley, 1956.

Dalitz, R. A., Sundaresan, M. K., and *Bethe, H. A.*, A Singular Integral Equation in the Theory of Meson-Nucleon Scattering, *Proc. Cambridge Phil. Soc.*, **52**, 251 (1956).

Schweber, Silvan S., *Bethe, Hans A.*, de Hoffmann, Frederic, *Mesons and Fields*, Evanston, Ill., Row, Peterson, (1955).

Bethe, H. A., and Hamilton, J., Anti-Proton Annihilation, *Nuovo Cimento*, (Ser. 10) **4**, 1 (1956).

Bethe, H. A., Nuclear Many-Body Problem, *Phys. Rev.*, **103**, 1353 (1956).

Bethe, H. A., Introduction to the Brueckner Theory, *Physica*, **22**, 987 (1956).

Bethe, H. A., Amsterdam Nuclear Reactions Conference, General Introduction, *Physica*, **22**, 941 (1956).

Bethe, H. A., Beyster, W. R., and Carter, R. E., Inelastic Cross-Sections for Fission-Spectrum Neutrons. I. *J. Nucl. Energy*, **3**, 207 (1956).

Bethe, H. A., Beyster, W. R., and Carter, R. E., Inelastic Cross Sections for Fission-Spectrum Neutrons. II. *J. Nucl. Energy*, **3**, 273 (1956).

Bethe, H. A., Reactor Safety and Oscillator Tests. Detroit, Atomic Power Development Associates, 1956.

Bethe, H. A., Beyster, W. R., and Carter, R. E., Inelastic Cross Sections for Fission-Spectrum Neutrons. III. *J. Nucl. Energy*, **4**, 3 (1957).

670   BIBLIOGRAPHY

Bethe, H. A., *Splitting of Terms in Crystals*, Complete English translation. New York, Consultants Bureau, 1958, Translated from *Annalen der Physik*, **3**, 133 (1929).

Bethe, H. A., Beyster, W. R., and Carter, R. E., Inelastic Cross-Sections for Fission-Spectrum Neutron. IV. *J. Nucl. Energy*, **4**, 147 (1957).

Bethe, H. A., and Goldstone, J., Effect of a Repulsive Core in the Theory of Complex Nuclei, *Proc. Roy. Soc.*, **239A**, 551 (1957).

Kivel, B., Mayer, H., and *Bethe, H. A.*, Radiation from Hot Air. I. Theory of Nitric Oxide Absorption. *Ann. Phys.*, **2**, 57 (1957).

Bethe, H. A., *Quantum Mechanics of One- and Two-Electron Atoms*, New York, Academic Press, 1957.

Bethe, H. A., Scattering and Polarization of Protons by Nuclei, *Ann. Phys.*, **3**, 190 (1958).

Bethe, H. A., *Strange Particles*, Lectures given at Cornell University in the spring of 1957. Ithaca, N.Y., 1958.

Suh, K. S., and *Bethe, H. A.*, Recoil Momentum Distribution in Electron Pair Production, *Phys. Rev.*, **115**, 672 (1959).

Bethe, H. A., Deviations from Thermal Equilibrium in Shock Waves. Ann Arbor, University Microfilms, 1961.

Schumacher, C. R., and *Bethe, H. A.*, Usefulness of Polarized Targets and the Polarization Transfer Tensor in Reconstruction of the Nucleon-Nucleon Scattering Matrix, *Phys. Rev.*, **121**, 1534 (1961).

Bethe, Hans A., and Teller, Edward, *The Future of Nuclear Tests*, New York, Foreign Policy Association—World Affairs Center, 1961.

Leon, M., and *Bethe, H. A.*, Negative Meson Absorption in Liquid Hydrogen, *Phys. Rev.*, **127**, 636 (1962).

Bethe, H. A., and Kinoshita, T., Behavior of Regge Poles in a Potential at Large Energy, *Phys. Rev.*, **128**, 1418 (1962).

Bethe, H. A., Brandow, B. H., and Petschek, A. G., Reference Spectrum Method for Nuclear Matter, *Phys. Rev.*, **129**, 225 (1963).

Read, A. L., Orear, J., and *Bethe, H. A.*, Exact Form for Scattering Amplitude in Regge Pole Theory, *Nuovo Cimento*, (10) **29**, 1051 (1963).

Bethe, H. A., Derivation of the Brueckner Theory, in Percus, J. K., Ed., *The Many-Body Problem*, Interscience, New York, 1963, p. 61.

Bethe, H. A., *Intermediate Quantum Mechanics*, W. A. Benjamin, New York, 1964.

Bethe, H. A., Note on High-Energy Proton-Proton Scattering, *Nuovo Cimento*, **33**, 1167 (1964).

Bethe, H. A., Nuclear Matter, *C. R. Congress International de Physique Nucleaire Paris: Centre Nat. de la Recherche Scientifique*, **I**, 99 (1964).

Bethe, H. A., The Fireball in Air, *J. Quant. Spectrosc. Radiative Transfer (GB)*, **5**, 9–12 Jan–Feb, 1965, (Opacities Conference, Albuquerque, 1964).

Bethe, H. A., Three-Body Correlations in Nuclear Matter, *Phys. Rev.*, **138**, B804 (1965).

Index

671